Function Theoretic Methods in Partial Differential Equations

This is Volume 54 in
MATHEMATICS IN SCIENCE AND ENGINEERING
A series of monographs and textbooks
Edited by RICHARD BELLMAN, *University of Southern California*

A complete list of the books in this series appears at the end of this volume.

FUNCTION THEORETIC METHODS IN PARTIAL DIFFERENTIAL EQUATIONS

ROBERT P. GILBERT

DEPARTMENT OF MATHEMATICS
INDIANA UNIVERSITY
BLOOMINGTON, INDIANA

1969

ACADEMIC PRESS New York and London

ACADEMIC PRESS, INC.
111 Fifth Avenue, New York, New York 10003

United Kingdom Edition published by
ACADEMIC PRESS, INC. (LONDON) LTD.
Berkeley Square House, London W.1

LIBRARY OF CONGRESS CATALOG CARD NUMBER: 68-23503

PRINTED IN THE UNITED STATES OF AMERICA

To Eileen

Preface

In traditional treatments of the partial differential equations of mathematical physics, particular stress is laid on solving boundary value problems and initial-boundary value problems. The reasons are that these problems were the *natural* ones to consider in classical physics, i.e., in fluid dynamics, elasticity, plasticity, and electromagnetics. In quantum mechanics and quantum field theory, however, one is usually not concerned with solving boundary value problems, but with investigating the *analytic* properties of solutions of partial differential equations.

The purpose of this monograph is to present a treatment of the analytic theory of partial differential equations which will be accessible to applied mathematicians, physicists, and quantum chemists. It is assumed that the reader approaching this subject already has a knowledge of functions of one complex variable, and an acquaintance with the equations of classical mathematical physics. However, it is not assumed that the reader has any knowledge of the theory of functions of several complex variables. In order to have the book self-contained, an introductory chapter to the local theory of several complex variables is included. The reader who has some acquaintance with the subject may skip this chapter and refer back to it as needed.

The point of view taken in this monograph is essentially that of the theory of integral operators. These procedures not only enable us to determine solutions of partial differential equations, but to translate most of the theorems of one and several complex variables to the theory of partial differential equations.

In the last chapter my "envelope method," which is a generalization of the idea used by Hadamard in the proof of his multiplication of singularities theorem, is applied to scattering problems in quantum mechanics and quantum field theory.

The material presented in this monograph is based on seminars and lectures given by me at Indiana University in connection with the Mathematical Physics Program, and at the Institute for Fluid Dynamics and Applied Mathematics, University of Maryland (1961–1965). I wish at this time to express my gratitude to Professor Alexander Weinstein for providing a pleasant and stimulating mathematical environment that encouraged my individual research and study at the Institute.

I have greatly appreciated having partial financial support while writing this book from the Air Force Office of Scientific Research under Grants AFOSR 400-64 and AFOSR 1206-67 and from the National Science Foundation under Grants NSF GP-3937, and NSF GP-5023.

I am indebted to Professor Stefan Bergman for his reading of and comments on certain sections of the manuscript, and for his encouragement to write this book. I also wish to thank Dr. Henry C. Howard for a thorough reading of the manuscript and many valuable suggestions. A careful proofreading of the galleys was performed by my students, Te Lung Chang, Wilma Loudin, Edward Newberger, and Thottathil Varughese.

Finally, I would like to thank Mrs. Katherine Smith, Mrs. Diane Boteler, and Mrs. Judy Hupp who competently typed and prepared the manuscript.

R. P. GILBERT

Bloomington, Indiana
October, 1968

Contents

4. *Singular partial differential equations*

5. *Applications of integral operators to scattering problems*

Introduction

This monograph deals with recent developments in the function theoretic approach to partial differential equations, and the application of these ideas to certain problems of current interest in mathematical physics. A cornerstone upon which much of this recent development rests is the results, which were first proved by the author in his doctoral dissertation in 1958 [G.6]; see also [G.7,8]. These results are essentially generalizations of the idea employed by Hadamard (1898 [H.1]) in the proof of his multiplication of singularities theorem, to the case of functions of one and several complex variables. Because of the usefulness of these results to the development of the function theoretic method it is of interest to sketch the historical development of the ideas involved and the contributions which were made along the way.

In 1954 Szegö [S.7] proved the following very interesting theorem concerning series of zonal harmonics:

Let $P_n(\cos\theta)$ denote the Legendre polynomial of degree n and let $a_1, a_2, \ldots$ be real constants such that $\limsup |a_n|^{1/n} \to 1$ *as $n \to \infty$. Let $u(r, \theta)$ be the harmonic function defined by*

$$u(r, \theta) = \sum_{n=0}^{\infty} a_n r^n P_n(\cos\theta), \tag{0.1}$$

and $f(z)$ the analytic function defined by

$$f(z) = \sum_{n=0}^{\infty} a_n z^n, \tag{0.2}$$

so that both functions are regular for $r = |z| < 1$. Then the boundary point $(1, \theta)$ is a singular point of $u(r, \theta)$, if and only if, the boundary point $z = e^{i\theta}$ is a singular point of $f(z)$.

Szegö goes on to conjecture that the same result would hold for complex coefficients $\{a_n\}$; however, Nehari [N.6] showed that this correspondence between singularities need not be one-to-one by proving a more general theorem which contained Szegö's as a special case. Nehari made direct use of the *original* Hadamard idea (see Chapter 1, Section 3 for a complete discussion of Hadamard's idea) to prove the following:

Let the $\{a_n\}$ *be constants such that* $\limsup |a_n|^{1/n} = \rho < 1$ *as* $n \to \infty$. *Furthermore, let the analytic functions* $g(t)$ *and* $f(z)$ *be defined by the expansions*

$$g(t) = \sum_{n=0}^{\infty} a_n P_n(t), \qquad |t+1| + |t-1| < \frac{1+\rho^2}{\rho}, \tag{0.3}$$

$$f(z) = \sum_{n=0}^{\infty} a_n z^n, \qquad |z| < \rho^{-1}, \tag{0.4}$$

which converge in the regions indicated. Under these assumptions, a point $t = \tau$, *which is reached by analytic continuation along a path* C_t *originating at* $t = 1$ *and otherwise avoiding the points* $t = \pm 1$, *will be a singularity of* $g(t)$ *if, and only if,*

$$\tau = \frac{1+\sigma^2}{2\sigma}, \tag{0.5}$$

where $z = \sigma$ *is a singularity of* $f(z)$ *which is reached by analytic continuation of* $f(z)$ *along a path* C_z *originating at* $z = 1$ *and coinciding with one of the two images of* C_t *under the conformal mapping*

$$t = \frac{1+z^2}{2z}. \tag{0.6}$$

What the author did in his doctoral dissertation was to generalize the results of Szegö and Nehari to the case of harmonic functions of three or more independent, complex variables. This goal was accomplished by discovering several generalizations of the original Hadamard idea to functions of one and several complex variables, which could be applied to completely general representations of harmonic functions. We shall refer to the author's generalization of the Hadamard idea as the *envelope method*. We restate Theorem (1.0) from page 8, and Theorem (3.0) from page 19 of the above-mentioned dissertation.

THEOREM (1.0) *Let* $f(\mathbf{X}; \zeta)$ *be a holomorphic function of* $\mathbf{X}$ *and* ζ, $\mathbf{X} \in \mathbb{C}^3$, $\zeta \in \mathbb{C}^1$, *and let* $S(\mathbf{X}; \zeta) = 0$ *be a global representation of the singularities of*

$f(\mathbf{X};\zeta)$. Then the integral, $H(\mathbf{X}) = \int_{\mathscr{L}} f(\mathbf{X};\zeta)\,d\zeta$, where $\mathscr{L}$ is a closed contour, is regular for all points not satisfying simultaneously

$$S(\mathbf{X};\zeta) = 0, \qquad \frac{\partial S(\mathbf{X};\zeta)}{\partial \zeta} = 0. \tag{0.7}$$

THEOREM (3.0) *Let $f(\mathbf{X};\zeta)$ be a holomorphic function of $\mathbf{X}$ and ζ, $\mathbf{X} \in \mathbb{C}^m$, $\zeta \in \mathbf{C}^n$, and let $S(\mathbf{X};\zeta) = 0$ be a global representation of the singularities of $f(\mathbf{X};\zeta)$. Then the integral, $H(\mathbf{X}) = \int_D f(\mathbf{X};\zeta)\,d\zeta$, where $D = \mathscr{L}_1 \times \mathscr{L}_2 \times \cdots \times \mathscr{L}_n$ is the cartesian product of closed contours in the $\zeta_1, \zeta_2, \ldots, \zeta_n$ planes, is regular for all points $\mathbf{X} \in \mathbb{C}^m$ which do not simultaneously satisfy*

$$S(\mathbf{X};\zeta) = 0, \qquad \frac{\partial S(\mathbf{X};\zeta)}{\partial \zeta_1} = 0, \ldots, \qquad \frac{\partial S(\mathbf{X};\zeta)}{\partial \zeta_n} = 0. \tag{0.8}$$

When Theorem (1.0) is applied to the Whittaker representation of the harmonic functions (Chapter 2, Section 2), one obtains a generalization of the results of Szegö and Nehari. Indeed, when one considers the special case of Theorem 2.2.1 of Chapter 2, where $f(u,\zeta) \equiv F(u) = \sum_{n=0}^{\infty} a_n u^n$, one reproduces the theorems of Szegö and Nehari. Another generalization of their theorems was provided somewhat later by the author [G.9] (see also Henrici [H.7]) in connection with the *complex* solutions of the generalized axially symmetric potential theory equation (GASPT),†

$$\frac{\partial^2 \Psi}{\partial x^2} + \frac{\partial^2 \Psi}{\partial y^2} + \frac{2\nu}{y}\frac{\partial \Psi}{\partial y} = 0 \qquad (\operatorname{Re} \nu > 0), \tag{0.9}$$

which are regular about the origin, i.e., the solutions,

$$\Psi(r,\theta) = \sum_{n=0}^{\infty} a_n r^n C_n^{\nu}(\cos\theta), \tag{0.10}$$

with $\limsup |a_n|^{1/n} = \rho < 1$. Here the $C_n^{\nu}(\cos\theta)$ are meant to be Gegenbauer or ultraspherical harmonics. When $\nu = \frac{1}{2}$, $C_n^{1/2}(\cos\theta) \equiv P_n(\cos\theta)$. It was shown that the singularities of the series (0.10) occurred in exactly the same positions as for the series (0.1)–(0.3). In Chapter IV, Theorem 4.2.5, a precise statement and proof of this result is given along with further extensions of these theorems to solutions of the more general equations,

$$\mathbf{S}_{\mu\nu}[\Psi] \equiv \Psi_{xx} + \frac{2\nu}{x}\Psi_x + \Psi_{yy} + \frac{2\mu}{y}\Psi_y + \{k^2 - V(r)\}\Psi = 0, \tag{0.11}$$

† The abbreviation GASPT is due to Weinstein who first considered fractional-dimensional space in potential theory, and showed the importance of this idea in applied mathematics problems [W.6–15].

where μ, $\nu \geq 0$, k is real and $rV(r) = \sum_{n=0}^{\infty} v_n r^n$ $(v_0 > 0)$ is an entire function, and to

$$\mathbf{L}_{\lambda,s}^{(n)}[\Psi] \equiv \frac{\partial^2 \Psi}{\partial x_1{}^2} + \cdots + \frac{\partial^2 \Psi}{\partial x_n{}^2} + \frac{\partial^2 \Psi}{\partial \rho^2} + \frac{s}{\rho}\frac{\partial \Psi}{\partial \rho} + \lambda^2 \Psi = 0, \tag{0.12}$$

where $s > -1$, and $\lambda \neq 0$ is real.

Chapters 2 and 4 contain a detailed survey of how the author's generalization of the Hadamard idea was useful in building up a function theoretic approach to the theory of linear partial differential equations, [G.6–28], [G.H.1–4].

Previous to the author's discovery of a generalized Hadamard lemma (*envelope method*) the study of singularities of solutions of partial differential equations was limited to fairly specific forms of integral representations. Bergman [B.22, pp. 54–57; B.3–10,13,24–27] thoroughly investigated the singularities of harmonic functions whose $\mathbf{B}_3$-associates were *rational* functions of u and ζ, i.e., harmonic functions having the integral representations

$$H(\mathbf{X}) = \mathbf{B}_3 f \equiv \frac{1}{2\pi i} \int_{|\zeta|=1} f(u, \zeta)\, d\zeta, \qquad f(u, \zeta) \equiv \frac{p_1(u, \zeta)}{p_2(u, \zeta)}, \tag{0.13}$$

where $\mathbf{X} \equiv (x_1, x_2, x_3)$, $u = (x_1 + ix_2)(\zeta/2) + x_3 - (x_1 - ix_2)(1/2\zeta)$, and $p_1(u, \zeta)$, $p_2(u, \zeta)$ are polynomials in u and ζ. The author's theorem (1.0) permitted one to study the singularities of harmonic functions of the most general kind by using the Whittaker representation. For instance, in the case where $p_1(u, \zeta)$ and $p_2(u, \zeta)$ were completely *arbitrary*, entire functions of two complex variables could now be treated for the first time.

Theorems (2.0) and (3.0) [G.6] have also been quite useful in certain problems of contemporary physics, such as investigating the singularities of Feynman integrals, and the singularities of the scattering amplitudes in quantum mechanics and quantum field theory (Chapter 5).

Indeed, Theorem (3.0) was conjectured by the physicist Landau (1959 [L4.5,]) in two papers on quantum field theory; see also Bjorken [B.37]. It was not until 1960 that Polkinghorne and Screaton [P.S.2] published an independently obtained proof of this theorem in the physics literature. Despite this coincidence, at that time function theoretic methods in the study of partial differential equations, as one may see from [B.22], was quite separated from quantum field theory, and in particular Feynman integrals. It was not until 1964 that the author became aware of the similar mathematical structure underlying certain aspects of the two areas. Shortly afterwards a survey paper on generalizations of the Hadamard idea, and a paper on applications of these results to the investigation of the singularities of the elastic unitarity integral were published by the author with his colleagues, Howard and Aks [G.H.A.1], [A.G.H.1]; these results are discussed in Chapters 1 and 5, respectively. (See notes added in proof, p. xviii.)

This monograph on function theoretic methods in partial differential equations has been planned so that it may be read independently of the other books in this area. It is assumed, however, that the reader is approaching the subject with some knowledge of the theory of analytic functions of one complex variable and the classical theory of partial differential equations. With this in mind, and the intention of making the book self-contained, a first chapter on the elements of functions of several complex variables has been included. Chapter 1 contains the definitions of Weierstrass and Cauchy–Riemann holomorphic functions, the generalization of Cauchy's formula to several complex variables, Osgood's lemma, Hartogs' theorem, the Weierstrass preparation theorem, the implicit function theorem, a Schwarz lemma for several complex variables, and growth estimates for entire functions of several complex variables. In addition, Chapter 1 contains a complete survey of this author's extensions of the Hadamard idea to both one and several complex variables, and certain recent theorems by the author [G.28] and Bergman [B.27] concerning criteria for locating singularities of functions of several complex variables from information about their series developments. In short, Chapter 1 comprises a concise introduction to the local theory of several complex variables, and is sufficient for the purposes of this monograph. The algebraic topological approach to the complex analytic theory of partial differential equations does not come within the scope of the present work. The reader interested in learning about this approach is directed to papers by Leray [L.8,9]; however, for this it is necessary to understand the global theory of several complex variables. (See for instance, the notes by Bers [B.35], or the books by Fuks [F.4,5], Gunning and Rossi [G.R.1], or Hormander [H.11].)

Chapter 2 deals with the analytic properties of harmonic functions of $(p+2)$ variables. The introduction to this material is designed to bridge the gap between traditional treatises on partial differential equations and the function theoretic approach. The following topics are discussed: harmonic functions of three variables, a derivation of the Whittaker representation, the use of the envelope method to locate singularities of harmonic functions of three variables, the Bergman–Whittaker operator $\mathbf{B}_3$, inverse operators for $\mathbf{B}_3$, other operators that generate harmonic functions, extensions of the operator $\mathbf{B}_3$ to higher dimension, the *envelope method* applied to the case of more than three variables, necessary conditions for harmonic functions to be singular in $\mathbb{R}^3$, projective geometric methods for classifying singularities, algebraic geometric methods for studying representations of harmonic functions, and solutions to the related elliptic partial differential equation

$$\mathbf{T}_{p+2}[\Psi] \equiv \sum_{\mu=1}^{n} \frac{\partial^2 \Psi}{\partial x_\mu{}^2} + A(r^2) r \frac{\partial \Psi}{\partial r} + C(r^2)\Psi = 0. \tag{0.14}$$

Chapter 3 is a study of the linear partial differential equation

$$\mathbf{e}[u] \equiv \frac{\partial^2 u}{\partial x^2} + \frac{\partial^2 u}{\partial y} + a(x, y)\frac{\partial u}{\partial y} + b(x, y)\frac{\partial u}{\partial y} + c(x, y)u = 0 \tag{0.15}$$

in domains $\mathfrak{S} \subset \mathbb{C}^1$, where the coefficients $a(x, y)$, $b(x, y)$, $c(x, y)$ are $\mathscr{C}^{(\infty)}$, and furthermore permit an analytic continuation in terms of the variables $z = x + iy$, $z^* = x - iy$ to the product space $\mathfrak{S} \times \mathfrak{S}^*$. This idea has been used by Bergman [B.22] and Vekua [V.1–3] to obtain representations of solutions to (0.15). A fairly complete survey of Bergman's work on this subject, including an existence proof for his E-function, and a discussion of the relation of the E-function to the solutions of special initial value problems is given. It is also pointed out what the connections are between the E-function method, the method of Diaz and Ludford [D.L.1–5], and the function theoretic method of Vekua [V.3]. The last mentioned method is not to be confused with the generalized analytic function approach of Vekua discussed in [V.4–6], or by the pseudoanalytic functions of Bers discussed in [C.H.1, Vol. II], and [B.30–35].

The function theoretic method of Vekua is concerned with obtaining the analogue of the Riemann function for the formally hyperbolic equation one obtains from (0.15) by introducing the variables z, z^*, i.e., for the equation

$$\mathbf{E}[U] \equiv U_{zz^*} + A(z, z^*)U_z + B(z, z^*)U_{z^*} + C(z, z^*)U = 0, \tag{0.16}$$

where the new coefficients are related in a simple way to the original ones (Chapter 3, Section 1). In order to obtain the Riemann function for (0.16) it is necessary to investigate multiple-integral Volterra equations, and to show that the solutions are holomorphic in a suitable product space in $\mathbb{C}^4$ (Chapter 3, Section 4). A complete discussion of this theory is included in this chapter along with several extensions made by using certain functional analysis methods [A.B.1], [A.G.2], [A.G.H.2], [S.8]. By introducing suitable Banach spaces and using fixed point theory, sufficient conditions can be obtained for a unique solution of (0.15) to exist in the large, satisfying the generalized Goursat data

$$\alpha_{i1} u_x + \alpha_{i2} u_y + \alpha_{i0} = f_i \tag{0.17}$$

on the analytic curves $\mathscr{C}_i$ $(i = 1, 2)$; $\mathscr{C}_1 \cap \mathscr{C}_2 \equiv \{(0, 0)\}$, $u(0, 0) = u_0$. Conditions for a correctly posed problem imply that the coefficients α_{ij} cannot all be real, and furthermore that their moduli must satisfy certain inequalities. A generalization of this approach to the normalized, nonlinear elliptic equation

$$\frac{\partial^2 u}{\partial x^2} + \frac{\partial^2 u}{\partial y^2} = f(x, y, u, u_x, u_y) \tag{0.18}$$

permits a uniqueness and existence theorem in the small (Section 5).

In our discussion of the Vekua approach we also include the interesting contributions of Henrici [H.6,8] who used the Vekua formulation to discuss Eq. (0.15) with Cauchy data. This particular item is *not* found in Chapter 3 but instead in Section 4 of Chapter 4, where we also include several of the new integral representations Henrici obtained (using these results), for solutions of the singular partial differential equation [H.4,8]

$$\mathbf{h}_{\mu\nu}[u] \equiv \frac{\partial^2 u}{\partial x^2} + \frac{\partial^2 u}{\partial y^2} + \frac{2\mu}{x}\frac{\partial u}{\partial x} + \frac{2\nu}{y}\frac{\partial u}{\partial y} + k^2 u = 0, \tag{0.19}$$

where $\mu, \nu > 0$, and k is real.

Chapter 4 is devoted to the study of singular elliptic partial differential equations of two and more independent variables. The first partial differential equation discussed is that of GASPT (0.9). This equation is one of the easiest to treat by our methods and consequently the most complete theory has been developed for this case [G.22]. In addition to developing a function theory for GASPT, approximation theorems are also presented. The function theoretic approach is also applied to the more general singular differential equations (0.11) and (0.12). One obtains in both of these cases theorems concerning the location of singularities and growth conditions for entire solutions.

We conclude Chapter 4 by giving a concise discussion of Weinstein's function theoretic approach as applied to the GASPT and EPD operators [W.6–15], and Eqs. (4.8.1), (4.8.2). Weinstein's approach is essentially different from the one taken in this monograph; however, his results are important for the reduction of boundary value problems to simpler forms [W.6, 8], and may be combined with other function theoretic methods to obtain new representation formulas, (4.8.5). Weinstein's formulas relating solutions of Eq. (4.8.8) have not been fully exploited for the purposes of obtaining new integral operators which may preserve different properties of classical function theory.

The final chapter of this monograph is concerned with illustrating how function theoretic methods may be used in the scattering problems of quantum mechanics and quantum field theory. The first section presents an introduction to potential scattering and the standard derivation of the phase shift formulas for the scattering amplitude. The scattering amplitude is obtained as a Legendre series of the form

$$A(k^2, \xi) = \sum_{l=0}^{\infty} a_l(k^2) P_l(\xi); \qquad (k, \xi) \in \mathbb{C}^2,$$

and its analytic properties are investigated for several physically relevant scattering potentials. Using information obtained about the solutions to (0.12), the potential scattering problem is generalized to the higher, fractional dimension problem associated with the equation

$$\mathbf{L}_{\lambda, s}^{(n)}[\Psi] = V(r)\Psi; \qquad r^2 = x_1^{\,2} + \cdots + x_n^{\,2} + \rho^2,$$

and the generalized radiation condition as $r \to \infty$

$$\Psi(\mathbf{X}) \approx e^{i(\mathbf{K}, \mathbf{X})} + \frac{f(k; \theta)}{r^{\frac{1}{2}(n+s)}} e^{ikr} + O(r^{-\frac{1}{2}(n+s)-1}).$$

Using the formulation given by Newton [N.12,13] for the scattering of particles with spin, and also his formulation of inelastic multiple channel scattering [N.9,12], it is shown how function theoretic methods may be used effectively in these general cases. A brief discussion is also given concerning the inverse scattering problem via the approach of Newton [N.11,13] and Sabatier [S.1,2].

For the case of relativistic scattering we use the Mandelstam hypothesis, and the elastic unitarity integral, to investigate the analytic properties of the scattering amplitude. The approach taken here is a modification, by the introduction of integral operators, of the approach taken by Gilbert *et al.* [G.H.A.1], [A.G.H.1].

Notes Added in Proof: In their paper "Algebraic curve theory and the envelope diagrams" (to appear, *Proc. Symp. Analytic Methods Math. Phys.*, Indiana Univ. Press, 1969), S. Abhyankar and C. Risk add some remarks concerning the Hadamard–Gilbert analyses of multivariable integrals.

Interesting applications of integral operator methods to the problems of classical physics, i.e., fluid dynamics, electromagnetism, and elasticity, can be found in the works of von Krzywoblocki [V.K. 1–8].

Function Theoretic Methods in Partial Differential Equations

I

An introduction to the theory of several complex variables

1. Fundamentals of the Local Theory

We begin by considering functions defined in an open region $\mathfrak{D}$ which is a subset of the space of n complex variables $\mathbb{C}^n$, i.e., the set of all n-tuples $(z_1, \ldots, z_n)$ where $z_k = x_k + iy_k$ and $x_k, y_k \in (-\infty, +\infty)$. Unless otherwise stated we shall assume that the function $f(z) \equiv f(z_1, \ldots, z_n)$ is single valued, and that $\mathfrak{D}$ is connected. Our definition of continuity is the usual one, i.e., $f(z)$ is continuous at $z^0 \in \mathfrak{D}$ if given an arbitrary $\varepsilon > 0$ we have

$$|f(z_1{}^0 + \Delta z_1, \ldots, z_n{}^0 + \Delta z_n) - f(z_1{}^0, \ldots, z_n{}^0)| < \varepsilon$$

provided that the euclidean norm of Δz is sufficiently small, i.e., $\|\Delta z\|_e = (|\Delta z_1|^2 + \cdots + |\Delta z_n|^2)^{1/2} < \delta(z)$. If $\delta(z)$ is independent of z for all $z \in \mathfrak{D}$ then we say $f(z)$ is uniformly continuous in $\mathfrak{D}$.

Definition *A complex-valued function $f(z)$ defined in a domain $\mathfrak{D}$ contained in the space of n-complex variables is said to be Weierstrass holomorphic in the domain $\mathfrak{D}$ if for each point $a \in \mathfrak{D}$ the function can be expanded as a power series of the form*

$$f(z) = \sum_{m=0}^{\infty} c_m(z - a)^m$$

$$\equiv \sum_{m_1, \ldots, m_n=0}^{\infty} c_{m_1 \cdots m_n}(z_1 - a_1)^{m_1} \cdots (z_n - a_n)^{m_n}, \qquad (1.1.1)$$

which converges in some nonvoid neighborhood of a. (The point $(z_1, \ldots, z_n) = (a_1, \ldots, a_n)$ is referred to as the *center* of the power series expansion.)

We now show that if the n-fold series (1.1.1) converges in some order at the point $z = z^0 \neq a$ it converges absolutely and uniformly to the same value independent of the order of summation for all z that are contained in the "polydisk"

$$\{z \mid |z_k - a_k| \leq |z_k{}^0 - a_k| - \varepsilon_k;\ \varepsilon_k > 0, \text{ and } k = 1, 2, \ldots, n\}. \tag{1.1.2}$$

Since (1.1.1) converges when summed in a certain order as a simple series, it is necessary that $|c_m(z^0 - a)^m| \leq B < \infty$ for all values of the indices, $m \equiv (m_1, \ldots, m_n)$. Setting $|z^0 - a| = r \equiv r_1 \cdot r_2 \cdot \cdots \cdot r_n$ one has $|c_m| \leq B/r^m$, from which it follows that

$$\sum_{m=0}^{\infty} \left| c_m(z - a)^m \right| \leq B \sum_{m=0}^{\infty} \left| \frac{z - a}{r} \right|^m = \frac{B}{\prod_{k=1}^{n} \left(1 - \dfrac{|z_k - a_k|}{r_k}\right)}, \tag{1.1.3}$$

and hence it is seen that (1.1.1) converges uniformly and absolutely in the set (1.1.2). (The interior of the set (1.1.2) is called an n-circular polycylindrical region.) Since the series (1.1.1) converges absolutely in the polycylinder (1.1.2) it may be summed as a simple series in any order and converges to the same value.

Definition *We shall say that a complex-valued function $f(z)$ is holomorphic in the sense of Cauchy–Riemann in the domain $\mathfrak{D} \subset \mathbb{C}^n$ if the first partial derivatives*

$$\frac{\partial f(z)}{\partial z_k} = \lim_{\Delta z_k \to 0} \frac{f(z_1, \ldots, z_k + \Delta z_k, \ldots, z_n) - f(z_1, \ldots, z_n)}{\Delta z_k} \qquad (k = 1, 2, \ldots, n), \tag{1.1.4}$$

exist at each point $z \in \mathfrak{D}$, and are continuous.

If one separates $f(z)$ into its real and imaginary parts, $u = \operatorname{Re} f(z)$, $v = \operatorname{Im} f(z)$, and if $f(z)$ is holomorphic in the sense of Cauchy–Riemann one has that

$$\frac{\partial u}{\partial x_k} = \frac{\partial v}{\partial y_k}, \qquad \text{and} \qquad \frac{\partial u}{\partial y_k} = -\frac{\partial v}{\partial x_k}, \tag{1.1.5}$$

with $z_k = x_k + iy_k$ ($k = 1, 2, \ldots, n$). In other words, "Cauchy–Riemann holomorphic" is equivalent to saying that $f(z)$ is holomorphic in each variable separately while the other variables are held fixed. If we formally introduce the variables $z_j = x_j + iy_j$ and $\bar{z}_j = x_j - iy_j$ then (1.1.5) is seen to be equivalent to the system of equations, $\partial f/\partial \bar{z}_j = 0$ ($j = 1, 2, \ldots, n$). The exact meaning of this statement will be made clear shortly; however, accepting this statement formally implies the result that *each Weierstrass holomorphic function is indeed also holomorphic in the Cauchy–Riemann sense*. This follows directly from the fact that in its polycylinder of convergence the power series (1.1.1) may be summed as a simple series, and hence if all the z_k except z_j ($k \neq j$) are held fixed, it represents a holomorphic function in the z_j variable. We shall see in what follows that the proof of the converse is not so obvious.

Definition *An ordinary polycylindrical region (or polycylinder) in $\mathbb{C}^n$ is the Cartesian product of n bounded, simply connected, regions $\mathfrak{D}_k$ in the z_k-planes.*

Theorem 1.1.1 *Let $f(z)$ be Cauchy–Riemann holomorphic and continuous in the closure of the polycylinder, $\mathfrak{D} \equiv \prod_{k=1}^{n} \mathfrak{D}_k$. Furthermore, let the boundaries, $\partial\mathfrak{D}_k$, of $\mathfrak{D}_k$ be piecewise smooth curves. Then if z is an interior point of $\mathfrak{D}$ we have*

$$f(z) = \left(\frac{1}{2\pi i}\right)^n \int_{\mathfrak{S}_n} \frac{f(\zeta)}{\prod_{k=1}^{n} (\zeta_k - z_k)}\, d\zeta_1 \cdots d\zeta_n, \tag{1.1.6}$$

where $\mathfrak{S}_n \equiv \prod_{k=1}^{n} \partial\mathfrak{D}_k$ is called the "skeleton" or "distinguished boundary" of $\mathfrak{D}$.

Proof We prove this theorem by making repeated application of Cauchy's formula for one variable. In the case $n = 2$ we have for $z_2 \in \mathfrak{D}_2$ and fixed

$$f(z_1, z_2) = \frac{1}{2\pi i} \int_{\partial\mathfrak{D}_1} \frac{f(\zeta_1, z_2)}{\zeta_1 - z_1}\, d\zeta_1$$

and hence we obtain the iterated integral

$$f(z_1, z_2) = \left(\frac{1}{2\pi i}\right)^2 \int_{\partial\mathfrak{D}_1} d\zeta_1 \int_{\partial\mathfrak{D}_2} d\zeta_2\, \frac{f(\zeta_1, \zeta_2)}{(\zeta_1 - z_1)(\zeta_2 - z_2)}$$

for $(z_1, z_2) \in \mathfrak{D}$. If the distance of z_k from the boundary $\partial\mathfrak{D}_k$ is greater than some $\delta_k > 0$, the integrand is absolutely integrable and we may rewrite this as the double integral

$$f(z) = \left(\frac{1}{2\pi i}\right)^2 \int_{\mathfrak{S}_2} \frac{f(\zeta)\, d\zeta_1\, d\zeta_2}{(\zeta_1 - z_1)(\zeta_2 - z_2)}.$$

The proof for n variables follows by induction.

Theorem 1.1.2 *Let $\{f_n(z)\}_{n=1}^{\infty}$ be a sequence of functions, Cauchy–Riemann holomorphic in $\mathfrak{D} \subset \mathbb{C}^n$. Furthermore, let the partial sums $F_n(z) = f_1(z) + \cdots + f_n(z)$ converge uniformly in $\mathfrak{D}$ to $F_0(z)$. Then $F_0(z)$ is Cauchy–Riemann holomorphic in $\mathfrak{D}$.*

Proof Let a be an arbitrary point in $\mathfrak{D}$ and let the closed polycylinder $\overline{\Delta(a; r)} \equiv \{z \,||z_k - a_k| \le r_k;\, k = 1, \ldots, n\} \subset \mathfrak{D}$. Since for each n $F_n(z)$ is a holomorphic function in the Cauchy–Riemann sense we have for $z \in \Delta(a; r)$ that

$$F_m(z) = \left(\frac{1}{2\pi i}\right)^n \int_{\mathfrak{S}_n} \frac{F_m(\zeta)\, d\zeta_1 \cdots d\zeta_n}{\prod_{k=1}^{n} (\zeta_k - z_k)},$$

where $\mathfrak{S}_n \equiv \prod_{k=1}^{n} \{\zeta \,||\zeta_k - a_k| = r_k\}$ is the skeleton of $\Delta(a; r)$. In that the partial sums $F_m(z)$ converge uniformly, as $m \to \infty$, to $F_0(z)$ for $\overline{\Delta(a; r)} \subset \mathfrak{D}$ we may pass to the limit under the integral sign, yielding

$$F_0(z) = \lim_{m \to \infty} \left(\frac{1}{2\pi i}\right)^n \int_{\mathfrak{S}_n} \frac{F_m(\zeta)\, d\zeta_1 \cdots d\zeta_n}{\prod_{k=1}^{n} (\zeta_k - z_k)}$$

$$= \left(\frac{1}{2\pi i}\right)^n \int_{\mathfrak{S}_n} \frac{F_0(\zeta)\, d\zeta_1 \cdots d\zeta_n}{\prod_{k=1}^{n} (\zeta_k - z_k)}.$$

We conclude from this that $F_0(z)$ is holomorphic in $\Delta(a; \rho)$, with $\rho_k < r_k$ $(k = 1, \ldots, n)$. Since any compact subset of $\mathfrak{D}$ can be covered by a finite number of polycylinders of the type $\Delta(a; r)$ we conclude that $F_0(z)$ is holomorphic in $\mathfrak{D}$.

From what has been said earlier it is clear that a function holomorphic in the Weierstrass sense at the point $z \in \mathfrak{D}$ is also holomorphic in the Cauchy–Riemann sense. It is easy to show that a function holomorphic in the Cauchy–Riemann sense and *continuous* (in all the variables) in a region $\mathfrak{D} \subset \mathbb{C}^n$ is also Weierstrass holomorphic. To show that this is also the case when we remove the condition of continuity is considerably more difficult, and we postpone this problem for somewhat later.

Theorem 1.1.3 *Let $f(z)$ be Cauchy–Riemann holomorphic and continuous (in all the variables) in the region $\mathfrak{D} \subset \mathbb{C}^n$. Then $f(z)$ is also holomorphic in the sense of Weierstrass. Furthermore, if $f(z)$ is Weierstrass holomorphic in $\mathfrak{D}$ then it is continuous (in all the variables) and Cauchy–Riemann holomorphic in $\mathfrak{D}$.*

Proof We prove this result for $n = 2$, the case of n variables follows by induction. If $a \in \mathfrak{D}$ there then exists a closed polycylinder $\overline{\Delta(a; r)} \subset \mathfrak{D}$ such that by Theorem 1.1.1 we have for $z \in \Delta(a; r)$

$$f(z) = \left(\frac{1}{2\pi i}\right)^2 \int_{\mathfrak{S}_2} \frac{f(\zeta)\, d\zeta}{(\zeta_1 - z_1)(\zeta_2 - z_2)},$$

where $d\zeta = d\zeta_1\, d\zeta_2$ and $\mathfrak{S}_2$ is the skeleton of $\Delta(a; \rho)$. Since

$$\frac{1}{(\zeta_1 - z_1)(\zeta_2 - z_2)} = \sum_{l, k=0}^{\infty} \frac{(z_1 - a_1)^l (z_2 - a_2)^k}{(\zeta_1 - a_1)^{l+1} (\zeta_2 - a_2)^{k+1}}$$

converges uniformly and absolutely for $|z_k - a_k| \le \rho_k < r_k$ $k = 1, 2$, and $f(\zeta)$ is continuous in $\mathfrak{D}$, then we may multiply this series by $f(\zeta)$ and integrate termwise. We obtain

$$f(z) = \sum_{l, k=0}^{\infty} c_{lk} (z_1 - a_1)^l (z_2 - a_2)^k,$$

where

$$c_{lk} \equiv \left(\frac{1}{2\pi i}\right)^2 \int_{\mathfrak{S}_2} \frac{f(\zeta)\, d\zeta}{(\zeta_1 - a_1)^{l+1} (\zeta_2 - a_2)^{k+1}}. \tag{1.1.7}$$

Furthermore, this series clearly converges uniformly in $\overline{\Delta(a; \rho)}$.

That $f(z)$ is Cauchy–Riemann holomorphic in $\mathfrak{D}$ if it is Weierstrass holomorphic follows, as remarked before, from the fact that we may differentiate a uniformly convergent series termwise in each variable separately. The fact that it must be continuous in all the variables we show as follows.

Proof Let $f(z)$ be expressed as its (m_1, m_2) partial sum plus a remainder term, i.e.,

$$f(z) = \sum_{k,l=0}^{m_1,m_2} c_{kl}(z_1 - a_1)^k(z_2 - a_2)^l + R_{m_1,m_2}(z),$$

and let us consider the difference $f(z + h) - f(z)$. We have then the estimate

$$|f(z + h) - f(z)| \le \left| \sum_{k,l=0}^{m_1,m_2} c_{kl}[(z_1 + h_1 - a_1)^k(z_2 + h_2 - a_2)^l \right.$$
$$\left. - (z_1 - a_1)^k(z_2 - a_2)^l] \right| + |R_{m_1,m_2}(z + h) - R_{m_1,m_2}(z)|.$$

For a given $\varepsilon > 0$ we may choose indices (N_1, N_2) such that

$$|R_{m_1,m_2}(z + h)| < \varepsilon/3, \; |R_{m_1,m_2}(z)| < \varepsilon/3 \quad \text{when} \quad m_k > N_k \; (k = 1, 2)$$

and h is sufficiently small. Clearly the (m_1, m_2) partial sum is continuous (as may be seen below) and hence for $\|h\| = (|h_1|^2 + |h_2|^2)^{1/2} < \delta(\varepsilon)$ we have

$$\left| \sum_{k,l=0}^{m_1,m_2} c_{kl}[(z_1 + h_1 - a_1)^k(z_2 + h_2 - a_2)^l - (z_1 - a_1)^k(z_2 - a_2)^l] \right|$$
$$\le \sum_{k,l=0}^{m_1,m_2} |c_{kl}| \left\{ \sum_{\substack{\mu,\nu=0 \\ \mu+\nu\neq 0}}^{k,l} |h_1|^\mu \cdot |h_2|^\nu \cdot |z_1 - a_1|^{k-\mu} \cdot |z_2 - a_2|^{l-\nu} \binom{k}{\mu}\binom{l}{\nu} \right\} < \frac{\varepsilon}{3}.$$

We conclude that $|f(z + h) - f(z)| < \varepsilon$, and hence Weierstrass holomorphic, is equivalent to Cauchy–Riemann holomorphic plus continuity (in all the variables), which is the desired result.

We remark that in what follows we shall develop the local theory of several complex variables for the case $n = 2$; most of our results carry over immediately to the case $n > 2$ by induction.

Let us suppose the function $f(z)$ is Weierstrass holomorphic in the domain $\mathfrak{D}$; then, about each point $a \in \mathfrak{D}$, $f(z)$ has a power series expansion of the form (1.1.1), which converges in a bicylindrical neighborhood. Considered as a power series in, say, just the variable z_1, for $z_2 = a_2$, the function is clearly analytic and hence its partial derivatives with respect to z_1 may be computed by differentiating the series termwise. Similarly, we may compute the partial derivatives with respect to z_2. Indeed, the derived series are also holomorphic in the two complex variables z_1 and z_2, which may be seen by using the method of dominants. We consider the following general series obtained by formally differentiating termwise with respect to z_1 and z_2:

$$\frac{1}{m!n!} \frac{\partial^{m+n} f(z)}{\partial z_1{}^m \, \partial z_2{}^n} = \sum_{l=m}^{\infty} \sum_{k=n}^{\infty} \binom{l}{m}\binom{k}{n} c_{lk}(z_1 - a_1)^{l-m}(z_2 - a_2)^{k-n} \quad (1.1.8)$$

Clearly one has from Eq. (1.1.7), the two-variable Cauchy estimates for the coefficient of (1.1.8), i.e.,

$$|c_{lk}| \leq M\rho_1^{-1}\rho_2^{-k}, \tag{1.1.9}$$

where $\rho_k < r_k$, and the series for $f(z)$ converges in the bicylinder $\Delta(a; r)$, $r = (r_1, r_2)$; here $M = M(\rho)$ is the maximum modulus of $f(z)$ on the skeleton of the bicylinder $\Delta(a; \rho)$. Using (1.1.9) we obtain the following estimate,

$$\begin{aligned}
&\frac{1}{m!n!}\left|\frac{\partial^{m+n}f(z)}{\partial z_1{}^m\,\partial z_2{}^n}\right| \\
&\quad \leq \frac{M}{\rho_1{}^m\rho_2{}^n}\left\{\sum_{l=m}^{\infty}\sum_{k=n}^{\infty}\binom{l}{m}\binom{k}{n}\left(\frac{|z_1 - a_1|}{\rho_1}\right)^{l-m}\left(\frac{|z_2 - a_2|}{\rho_2}\right)^{k-n}\right. \\
&\quad = \frac{M}{\rho_1{}^m\rho_2{}^n}\left(1 - \frac{|z_1 - a_1|}{\rho_1}\right)^{-m-1}\left(1 - \frac{|z_2 - a_2|}{\rho_2}\right)^{-n-1},
\end{aligned}$$

from which it follows that the derived series for $\partial^{m+n}f/\partial z_1{}^m \partial z_2{}^n$ is holomorphic at $z = a$. Since this holds for all points $a \in \mathfrak{D}$ we obtain that the derived series is holomorphic in $\mathfrak{D}$. By induction one then has:

Theorem 1.1.4 *If $f(z)$ is Weierstrass holomorphic in the domain $\mathfrak{D}$, then its partial derivatives of all orders are Weierstrass holomorphic in $\mathfrak{D}$.*

We have already observed that if $f(z)$ is Weierstrass holomorphic in $\mathfrak{D}$ then it is also Cauchy–Riemann holomorphic, and the coefficients of the series (1.1.1) are given by (1.1.7). Comparing this with the expression (1.1.8) yields the well-known relationships between the Taylor coefficients and the partial derivatives:

$$\frac{1}{m!n!}\frac{\partial^{m+n}f(a)}{\partial z_1{}^m\,\partial z_2{}^n} = c_{mn}, \tag{1.1.10}$$

and

$$f(z) = \sum_{m=0}^{\infty}\sum_{n=0}^{\infty}\frac{1}{m!n!}\frac{\partial^{m+n}f(a)}{\partial z_1{}^m\,\partial z_2{}^n}(z_1 - a_1)^m(z_2 - a_2)^n. \tag{1.1.11}$$

Let us suppose that the series (1.1.11) converges in the bicylinder $\Delta_r(a) \equiv \{z \,||z_k - a_k| < r_k;\, k = 1, 2\}$, and consider the formal power series

$$\tilde{f}(z) \equiv \sum_{m=0}^{\infty}\sum_{n=0}^{\infty}\frac{1}{m!n!}\frac{\partial^{m+n}f(z^0)}{\partial z_1{}^m\,\partial z_2{}^n}(z_1 - z_1{}^0)^m(z_2 - z_2{}^0)^n, \tag{1.1.12}$$

where $(z_1{}^0, z_2{}^0) \in \Delta_r(a)$. We shall show that the series for $\tilde{f}(z)$ converges in the bicylinder $\Delta_\rho(z^0)$, where $\rho_k = r_k - |z_k{}^0 - a_k|$, and furthermore in this region $\tilde{f}(z) \equiv f(z)$. It follows then that $f(z)$ as defined by (1.1.11) is Weierstrass holomorphic in the interior of $\Delta_r(a)$.

From (1.1.8) we have

$$\frac{\partial^{m+n} f(z^0)}{\partial z_1{}^m \, \partial z_2{}^n} = \sum_{l=0}^{\infty} \sum_{k=0}^{\infty} \frac{(l+m)!}{l!} \frac{(k+n)!}{k!} c_{l+m,\,k+n} (z_1{}^0 - a_1)^l (z_2{}^0 - a_2)^k,$$

and hence we have

$$\left| \frac{\partial^{m+n} f(z^0)}{\partial z_1{}^m \, \partial z_2{}^n} \right| \le \sum_{l=0}^{\infty} \sum_{k=0}^{\infty} \frac{(l+m)!}{l!} \frac{(k+n)!}{k!} |c_{l+m,\,k+n}| \, |z_1{}^0 - a_1|^l \, |z_2{}^0 - a_2|^k.$$

Consequently, one has for an estimate on $\tilde{f}(z)$, when $|z_k - z_k{}^0| \le \tilde{\rho}_k < \rho_k$, $\rho_k = r_k - |z_k{}^0 - a_k| \qquad (k = 1, 2)$,

$$\begin{aligned} |\tilde{f}(z)| &\le \sum_{m=0}^{\infty} \sum_{n=0}^{\infty} \frac{1}{m!n!} \left| \frac{\partial^{m+n} f(z^0)}{\partial z_1{}^m \, \partial z_2{}^n} \right| |z_1 - z_1{}^0|^m \, |z_2 - z_2{}^0|^n \\ &\le \sum_{m,n=0}^{\infty} \frac{\tilde{\rho}_1{}^m \tilde{\rho}_2{}^n}{m!n!} \left(\sum_{l,k=0}^{\infty} \frac{(l+m)!(k+n)!}{l!k!} \right. \\ &\qquad \left. \times |c_{l+m,\,k+n}| \, |z_1{}^0 - a_1|^l \, |z_2{}^0 - a_2|^k \right) \\ &\le \sum_{p,q=0}^{\infty} |c_{p,q}| \left(\sum_{l=0}^{p} \sum_{k=0}^{q} \frac{p!q! \tilde{\rho}_1^{p-l} |z_1{}^0 - a_1|^l \tilde{\rho}_2^{q-k} |z_2{}^0 - a_2|^k}{(p-l)!l!(q-k)!k!} \right) \\ &\le \sum_{p,q=0}^{\infty} |c_{p,q}| \, \tilde{r}_1{}^p \tilde{r}_2{}^q < \infty. \end{aligned}$$

Since $\tilde{r}_k \equiv \tilde{\rho}_k + |z_k{}^0 - a_k| < r_k$ $(k = 1, 2)$, the series (1.1.1) with

$$c_{p,q} = \frac{1}{p!q!} \frac{\partial^{p+q} f(a)}{\partial z_1{}^p \, \partial z_2{}^q}$$

is uniformly and absolutely convergent in the bicylinder, $\Delta_{\tilde{r}}(a) \subset \Delta_r(a)$. We realize from this that the series (1.1.12) converges absolutely in $\Delta_{\tilde{\rho}}(z^0)$ and hence we may sum this series by regrouping the terms in various ways. For instance one such grouping gives us

$$\tilde{f}(z) = \sum_{m,n=0}^{\infty} \frac{1}{m!n!} \frac{\partial^{m+n} f(z^0)}{\partial z_1{}^m \, \partial z_2{}^n} (z_1 - z_1{}^0)^m (z_2 - z_2{}^0)^n$$

$$= \sum_{m,n=0}^{\infty} \frac{1}{m!n!} (z_1 - z_1^0)^m (z_2 - z_2^0)^n$$

$$\cdot \left(\sum_{l,k=0}^{\infty} \frac{(l+m)!(k+n)!}{l!k!} c_{l+m,k+n} (z_1^0 - a_1)^l (z_2^0 - a_2)^k \right)$$

$$= \sum_{p,q=0}^{\infty} c_{p,q}$$

$$\times \left(\sum_{l=0}^{p} \sum_{k=0}^{q} \frac{p!q!(z_1 - z_1^0)^{p-l}(z_1^0 - a_1)^l (z_2 - z_2^0)^{q-k} (z_2^0 - a_2)^k}{(p-l)!l!(q-k)!k!} \right)$$

$$= \sum_{p,q=0}^{\infty} c_{p,q}[(z_1 - z_1^0) + (z_1^0 - a_1)]^p [(z_2 - z_2^0) + (z_2^0 - a_2)]^q$$

$$= f(z).$$

We summarize the above discussion by the following theorem.

Theorem 1.1.5 *Let $f(z)$ be Weierstrass holomorphic at the point $a \in \mathfrak{D}$ and be represented there by the power series* (1.1.1), *which converges in the bicylinder $\Delta_r(a) \subset \mathfrak{D}$. Then $f(z)$ is Weierstrass holomorphic at each point $z^0 \in \Delta_r(a)$, and has a power series representation, which converges in the bicylinder $\Delta_\rho(z^0)$, where $\rho_k = r_k - |z_k^0 - a_k|$ $(k = 1, 2)$.*

The previous theorem tells us that the regrouped series (1.1.12) must converge at least in the original bicylinder. If on the other hand this series converges in a larger bicylinder, $\Delta_{\rho'}(z^0)$, i.e., where $\rho_k' > r_k - |z_k^0 - a_k|$, this regrouped series serves to provide a direct holomorphic continuation of the function element $(f(z), z^0)$. Choosing a point $z' \in \Delta_{\rho'}(z^0)$ we may again regroup terms of this series about the center z', and if its bicylinder of convergence extends past the boundary of $\Delta_{\rho'}(z^0)$ we have again obtained a continuation of our original function element. Indeed, we shall refer (as in the case of one complex variable) to any function element obtained by a finite chain of direct holomorphic continuations (using bicylinders) as a holomorphic continuation of the original function element.

Let us now define as the *real environment* [B.M. 1, p. 34] of a point $z^0 \in \mathfrak{D}$, any point set containing the rectangle

$$\mathfrak{r} \equiv \{z \mid |x_k - x_k^0| < d;\ y_k = y_k^0;\ k = 1, 2\}.$$

We note that since the partial derivatives $\partial^{m+n} f / \partial z_1^m \, \partial z_2^n$ may be evaluated at $z = z^0$ by just using points of $\mathfrak{r}$, that if $f(z) = 0$ for z in $\mathfrak{r}$, then $f(z) \equiv 0$ in a full neighborhood of z^0. Now if $f(z)$ is given to be holomorphic in the domain $\mathfrak{D}$, then it follows that $f(z) \equiv 0$ in $\mathfrak{D}$, since the value of the function $f(z)$ at each point of $\mathfrak{D}$ may be found with a finite chain of direct holomorphic continuations by bicylinders. From this fact it follows immediately that if two functions, $f_1(z)$ and $f_2(z)$, which are defined in the domains $\mathfrak{D}_1$ and $\mathfrak{D}_2$, respectively, coincide on a real environment of a point $z^0 \in \mathfrak{D}_1 \cap \mathfrak{D}_2$, then there exists a unique function defined in $\mathfrak{D}_1 \cup \mathfrak{D}_2$, which coincides with each of the $f_k(z)$ $(k = 1, 2)$ in their respective domains of definition.†

We are now able, using the information above, to give a precise meaning to the complex form of the Cauchy–Riemann equations. For instance, let us suppose the function $f(z)$ is Weierstrass holomorphic in the domain $\mathfrak{D}$. Then for each point $z^0 \in \mathfrak{D}$ there exists a bicylinder $\Delta_r(z^0)$ such that the power series

$$f(z) = \sum_{l,\,k=0}^{\infty} c_{lk}(x_1 + iy_1 - z_1{}^0)^l(x_2 + iy_2 - z_2{}^0)^k$$

converges for each $(x_1 + iy_1, x_2 + iy_2) \in \Delta_r(z^0)$. Indeed this series is seen to converge for complex values of x_k, and y_k also, provided that $|x_k| < r_k/2$, $|y_k| < r_k/2$ $(k = 1, 2)$. Hence regrouping the series in terms of powers of x_1, y_1, x_2, y_2, we see that it represents a Weierstrass holomorphic function of these four complex variables in the polycylinder $\Delta_{r/2}^{(4)}(x^0, y^0)$. If we now introduce the linear transformation $z_k = x_k + iy_k$, $z_k{}^* = x_k - iy_k$ $(k = 1, 2)$, the composite function is certainly Weierstrass holomorphic in at least the polycylinder,

$$\Delta_{r/4}^{(4)}(z^0, z^{*0}) \equiv \{(z, z^*) \,|\, |z_k - z_k{}^0| < r_k/4, |z_k{}^* - z_k^{0*}| < r_k/4; k = 1, 2\}.$$

If the closure of $\mathfrak{D}$ is compact in $\mathbb{C}^2$, then $\mathfrak{D}$ has a finite covering with bicylinders $\Delta_r(z^{(n)})$, each suitably chosen for direct holomorphic continuation of $f(z)$ between overlapping bicylinders. We conclude that in the space of four complex variables, $(x_1, x_2, y_1, y_2) \in \mathbb{C}^4$, the function $\Psi(x, y) \equiv f(z)$ is holomorphic in a four-complex dimensional neighborhood of $\mathfrak{D}$, $\mathcal{N}^{(4)}(\mathfrak{D})$. Likewise the composite function, $\Phi(z, z^*) = \Psi(x, y)$ (obtained by the linear mapping above), and the derived functions $\partial\Phi/\partial z_k{}^*$ $(k = 1, 2)$, are also holomorphic in $\mathcal{N}^{(4)}(\mathfrak{D})$.

Now if as we have assumed, $f(z)$ is holomorphic in $\mathfrak{D}$, then for each point $z^0 \in \mathfrak{D}$, the Weierstrass holomorphic function $\partial\Phi(z, z^*)/\partial z_k{}^*$ $(k = 1, 2)$, defined in the polydisk $\Delta_{r/4}^{(4)}(z^0, z^{*0})$ by the regrouped series, converges there identically to zero. We conclude from this that $\partial\Phi/\partial z_k{}^* \equiv 0$ for $(z, z^*) \in \mathcal{N}^{(4)}(\mathfrak{D})$, and hence in the restriction, $\bar{z}_k = z_k{}^*$ $(k = 1, 2)$, (i.e., x_k and y_k are

† For further results of this kind the reader is referred to [B.M.1, Chapter II].

real), $\partial\Phi/\partial\bar{z}_k \equiv 0$ ($k = 1, 2$). Hence, if we assume $f(z)$ is Weierstrass holomorphic, the complex forms of the Cauchy–Riemann equations have a clearly understood meaning.

2. *Hartogs' Theorem and Holomorphic Continuation*

At this point we are ready to demonstrate that Cauchy–Riemann and Weierstrass holomorphic are equivalent concepts. Afterwards we shall just refer to functions being simply holomorphic. To this end we first prove a theorem known as Hartogs' lemma.

Theorem 1.2.1 (Hartogs' Lemma) *Let $f(z)$ be Cauchy–Riemann holomorphic in the closed bicylinder $\Delta \equiv \{z \,||z_k| \le r_k;\ k = 1, 2\}$, and bounded in the closed bicylinder, $\tilde{\Delta} \equiv \{z \,||z_1| \le r_1, |z_2| \le \rho < r_2\}$. Then $f(z)$ is a continuous function of z_1 and z_2 simultaneously for $z \in \Delta$.*

Proof Since $f(z)$ is Cauchy–Riemann holomorphic it is holomorphic in each variable separately, and (since for one complex variable Cauchy–Riemann and Weierstrass holomorphic are obviously equivalent) we have that the series

$$f(z) = \sum_{k=0}^{\infty} f_k(z_1){z_2}^k \tag{1.2.1}$$

converges uniformly for z_2 such that $|z_2| \le r_2$. Here the variable z_1 is arbitrary with $|z_1| \le r_1$; we remark that it is not self-evident at this time that the functions $f_k(z_1)$ are analytic in $|z_1| \le r_1$. In order to see this we proceed as follows: first, $f(z_1, 0) \equiv f_0(z_1)$ must be holomorphic in $|z_1| \le r_1$; second, so are the functions $F^{(n)}(z_1, z_2)$ (for each fixed z_2, $0 < |z_2| \leqslant r_2$) defined recursively by

$$F^{(n)}(z_1, z_2) = \frac{f(z_1, z_2) - \sum_{k=0}^{n-1} f_k(z_1){z_2}^k}{{z_2}^n}$$

$$= \sum_{l=0}^{\infty} f_{l+n}(z_1){z_2}^l. \tag{1.2.2}$$

Evidently, the function $F^{(n)}(z_1, z_2)$ is Cauchy–Riemann holomorphic in the bicylinder $\{0 < |z_2| < r_2\} \times \{|z_1| < r_1\}$. Let $\{z_2^{(i)}\}$, $i \in I$ (a suitable index set), be a sequence of points in $\{0 < |z_2| < r_2\}$ which converge to $z_2 = 0$. Then

Proof Without loss of generalization we take $a_k = 0$ $(k = 1, 2)$. In order to see this let us define

$$M(z_2) = \sup_{|z_1| \leq r_1} |f(z_1, z_2)|,$$

where z_2 is arbitrary with $|z_2| \leq r_2$, and let $\Omega_n \subset \{|z_2| \leq r_2\}$ be the set of points for which $M(z_2) \leq n$. Clearly $\Omega_n \subset \Omega_{n+1}$, and each point $\tilde{z}_2 \in \{|z_2| \leq r_2\}$ must be contained in some Ω_n for $n \geq n(\tilde{z}_2)$. If this latter were not true for $z_2 = z_2{}^1$, say, then $f(z_1, z_2{}^1)$ would not be holomorphic in $|z_1| \leq r_1$, contrary to the hypothesis. In addition, we note that the point sets Ω_n are closed; this follows directly from the fact that $M(z_2)$ is a continuous function of z_2 in the disk $\Delta \equiv \{|z_2| \leq r_2\}$.

We shall now show that there exists a set Ω_n containing a disk $\{|z_2 - z_2{}^0| \leq b\}$. If this were not the case, then the sets Ω_n would be nowhere dense in $\Delta \equiv \{|z_2| \leq r_2\}$, and we would find a closed disk $D_1 \subset \Delta$, such that $D_1 \cap \Omega_1 = \varnothing$. Likewise, we may find another closed disk D_2, entirely within D_1, such that $D_2 \cap \Omega_2 = \varnothing$. Proceeding in this manner, we construct a nested sequence of closed disks D_n, with $D_n \cap \Omega_n = \varnothing$. Consequently, there would have to exist at least one point common to all the D_n, and hence exterior to all the Ω_n. This, however, is impossible, which proves our contention, that there exists a set Ω_n, containing a disk $\{|z_2 - z_2{}^0| \leq b\}$, i.e., the function $f(z_1, z_2)$ is bounded in the bicylinder

$$\{|z_1| \leq r_1\} \times \{|z_2 - z_2{}^0| \leq b\} \subset \Delta_r(0).$$

The equivalence of Cauchy–Riemann and Weierstrass holomorphic now follows by noting that if $f(z)$ is Cauchy–Riemann holomorphic in $\Delta_r(0)$ then it is also Cauchy–Riemann holomorphic in the subset $\Delta^{(1)}(0) \equiv \{|z_1| \leq r_1\} \times \{|z_2| \leq r_2/3\} \subset \Delta_r(0)$, and hence from the preceding lemma there exists a bicylinder, $\mathfrak{K}^{(1)} \equiv \{|z_1| \leq r_1\} \times \{|z_2 - z_2{}^0| \leq b\} \subset \Delta^{(1)}(0)$, in which $|f(z)|$ is bounded. From Hartogs' lemma, since $|z_2{}^0| \leq r_2/3$ we see that $f(z)$ is continuous (in all the variables) in the set $\mathfrak{K}^{(2)} \equiv \{|z_1| \leq r_1\} \times \{|z_2 - z_2{}^0| \leq \tfrac{2}{3}r_2\} \subset \Delta_r(0)$, and consequently Weierstrass holomorphic there. We conclude that $f(z)$ is bounded in $\Delta^{(1)}(0) \subset \mathfrak{K}^{(2)}$, and hence again by Hartogs' lemma (applying it to the bicylinders $\Delta^{(1)}(0)$, and $\Delta_r(0)$) continuous in $\Delta^{(1)}(0)$. This concludes our proof.

We define the *associated radii of convergence* of the power series

$$(z) = \sum_{l,\,k=0}^{\infty} c_{lk}(z_1 - a_1)^l (z_2 - a_2)^k \tag{1.2.6}$$

to be the ordered pairs of positive numbers (r_1, r_2) such that the series (1.2.1) converges in the bicylinder $\{|z_1 - a_1| < r_1\} \times \{|z_2 - a_2| < r_2\}$, but diverges in the bicylinder $\{|z_1 - a_1| < \rho_1\} \times \{|z_2 - a_2| < \rho_2\}$ if either (1) $\rho_1 > r_1$ with $\rho_2 = r_2$, or (2) $\rho_1 = r_1$ with $\rho_2 > r_2$. We remark that if $\rho_1 < r_1$ it is possible for the series (1.2.6) to converge when $\rho_2 > r_2$, which implies a functional dependence between the numbers r_1 and r_2. Clearly, if $r_2 = \Phi(r_1)$ represents such a function, then it must be monotone decreasing.

It is easy to show that the associated radii of convergence satisfy an analogue of the Cauchy–Hadamard formula for one complex variable, i.e., the relation

$$\limsup_{l+k\to\infty} {}^{l+k}\sqrt{|c_{lk}|\, r_1{}^l r_2{}^k} = 1. \tag{1.2.7}$$

To this end we consider, for $|t| < 1$, the related series,

$$\begin{aligned} f(r_1 t, r_2 t) &= \sum_{l,k=0}^{\infty} c_{lk}(r_1 t)^l (r_2 t)^k \\ &\ll \sum_{l,k=0}^{\infty} |c_{lk}|\, r_1{}^l r_2{}^k t^{l+k} \\ &= \sum_{m=0}^{\infty} \left(\sum_{j=0}^{m} |c_{j,m-j}|\, r_1{}^j r_2^{m-j} \right) t^m. \end{aligned} \tag{1.2.8}$$

Using the Cauchy–Hadamard formula for one complex variable we have

$$\limsup_{m\to\infty} \left(\sum_{j=0}^{m} |c_{j,m-j}|\, r_1{}^j r_2^{m-j} \right)^{1/m} = 1.$$

Let α be the value of the index j $(0 \le j \le m)$ for which the terms $|c_{j,m-j}|$ $r_1{}^j r_2^{m-j}$ take on the maximum value. Then one has

$$|c_{\alpha,m-\alpha}|\, r_1{}^\alpha r_2^{m-\alpha} \le \sum_{j=0}^{m} |c_{j,m-j}|\, r_1{}^j r_2^{m-j} \le (m+1)\, |c_{\alpha,m-\alpha}|\, r_1{}^\alpha r_2^{m-\alpha},$$

from which we conclude our result, namely that

$$\limsup_{m\to\infty} (|c_{\alpha,m-\alpha}|\, r_1{}^\alpha r_2^{m-\alpha})^{1/m} = \limsup_{m\to\infty} \left(\sum_{j=0}^{m} |c_{j,m-j}|\, r_1{}^j r_2^{m-j} \right)^{1/m} = 1.$$

We define a *Reinhardt circular domain*, $\mathfrak{D} \subset \mathbb{C}^2$, to be a region having the following property: There exists a point $a \equiv (a_1, a_2) \in \mathfrak{D}$ such that for each point $z \equiv (z_1, z_2) \in \mathfrak{D}$ the points $([z_1 - a_1]e^{i\theta_1} + a_1,\ [z_2 - a_2]e^{i\theta_2} + a_2) \in \mathfrak{D}$ for all $\theta_k \ni$, $0 \leq \theta_k \leq 2\pi$ $(k = 1, 2)$. We may schematically represent circular regions by making use of the *absolute quadrant*, i.e., those points in $\mathbb{R}^{(2)}$ which are represented by

$$\mathbb{R}_2^{(+)} \equiv \{(|z_1|, |z_2|) \,|\, (z_1, z_2) \in \mathfrak{D}\}. \tag{1.2.9}$$

Let us suppose now that a function $f(z_1, z_2)$ is holomorphic in a hyperspherical shell of "thickness" ε ($\varepsilon > 0$ is assumed to be small):

$$\mathfrak{D}_1 \equiv \{(z_1, z_2) \,|\, R^2 \leq |z_1|^2 + |z_2|^2 \leq (R + \varepsilon)^2\}$$

We note that $\mathfrak{D}_1$ is a circular domain, which may be represented schematically in the absolute quadrant as shown in Fig. 1. For each fixed value of z_2,

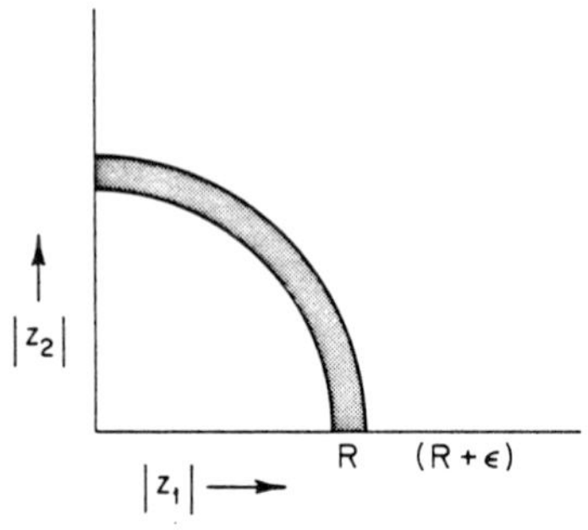

FIGURE 1

$\ni |z_2| < R + \varepsilon$, we may define a holomorphic function of z_1 in the disk $\{|z_1|^2 < (R + \eta)^2 - |z_2|^2\}$ by the Cauchy formula

$$\varphi(z_1, z_2) = \frac{1}{2\pi i} \int_{|z_1| = a} \frac{f(\zeta_1, z_2)}{\zeta_1 - z_1}\, d\zeta_1, \tag{1.2.10}$$

where $a = ((R + \eta)^2 - |z_2|^2)^{1/2}$, $\varepsilon/2 < \eta < \varepsilon$. We remark that the representation (1.2.10) yields a function $\varphi(z_1, z_2)$ which is holomorphic in each variable (i.e., holomorphic) in the circular region $\{|z_1|^2 + |z_2|^2 \leq (R + \eta)^2;\ \eta < \varepsilon\}$. If we can show that $\varphi(z_1, z_2) = f(z_1, z_2)$ in a complete neighborhood of some point in the hyperspherical shell, then $\varphi(z_1, z_2)$ provides an analytic continuation of $f(z_1, z_2)$ to the entire hypersphere $\{|z_1|^2 + |z_2|^2 \leq (R + \varepsilon)^2\}$. To this end we consider z_2 as lying in the annulus, $\{R \leq |z_2| \leq R + \varepsilon/2\}$; then inside the disk $\{|z_1| < \eta - \varepsilon/2\}$ $(\varepsilon/2 < \eta < \varepsilon)$ the function $\varphi(z_1, z_2)$, as defined by the Cauchy integral (1.2.10), equals $f(z_1, z_2)$ (Fig. 2). The point

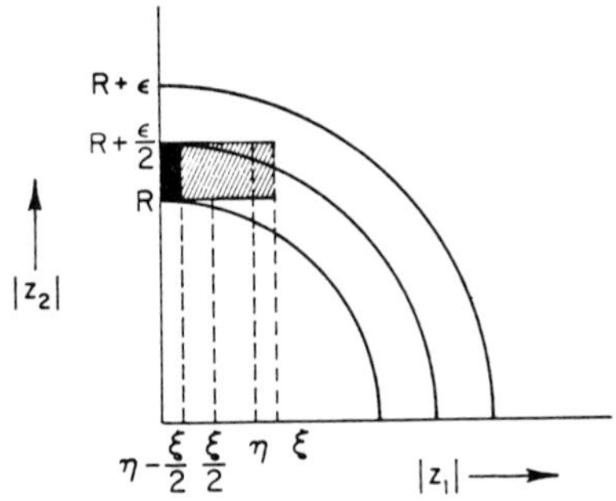

FIGURE 2

$(z_1{}^0, z_2{}^0) \equiv (0, (R + \varepsilon/4)e^{i\Psi_0})$ lies in the convex shell, and $\{|z_1| < \eta - \varepsilon/2\} \times \{|z_2 - z_2{}^0| < \varepsilon/5\}$ is a complete neighborhood of this point lying in the shell. Clearly from the above, it is seen that $\varphi(z_1, z_2) \equiv f(z_1, z_2)$ in this neighborhood, which completes our proof.

In the same way one is able to show that a function holomorphic in the circular domain,

$$\{(z_1, z_2) \mid 1 - \varepsilon \leq |z_1| \leq 1;\, |z_2| \leq 1\} \cup \{(z_1, z_2) \mid |z_1| \leq 1;\, |z_2| \leq \varepsilon\},$$

where $\varepsilon > 0$, is also holomorphic in the bicylinder, $\{(z_1, z_2) \mid |z_1| \leq 1;\, |z_2| \leq 1\}$. Phenomena such as these, where an arbitrary holomorphic function defined in a particular domain has an automatic continuation to a larger domain, are known as *analytic completions*, or *simultaneous holomorphic continuations*, etc. We remark that this concept occurs solely in the theory of *several* complex variables, and has no counterpart for analytic functions of one complex variable.

We remark that the above results may be extended considerably, and refer the reader to [B.M.1, Chapter IV] for further details. It suffices for our purpose to state the following theorem (the proof of which is similar to the method discussed above), and leave the details as an exercise for the reader.

Theorem 1.2.4 *Let* $\mathfrak{Q} \subset \mathfrak{B}$ *be two convex domains in* $\mathbb{C}^2$. *If* $f(z_1, z_2)$ *is holomorphic in the domain* $(\mathfrak{B} - \mathfrak{Q})$ *(a convex shell), then* $f(z_1, z_2)$ *has an analytic completion into the set* $\mathfrak{B}$.

At this point we make a slight digression on the zeros of holomorphic functions. To this end we shall use Hartogs' result to prove the following theorem.

Theorem 1.2.5 (The Weierstrass Preparation Theorem) *Let $F(z; w) \equiv F(z_1, \ldots, z_n, w)$ be holomorphic in a neighborhood of the origin $\mathbb{C}^{n+1}$, and let $F(0; 0) = 0$, but $F(0, w) \not\equiv 0$. Then in some neighborhood of the origin, $\mathcal{N}^{(n+4)}(0)$ there exists a representation for $F(z; w)$ of the form*

$$F(z; w) \equiv [w^m + A_1(z)w^{m-1} + \cdots + A_m(z)]\Omega(z; w),$$

with $\Omega(z, w)$ holomorphic in $\mathcal{N}^{(n+1)}(0)$, and the $A_k(z)$ $(k = 1, \ldots, m)$ holomorphic in a neighborhood of $(z) = (0)$, $\mathcal{N}^{(n)}(0)$. The functions $A_k(0) = 0$ $(k = 1, 2, \ldots, m)$; however $\Omega(0; 0) \neq 0$. Finally, if m is taken to be the order of the zero of $F(0, w)$ then the $A_k(z)$ $(k = 1, 2, \ldots, m)$ and $\Omega(z; w)$ are uniquely determined.

Proof There exists a polydisk

$$\Delta^{(n+1)} \equiv \{(z; w) \mid |w| < a; |z_k| \leq b \ (k = 1, 2, \ldots, n)\} \subset \mathcal{N}^{(n+1)}(0)$$

in which $F(z; w)$ is holomorphic. Further, by choosing a sufficiently small we may ensure that $w = 0$ is the sole zero of $F(0; w)$ in the disk $\{|w| \leq a\}$. Since $F(z; w)$ is continuous we may clearly choose b small enough so that $F(z; w) \neq 0$ for $\Delta^{(n)} \equiv \{(z) \mid |z_k| \leq b \ (k = 1, 2, \ldots, n\}$ when $|w| = a$. It follows from the argument principle and the fact that $F(z; w)$ is continuous, that the order (m) of the zero of $F(0; w)$ at $w = 0$ is the same as the number of zeros of $F(z^{(0)}; w)$ in the disk $\{|w| \leq a\}$ when $(z^0) \in \Delta^{(n)}$; consequently, one has

$$m = \frac{1}{2\pi i} \int_{|w|=a} \frac{F_w(z^{(0)}; w)}{F(z^0; w)} \, dw.$$

If the roots of $F(z; w) = 0$ are designated by $w_k(z)$ $(k = 1, 2, \ldots, m)$ for $(z) \in \Delta^{(n)}$, and $\Phi(w)$ is a function holomorphic in the disk $\{|w| \leq a\}$, then one has by the residue theorem,

$$\sum_{k=1}^{m} \Phi(w_k(z)) = \frac{1}{2\pi i} \int_{|w|=a} \Phi(w) \frac{F_w(z; w)}{F(z; w)} \, dw.$$

By choosing for $\Phi(w)$ the particular functions w^l $(1 = 1, 2, \ldots, m)$, one obtains the following relations for each fixed $(z) \in \Delta^{(n)}$:

$$Q_l(z) \equiv w_1{}^l(z) + \cdots + w_m{}^l(z) = \frac{1}{2\pi i} \int_{|w|=a} \frac{w^l F_w(z; w)}{F(z; w)} \, dw.$$

Furthermore, since $F(z; w) \neq 0$ for $(z) \in \Delta^{(n)}$ when $|w| = a$, we conclude that the functions $Q_1(z)$ $(l = 1, 2, \ldots, m)$ are holomorphic in the polycylinder $\Delta^{(n)}$. Now, it is a well-known result from algebra that the elementary symmetric functions $A_s(z)$ $(s = 1, 2, \ldots, m)$ associated with the *pseudopolynomial*,

$$\prod_{k=1}^{m} [w - w_k(z)] \equiv w^m + A_1(z)w^{m-1} + \cdots + A_m(z),$$

may be expressed as polynomials consisting of the functions $Q_l(z)$. Since $w_k(0) = 0$ $(k = 1, 2, \ldots, m)$ we have that $Q_l(0) = 0$ $(l = 1, 2, \ldots, m)$, which in turn implies the $A_s(0) = 0$ $(s = 1, 2, \ldots, m)$. Clearly this pseudopolynomial is well defined by our hypotheses concerning the function $F(z; w)$.

We turn our attention next to the function $\Omega(z; w)$, which we define as

$$\Omega(z; w) \equiv F(z; w)\left(\prod_{k=1}^{m} [w - w_k(z)]\right)^{-1}.$$

For each fixed $(z^0) \in \Delta^{(n)}$, $\Omega(z^{(0)}; w)$ is holomorphic in w for $|w| \leq a$ with the exception of the m-points, $w_s(z^{(0)})$ $(s = 1, 2, \ldots, m)$. These points must lie strictly inside the disk $\{|w| < a\}$, since for $|w| = a$ we have chosen $\Delta^{(n)}$ such that $F(w; z) \neq 0$. We may conclude from this that the only singularities of $\Omega(z; w)$ are removable, and that at these points the function $\Omega(z; w)$ may be defined by its Cauchy integral,

$$\Omega(z; w) = \frac{1}{2\pi i} \int_{|\omega| = a} \frac{\Omega(z; \omega)\, d\omega}{\omega - w}.$$

This integral shows that $\Omega(z; w)$ is holomorphic as a function of w for all $(z) \in \Delta^{(n)}$. Likewise, since $\Omega(z; w)$ is holomorphic for $(z) \in \Delta^{(n)}$ when $|w| < a$, we have by Hartogs' theorem (1.2.2) that $\Omega(z; w)$ is holomorphic in $\Delta^{(n+1)}$. This concludes our proof.

3. *Singular Points of Holomorphic Functions*

The singularities of functions of several complex variables have a much more complicated structure than in the case of one complex variable, and we shall only treat this topic for the space $\mathbb{C}^n$. To go into further details, for instance where the functions are defined in complex spaces, would be beyond the scope of this monograph. The reader interested in these aspects is referred in particular to [G.R.1], [H.11], and [F.5].

It is well known, that in the domain of definition of a holomorphic function of one complex variable the singularities of such a function are all isolated. This is not the case for functions of several complex variables, as is illustrated by the simple example

$$f(z_1, z_2) \equiv 1/z_1.$$

Here, every point, $(0, z_2)$, on the analytic plane, $z_1 = 0$, is a singular point of $f(z_1, z_2)$. However, in the sense that the value of the function $f(z_1, z_2) \to \infty$ as (z_1, z_2) approaches (in any manner) a point on this analytic plane, these singular points are analogous to polar singularities in the theory of one complex variable.

Definition *The point $(z_1, z_2) = (a_1, a_2)$ will be termed a polar point (or a nonessential singularity of the first kind) of the holomorphic function $f(z_1, z_2)$ if in a suitably small bicylindrical neighborhood of this point the function may be represented in the form*

$$f(z_1, z_2) = \frac{h(z_1, z_2)}{g(z_1, z_2)},$$

where $g(z_1, z_2)$ and $h(z_1, z_2)$ are both holomorphic at $(z) = (a)$, and where $g(a_1, a_2) = 0$ but $h(a_1, a_2) \neq 0$.

An entirely different type of singular point occurs at $(z) = (a)$ when $h(z_1, z_2)$ also vanishes at (a), providing $g(z_1, z_2)$ and $h(z_1, z_2)$ are relatively prime. In this sense it is easy to see that the value the function $f(z_1, z_2)$ approaches as $(z) \to (a)$ depends on the path, and indeed, that $f(z_1, z_2)$ may be made to approach any preassigned value. In general, in the neighborhood of such a point it may be shown, using the Weierstrass preparation theorem, that $f(z_1, z_2)$ may be written in the form

$$f(z_1, z_2) = \frac{(z_2 - a_2)^m + A_1(z_1)(z_2 - a_2)^{m-1} + \cdots + A_m(z_1)}{(z_2 - a_2)^n + B_1(z_1)(z_2 - a_2)^{n-1} + \cdots + B_n(z_1)} \Omega(z_1, z_2),$$

where the $A_k(z_1)$, $B_l(z_1)$ $(k = 1, \ldots, m)$ $(l = 1, \ldots, n)$ are analytic in a neighborhood of $z_1 = a_1$, $A_k(a_1) = B_l(a_1) = 0$, and the polynomials are prime to one another. Furthermore, $\Omega(z_1, z_2)$ is holomorphic amd nonvanishing in a suitably small bicylindrical neighborhood of $(z) = (a)$. It is clear that for the case of functions of two complex variables these nonessential singularities of the second kind are isolated points.

For what follows it is useful for us to have an analog of the implicit function theorem for several complex variables.

The Implicit Function Theorem *Let the functions* $F_k(z;\zeta) \equiv F_k(z_1, \ldots, z_n; \zeta_1, \ldots, \zeta_m)$ $(k = 1, 2, \ldots, n)$ *be holomorphic in a neighborhood of the origin in* $\mathbb{C}^{n+m}$. *Furthermore, let* $F_k(0; 0) = 0$ $(k = 1, 2, \ldots, n)$, *and the functional determinant* $\partial(F_1, \ldots, F_n)/\partial(z_1, \ldots, z_n) \neq 0$ *at the origin. Then there exists a unique solution* $z_k = z_k(\zeta)$ $(k = 1, \ldots, n)$ *of the system* $F_k(z; \zeta) = 0$ $(k = 1, 2, \ldots, n)$ *where the* $z_k(\zeta)$ *are holomorphic in a suitably small neighborhood of* $(\zeta) = (0)$.

Proof In order to show that the solution is unique we need only to reduce the above situation to the case of real functions of real variables and use the real implicit function theorem. To this end we note, by continuity, that $\partial(F_1, \ldots, F_n)/\partial(z_1, \ldots, z_n) \neq 0$ in a full neighborhood of the origin. We also note, that if U_k and V_k are the real and imaginary parts of F_k, and if the $z_k = x_k + iy_k$ $(k = 1, 2, \ldots, n)$ (with x_k and y_k real), then one has the following identity:

$$\frac{\partial(U_1, V_1, \ldots, U_n, V_n)}{\partial(x_1, y_1, \ldots, x_n, y_n)} \equiv \frac{\partial(F_1, \bar{F}_1, \ldots, F_n, \bar{F}_n)}{\partial(z_1, \bar{z}_1, \ldots, z_n, \bar{z}_n)}$$

$$= \frac{\partial(F_1, \ldots, F_n)}{\partial(z_1, \ldots, z_n)} \frac{\partial(\bar{F}_1, \ldots, \bar{F}_n)}{\partial(\bar{z}_1, \ldots, \bar{z}_n)}$$

$$= \left| \frac{\partial(F_1, \ldots, F_n)}{\partial(z_1, \ldots, z_n)} \right|^2.$$

Consequently, the functional determinant corresponding to the real system

$$(\zeta_k = \xi_k + i\eta_k, \bar{\zeta}_k = \xi_k - i\eta_k) \qquad U_k(x, y; \xi, \eta) = 0, \qquad V_k(x, y; \xi, \eta) = 0$$
$$(k = 1, \ldots, n)$$

does not vanish in a full neighborhood of the origin in $\mathbb{R}^{2(n+m)}$. We conclude that in a neighborhood of $(0) \in \mathbb{C}^m$ there exists a unique solution

$$z_k = x_k(\xi, \eta) + iy_k(\xi, \eta),$$

where the $x_k(\xi, \eta)$, $y_k(\xi, \eta)$ have continuous first partial derivatives with respect to the ξ_j and η_j. In order to see that the functions $z_k(\xi, \eta) \equiv x_k(\xi, \eta) + iy_k(\xi, \eta)$ are indeed holomorphic functions of ζ_j, we differentiate the system of equations with respect to the $\bar{\zeta}_j$, and obtain

$$\frac{\partial F_k}{\partial \bar{\zeta}_j} \equiv \sum_{l=1}^{m} \frac{\partial F_k}{\partial \bar{z}_l} \frac{\partial \bar{z}_l}{\partial \bar{\zeta}_j} + \sum_{p=1}^{m} \frac{\partial F_k}{\partial z_p} \frac{\partial z_p}{\partial \bar{\zeta}_j} = 0 \qquad (k = 1, 2, \ldots, n).$$

Since the F_k are *not* holomorphic functions of the $\bar{\zeta}_j$ we obtain the following system of linear equations for the $\partial z_l / \partial \bar{\zeta}_j$:

$$\sum_{l=1}^{m} \frac{\partial F_k}{\partial z_l} \frac{\partial z_l}{\partial \bar{\zeta}_j} = 0 \qquad (k = 1, \ldots, n).$$

The only solution of this system is the trivial solution $\partial z_1 / \partial \bar{\zeta}_j = 0$ $(l = 1, \ldots, n)$ $(j = 1, \ldots, m)$. This concludes our proof.

We now turn to the investigation of the location of singular points of holomorphic functions. We begin by considering several extensions of the idea used by Hadamard in his celebrated theorem on the multiplication of singularities [H.1], [D.4, p. 346], [T.1, p. 157]. Our first result, when $n = 1$, may be seen to actually contain Hadamard's theorem as a special case. (The reader is directed to the following papers by the present author for a survey of the development of these results: [G.6–9,11,23,24], [G.H.A.1].

Hadamard's Multiplication of Singularities Theorem *Let $f(z)$ and $g(z)$ be defined by the Taylor series*

$$f(z) = \sum_{n=0}^{\infty} a_n z^n, \qquad |z| < R,$$

$$g(z) = \sum_{n=0}^{\infty} b_n z^n, \qquad |z| < R';$$

furthermore, if $f(z)$ has singularities at $\alpha_1, \alpha_2, \ldots$, and $g(z)$ has singularities at $\beta_1, \beta_2, \ldots$, then the singularities of $F(z) = \sum a_n b_n z^n$ are to be found at the points $\alpha_m \beta_n$.

To prove this theorem we first consider the representation for $F(z)$ in a sufficiently small neighborhood of the origin,

$$F(z) = \frac{1}{2\pi i} \int_{\mathscr{L}} f(\zeta) g(z/\zeta) \, d\zeta/\zeta,$$

where $\mathscr{L}$ is a simple contour lying in the annulus $|z| R'^{-1} < |\zeta| < R$. This representation may be continued analytically along a curve γ to z_1, provided no point of γ coincides with a singularity of the integrand on the path of integration. Hadamard notes that this representation may be continued further along γ by continuously deforming $\mathscr{L}$, such that $\mathscr{L}$ at no time crosses a singularity of the integrand. Since the singularities of $f(z)$ are at $\{\alpha_m\}$ and those of $g(z/\zeta)$ are at $\{z/\beta_n\}$ we see that it is always possible to make such a deformation except when a point z/β_n coincides with a point α_m, that is, for $z = \alpha_m \beta_n$. For further details the reader is referred to [T.1, p. 157], [D.4, p. 346], and [H.9, Vol. II].

Notation For conciseness of presentation in what follows we shall adopt the notation that

$$\mathfrak{S}_0 = \mathfrak{S}_1 \cap \mathfrak{S}_2,$$

where

$$\mathfrak{S}_1 \equiv \{(z) \mid F_1(z;\zeta) = 0;\ \zeta \in \mathbb{C}^1\},$$

$$\mathfrak{S}_2 \equiv \{(z) \mid F_2(z;\zeta) = 0;\ \zeta \in \mathbb{C}^1\},$$

is to mean

$$\mathfrak{S}_0 \equiv \{(z) \mid \exists\ a\zeta \in \mathbb{C}^1 \ni F_1(z;\zeta) = F_2(z;\zeta) = 0\}.$$

Theorem 1.3.1 (The Envelope Method [G.6]) *Let* $F(z) \equiv F(z_1, z_2, \ldots, z_n)$ *be defined by the integral representation*

$$F(z) = \int_{\mathscr{L}} K(z;\zeta)\, d\zeta,$$

where $K(z;\zeta)$ *is a holomorphic function of* $(n+1)$ *complex variables for* $(z;\zeta)$ *contained in, save for certain singularities indicated below,* $\mathbb{C}^{n+1}$. *Furthermore, let the integration path* $\mathscr{L} \subset \mathbb{C}^{(1)}$ *be a closed rectifiable contour, and let all of the singular points of* $K(z;\zeta)$ *be contained on the analytic set* $\mathfrak{S}_0^{(n)} \equiv \{(z) \mid S(z;\zeta) = 0;\ \zeta \in \mathbb{C}^1\}$. *Then* $F(z)$ *is regular for all points,*

$$(z) \notin \mathfrak{S}^{(n-1)} \equiv \mathfrak{S}_0^{(n)} \cap \mathfrak{S}_1^{(n)}, \tag{1.3.1}$$

where

$$\mathfrak{S}_1^{(n)} \equiv \{(z) \mid S_\zeta(z;\zeta) = 0;\ \zeta \in \mathbb{C}^1\}.$$

Proof Since $F(z)$ is regular-analytic in some domain $\mathfrak{D}^{(n)}$, one may choose a point $(z^0) \in \mathfrak{D}^{(n)}$ and a neighborhood of (z^0), $\mathscr{N}^{(n)}(z^0)$, in which the integral defines a regular function element of $F(z)$. Starting with this function element we may continue it analytically along any contour, γ, initiating at (z^0) and terminating with the point (z), providing no point of γ corresponds to a singularity of the integrand on the path of integration, $\mathscr{L}$. We shall refer to the union of all such points (z) as the *initial domain of definition* of $F(z)$.

Since all of the singularities of $K(z; \zeta)$ lie on $\mathfrak{S}_0^{(n)}$ it is clear that as $F(z)$ is continued along γ the singularities of the integrand move in the ζ-plane. It follows that the initial domain of definition consists of all points (z) which may be reached without a singularity in the ζ-plane passing over $\mathscr{L}$. It is is possible, however, that the integral representation for $F(z)$ may be extended to other points by continuously deforming the path of integration, provided that in so doing we do not cross a singularity in the ζ-plane. All such points (z) reached by continuing $F(z)$ along paths γ (which can be reached by suitably deforming the path of integration) we shall refer to as the *domain of association* of $F(z)$. It is clear that the domain of association consists of the set of all points at which there exists a regular function element of $F(z)$, and furthermore, if one considers all such possible paths, γ, one constructs in this way all the regular function elements associated with $F(z)$.

We now consider when it may be no longer possible to continue $F(z)$ along a path γ_1. This case occurs (assuming we can solve $S(z, \zeta) = 0$ as a function of z, $\zeta = \alpha(z)$, say) when a singularity $\zeta = \alpha(z)$ threatens to cross the contour $\mathscr{L}$ and it is no longer possible to deform $\mathscr{L}$ and avoid it. In other words, when $F(z)$ has been continued along γ_1 up to a point (z_1), and at that point $(z) = (z_1)$ there exists a singularity $\zeta = \alpha$ on the path of integration. If $S(z_1; \zeta)$ has a simple zero at $\zeta = \alpha_1$ one may, in a suitably small neighborhood $\mathscr{N}(\alpha) \equiv \{\zeta \mid |\zeta - \alpha| < \varepsilon\}$, approximate

$$S(z_1; \zeta) \approx (\zeta - \alpha) \frac{\partial S(z_1; \alpha)}{\partial \zeta}.$$

In this case, it is clear that for $\zeta \in \mathscr{N}(\alpha)$, $S(z_1; \zeta) \neq 0$ except for $\zeta = \alpha$, and one may deform $\mathscr{L}$ about the point $\zeta = \alpha$ by letting it follow a portion of the circle $\{|\zeta - \alpha| = \frac{1}{2}\varepsilon\}$. This completes the proof of our theorem.

Remark If $\mathscr{L}$ is not a closed contour, but rather an open contour between two fixed points ζ_1 and ζ_2, then there is an additional set which must be considered as candidates for singularities. Indeed, since the points ζ_1 and ζ_2 are fixed they are distinguished in the sense that it is impossible to deform the contour away from a singularity which tends to either of these points. In the case of Theorem 1.3.1 we would also have the set

$$\mathfrak{S}^{(n-1)} \equiv \{(z) \mid S(z; \zeta) = 0;\ \zeta = \zeta_1 \text{ and } \zeta = \zeta_2\}$$

as possible singularities of $F(z)$ ([G.9, p. 175]). We refer to such singularities as *boundary-pinch* or *endpoint-pinch singularities*.

By replacing the kernel $K(z;\zeta)$ by $f_1(z;\zeta)f_2(z;\zeta)$ we may obtain a variation of this result, namely:

Theorem 1.3.2 *Let $K(z;\zeta)$ be a holomorphic function of $(n+1)$ variables as in Theorem* 1.3.1 *with a decomposition in that domain into a product of nonconstant, holomorphic functions,* i.e., $K(z;\zeta) \equiv f_1(z;\zeta)f_2(z;\zeta)$. *Furthermore, let the functions $f_\nu(z;\zeta)$, $(\nu = 1, 2)$, be singular on the analytic set $\mathfrak{S}_\nu^{(n)} \equiv \{(z) \mid \zeta = \alpha_\nu(z);\ \zeta \in \mathbb{C}^1\}$ $(\nu = 1, 2)$, respectively with $\mathfrak{S}_\nu^{(n)} \neq \varnothing$ $(\nu = 1, 2)$. Then the "possible singularities" of the function $F(z)$ (defined by the Cauchy integral above) generated from the singularity sets $\mathfrak{S}_\nu^{(n)}$, as given by the "envelope method", are the same as the coincidence set $\tilde{\mathfrak{S}}^{(n-1)} \equiv \mathfrak{S}_1^{(n)} \cap \mathfrak{S}_2^{(n)}$.*

Proof By singularities obtained by the "Hadamard method" we mean those points which are computed by eliminating ζ from the two representations corresponding to the singularity sets $\mathfrak{S}_1^{(n)}$ and $\mathfrak{S}_2^{(n)}$. These candidates for singularities occur, as in Hadamard's theorem cited above, because of a coincidence of singular points of the integrand in the ζ-planes. By the term "possible singularities" we mean those points which we are unable to list as regular points by either the "envelope" or "Hadamard methods."

Applying the envelope method by constructing as the singularity manifold of $K(z;\zeta)$, the analytic set

$$\mathfrak{S}^{(n)} \equiv \{(z) \mid [\zeta - \alpha_1(z)][\zeta - \alpha_2(z)] = 0;\ \zeta \in \mathbb{C}^1\},$$

and following Theorem 1.3.1, we compute

$$\mathfrak{A}^{(n)} \equiv \{(z) \mid [\zeta - \alpha_1(z)] + [\zeta - \alpha_2(z)] = 0;\ \zeta \in \mathbb{C}^1\}.$$

Since the singularities must lie on $\mathfrak{S}^{(n)} \cap \mathfrak{A}^{(n)}$, this means (z) is a regular point providing $(z) \notin [\{(z) \mid \zeta = \alpha_1(z); \zeta \in \mathbb{C}^1\} \cap \{(z) \mid \zeta = \alpha_2(z); \zeta \in \mathbb{C}^1\}] \equiv \mathfrak{S}_1^{(n)} \cap \mathfrak{S}_2^{(n)}$.

The assumption of "explicit representations" of the singularity sets of $f_\nu(z;\zeta)$ $(\nu = 1, 2)$ (i.e., $\zeta = a_\nu(z)$, $\nu = 1,2$) rules out singularities due to coincidences involving the functions $f_1(z;\zeta)$ or $f_2(z;\zeta)$ alone. For instance, let us consider the envelope method where $f_\nu(z;\zeta)$ $(\nu = 1, 2)$ is singular on $\mathfrak{S}_\nu^{(n)} = \{(z) \mid S_\nu(z;\zeta) = 0;\ \zeta = \mathbb{C}^1\}$ where $S_\nu(z;\zeta)$ is a global representation of the singularities. Then by setting

$$\mathfrak{S}^{(n)} = \{(z) \mid S_1(z;\zeta)S_2(z;\zeta) = 0;\ \zeta \in \mathbb{C}^1\},$$

and

$$\mathfrak{A}^{(n)} = \left\{(z) \middle| \frac{\partial}{\partial \zeta} S_1 S_2 = 0;\ \zeta \in \mathbb{C}^1\right\},$$

it is seen by the envelope method that it is possible for $F(z)$ to be singular on $\mathfrak{S}_1^{(n)} \cap \mathfrak{A}_1^{(n)}$, which is a subset of $\mathfrak{S}^{(n)} \cap \mathfrak{A}^{(n)}$. If $S_1 = 0$ but $S_2 \neq 0$ and if $\partial S_1/\partial\zeta = 0$ it is evident that z may satisfy both intersection conditions but not be one of the singularities mentioned in Theorem 1.3.2. However, in this case it is not possible to represent $\mathfrak{S}_1^{(n)}$ in the form $\{(z) \mid \zeta = \alpha(z);\ \zeta \in \mathbb{C}^1\}$ where the first derivative $\partial S_1/\partial\zeta$ vanishes. The requirement that the singularity sets of $f_\nu(z;\zeta)$ $(\nu = 1, 2)$ have the above representation is equivalent to

$$\bigcup_{\nu=1,2} \mathfrak{S}_\nu^{(n)} \cap \mathfrak{A}_\nu^{(n)} = \varnothing \qquad \text{with} \quad \mathfrak{A}_\nu^{(n)} = \left\{(z) \,\middle|\, S_\zeta\,(z;\zeta) = 0;\ \zeta \in \mathbb{C}^1\right\}.$$

A natural extension of these results may be made by considering multiple integrals, and combinations of the Hadamard and envelope methods used alternately. We offer the following theorem as an example of the type of results one may obtain using this approach.

Theorem 1.3.3 *Let $K(z;\zeta_1,\zeta_2)$ be, save for certain singularities indicated below an analytic function of $(n+2)$ variables, $(z;\zeta_1,\zeta_2) \equiv (z_1,\ldots,z_n;\zeta_1,\zeta_2)$, regular in $(\mathbb{C}^n \times \mathbb{C}^2)$. Let $\mathscr{L}_\nu \subset \mathbb{C}^1(\nu = 1, 2)$ be closed rectifiable curves in the ζ_ν-planes, respectively. and let $K(z;\zeta_1,\zeta_2)$ be singular on the analytic set $\mathfrak{S}^{(n)} \equiv \{(z) \mid S(z;\zeta_1,\zeta_2) = 0;\ (\zeta) \in \mathbb{C}^2\}$. Then, the function $F(z)$ defined by the representation*

$$F(z) \equiv \int_{\mathscr{L}_1} d\zeta_1 \int_{\mathscr{L}_2} d\zeta_2\, K(z;\zeta_1,\zeta_2), \qquad (z) \in \mathfrak{D}^{(n)} \quad (\textit{a domain of definition})$$

is regular for all $(z) \notin \mathfrak{S}_1^{(n)} \cap \mathfrak{A}_1^{(n)} \cap \mathfrak{A}_2^{(n)}$, where

$$\mathfrak{A}_\nu^{(n)} \equiv \left\{(z) \,\middle|\, S_{\zeta_\nu}\,(z;\zeta_1,\zeta_2) = 0;\ (\zeta) \in \mathbb{C}^2\right\} \qquad (\nu = 1, 2). \qquad (1.3.2)$$

Proof Our proof is similar to those given before. (Results of this kind were first given by the present author in [G.6]). We consider all points (z) which may be reached by continuing $F(z)$ along a contour γ, such that no point on this contour corresponds to a singularity of the integrand on the domain of integration $\mathscr{L}_1 \times \mathscr{L}_2$. Again, we attempt to enlarge this initial domain of definition by continuously deforming $\mathscr{L}_1$ and $\mathscr{L}_2$, providing we do not let either curve pass over a singularity in its respective plane. (As we deform one of the curves we must be careful that a singularity does not move over the "stationary" curve in the other plane.) We assume we have been able to continue $F(z)$ to the point $(z) = (z_1)$, where the singularity $(\zeta_1, \zeta_2) = (\alpha_1, \alpha_2)$ threatens to meet $\mathscr{L}_1 \times \mathscr{L}_2$. If both $S_{\zeta_\nu}(z; \alpha_1, \alpha_2)$ $(\nu = 1, 2)$ do not vanish, then in a suitably small bicylindrical neighborhood of (α_1, α_2), $\mathscr{N}^{(2)}(\alpha_1, \alpha_2) \equiv \{(\zeta_1, \zeta_2) \,\|\, \zeta_\nu - \alpha_\nu| < \varepsilon_\nu;\ \nu = 1, 2\}$, we may approximate:

$$S(z_1; \zeta_1, \zeta_2) \approx (\zeta_1 - \alpha_1)\frac{\partial S(z_1; \alpha_1, \alpha_2)}{\partial \zeta_1} + (\zeta_2 - \alpha_2)\frac{\partial S(z_1; \alpha_1, \alpha_2)}{\partial \zeta_2}$$

In this case we may deform $\mathscr{L}_1, \mathscr{L}_2$ about the point (α_1, α_2) in such a manner that $S(z_1; \zeta_1, \zeta_2) \neq 0$ for (ζ_1, ζ_2) on the set

$$\left\{|\zeta_1 - \alpha_1| = \frac{\varepsilon_1}{2}\right\} \times \left\{|\zeta_2 - \alpha_2| = \frac{\varepsilon_1}{4}\left|\frac{\partial S/\partial \zeta_1}{\partial S/\partial \zeta_2}\right|\right\}.$$

If one of the terms $S_{\zeta_\nu}(z; \alpha_1, \alpha_2)$ $(\nu = 1, 2)$ vanishes, then the proof follows that of Theorem 1.3.1. This concludes our argument.

We consider next several extensions of this last result. Let us assume first that $K(z; \zeta_1, \zeta_2)$ may be decomposed into the form $K(z; \zeta_1, \zeta_2) \equiv f_1(z; \zeta_1, \zeta_2) \times f_2(z; \zeta_1, \zeta_2)$, where the $f_\nu(z; \zeta_1, \zeta_2)$ are analytic in $\mathbb{C}^{n+2}$ with the exception of singularities on the respective analytic sets $\mathfrak{S}_{\nu,0}^{(n)} = \{(z) \mid S_\nu(z; \zeta_1, \zeta_2) = 0;\ (\zeta) \in \mathbb{C}^2\}$; let γ be a curve in the space of the (z) variables starting at an initial point $(z^0) \in \mathfrak{D}^{(n)}$ (a domain of definition), and terminating at (z).

We are able to obtain the following result concerning the continuation of function elements defined about $(z^0) \in \mathfrak{D}^{(n)}$ by the integral representation:

$$F(z) = \int_{\mathscr{L}_1}\int_{\mathscr{L}_2} f_1(z; \zeta_1, \zeta_2) f_2(z; \zeta_1, \zeta_2)\, d\zeta_1\, d\zeta_2,$$

Theorem 1.3.4 *Let $f_\nu(z; \zeta_1, \zeta_2)$ $(\nu = 1, 2)$, with the exception of certain singularities indicated below, be analytic in $\mathbb{C}^{n+2}$ with the singular sets $\mathfrak{S}_{\nu,0}^{(n)}$ as described above. Further, let $\mathscr{L}_\nu$ be rectifiable contours in the ζ_ν-planes respectively; then the continuation of the analytic function element $F(z)$ as given by the double Cauchy integral above is regular at all points which may be arcwise connected to the initial point of definition by a curve not passing through the set $\mathfrak{h}^{(n-1)} \cup \mathfrak{E}_{1,2}^{(n-1)} \subset \mathfrak{E}^{(n-1)}$.*

Proof Let us first introduce some notation for the singularity sets that are involved:

$$\mathfrak{S}_{\nu,1}^{(n)} \equiv \left\{(z) \left| \frac{\partial}{\partial \zeta_1} S_\nu(z; \zeta_1, \zeta_2) = 0; (\zeta) \in \mathbb{C}^2 \right.\right\} \qquad (\nu = 1, 2)$$

$$\mathfrak{S}_{\nu,2}^{(n)} \equiv \left\{(z) \left| \frac{\partial}{\partial \zeta_2} S_\nu(z; \zeta_1, \zeta_2) = 0; (\zeta) \in \mathbb{C}^2 \right.\right\} \qquad (\nu = 1, 2)$$

$$\mathfrak{E}^{(n)} \equiv \left\{(z) \left| \frac{\partial S_1}{\partial \zeta_1}\frac{\partial S_2}{\partial \zeta_2} - \frac{\partial S_1}{\partial \zeta_2}\frac{\partial S_2}{\partial \zeta_1} = 0; (\zeta) \in \mathbb{C}^2 \right.\right\} \qquad (1.3.3)$$

$$\mathfrak{Q}_0^{(n)} \equiv \{(z) \mid S_1(z; \zeta_1, \zeta_2) S_2(z; \zeta_1, \zeta_2) = 0; (\zeta) \in \mathbb{C}^2\}$$

$$\mathfrak{Q}_1^{(n)} \equiv \left\{(z) \left| \frac{\partial S_1}{\partial \zeta_1} S_2 + S_1 \frac{\partial S_2}{\partial \zeta_1} = 0; (\zeta) \in \mathbb{C}^2 \right.\right\}$$

$$\mathfrak{Q}_2^{(n)} \equiv \left\{(z) \left| \frac{\partial S_1}{\partial \zeta_2} S_2 + S_1 \frac{\partial S_2}{\partial \zeta_2} = 0; (\zeta) \in \mathbb{C}^2 \right.\right\}.$$

We notice first that "candidates" for singularities occur which correspond to the "envelope" of either $\mathfrak{S}_{1,0}^{(n)}$ or $\mathfrak{S}_{2,0}^{(n)}$. We conclude, singular points of $F(z)$ may be contained in the set

$$\bigcup_{\nu=1,2} \left\{ \bigcap_{\mu=0,1,2} \mathfrak{S}_{\nu,\mu}^{(n+1)} \right\} \equiv \bigcup_{\nu=1,2} \mathfrak{E}_\nu^{(n-1)} \equiv \mathfrak{E}_{1,2}^{(n-1)},$$

where $\mathfrak{E}_\nu^{(n-1)}$ is the "envelope" corresponding to $\mathfrak{S}_{\nu,0}^{(n)}$. The Hadamard approach, on the other hand (eliminating ζ_1 or ζ_2 between the equations $S_1 = 0$ and $S_2 = 0$), applied to either variable ζ_1, or ζ_2, followed by the envelope method applied to the eliminant, yields the following set of possible singularities,

$$\mathfrak{H}^{(n-1)} \equiv \mathfrak{S}_{1,0}^{(n)} \cap \mathfrak{S}_{2,0}^{(n)} \cap \mathfrak{H}_{1,2}^{(n)},$$

$$\mathfrak{H}_{1,2}^{(n)} \equiv \left\{(z) \left| \frac{\partial S_1}{\partial \zeta_1}\frac{\partial S_2}{\partial \zeta_2} - \frac{\partial S_1}{\partial \zeta_2}\frac{\partial S_2}{\partial \zeta_1} = 0; (\zeta) \in \mathbb{C}^2 \right.\right\}.$$

The set $\mathfrak{H}^{(n-1)}$ is computed by applying the envelope method to the eliminant of $\mathfrak{S}_{1,0}^{(n)} \cap \mathfrak{S}_{2,0}^{(n)}$, regardless which variable ζ_1 or ζ_2 has been eliminated (by the Hadamard approach), providing no $\partial S_\nu/\partial \zeta_\mu = 0$ ($\nu, \mu = 1, 2$). The case where all the $\partial S_\nu/\partial \zeta_\mu = 0$ is contained above (in the envelope method approach), and if *not all* the $\partial S_\nu/\partial \zeta_\mu = 0$, we may compute $\mathfrak{H}^{(n)}$ by eliminating a *particular* variable first. Finally, by applying Theorem 1.3.3 to the combined singularity manifold of the integrand, $\mathfrak{Q}_0^{(n)}$, we obtain as the set of possible singularities for $F(z)$,

$$\mathfrak{E}^{(n-1)} \equiv \mathfrak{Q}_0^{(n)} \cap \mathfrak{Q}_1^{(n)} \cap \mathfrak{Q}_2^{(n)}.$$

Moreover, it is easy to see from the definitions of $\mathfrak{H}^{(n-1)}$ and $\mathfrak{E}^{(n-1)}$ that $\mathfrak{H}^{(n-1)} \subset \mathfrak{E}^{(n-1)}$. This concludes our proof.

As a final illustration of the type of results we may obtain by this approach we shall obtain the following theorem, which will be of direct use to us later, in the section on applications to scattering theory (Chapter V). Let us consider the integral

$$F(z) = \int_{\mathscr{L}_1} \int_{\mathscr{L}_2} K(z; \zeta_1, \zeta_2) \times f_1(z; \zeta_1) f_2(z; \zeta_2)\, d\zeta_1\, d\zeta_2, \qquad (1.3.4)$$

and furthermore, let $\mathfrak{S}^{n}_{0,0} \equiv \{(z) \mid S(z; \zeta_1, \zeta_2) = 0; (\zeta) \in \mathbb{C}^2\}$, $\mathfrak{S}^{(n)}_{v,0} \equiv \{(z) \mid \zeta_v = \Phi_v(z);\ \zeta_v \in \mathbb{C}^1\}$ $(v = 1, 2)$ be singular sets of $K(z; \zeta_1, \zeta_2)$, and $f_v(z; \zeta_v)$ $(v = 1, 2)$, respectively. Let $\mathfrak{S}^{(n)}_{0,\mu} \equiv \{(z) \mid S_{\zeta_\mu}(z; \zeta_1, \zeta_2) = 0; \zeta \in \mathbb{C}^2\}$ $(\mu = 1, 2)$. The singularity manifold of the integrand is

$$\mathfrak{Q}_0^{(n)} \equiv \{(z) \mid S(z; \zeta_1, \zeta_2)(\zeta_1 - \Phi_1(z))(\zeta_2 - \Phi_2(z)) = 0; (\zeta) \in \mathbb{C}^2\},$$

and we define as usual

$$\mathfrak{Q}_1^{(n)} \equiv \{(z) \mid S_{\zeta_1}(z; \zeta)(\zeta_1 - \Phi_1)(\zeta_2 - \Phi_2) - S(z; \zeta)(\zeta_2 - \Phi_2) = 0; (\zeta) \in \mathbb{C}^2\},$$

and

$$\mathfrak{Q}_2^{(n)} \equiv \{(z) \mid S_{\zeta_2}(z; \zeta)(\zeta_1 - \Phi_1)(\zeta_2 - \Phi_2) - S(z; \zeta)(\zeta_1 - \Phi_1) = 0; (\zeta) \in \mathbb{C}^2\}.$$

Clearly, if we apply the envelope method to the entire integrand we have as "possible" singularities points contained in the set $\bigcap_{v=0,1,2} \mathfrak{Q}_v^{(n)}$.

If we apply the envelope method to the singularities of the kernel we obtain the set

$$\bigcap_{\mu=0,1,2} \mathfrak{S}^{(n)}_{0,\mu} \subset \bigcap_{v=0,1,2} \mathfrak{Q}_v^{(n)}.$$

Applying the Hadamard method to both ζ_v $(v = 1, 2)$ variables we obtain

$$\mathfrak{S}^{(n)}_{0,0} \cap \mathfrak{S}^{(n)}_{1,0} \cap \mathfrak{S}^{(n)}_{2,0} \equiv \{(z) \mid S(z; \Phi_1(z), \Phi_2(z)) = 0\} \subset \bigcap_{v=0,1,2} \mathfrak{Q}_v^{(n)}.$$

Corollary to Theorem 1.3.4 *The possible singularities of the analytic continuation of the function element given in* $\mathfrak{D}^{(n)}$ *by* (1.3.4) *lie on the set*

$$\mathfrak{S}^{(n)}_{0,0} \cap \left[\left(\bigcap_{\mu=1,2} \mathfrak{S}^{(n)}_{0,\mu}\right) \cup \left(\bigcap_{v=1,2} \mathfrak{S}^{(n)}_{v,0}\right) \cup (\mathfrak{S}^{(n)}_{0,1} \cap \mathfrak{S}^{(n)}_{2,0}) \cup (\mathfrak{S}^{(n)}_{0,2} \cap \mathfrak{S}^{(n)}_{1,0})\right] \subset \bigcap_{\mu=0,1,2} \mathfrak{Q}_\mu^{(n)}.$$

Bergman has recently obtained results concerning the location of certain singular points of a holomorphic function represented by a series development

$$f(z_1, z_2) = \sum_{m=0}^{\infty} \sum_{l=0}^{\infty} a_{ml} z_1{}^m z_2{}^l. \tag{1.3.5}$$

He does this by considering the restriction of $f(z_1, z_2)$ to an analytic plane through the origin, thereby obtaining a function of just a single complex variable, and then employing several results from classical function theory. We shall reproduce with some modification his results after a short digression on the geometry of analytic planes, which is necessary for greater clarity of presentation.

Let $\mathfrak{P}(\alpha) \equiv \{(z) \mid z_2 = \alpha z_1; \operatorname{Re}[\alpha] \geq 0\}$ be an analytic plane through the origin. Then it is clear that for each point $(z_1^{(0)}, z_2^{(0)}) \neq (0)$, there exists just one analytic plane $\mathfrak{P}(\alpha^{(0)})$ with $\alpha^{(0)} = z_2{}^0/z_1^{(0)}$. (In the case $z_1^{(0)}) = 0$ we shall take $\alpha^{(0)} = \infty$, or rather consider instead the analytic surfaces corresponding to $z_1 = \beta^{(0)} z_2$ with $\beta^{(0)} = z_1^{(0)}/z_2^{(0)} = 0$.) We shall refer to α as being the *plane parameter* for $\mathfrak{P}(\alpha)$.

We remark that if $\mathfrak{P}(\alpha^{(0)})$ and $\mathfrak{P}(\alpha^{(1)})$ are analytic planes corresponding to the complex points $(z^{(0)}) \equiv (z_1^{(0)}, z_2^{(0)})$ and $(z^{(1)}) \equiv (z_1^{(1)}, z_2^{(1)})$ respectively, then one may compute the *angle* between the two analytic planes as follows: clearly the angle between the vectors drawn from the origin to the points $(z^{(0)})$ and $(z^{(1)})$, respectively, may be computed by the formula

$$\cos \Psi = \frac{\operatorname{Re} \sum_{k=1}^{2} z_k^{(0)} \overline{z_k^{(1)}}}{\|z^{(0)}\| \cdot \|z^{(1)}\|}, \tag{1.3.6}$$

where $\|z\| \equiv (|z_1|^2 + |z_2|^2)^{1/2}$. The planes $\mathfrak{P}(\alpha^{(k)})$ $(k = 1, 2)$ consist of the collection of points $(z_1, z_2) \equiv (\lambda z_1^{(k)}, \lambda z_2^{(k)})$, where $\lambda \in \mathbb{C}^1$. The angle between the two planes $\mathfrak{P}(\alpha^{(0)})$, $\mathfrak{P}(\alpha^{(1)})$ is defined to be the minimum angle between arbitrary vectors drawn from the origin to the points $(w_1^{(k)}, w_2^{(k)}) \in \mathfrak{P}(\alpha^{(k)})$ $(k = 0, 1)$. Hence, in order to determine this angle, θ, we compute its cosine to be the maximum for all $(\lambda, \mu) \in \mathbb{C}^2$ of

$$\operatorname{Re}\left\{\frac{\lambda\bar{\mu}}{|\lambda\mu|} \sum_{k=1}^{2} z_k^{(0)} \overline{z_k^{(1)}}\right\}.$$

If we set the value of $\lambda\bar{\mu}/|\lambda\mu|$, which maximizes this term, equal to $e^{-i\varphi}$, then φ is clearly the angle of rotation necessary to make the complex number $\sum_{k=1}^{2} z_k^{(0)} \overline{z_k^{(1)}}$ a positive real. Consequently, one has

$$e^{i\varphi} \cos \theta = \frac{\sum_{k=1}^{2} z_k^{(0)} \overline{z_k^{(1)}}}{\|z^{(0)}\| \cdot \|z^{(1)}\|}. \tag{1.3.7}$$

By rearranging terms we have

$$\begin{aligned}\sin\theta &= (1-|e^{i\varphi}\cos\theta|^2)^{1/2}\\ &= \left[1-\left(\frac{|\sum_{k=1}^{2} z_k^{(0)}\overline{z_k^{(1)}}|}{\|z^{(0)}\|\cdot\|z^{(1)}\|}\right)^2\right]^{1/2}\\ &= \frac{[(\sum_{k=1}^{2}|z_k^{(0)}|^2)(\sum_{k=1}^{2}|z_k^{(1)}|^2)-|\sum_{k=1}^{2} z_k^{(0)}\overline{z_k^{(1)}}|^2]^{1/2}}{\|z^{(0)}\|\cdot\|z^{(1)}\|}\\ &= \frac{|z_1^{(0)}z_2^{(1)}+z_2^{(0)}z_1^{(1)}|}{\|z^{(0)}\|\cdot\|z^{(1)}\|}. \end{aligned} \tag{1.3.8}$$

The angles θ and φ are referred to as the first and second analytic angles respectively, between the vectors $\{z^{(0)}\}$ and $\{z^{(1)}\}$.

In each plane $\mathfrak{P}(\alpha)$ we introduce a polar coordinate system ρ_α, φ_α, whose origin coincides with the origin in the space of two complex variables z_1, z_2. The positive real axis is chosen in the plane $\mathfrak{P}(\alpha)$ to be the points of the intersection $\mathfrak{P}(\alpha) \cap \{y_1 = 0\}$, which correspond to $x_2 > 0$.

In each plane $\mathfrak{P}(\alpha)$ the function $f(z_1, z_2)$ becomes a holomorphic function of a single complex variable, i.e.,

$$F_\alpha(z_1) \equiv f(z_1, \alpha z_1) = \sum_{n=0}^{\infty} z_1{}^n\left(\sum_{k=0}^{n} a_{n-k,k}\alpha^k\right); \tag{1.3.9}$$

clearly at each point (z_1, z_2) at which $f(z_1, z_2)$ is regular the restriction $F_\alpha(z_1)$ is regular. By the Cauchy–Hadamard formula $F_\alpha(z_1)$ is regular in the disk $|z_1| < \tilde{\rho}(\alpha)$, where

$$\tilde{\rho}(\alpha) \equiv \limsup_{n\to\infty}\left[\left|\sum_{k=0}^{n} a_{n-k,k}\alpha^k\right|^{1/n}\right]. \tag{1.3.10}$$

Using the Mandelbrojt theorems [M.2] for the location of the first singular point on the circle of convergence, $|z| = \tilde{\rho}(\alpha)$, one obtains as the argument of said point,

$$\tilde{\varphi}(\alpha) = \liminf_{\beta\to\infty}|\varphi(\beta)| \qquad (0 \le \arg(\beta-\alpha) \le 2\pi); \tag{1.3.11}$$

where $\cos\varphi(\beta) \le R^{(+)\prime}(0, \beta)$. Here $R^{(+)\prime}(0, \beta)$ is the right-hand derivative (at $h = 0$) of the function

$$\mathrm{R}(h, \alpha) \equiv \limsup_{n\to\infty}[|d_n(h, \alpha)|^{1/n}], \tag{1.3.12}$$

where

$$d_n(h, \alpha) \equiv \sum_{k=0}^{n} \left[\binom{n}{k} \tilde{\rho}^k(\alpha) h^{n-k} \left(\sum_{l=0}^{n-k} a_{n-k-l,l} \alpha^l \right) \right]. \tag{1.3.13}$$

We are now in a position to establish Bergman's coefficient theorem.

Theorem 1.3.5 *Let $f(z_1, z_2)$ be a holomorphic function of two complex variables in a neighborhood of the origin and having the Taylor expansion* (1.3.5). *If for every $\alpha_0 \in \mathbb{C}^1$, there exists a neighborhood $\mathcal{N}(\alpha_0)$, such that for each $\alpha \in \mathcal{N}(\alpha_0)$, and $h > 0$ sufficiently small one has*

$$\tilde{\rho}(\alpha)[R^{(+)'}(0, \alpha) + h - 1] \geq s > 0, \tag{1.3.14}$$

then $f(z_1, z_2)$ is regular in the Behnke–Caratheodory circular domain $\mathcal{L} \cup \mathfrak{L}^{(3)}$, where

$$\mathcal{L} \equiv \{(z) \,|\, |\alpha| \leq \infty, \rho < \tilde{\rho}(\alpha), 0 \leq \varphi \leq 2\pi\}, \tag{1.3.15}$$

and

$$\mathfrak{L}^{(3)} \equiv \{(z) \,|\, \rho = \tilde{\rho}(\alpha), |\varphi| \leq \tilde{\varphi}(\alpha)\}. \tag{1.3.16}$$

Proof In our discussion above we have already seen that $F_\alpha(z_1)$ is regular in $[\mathcal{L} \cup \mathfrak{L}^{(3)}] \cap \mathfrak{P}(\alpha)$. To show that $f(z_1, z_2)$ is regular in $\mathcal{L}$ we first note that $F_\alpha(z_1)$ is regular in $\mathcal{L} \cap \mathfrak{P}(\alpha)$ and that $\tilde{\rho}(\alpha)$ is its radius of convergence. Since $F_\alpha(z_1)$ is also a power series in α, and $|F_\alpha(z_1)| < \infty$ in the set $\{(z_1, \alpha) \,|\, |\alpha| < M < \infty; |z_1| < \tilde{\rho}(\alpha)\}$, one may conclude by the use of the analytic completion theorem (1.2.1) that $F_\alpha(z_1)$ is holomorphic in this set as a function of z_1 and α. Consequently, $f(z_1, z_2)$ is seen to be holomorphic as a function of z_1, z_2 in this set. We are given the fact that $f(z_1, z_2)$ is holomorphic in a neighborhood of the origin; this combined with the fact that M may be chosen arbitrarily large is sufficient for us to conclude that $f(z_1, z_2)$ is holomorphic in $\mathcal{L}$.

In order to show $f(z_1, z_2)$ is holomorphic in $\mathfrak{L}^3$ we again consider the coordinates z_1, α, and consider $F_\alpha(z_1)$ as a function of these two variables. If the point $(z_1^{(0)}, \alpha_0)$ lies *in* the arc

$$\{(z_1, \alpha) \,|\, \alpha = \alpha_0; z_1 = \tilde{\rho}(\alpha_0)e^{i\varphi}, -\varphi(\alpha_0) \leq \varphi \leq \varphi(\alpha_0)\},$$

then we may show that in a suitably small bicylindrical neighborhood about $(z_1^{(0)}, \alpha_0)$, $F_\alpha(z_1)$ is a holomorphic function of z_1 and α. In this way we are able to cover the set $\mathfrak{L}^3$ with bicylindrical neighborhoods in which $F_\alpha(z_1)$ is holomorphic and hence obtain our result.

To this end we consider $\mathscr{L}$ in the coordinates $|z_1|$, $|\alpha|$ (see Fig. 1). If β is the angle that the tangent to the curve $|z_1| = \rho(|\alpha|)$ makes at the point $(|z_1^{(0)}|, |\alpha_0|)$, then by a simple application of our analytic completion theorem (1.2.1) one realizes that β must lie within the limits $\pi/2 \leq \beta \leq \pi$. We assume tentatively that $\pi > \beta > \pi/2$. Since $\rho(\alpha)$ is continuous we may choose a $z_1{}^* = z_1^{(0)} - \eta$ (with $\arg[\eta] = \arg[z_1^{(0)}]$), such that the disk $\{(z_1, \alpha) \,|\, |\alpha - \alpha_0| < |\varepsilon|;$ $z_1{}^* = z_1^{(0)} - \eta\} \subset \mathscr{L}$, providing that $|\varepsilon| > 0$ is chosen sufficiently small. The constant ε may be further chosen so that $\arg[\varepsilon] = \arg[\alpha_0]$. Further, let η' be taken to lie in the range, $\tilde{\rho}(\alpha_0) - |z_1{}^*| < \eta' < \tilde{\rho}(\alpha_0 - \varepsilon) - |z_1{}^*|$ and let $\mathfrak{B}$ be the bicylinder

$$\mathfrak{B} \equiv \{(z_1, \alpha) \,|\, |z_1 - z_1{}^*| < \eta';\ |\alpha - \alpha_0| < |\varepsilon|\}. \tag{1.3.17}$$

These sets are indicated in Fig. 3. From the Mandelbrojt theorem [M.2] it is

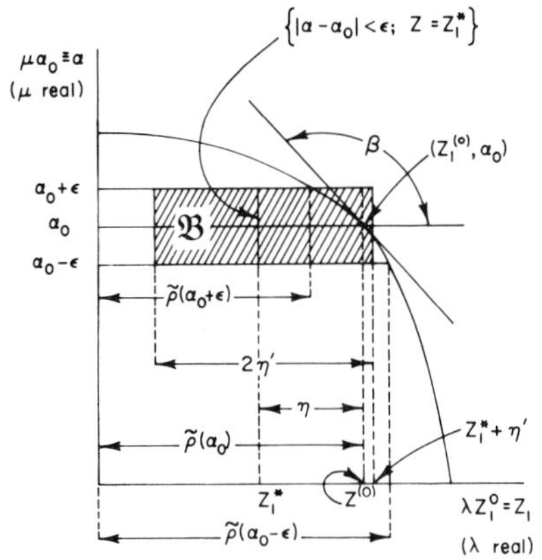

FIGURE 3

clear that if for $\alpha = \alpha_0$ $z_1{}^0$ is not a singular point of $F_\alpha(z_1)$, then $F_\alpha(z_1)$ has a continuation into a disk $\mathfrak{M}^{(2)}_{(\alpha)} \equiv \{z_1 \,|\, |z_1 - z_1{}^0| < \eta'\}$ where η' is chosen sufficiently small. If we define the set $\mathfrak{M}$ to be the topological sum

$$\mathfrak{M} \equiv \bigcup_{|\alpha - \alpha_0| < |\varepsilon|} \mathfrak{M}^{(2)}(\alpha), \tag{1.3.18}$$

then it is clear that the function $F_\alpha(z_1)$ can be holomorphically continued into the bicylinder $\mathfrak{B}$, providing $\mathfrak{B} \subset \mathscr{L} \cup \mathfrak{M}$. If the angle β, introduced earlier, lies in the open interval $\pi > \beta > \pi/2$, this establishes our result since $f(z_1, z_2)$ must be holomorphic in $\mathscr{L} \cup \mathfrak{M}$ by the composite function theorem. The case where β is either $\pi/2$ or π clearly does not lead to further difficulties since we may repeat our previous arguments with respect to $\mathfrak{B}^* \equiv \mathbf{T}\,\mathfrak{B}$, $\mathbf{T}$: $z^* = z + \tau\alpha$, $\alpha^* = \alpha$, $\tau > 0$ taken sufficiently small. This completes our proof. Further details are contained in the papers of Bergman [B.27, pp. 254–260], and Mandelbrojt [M. 2].

Bergman generalizes this result to contain analogues of the Hadamard theorems as follows: let $\mathfrak{U}$ be the set of singularities of the function $f(z_1, z_2)$, and let the $\mathfrak{U}$ be subdivided into sets $\mathfrak{U}_{\mu\nu}$ according to the procedure below. For each fixed α, the radii of the circles $\tilde{\rho}_\nu(\alpha)$, on which the singular points $z_1 = \tilde{\rho}_\nu(\alpha)\exp\{i\tilde{\varphi}_{\mu\nu}(\alpha)\}$ of $F_\alpha(z_1)$ lie, are to be ordered so that $\tilde{\rho}_\nu < \tilde{\rho}_{\nu+1}(\alpha)$. Similarly the arguments $\tilde{\varphi}_{\mu\nu}(\alpha)$ are ordered for each fixed ν, so that $\tilde{\varphi}_{\mu,\,\nu}(\alpha) < \tilde{\varphi}_{\mu+1,\nu}(\alpha)$. The sets $\mathfrak{U}_{\mu\nu}$ are defined to be

$$\mathfrak{U}_{\mu\nu} \equiv \bigcup_{\alpha \in \mathbb{C}^1} \{(z) \mid z_1 = \tilde{\rho}_\nu(\alpha)\exp\{i\tilde{\varphi}_{\mu\nu}(\alpha)\};\ z_2 = z_1\alpha^{-1}\}; \tag{1.3.19}$$

whereas the set $\mathfrak{U} \equiv \bigcup_{\mu,\nu} \mathfrak{U}_{\mu\nu}$.

Theorem 1.3.6 *Let the following functions of the variable α be defined:*

$$_\mu(\alpha) \equiv \limsup_{n\to\infty} |D_n^{(\mu)}(\alpha)|^{1/n},$$

where $D_n^{(\mu)}(\alpha) \equiv$

$$\begin{vmatrix} \sum_{k=0}^{n} a_{n-k,k}\alpha^k, & \sum_{k=0}^{n+1} a_{n+1-k,k}\alpha^k, & \ldots, & \sum_{k=0}^{n+\mu} a_{n+\mu-k,k}\alpha^k \\ \sum_{k=0}^{n+1} a_{n+1-k,k}\alpha^k, & \sum_{k=0}^{n+2} a_{n+2-k,k}\alpha^k, & \ldots, & \sum_{k=0}^{n+\mu+1} a_{n+\mu+1-k,k}\alpha^k \\ \vdots & & \vdots & \\ \sum_{k=0}^{n+\mu} a_{n+\mu-k,k}\alpha^k, & \sum_{k=0}^{n+\mu+1} a_{n+\mu+1-k,k}\alpha^k, & \ldots, & \sum_{k=0}^{n+2\mu} a_{n+2\mu-k,k}\alpha^k \end{vmatrix}.$$

Then the following conclusions may be drawn concerning the singular sets $\mathfrak{U}_{\mu\nu}$.

(1) *The necessary and sufficient condition that the function $f(z_1, z_2)$ have at most one singular set of the form $\mathfrak{U} = \bigcup_{\mu=1}^{p} \mathfrak{U}_{\mu\nu}$ is that*

$$l_j(\alpha) = [\tilde{\rho}(\alpha)]^{-(j+1)} \qquad \textit{for} \quad j = 0, 1, \ldots, (p-1),$$

and

$$l_p(\alpha) < [\tilde{\rho}(\alpha)]^{-(p+1)}.$$

(2) *If there exists a q, $q < \infty$, such that*

$$[l_q(\alpha)/l_{q-1}(\alpha)] = 0,$$

then there at most q singular sets of the form $\mathfrak{U}_{\mu\nu}$.

(3) *If the ratio $[l_\mu(\alpha)/l_{\mu-1}(\alpha)] \to 0$ uniformly in α as $\mu \to \infty$, then $f(z_1, z_2)$ has at most a finite number of singular sets $\mathfrak{U}_{\mu\nu}$ in any compact set in $\mathbb{C}^2$.*

(4) *If $[l_\mu(\alpha)/l_{\mu-1}(\alpha)] \to 1/R(\alpha)$ uniformly in α, then $f(z_1, z_2)$ has at most a finite number of singular sets in the circular domain,*

$$\{(z) \,|\, |z_1| < \rho \leq R(\alpha);\, \alpha \in \mathbb{C}^1\};$$

however, it has an essential singularity (i.e., an infinite number of singular sets) in the neighborhood of the boundary, $\{(z) \,|\, |z_1| = R(\alpha);\, \alpha \in \mathbb{C}^1\}$.

We remark, Bergman [B.27] has also shown that in the neighborhood of the singular sets $\mathfrak{U}_{\mu\nu}$ the function $f(z_1, z_2)$ tends to ∞ as an integral power of the inverse distance to the set. Hence the sets $\mathfrak{U}_{\mu\nu}$ are the polar singularities of $f(z_1, z_2)$. The reader is directed to Bergman's paper [B.27] for further details.

Theorem 1.3.7 (A Fabry Theorem for Functions of Two Complex Variables) *Let $f(z_1, z_2)$ be a holomorphic function defined in a neighborhood of the origin with the series development*

$$f(z_1, z_2) = \sum_{m=0}^{\infty} \sum_{n=0}^{\infty} a_{mn} z_1{}^m z_2{}^n.$$

Let us suppose further that $a_{mn} = 1 + O(1/M)$, where $M = \max\{m, n\}$; then $f(z_1, z_2)$ is singular on the analytic planes $z_1 = 1$ and $z_2 = 1$.

Proof Let $\mathfrak{P}(\alpha) \equiv \{(z_1, z_2) \,|\, z_2 = \alpha z_1\}$ be an analytic plane through the origin, and let us define the function of one complex variable ($z_1 = z$)

$$f_\alpha(z) \equiv \sum_{k=0}^{\infty} \left\{ \sum_{m+n=k} z^k a_{mn} \alpha^n \right\} \equiv \sum_{k=0}^{\infty} b_k(\alpha) z^k.$$

First, we have for N sufficiently large,

$$b_N(\alpha) = \sum_{\mu=0}^{N} a_{\mu, N-\mu} \alpha^{N-\mu} = \frac{1 - \alpha^{N+1}}{1 - \alpha} (1 + O(1/N));$$

hence, when $|\alpha| > 1$ the radius of convergence of $f_\alpha(z)$ is seen to be $\rho(\alpha) = 1/|\alpha|$. Likewise, for $|\alpha| < 1$, the radius of convergence is $\rho(\alpha) = 1$.

By the Fabry theorem for functions of one complex variable [D.4, p. 377] we may compute the singular point for $f_\alpha(z)$ in the cases where $|\alpha| > 1$ and $|\alpha| < 1$. We have that

$$\frac{b_N(\alpha)}{b_{N+1}(\alpha)} = \frac{1 - \alpha^{N+1}}{1 - \alpha^{N+2}};$$

hence, $f_\alpha(z)$ is singular at the point $z = 1/\alpha$ when $|\alpha| > 1$, and at the point $z = 1$ when $|\alpha| < 1$. Consequently, $f(z_1, z_2)$ is singular on the union $\mathfrak{S} \equiv \mathfrak{S}_1 \cup \mathfrak{S}_2$, where

$$\mathfrak{S}_1 \equiv \{(z_1, z_2) \,|\, |z_1| < 1, z_2 = 1\},$$

$$\mathfrak{S}_2 \equiv \{(z_1, z_2) \,|\, z_1 = 1, |z_2| < 1\}.$$

$\mathfrak{S}_1$ and $\mathfrak{S}_2$ are, however, elements of analytic sets which upon completion become the analytic planes $z_2 = 1$ and $z_1 = 1$, respectively.

The case where $\alpha = e^{it}$ we treat as follows. Clearly, for $|\alpha| < 1$ the remainder series

$$R_N(z;\alpha) \equiv \left\{\frac{1}{1-\alpha}\sum_{K=N+1}^{\infty} z^K - \frac{1}{1-\alpha}\sum_{K=N+1}^{\infty} \alpha^{K+1} z^K\right\}\left(1 + O\left(\frac{1}{N}\right)\right)$$

converges absolutely. The series $f_\alpha(z)$ is seen to have the following singular points on the unit circle, $z = 1$, and $z = e^{-it}$. We conclude that $f(z_1, z_2)$ must also be singular for $\{z_1 = e^{it}, z_2 = 1; t \neq 0, 2\pi\}$ and for $\{z_1 = 1, z_2 = e^{+it}; t \neq 0, 2\pi\}$; interchanging the roles played by z_1 and z_2, i.e., setting $z_1 = \alpha z_2$ and repeating our arguments shows that we must also include the points $\{z_1 = e^{+it}, z_2 = 1; t \neq 0, 2\pi\}$ and $\{z_1 = 1, z_2 = e^{-it}; t \neq 0, 2\pi\}$. However this set of points for all $t \in (0, 2\pi)$ is contained in the analytic planes $z_1 = 1$ and $z_2 = 1$. This proves our result.

We remark that by the above construction it is seen that no other singularity set contains points closer to the origin than the closest points of this set.

Theorem 1.3.8 *Let $f(z_1, z_2)$ and $g(z_1, z_2)$ be holomorphic functions defined in a neighborhood of the origin with the series developments*

$$f(z_1, z_2) = \sum_{m=0}^{\infty}\sum_{n=0}^{\infty} a_{mn} z_1{}^m z_2{}^n$$

and

$$g(z_1, z_2) = \sum_{m=0}^{\infty} \sum_{n=0}^{\infty} b_{mn} z_1{}^m z_2{}^n,$$

where

$$b_{mn} = a_{mn} + O\left(\frac{1}{M}\right) \quad \text{and} \quad M = \max\{m, n\}.$$

Furthermore, let the singularity set of $f(z_1, z_2)$ that is closest to the origin consist of the points on the analytic set $\mathfrak{S} \equiv \{(z_1, z_2) \mid \Psi(z_1, z_2) = 0\}$, where $\Psi(z_1, z_2)$ is a holomorphic function. Then $g(z_1, z_2)$ is also singular on the set $\mathfrak{S}$ and this is the closest singular set to the origin.

Proof Let us define the coefficients c_{mn} by $c_{mn} a_{mn} = b_{mn}$; hence, $c_{mn} = 1 + O(1/M)$ for M sufficiently large. Since $f(z_1, z_2)$ is holomorphic at the origin $\Psi(0, 0) \neq 0$; hence, for (z_1, z_2) taken in a suitably small bicylinder we may represent $g(z_1, z_2)$ by a double Cauchy integral, i.e.,

$$g(z_1, z_2) = \frac{-1}{4\pi^2} \int_{\mathscr{L}_1} \frac{d\zeta_1}{\zeta_1} \int_{\mathscr{L}_2} \frac{d\zeta_2}{\zeta_2} h\left(\frac{z_1}{\zeta_1}, \frac{z_2}{\zeta_2}\right) f(\zeta_1, \zeta_2).$$

where

$$h(z_1, z_2,) \equiv \sum_{m=0}^{\infty} \sum_{n=0}^{\infty} c_{mn} z_1^m z_2^n.$$

The power series representation for $h(z_1/\zeta_1, z_2/\zeta_2)$ converges in the bicylinder $\{|z_1/\zeta_1| < 1\} \times \{|z_2/\zeta_2| < 1\}$, whereas the series for $f(\zeta_1, \zeta_2)$ converges in any sufficiently small bicylinder that does not meet the analytic surface $\Psi(\zeta_1, \zeta_2) = 0$. It is clear that we may choose a pair of annuli $\{r_k \leq |\zeta_k| \leq R_k\}$ $(k = 1, 2)$ in which the integral representation for $g(z_1, z_2)$ is valid.

In order to study the singularities of the integral representation for $g(z_1, z_2)$ we consider the analytical continuation of this function along all admissible contours initiating at the origin. We note that $g(z_1, z_2)$ will be analytic at all points (z_1, z_2) that may be reached by such a contour, providing no point of this contour corresponds to a singularity of the integrand on the domain of integration. Furthermore, this initial domain of analyticity for $g(z_1, z_2)$ can be extended whenever it is possible to deform the domain of integration to avoid passing over a singularity of the integrand. We note that this can be done whenever the singularities of $h(z_1/\zeta_1, z_2/\zeta_2)$ and $f(\zeta_1, \zeta_2)$ do not "pinch" the integration curves $\mathscr{L}_1$ and $\mathscr{L}_2$, i.e., whenever z_1, z_2 do not satisfy $\Psi(z_1, z_2) = 0$. This concludes our proof.

We remark that Theorems 1.3.7 and 1.3.8 may be extended to the case of n complex variables by induction. For instance, we sketch a proof for a Fabry-type theorem when $n = 3$, and we consider the Taylor series representation

$$f(z_1, z_2, z_3) \equiv \sum_{m,n,l=0}^{\infty} a_{m,n,l} z_1{}^m z_2{}^n z_3{}^l,$$

and also consider the restriction of this function to the analytic plane $z_3 = \alpha z_2$, where α is an arbitrary but fixed complex number. We obtain

$$f_\alpha(z_1, z_2) \equiv \sum_{m,k=0}^{\infty} \left\{ \sum_{n+l=k} a_{mnl} \alpha^l \right\} z_1{}^m z_2{}^k.$$

We consider the case where $|\alpha| < 1$; then the Taylor coefficients

$$c_{mk}(\alpha) \equiv \sum_{n+l=k} a_{mnl} \alpha^l$$

are for sufficiently large k,

$$c_{mk}(\alpha) \approx \frac{1 - \alpha^{k+1}}{1 - \alpha} \left(1 + O\left(\frac{1}{m+k}\right)\right)$$

From which we may conclude that for $|\alpha| < 1$ we have in $\{z_1 = 1;\ z_2 \in \mathbb{C}^1\}$, and $\{z_2 = 1;\ z_1 \in \mathbb{C}^1\}$ as singular sets. Interchanging the roles played by z_1, z_2, z_3, and completing the elements for these analytic sets, yield the result that the analytic planes $z_1 = 1$, $z_2 = 1$, and $z_3 = 1$ are singular sets for $f(z_1, z_2, z_3)$.

4. *Elementary Bounds for Holomorphic Functions*

In this section we will present two results concerning the bounds on the absolute value of a holomorphic function of n complex variables. The first result is a generalized Schwarz lemma and is a variation of the result to be found in the book of Bochner and Martin [B.M.1, p. 57].

Theorem 1.4.1 *Let* $\|z\| = \|(z_1, z_2, \ldots, z_n)\|$ *be an arbitrary but fixed norm for the elements* $(z) \in \mathbb{C}^n$, *and let* $f(z_1, \ldots, z_n)$ *be holomorphic in the unit* *hypersphere, defined in terms of this norm,* $\mathbf{S} \equiv \{(z) \mid \|z\| \leq 1\}$. *Furthermore, let* $f(0, 0, \ldots, 0) = 0$. *Then one has the following inequality for all points* $(z) \in \mathbf{S}$,

$$\max_{\|z\|=\rho} |f(z_1, z_2, \ldots, z_n)| \leq \|(z)\| \cdot \max_{\|z\|=1} |f(z_1, z_2, \ldots, z_n)|. \tag{1.4.1}$$

Proof We introduce as in [B.M.1] the auxiliary function $g(t; z) \equiv f(z_1 t, z_2 t, \ldots, z_n t)$. We note that $g(0; z) = f(0) = 0$; hence we may apply the Schwarz lemma (for one complex variable) to obtain

$$\max_{|t|=\rho} |g(t; z^0)| \leq \rho \cdot \max_{|t|=1} |g(t; z^0)|, \tag{1.4.2}$$

where $\|z^0\| = 1$, and $\|tz^0\| = |t|$. Since

$$\max_{\|z\|=\rho} \{|f(z)|\} = \max_{\|z^0\|=1} \{\max_{|t|=\rho} |g(t; z^0)|\}, \tag{1.4.3}$$

we obtain our result immediately by successively computing the maxima of (1.4.2), first on the left and then on the right.

We remark that Bochner and Martin give several other bounds of this type, i.e., a generalization to several functions, and Hadamard three-hypersphere theorems. The reader interested in further details is directed to this reference [B.M.1].

The next result we shall present is an analog of the bounds given in terms of the order and type of an entire function of one complex variable. There are numerous ways in which these bounds may be generalized to the case of functions of several complex variables; however, we shall present just one such result in this direction, [F.4].

Theorem 1.4.2 (Gol'dberg) *Let* $f(z) \equiv f(z_1, z_2, \ldots, z_n)$ *be a holomorphic function of n complex variables in* $\mathbb{C}^n$, *and let* $f(z)$ *have the Taylor expansion* $f(z) = \sum c_k z^k$ *about the origin. Furthermore, let* $\mathfrak{D} \subset \mathbb{C}^n$ *be a complete, n-circular domain. Then the following inequalities hold,*

$$\sup_{(z) \in \mathfrak{D}} |f(zR)| \leq \exp(R^{\rho+\varepsilon}), \tag{1.4.4}$$

and

$$\sup_{(z) \in \mathfrak{D}} |f(zR)| \leq \exp[(\sigma_{\mathfrak{D}} + \varepsilon')R^{\rho}], \tag{1.4.5}$$

where R is sufficiently large and $\varepsilon, \varepsilon' > 0$ are arbitrarily small. The numbers, ρ and $\sigma_{\mathfrak{D}}$, may be found from the formulas

$$\rho = \limsup_{\|k\| \to \infty} \frac{\|k\| \ln \|k\|}{-\ln |c_k|}, \tag{1.4.6}$$

$$(e\rho\sigma_{\mathfrak{D}})^{1/\rho} = \limsup_{\|k\| \to \infty} \{\|k\|^{1/\rho} [|c_k|\, d_k(\mathfrak{D})]^{1/\|k\|}\}, \tag{1.4.7}$$

where $\|k\| = k_1 + k_2 + \cdots + k_n$, and

$$d_k(\mathfrak{D}) = \sup_{(z) \in \mathfrak{D}} \{|z_1|^{k_1} |z_2|^{k_2} \cdots |z_n|^{k_n}\}.$$

The order, ρ, is independent of the n-circular domain $\mathfrak{D}$; however, the type, $\sigma_{\mathfrak{D}}$, depends on $\mathfrak{D}$.

Proof The proof we offer is the standard one and is much the same as the proof given for functions of one complex variable [D.4, pp. 291–293]. The basic idea we use is to introduce a new function,

$$F(t; z) \equiv \sum_{\kappa=0}^{\infty} t^{\kappa} \sum_{\|k\|=\kappa} c_k z^k = \sum_{\kappa=0}^{\infty} t^{\kappa} f_{\kappa}(z),$$

which is related to the original function by $F(1; z) \equiv f(z)$, and to employ the classical results to $F(t; z)$ as a function of the single complex variable t. One has immediately by the Cauchy estimates that

$$\sup_{(z) \in \mathfrak{D}} |f_{\kappa}(z)| \leq \frac{1}{R^{\kappa}} \sup_{\substack{(z) \in \mathfrak{D} \\ |t| = R}} |F(t; z)| = \frac{1}{R^{\kappa}} \sup_{(z) \in \mathfrak{D}} |f(Rz)|.$$

We assume that the n-circular domain $\mathfrak{D}$ is held fixed in what follows. Let us suppose that for R sufficiently large there exist numbers a and λ, such that the inequality

$$\sup_{(z) \in \mathfrak{D}} |f(Rz)| \leq \exp[(a + \varepsilon) R^{\lambda}] \tag{1.4.8}$$

holds with $\varepsilon > 0$ arbitrarily small. Then one obtains

$$\sup_{(z) \in \mathfrak{D}} |f_{\kappa}(z)| \leq (1/R^{\kappa}) \exp[(a + \varepsilon) R^{\lambda}]; \tag{1.4.9}$$

the right-hand side assumes its minimum as R varies for $R = [n/(a+\varepsilon)\lambda]^{1/\lambda}$, and this then yields the further inequality

$$\sup_{(z)\in\mathfrak{D}} |f_\kappa(z)| \le \left(\frac{(a+\varepsilon)e\lambda}{\kappa}\right)^{\kappa/\lambda} \tag{1.4.10}$$

for κ sufficiently large, say for $\kappa \ge N(R)$. In order to obtain an estimate for the Taylor coefficients we choose a polydisk $\Delta \equiv \{(z) \,|\, |z_\mu| < |z_\mu{}^0|;\ \mu = 1, 2, \ldots, n\} \subset \mathfrak{D}$, where $(z^0) \in \partial\mathfrak{D}$, and such that

$$|(z^0)|^k \equiv |z_1{}^0|^{k_1} \cdots |z_n{}^0|^{k_1} = \max_{(z)\in\mathfrak{D}} |(z)|^k \equiv d_k(\mathfrak{D}).$$

The several variable Cauchy estimates then lead immediately to the bound

$$|c_k|\, d_k(\mathfrak{D}) \le \left(\frac{(a+\varepsilon)e\lambda}{\kappa}\right)^{\kappa/\lambda}, \tag{1.4.11}$$

where $\kappa = k_1 + k_2 \cdots + k_n$.

Conversely, if inequality (1.4.11) holds, then for a fixed value of R and for sufficiently large $\kappa \ge \tilde{N}(R)$, one has

$$R^\kappa\, |c_k|\, d_k(\mathfrak{D}) \le \left(\frac{(a+\varepsilon)e\lambda}{\kappa}\right)^{\kappa/\lambda} R^\kappa \le \frac{1}{2^\kappa}. \tag{1.4.12}$$

Consequently,

$$\begin{aligned}
\sup_{(z)\in\mathfrak{D}} |f(Rz)| &\le \sum_{\kappa=0}^{\infty} \left\{ R^\kappa \sum_{\|k\|=\kappa}^{\infty} |c_k|\, d_k(\mathfrak{D}) \right\} \\
&\le \sum_{\kappa=0}^{\tilde{N}(R)-1} \left\{ R^\kappa \sum_{\|k\|=\kappa} |c_k|\, d_k(\mathfrak{D}) \right\} + \sum_{\kappa=\tilde{N}(R)}^{\infty} \sum_{\|k\|=\kappa} \{1/2^k\} \\
&\le \sum_{\kappa=0}^{\tilde{N}(R)-1} \left\{ R^\kappa \sum_{\|k\|=\kappa} |c_k|\, d_k(\mathfrak{D}) \right\} + \sum_{\kappa=\tilde{N}(R)}^{\infty} (\kappa+1)^n \{1/2^\kappa\}.
\end{aligned}$$

We next attempt an estimate of the first sum, and to this end consider the maximum term of the sequence $\{R^\kappa \sum_{\|k\|=\kappa} |c_k| d_k(\mathfrak{D})\}$, $[\kappa = 0, 1, \ldots, \tilde{N}(R)]$. We note that as $R \to \infty$, $\tilde{N}(R)$ must also $\to \infty$, hence the maximum value of the individual terms in the preceding sequence of sums is bounded above by $[(a+\varepsilon)e\lambda/\kappa]^{\kappa/\lambda} R^\kappa$. We may obtain the maximum of this value, as κ varies from 1 to ∞, by differentiating with respect to κ; we notice that the maximum occurs for $\kappa = (a + \varepsilon)\lambda R^\lambda$, and the corresponding upper bound for these terms is then seen to be $\exp[(a + \varepsilon)R^\lambda]$. We obtain the estimate

$$\sup_{(z) \in \mathfrak{D}} |f(Rz)| \leq \sum_{\kappa=0}^{\tilde{N}(R)-1} \{(\kappa + 1)^n \exp[(a + \varepsilon)R^\lambda]\} + c_0, \qquad c_0 < \infty.$$

From the choice of $\tilde{N}(R)$ it is clear that $\tilde{N}(R) = O(R^\lambda)$ as $R \to \infty$, hence we obtain further the following asymptotic estimate,

$$\sup_{(z) \in \mathfrak{D}} |f(Rz)| \leq \exp[(a + \varepsilon')R^\lambda] \qquad \text{as} \quad R \to \infty,$$

where $\varepsilon' > \varepsilon > 0$ may be taken arbitrarily small since ε can be made arbitrarily small.

From the above discussion we see that the condition

$$\sup_{(z) \in \mathfrak{D}} |f(Rz)| \leq \exp[(a + \varepsilon)R^\lambda]$$

implies $|c_k| d_k(\mathfrak{D}) \leq [e\lambda(a + \varepsilon)/\kappa]^{\kappa/\lambda}$, whereas on the other hand this latter inequality implies the condition

$$\sup_{(z) \in \mathfrak{D}} |f(Rz)| \leq \exp[(a + \varepsilon')R^\lambda].$$

(Here ε, and ε' are positive but arbitrarily small.) We conclude from this that a is the smallest number for which the bound on the Taylor coefficients and the maximum modulus of $f(Rz)$ coincide, and from this we obtain our conditions (1.4.6) and (1.4.7). Finally, in order to see that the number ρ given by Eq. (1.4.6) is independent of the domain we choose two polydisks, Δ_1 and Δ_2 such that $\Delta_1 \subset \mathfrak{D} \subset \Delta_2$. It is clear from Eq. (1.4.6) and the definition of $d_k(\Delta_m)$ $(m = 1, 2)$ that $\rho_{\Delta_1} = \rho_{\Delta_2} = \rho_{\mathfrak{D}}$.

Remark If one considers functions of a single complex variable and takes for $\mathfrak{D}$ the unit disk, then Eqs. (1.4.6) and (1.4.7) yield the results of classical function theory.

References and Additional Reading

[A.1]
[B.15]
[B.16]
[B.19]
[B.36]
[B.37]
[B.39]
[B.40]
[B.41]
[B.M.1]
[B.T.1]
[C.2]
[C.4]
[D.4]
[F.2]
[F.3]
[F.4]
[F.5]
[G.6]
[G.7]
[G.8]
[G.28]
[G.H.A.1]
[G.R.1]
[G.K.L.1]
[H.1]
[H.2]
[H.9]
[H.11]
[L.1]
[L.2]
[L.8]
[L.9]
[M.2]
[N.7]
[O.2]
[P.S.2]
[W.W.1]

2

Harmonic functions in (p + 2) variables

Introduction

In this chapter we shall study the analytic properties of solutions to Laplace's equation,

$$\Delta\Psi \equiv \frac{\partial^2\Psi}{\partial x_1{}^2} + \cdots + \frac{\partial^2\Psi}{\partial x_{p+2}^2} = 0, \qquad p \geq 0, \tag{2.0.1}$$

by introducing certain integral operators. The case where $p = 0$ is from our point of view trivial in that these solutions are simply the real or imaginary parts of an analytic function. This property, which relates harmonic functions to the real or imaginary parts of an analytic function, is no longer available when $p \geq 1$. For instance, if $f(z_1, \ldots, z_n) = u + iv$ is a holomorphic function of n complex variables, its real and imaginary parts are *pluriharmonic* functions, i.e., they satisfy the equations

$$\frac{\partial^2 u}{\partial z_\mu\, \partial \bar{z}_\nu} = 0, \qquad \frac{\partial^2 v}{\partial z_\mu\, \partial \bar{z}_\nu} = 0 \qquad (\mu, \nu = 1, 2, \ldots, n).$$

On the other hand, harmonic function of $2n$ real variables, satisfy the equations

$$\sum_{\mu=1}^{n} \frac{\partial^2 w}{\partial z_\mu\, \partial \bar{z}_\mu} = 0.$$

Clearly, the class of pluriharmonic functions is more restricted than the class of harmonic functions. Indeed, they form a proper subclass in the following sense: in general one cannot solve the Dirichlet problem for real continuous boundary data with the pluriharmonic functions. Several attempts have been made to extend the class of pluriharmonic functions, namely by Bergman and Bremermann, so that in this larger class it would be possible to solve the Dirichlet problem. For further information on this topic see Bergman [B.15, 16, 19], and Bremermann [B.41].

Another approach to the problem is to develop an integral operator which maps holomorphic functions of one or several complex variables onto harmonic functions. This method was originally discovered by Bergman [B.3–14] and extensively developed over the next three and a half decades by him in a series of papers [B.17–29]. For further details the reader is referred to the above literature, and in particular the book [B.22].

We remark that the methods developed in this section apply not only to harmonic functions, but also to solutions of certain classes of elliptic equations, in particular the equation

$$\mathbf{T}_{p+2}[\Psi] \equiv \sum_{\mu=1}^{p+2} \frac{\partial^2 \Psi}{\partial x_\mu{}^2} + A(r^2) \sum_{\mu=1}^{p+2} x_\mu \frac{\partial \Psi}{\partial x_\mu} + C(r^2)\Psi = 0,$$

where $A(r^2)$ and $C(r^2)$ are analytic functions of $r^2 = \sum_{\mu=1}^{p+2} x_\mu{}^2$.

1. *Harmonic Functions of Three Variables*

Let $\mathbf{X} \equiv (x_1, x_2, x_3) \in \mathbb{R}^3$ be cartesian coordinates, and let $u = N_\mu x_\mu$. (Repeated indices indicate that the summation convention is employed. Here the summation is taken from 1 to 3, where $N_\mu \equiv N_\mu(\zeta)$ ($\mu = 1, 2, 3$) are analytic functions of an auxiliary complex variable, ζ.) Furthermore, let us assume that the vector $\mathbf{N} \equiv (N_1, N_2, N_3)$ is isotropic, i.e., $N_\mu N_\mu = 0$. We consider next the formal power series in u,

$$f(u) = \sum_{n=0}^{\infty} a_n u^n \equiv \sum_{n=0}^{\infty} a_n (N_\mu x_\mu)^n. \tag{2.1.1}$$

If the series (2.1.1) converges uniformly we may differentiate with respect to x_ν termwise and obtain

$$\frac{\partial}{\partial x_\nu} f(u) = f'(u) N_\nu = \sum_{n=1}^{\infty} n a_n N_\nu (N_\mu x_\mu)^{n-1},$$

from which follows:

$$\frac{\partial^2 f}{\partial x_\nu \, \partial x_\nu} = f''(u) N_\nu N_\nu = \sum_{n=1}^{\infty} n(n-1) a_n N_\nu N_\nu u^{n-2} \equiv 0.$$

These operations are clearly valid for all X, and ζ such that

$$|N_\mu x_\mu| \le \rho < \rho_0 = \left[\overline{\lim_{n\to\infty}} |a_n|^{1/n}\right]^{-1}.$$

A suitable choice for the components of the isotropic vector $\mathbf{N}$ is $N_1 = (1/2)(\zeta - 1/\zeta)$, $N_2 = (i/2)(\zeta + 1/\zeta)$, $N_3 = 1$, [with $u = (\zeta/2)(x_1 + ix_2) + x_3 - (1/2\zeta)(x_1 - ix_2)$], which we note becomes $\mathbf{N} \equiv (i \sin \alpha, i \cos \alpha, 1)$ when $\zeta = e^{i\alpha}$, i.e., where ζ is restricted to lie on the unit circle. Integral powers of u are by definition spherical harmonics (cf. Hobson [H.10], p. 135). Furthermore, by expanding u^n in powers of ζ one obtains as the coefficients of ζ^m, homogeneous-harmonic polynomials of degree n, i.e.,

$$u^n = \sum_{m=-n}^{n} h_{nm}(x_1, x_2, x_3)\zeta^m.$$

(It is shown below that these functions $h_{nm}(X)$ $(n = 0, 1, \ldots)$ $(m = 0, \pm 1, \ldots, \pm n)$ form a complete system of harmonic functions.)

If we replace x_1, x_2, x_3 by the spherical polar coordinates

$$\begin{aligned} x_3 &= r \cos \theta, \\ x_2 &= r \sin \theta \cos \varphi \\ x_1 &= r \sin \theta \sin \varphi \end{aligned} \tag{2.1.2}$$

then Laplace's equation,

$$\Delta_3 H \equiv \frac{\partial^2 H}{\partial {x_1}^2} + \frac{\partial^2 H}{\partial {x_2}^2} + \frac{\partial^2 H}{\partial {x_3}^2} + 0,$$

becomes

$$\frac{\partial^2 V}{\partial r^2} + \frac{2}{r}\frac{\partial V}{\partial r} + \frac{1}{r^2}\frac{\partial^2 V}{\partial \theta^2} + \frac{\cot \theta}{r^2}\frac{\partial V}{\partial \theta} + \frac{1}{r^2 \sin^2 \theta}\frac{\partial^2 V}{\partial \varphi^2} = 0, \tag{2.1.3}$$

where $V(r, \theta, \varphi) \equiv H(r \sin \theta \sin \varphi, r \sin \theta \cos \varphi, r \cos \theta)$. If we seek solutions of Laplace's equation in spherical polar coordinates by separation of variables, i.e., $V(r, \theta, \varphi) \equiv R(r)\Theta(\theta)\Phi(\varphi)$, we find the following set of solutions,

$r^n P_n^m(\cos\theta)\ \ \exp(\pm\, im\,\varphi)$. $(n = 0, 1, 2, \ldots)$ $(m = 0, 1, 2, \ldots, n)$, which are regular about the origin. The $P_n^m(\xi)$ are associated Legendre functions of the first kind, nth degree and order m, and are solutions of the ordinary differential equation

$$(1-\xi^2)\frac{d^2w}{d\xi^2} - 2\xi\frac{dw}{d\xi} + \left[n(n+1) - \frac{m^2}{1-\xi^2}\right]w = 0,$$

$w(\xi) \equiv \Theta(\cos^{-1}\xi)$. When m is an integer, solutions of this equation, may be defined also by Rodrigues' formula [E.6, Vol. 1, p. 148],

$$P_n^m(\xi) = \frac{(1-\xi^2)^{m/2}}{2^n n!}\frac{d^{n+m}(\xi^2-1)^n}{d\xi^{n+m}}. \tag{2.1.4}$$

The set of separated solutions, $r^n P_n^m(\cos\theta)\exp(\pm\, i\, m\,\varphi)$, are called solid tesseral harmonics. It is well known that these functions form a complete system with respect to the class of harmonic functions regular about the origin. Indeed any such solutions of Laplace's eqation, regular, say, for $0 \le r \le r_0$, $r_0 > 0$, can be expanded in the form [W.W.1, p. 393]†

$$V(r,\theta,\varphi) = \sum_{n=0}^{\infty} r^n \Big\{ A_{n0} P_n(\cos\theta) + \sum_{m=1}^{n} (A_{nm}\cos m\varphi + B_{nm}\sin m\varphi)$$

$$\times P_n^m(\cos\theta)\Big\} \qquad (0 \le r \le r_0) \tag{2.1.5}$$

where the Fourier coefficients A_{n0}, A_{nm}, B_{nm} may be determined by the formulas

$$A_{n0} = \frac{2n+1}{4\pi r_0{}^n}\int_0^{2\pi} d\varphi \int_0^{\pi} d\theta\, V(r_0, \theta, \varphi) P_n(\cos\theta)\sin\theta,$$

$$A_{nm} = \frac{2n+1}{2\pi r_0{}^n}\frac{(n-m)!}{(n+m)!}\int_0^{2\pi} d\varphi \int_0^{\pi} d\theta\, V(r_0, \theta, \varphi) P_n^m(\cos\theta)\cos m\varphi\sin\theta,$$

$$B_{nm} = \frac{2n+1}{2\pi r_0{}^n}\frac{(n-m)!}{(n+m)!}\int_0^{2\pi} d\varphi \int_0^{\pi} d\theta\, V(r_0, \theta, \varphi) P_n^m(\cos\theta)\sin m\varphi\sin\theta. \tag{2.1.6}$$

Certainly, whenever $V(r_0, \theta, \varphi) \equiv g(\theta, \varphi)$ is continuous on $\{0 \le \theta \le \pi\} \times \{0 \le \varphi \le 2\pi\}$ these formulas determine the Fourier coefficients of a regular

† The function $P_n(\xi) = P_n^0(\xi)$ is Legendre's polynomial.

solution of Laplace's equation in the interior of the sphere $r \le r_0$. This solution may also be represented in the interior by means of the Poisson formula, namely,

$$V(r, \theta, \varphi) = \frac{1}{4\pi} r_0(r_0{}^2 - r^2) \int_0^{2\pi} d\varphi' \int_0^{\pi} d\theta' \frac{g(\theta', \varphi')\sin\theta'}{[r^2 - 2r_0 r \cos\Psi + r_0{}^2]^{3/2}} \quad (2.1.7)$$

where $\cos\Psi \equiv \cos\theta \cos\theta' + \sin\theta \sin\theta' \cos(\varphi - \varphi')$.

If we now rewrite the auxiliary variable u in terms of the spherical polar coordinates we have (cf. Courant–Hilbert, Vol. I, p. 540)

$$\begin{aligned} u^n &= r^n\{i \sin\alpha \sin\theta \sin\varphi + i \cos\alpha \sin\theta \cos\varphi + \cos\theta\}^n \\ &= r^n\{\cos\theta + i \sin\theta \cos(\varphi - \alpha)\}^n \\ &= r^n \sum_{m=-n}^{+n} \frac{n!\, i^m}{(n+m)!} P_n^m(\cos\theta) \exp[im(\varphi - \alpha)], \end{aligned} \quad (2.1.8)$$

where $\zeta = e^{i\alpha}$. This expression involving the connection between the solid tesseral harmonics and the solid spherical harmonic u^n may be realized by considering the Heine integral representation for the Legendre polynomials [W.W.1, pp. 326, 392], i.e.,

$$P_n^m(\cos\theta)e^{im\varphi} = \frac{1}{2\pi} \frac{(n+m)!}{n!\, i^m} \int_0^{2\pi} (\cos\theta + i \sin\theta \cos(\varphi - \alpha))^n e^{im\varphi}\, d\alpha, \quad (2.1.9)$$

which itself may be obtained by applying Cauchy's formula to the Rodrigues' definition of the $P_n^m(\xi)$ [C.6, p. 301].

The expressions (2.1.8), (2.1.9) permit us to construct an integral operator which generates solutions of Laplace's equation which are regular about the origin. For instance, if one introduces as a formal sum the kernel [G.19]

$$B^{(+)}\left(\frac{r}{s}, \cos\theta, \frac{e^{i\varphi}}{\zeta}\right) \equiv \sum_{n=0}^{\infty} \sum_{m=-n}^{+n} \frac{n!}{(n+m)!} \left(\frac{r}{s}\right)^n P_n^m(\cos\theta) \left(\frac{ie^{i\varphi}}{\zeta}\right)^m, \quad (2.1.10)$$

defined for, say $|r/s| < 1$, $1 - \delta \le |\zeta| \le 1 + \delta$, we realize that this sum converges uniformly for

$$(r/s \equiv t,\ \cos\theta \equiv \xi,\ e^{i\varphi}/\zeta = \eta),$$

$$(t, \xi, \eta) \in \mathfrak{D}(\varepsilon, \delta) \equiv \{|t| \le 1 - \varepsilon\} \times \{-1 \le \xi \le +1\} \times \{1 - \tilde{\delta} \le |\eta| \le 1 + \tilde{\delta}\},$$

with

$$0 < \varepsilon < 1 \qquad \text{and } \tilde{\delta} \text{ sufficiently small.}$$

We remark that the fact that this sum converges uniformly in the bicylindrical region follows from considering the generating function expression (2.1.8) and by rewriting the auxiliary variable u as

$$u = r\{\cos\theta + iz(\varphi)\sin\theta\} \qquad \text{with} \quad z(\varphi) \equiv \frac{1}{2}\left(\frac{\zeta}{e^{i\varphi}} + \frac{e^{i\varphi}}{\zeta}\right),$$

and by considering $z(\varphi)$ as a conformal mapping depending on the parameter φ. We notice that $z(\varphi)$ takes both the interior and exterior of the unit disk onto the extended complex plane slit from -1 to $+1$; if $|\zeta| = 1$, then $z(\varphi)$ lies on this slit and $|u| = r$. On the other hand, if ζ satisfies $1 - \tilde{\delta} < |\zeta| < 1 + \tilde{\delta}$, then $z(\varphi)$ lies in an ellipse with foci at ± 1, $\{|z(\varphi) - 1| + |z(\varphi) + 1| < 2 + \varepsilon(\tilde{\delta})$ where $\varepsilon(\tilde{\delta}) \to 0$ as $\tilde{\delta} \to 0$. For $\tilde{\delta}$ sufficiently small, it follows from elementary geometry that

$$|u/s| < |r/s|\{1 + \varepsilon(\tilde{\delta})\} < 1.$$

With this information we conclude that $B^{(+)}(r/s, \cos\theta, e^{i\varphi}/\zeta)$ converges in the above bicylinder. Hartogs' theorem for bounded functions, combined with the fact that $B^{(+)}$ may be approximated by partial sums which are Cauchy–Riemann analytic in the variables $t = r/s$, $\xi = \cos\theta$, and $\eta = e^{i\varphi}/\zeta$ for $(t, \xi, \eta) \in \mathfrak{D}(\varepsilon_1, \varepsilon_2, \varepsilon_3) \equiv \{|t| \le 1 - \varepsilon_1;\ \varepsilon_1 > 0\} \times \{|1 - \xi| + |1 + \xi| \le 2 + \varepsilon_2;\ \varepsilon_2 > 0, \xi \not\equiv 1, \xi \not\equiv -1\} \times \{1 - \varepsilon_3 \le |\eta| \le 1 + \varepsilon_3\}$, leads us to the conclusion that $B^{(+)}(t, \xi, \eta)$ is a holomorphic function in this polycylinder. Indeed, for t, ξ, η in this region we may sum $B^{(+)}$ to obtain

$$B^{(+)}\left(\frac{r}{s}, \cos\theta, \frac{e^{i\varphi}}{\zeta}\right) = \frac{s}{s - u}, \tag{2.1.11}$$

where u is given above.

If $f(s, \zeta)$ is a holomorphic function of two complex variables s, ζ for $(s, \zeta) \in \mathfrak{B}(\rho, \delta) \equiv \{|s| < \rho\} \times \{1 - \delta \le |\zeta| \le 1 + \delta\}$, and has there the Laurent series representation

$$f(s, \zeta) = \sum_{n=0}^{\infty} \sum_{m=-n}^{+n} a_{nm} s^n \zeta^m, \tag{2.1.12}$$

then one may formally represent the associated function given by the series below:

$$V(r, \theta, \varphi) \equiv H(r \sin\theta \sin\varphi, r \sin\theta \cos\varphi, r \cos\theta),$$
$$V(r, \theta, \varphi) = \sum_{n=0}^{\infty} \sum_{m=-n}^{+n} \frac{a_{nm}\, n!}{(n + m)!} i^m r^n P_n^m(\cos\theta) e^{im\varphi} \tag{2.1.13}$$

by the integral

$$V(r, \theta, \varphi) = \frac{-1}{4\pi^2} \int_{|\zeta|=1} \frac{d\zeta}{\zeta} \int_{|s-u|=\varepsilon/2} \frac{f(s, \zeta)}{s-u} \, ds = \frac{1}{2\pi i} \int_{|\zeta|=1} f(u, \zeta) \frac{d\zeta}{\zeta}, \quad (2.1.14)$$

($\varepsilon < \rho - |s|$) which is the Bergman–Whittaker representation. Bergman [B.3, 4] introduced the idea of considering this integral as an operator which maps the linear space of functions holomorphic in the bicylinder $\mathfrak{B}(\rho, \delta)$ (given above) onto the linear space of functions harmonic in a neighborhood of the origin. Indeed, if the path of integration, $|\zeta| = 1$, of (2.1.14) can be continuously deformed into another path, homologous to $\{|\zeta| = 1\}$, without passing over a singularity of the integrand, then this operation may be written as

$$H(\mathbf{X}) = \mathbf{B}_3 f, \qquad \mathbf{B}_3 f \equiv \frac{1}{2\pi i} \int_{\mathscr{L}} f(u, \zeta) \frac{d\zeta}{\zeta}, \qquad \mathscr{L} \sim \{|\zeta| = 1\}, \quad (2.1.15)$$

where $\|\mathbf{X} - \mathbf{X}_0\| \equiv [(x_1 - x_1{}^0)^2 + (x_2 - x_2{}^0)^2 + (x_3 - x_3{}^0)^2]^{1/2} < \varepsilon$, for $\varepsilon > 0$ arbitrarily small. Here $\mathbf{X}_0 \equiv (x_1{}^0, x_2{}^0, x_3{}^0)$ is to be taken as some initial point of definition for which the integral (2.1.15) exists. The operator $\mathbf{B}_3$ then defines a harmonic function, so to speak, "in the small," i.e., for some neighborhood of the initial point $\mathbf{X}_0$.

2. *The Bergman–Whittaker Operator*

We have seen that if $f(s, \zeta)$ has a Laurent series expansion in $\mathfrak{B}(\rho, \delta)$, then the operator $\mathbf{B}_3$ generates a harmonic function $H(\mathbf{X})$ which is regular for all $\mathbf{X}$ such that $\|\mathbf{X}\| \leq \rho$. This follows from the fact that when $\mathscr{L}$ is the unit circle we have the bound $|u| \leq \|\mathbf{X}\|$; hence for $\|\mathbf{X}\| \leq \rho$, $|\zeta| = 1$ the series expansion for $f(u, \zeta)$ converges uniformly and the integration involved in the representation (2.1.15) may be performed termwise. In this case it is clear that the harmonic function with the series representation (2.1.13) generated by $\mathbf{B}_3 f$ [from the holomorphic function given by (2.1.12)] converges uniformly in the closed sphere $S_\rho \equiv \{\mathbf{X} \mid \|\mathbf{X}\| \leq \rho\}$. On the other hand any harmonic function regular in the closed sphere S_ρ can be represented there by a series of the form (2.1.5), which we may rewrite in the form ($r \leq \rho$)

$$V(r, \theta, \varphi) = \sum_{n=0}^{\infty} \sum_{m=-n}^{+n} r^n C_{nm} P_n^m(\cos \theta) e^{im\varphi}, \quad (2.2.1)$$

by setting for $m > 0$, $C_{nm} = \frac{1}{2}[A_{nm} - iB_{nm}]$; for $m < 0$, $C_{nm} = \frac{1}{2}[A_{nm} + iB_{nm}]$, and finally for $m = 0$, $C_{n0} = A_{n0}$.

Bergman showed that each harmonic function regular in a neighborhood of the origin may be represented, in a smaller neighborhood, in terms of the operator $\mathbf{B}_3$, and an associated holomorphic function (2.1.12) [B.22, pp. 41–43]. The holomorphic function element $f(u, \zeta)$, which we associate with (2.2.1) by means of the operator $\mathbf{B}_3$, is defined by the formal sum (2.1.12), where the Laurent coefficients a_{nm} are given by $a_{nm} = [(n+m)!/(n!i^m)]C_{nm}$ $(n = 0, 1, 2, \ldots)$ $(m = 0, \pm 1, \ldots, \pm n)$. Using the orthogonality condition for the Legendre functions,

$$\int_{-1}^{+1} P_n^m(\xi) P_l^m(\xi)\, d\xi = \delta_{nl}\left(\frac{1}{2n+1}\right)^{-1} \frac{(n+m)!}{(n-m)!}, \tag{2.2.2}$$

and the Bessel–Schwarz inequality we have

$$\begin{aligned} &\int_0^{2\pi}\int_0^{\pi} |V(r, \theta, \varphi)|_{r=r_0}^2 \sin\theta\, d\theta\, d\varphi \\ &\quad \leq 2\pi \sum_{n=0}^{\infty}\sum_{m=-n}^{+n} |C_{nm}|^2 r_0^{2n} \int_0^{\pi} (P_n^m(\cos\theta))^2 \sin\theta\, d\theta \\ &\quad \leq 2\pi \sum_{n=0}^{\infty}\sum_{m=-n}^{+n} |a_{nm}|^2 r_0^{2n} \frac{2[n!]^2}{(2n+1)(n+m)!(n-m)!} < 4\pi M, \end{aligned} \tag{2.2.3}$$

where

$$M = \max_{r=r_0} |V(r, \theta, \varphi)|, \qquad \text{with} \quad r_0 < \rho.$$

Since $(n!)^2 \geq 2^{-2n}(2n)!$ we have, following Bergman [B.22, pp. 40–41],

$$\sum_{n=0}^{\infty}\sum_{m=-n}^{+n} \frac{|a_{nm}|^2}{2n+1}\left(\frac{r_0}{2}\right)^{2n} \leq \sum_{n=0}^{\infty}\sum_{m=-n}^{+n} \frac{|a_{nm}|^2 (2n)!}{(n+m)!(n-m)!}\left(\frac{r_0}{2}\right)^{2n} < M.$$

For $|\zeta| = 1$, we have, by the Schwarz inequality, that

$$\begin{aligned} \left|\sum_{n=0}^{\infty}\sum_{m=-n}^{+n} a_{nm} u^n \zeta^m\right| &\leq \left(\sum_{n=0}^{\infty}\sum_{m=-n}^{+n} \frac{|a_{nm}|^2}{2n+1}\left(\frac{r_0}{2}\right)^{2n}\right)^{1/2} \\ &\quad \times \left(\sum_{n=0}^{\infty}\sum_{m=-n}^{+n} \left|\frac{2u}{r_0}\right|^{2n} (2n+1)\right)^{1/2} \\ &\leq M\left(\sum_{n=0}^{\infty}\left(\frac{2u}{r_0}\right)^{2n}(2n+1)^2\right)^{1/2}. \end{aligned}$$

Hence the series representation (2.1.12) converges uniformly and absolutely on the product set $\{|u| < r_0/2\} \times \{|\zeta| = 1\}$. From this we conclude that every harmonic function $V(r, \theta, \varphi)$ regular in a neighborhood of the origin may be represented in (a suitably small) neighborhood of the origin by the Bergman–Whittaker operator $\mathbf{B}_3$, i.e., to each such solution $V(r, \theta\ \varphi)$ there corresponds a $\mathbf{B}_3$-associate $f(u, \zeta)$. Later we shall show by analytic continuation methods that $f(u, \rho)$ converges uniformly on the set $\mathfrak{B}(\rho - \varepsilon, 0)$, where $\varepsilon > 0$ may be taken arbitrarily small. Furthermore, it will be seen that this set of uniform convergence may be extended to include the circular domain $\mathfrak{B}(\rho - \varepsilon, \delta(\varepsilon))$, where $\delta(\varepsilon)$ depends on our choice of ε.

At this point we wish to mention something concerning the motivation behind the integral operator method. The operator $\mathbf{B}_3$, defined above, associates with each holomorphic function $f(u, \zeta)$ a harmonic function element $\{H(\mathbf{X}); \Delta_\rho\}$ $\Delta_\rho \equiv \{\|\mathbf{X}\| < \rho\}$. By the usual means of analytic continuation one can investigate the continuation of this harmonic function element. Clearly $\{H(\mathbf{X}); \Delta_\rho\}$ may be continued along any contour $\Gamma \subset \mathbb{R}^3$ provided no point of Γ corresponds to a singularity of the integrand $(f(u, \zeta)\zeta^{-1})$ on the path of integration, $|\zeta| = 1$. The union of all such points we refer to as the *initial domain of definition of the harmonic function* $H(\mathbf{X})$ *identified with the function element* $\{H(\mathbf{X}); \Delta_\rho\}$. However, it may be possible to extend this domain further by deforming the integration path continuously providing one does not pass over a singularity of the integrand. The study of this problem was first instigated by Bergman [B.3,4] (see his book [B.22, pp. 47–54]). Another problem associated with this investigation is to determine what happens when the path of integration does pass over a singularity. In the case of polar singularities the answer is simple, the value of the integral goes through a jump equivalent to the residue introduced by the polar singularity. This phenomenon, however, gives rise to the occurrence of certain surfaces, called by Bergman, *surfaces of separation* [B.22, p. 49], which have properties similar to the branch lines of analytic function theory.

We see by the above-mentioned examples how the integral operator method tends to generalize or extend some of the results of classical function theory to the case of harmonic functions in three variables. Actually these methods will be seen in what follows to extend to solutions of a wide class of linear partial differential equations. The original research in this direction was accomplished by Bergman for harmonic functions in three variables and the reader is referred to Chapters II, III, and IV of his book [B.22] for a survey of his results. We shall postpone discussing results of this kind until the chapter on singular partial differential equations in two variables (Chapter 3). Our results on singular differential equations are analogous to those obtained by Bergman in the present case; however, because of the smaller number of independent variables (two instead of three) these results have an even more direct connection with the results of classical function theory.

The harmonic functions which are regular at infinity may be obtained from the linear space of harmonic functions regular about the origin by means of a Kelvin transformation (cf. Courant–Hilbert, Vol. II, p. 243), i.e., if $H(\mathbf{X})$ is harmonic-regular for $\|\mathbf{X}\| \leq 1$ then $H^{\infty}(\mathbf{X}) = (1/r)H(x_1/r^2, x_2/r^2, x_3/r^2)$ is harmonic-regular for $\|\mathbf{X}\| \geq 1$. The harmonic functions regular at infinity may also be generated by means of a Bergman–Whittaker operator; however, in this case we use the following linear space of holomorphic functions,

$$\mathscr{G} \equiv \left\{ g \mid g(u, \zeta) = \sum_{n=0}^{\infty} \sum_{m=-n}^{+n} a_{nm} u^{-n-1} \zeta^m \right\}. \tag{2.2.4}$$

How these functions transform under the operator $\mathbf{B}_3$ may be seen by noting another of Heine's representations,

$$\begin{aligned} \frac{(n-m)!}{n!}(-i)^m r^{-n-1} P_n^m(\cos\theta) e^{im\varphi} &\equiv \frac{(n-m)!(n+m)!}{(n!)^2 2^n} \frac{1}{r} h_{n,m}\left(\frac{x_1}{r^2}, \frac{x_2}{r^2}, \frac{x_3}{r^2}\right) \\ &= h_{n,m}^{\infty}(x_1, x_2, x_3) \\ &= \frac{1}{2\pi i} \int_{|\zeta|=1} u^{-n-1} \zeta^m \frac{d\zeta}{\zeta}. \end{aligned} \tag{2.2.5}$$

Bergman has considered certain special classes of harmonic functions generated by the operator $\mathbf{B}_3$, for instance when $f(u,\zeta)\zeta^{-1}$ is either a rational function of u, ζ, or when it is an algebraic function. Both of these cases lead to interesting results which may be considered as generalizations of properties associated with analytic functions.

In the case where $f(u, \zeta)\zeta^{-1} \equiv p(u, \zeta)/q(u, \zeta)$, with p and q polynomials, one may give a rather simple representation to the corresponding harmonic functions [B.3, 13, 22]. To investigate the harmonic function

$$H(\mathbf{X}) = \mathbf{B}_3 \frac{\zeta p}{q} \equiv \frac{1}{2\pi i} \int_{\mathscr{L}} \frac{p(u, \zeta)}{q(u, \zeta)} d\zeta, \tag{2.2.6}$$

we consider the singularity manifold of the integrand, i.e., the set of points $(\mathbf{X}; \zeta) \in \mathfrak{Z}^{(3)}$, where

$$\mathfrak{Z}^{(3)} \equiv \{Q(X; \zeta) \equiv q(u, \zeta) = 0\} \subset \mathbb{C}^{(4)}. \tag{2.2.7}$$

The manifold $\mathfrak{Z}^{(3)}$ may also be written in the form

$$\mathfrak{Z}^{(3)} \equiv \{\zeta = \phi_\nu(\mathbf{X}); \nu = 1, 2, \ldots, m\}, \tag{2.2.8}$$

where the $\phi_\nu(\mathbf{X})$ are algebraic functions of x_1, x_2, x_3, and the degree of ζ in $Q(\mathbf{X};\zeta)$ is m. At every point $\mathbf{X}$ such that

$$\mathbf{X} \notin \left\{\mathbf{X} \,\middle|\, \prod_{0\le\mu<\nu\le m} [\phi_\mu(\mathbf{X}) - \phi_\nu(\mathbf{X})] = 0\right\} \tag{2.2.9}$$

these are m distinct branches of the singularity manifold. In this case it is possible for us to represent $\mathscr{L}$ as a sum of contours $\mathscr{L}_\nu$ $(\nu = 1, 2, \ldots, m)$ plus a contour $\mathscr{L}_0$ chosen in the following manner. The contour $\mathscr{L}_\nu$ is to have winding numbers 1 and 0 with respect to the points $\zeta = \phi_\nu(\mathbf{X})$ and $\zeta = \phi_\mu(\mathbf{X})$ $(\mu \neq \nu)$ respectively. $\mathscr{L}_0$ is chosen to have winding number zero with respect to all the points $\zeta = \phi_\nu(\mathbf{X})$ $(\nu = 1, \ldots, m)$. Consequently, one has when $\mathscr{L}$ is an arbitrary piecewise smooth, closed curve

$$\begin{aligned} H(\mathbf{X}) &= \frac{1}{2\pi i}\int_{\mathscr{L}} \frac{P(\mathbf{X};\zeta)}{Q(\mathbf{X};\zeta)}\,d\zeta \\ &= \sum_{\nu=1}^{m} \frac{1}{2\pi i}\,\eta(\mathscr{L};\phi_\nu(\mathbf{X}))\int_{\mathscr{L}_\nu} \frac{P(\mathbf{X};\zeta)}{Q(\mathbf{X};\zeta)}\,d\zeta; \end{aligned} \tag{2.2.10}$$

here $\eta(\mathscr{L};\phi_\nu(\mathbf{X}))$ is the index of $\zeta = \phi_\nu(\mathbf{X})$ with respect to the curve $\mathscr{L}$. From the residue theorem it follows that

$$\begin{aligned} H_\nu(\mathbf{X}) &\equiv \frac{1}{2\pi i}\int_{\mathscr{L}_\nu} \frac{P(\mathbf{X};\zeta)}{Q(\mathbf{X};\zeta)}\,d\zeta \\ &= \frac{p\left([x_1 + ix_2]\dfrac{\phi_\nu(\mathbf{X})}{2} + x_3 - (x_1 - ix_2)\dfrac{1}{2\phi_\nu(\mathbf{X})};\phi_\nu(\mathbf{X})\right)}{\dfrac{\partial}{\partial\zeta}\,q\left([x_1 + ix_2]\dfrac{\zeta}{2} + x_3 - (x_1 - ix_2)\dfrac{1}{2\zeta};\zeta\right)\Bigg|\,\zeta = \phi_\nu(\mathbf{X})}. \end{aligned} \tag{2.2.11}$$

We notice then [B.3,13,22] that $H(\mathbf{X})$ becomes singular for those values of $\mathbf{X}$, which satisfy simultaneously the equations

$$\begin{aligned} q\left([x_1 + ix_2]\frac{\zeta}{2} + x_3 - (x_1 - ix_2)\frac{1}{2\zeta};\zeta\right) &\equiv Q(\mathbf{X};\zeta) = 0, \\ \frac{\partial q}{\partial\zeta}\left([x_1 + ix_2]\frac{\zeta}{2} + x_3 - (x_1 - ix_2)\frac{1}{2\zeta};\zeta\right) &\equiv \frac{\partial}{\partial\zeta}\,Q(\mathbf{X};\zeta) = 0. \end{aligned} \tag{2.2.12}$$

Actually, this type of result holds under more general conditions than $f(u,\zeta)\zeta^{-1}$ be a rational function [G.6,7].

Theorem 2.2.1 (Gilbert) *Let the defining function for the set of singularities of* $f(u, \zeta)\zeta^{-1}$ *be a global defining function in* $\mathbb{C}^2$. *Then if* $h(u, \zeta) \equiv S(\mathbf{X}; \zeta) = 0$ *is such a defining function we have that*

$$H(\mathbf{X}) = \frac{1}{2\pi i} \int_{|\zeta|=1} f(u, \zeta) \frac{d\zeta}{\zeta}$$

is regular for all points $\mathbf{X}$, *which may be reached by continuation along a curve* Γ *starting at some initial point of definition* $\mathbf{X}^0$, *provided* $\mathbf{X}$ (*and hence the curve* Γ) *does not lie on the intersection*

$$\mathfrak{S} \equiv \{\mathbf{X} \,|\, S(\mathbf{X}; \zeta) = 0\} \cap \{\mathbf{X} \,|\, S_\zeta(\mathbf{X}; \zeta) = 0\}. \tag{2.2.13}$$

Proof This result is a corollary of Theorem 1.3.1 of the previous chapter. We remark that the word "intersection" in the above context may be an "abuse of language." However, the meaning is clear, i.e., for each $\zeta \in \mathbb{C}^1$ we consider those points $\mathbf{X}$ which satisfy both $S(\mathbf{X}; \zeta) = 0$ and $S_\zeta(\mathbf{X}; \zeta) = 0$.

Bergman [B.4,22] has given an inverse integral operator for $\mathbf{B}_3$, i.e. an integral formula which transforms the harmonic function $H(\mathbf{X})$ back into its $\mathbf{B}_3$-associate. Before proceeding to derive this representation we should like to remark that the mapping of holomorphic functions $f(u, \zeta)$, regular in the circular domain $\mathfrak{B}(\rho, \delta)$ is many-to-one. For instance, both of the formal sums

$$f_1(u, \zeta) = \sum_{n=0}^{\infty} \sum_{m=-n}^{+n} a_{nm} u^n \zeta^m; \qquad \text{and} \qquad f_2(u, \zeta) = \sum_{n=0}^{\infty} \sum_{m=-\infty}^{+\infty} a_{nm} u^n \zeta^m$$

map onto the same harmonic function given by the series (2.1.13). This may be realized by considering the identities

$$0 = \frac{1}{2\pi i} \int_{|\zeta|=1} u^n \zeta^m \frac{d\zeta}{\zeta}, \qquad \text{for} \quad |m| > n, \tag{2.2.14}$$

which follow from an elementary application of the residue theorem.

In order to obtain an inverse for the integral operator $\mathbf{B}_3$, Bergman [B.22] introduces the characteristic space $\mathfrak{C}^2 \equiv \{\mathbf{X} \,|\, {x_1}^2 + {x_2}^2 + {x_3}^2 = 0\} \subset \mathbb{C}^3$. We shall obtain his result below in a slightly modified form.

If we introduce the new coordinates† $x = x_3$, $z = \frac{1}{2}(x_1 + ix_2)$, $z^* = -\frac{1}{2}(x_1 - ix_2)$ then we may write the equation defining the characteristic space as, $x = 2(zz^*)^{1/2}$.

† Our definition of the auxilliary variable u and the variables z, z^* differ from Bergman's, [B.22, p. 39], in that we have replaced his variables x, y, z, by x_3, x_2, x_1, respectively.

We also introduce the function $\tilde{H}(x, z, z^*) \equiv H(z - z^*, -i(z + z^*), x)$ where $H(x_1, x_2, x_3)$ is taken to be harmonic-regular in a neighborhood of the origin. From our above discussion this implies there exists a $\mathbf{B}_3$-associate of $H(x_1, x_2, x_3)$ holomorphic in a domain $\mathfrak{B}(\rho, \delta)$, which in turn implies $H(x_1, x_2, x_3)$ considered as a function of its complex arguments is holomorphic in a sufficiently small polycylindrical neighborhood of the origin. In this sense $\tilde{H}(x, z, z^*)$ is considered as an analytic continuation of $H(\mathbf{X})$ from S_ρ to a larger region $\mathfrak{Q}$ whose intersection with $\mathfrak{C}^2$ is of complex dimension two. The restriction of $\tilde{H}(x, z, z^*)$ to $\mathfrak{Q} \cap \mathfrak{C}^2$ we shall call $\chi(z, z^*) \equiv \tilde{H}(2(zz^*)^{1/2}, z, z^*)$.

The auxiliary variable u may be rewritten in terms of the coordinates x, z, z^* as

$$u = z\zeta + x + z^*\zeta^{-1}, \tag{2.2.15}$$

which, when restricted to the characteristic space, becomes

$$u = z\zeta + 2(zz^*)^{1/2} + z^*\zeta^{-1} = [(z\zeta)^{1/2} + (z^*/\zeta)^{1/2}]^2.$$

The generating function, u^n, for the tesseral harmonics may also be simplified to read

$$u^n|_{\mathfrak{C}^2} = [(z\zeta)^{1/2} + (z^*/\zeta)^{1/2}]^{2n} = \sum_{m=-n}^{+n} \binom{2n}{n-m} (z)^{(n+m)/2}(z^*)^{(n-m)/2}\zeta^m;$$

hence in the characteristic space the solid tesseral harmonics

$$h_{n,m}(\mathbf{X}) \equiv r^n \frac{n!\, i^m}{(n+m)!} P_n^m(\cos\theta)e^{im\varphi}$$

become simply

$$\tilde{h}_{n,m}(2(zz^*)^{1/2}, z, z^*) \equiv \chi_{n,m}(z, z^*) = \binom{2n}{n-m} z^{(n+m)/2} z^{*(n-m)/2}. \tag{2.2.16}$$

If we replace z by $\zeta u t^2$, and z^* by $(u/\zeta)(1-t)^2$, then we have

$$\chi_{nm}\left(\zeta u t^2, \frac{u}{\zeta}[1-t]^2\right) = (u)^n \zeta^m \binom{2n}{n-m} t^{n-m}(1-t)^{n+m},$$

and hence

$$u^{1/2}\frac{\partial}{\partial u}\left\{u^{1/2}\chi_{nm}\left(\zeta u t^2, \frac{u}{\zeta}[1-t]^2\right)\right\} = \left(n + \frac{1}{2}\right)\chi_{nm}\left(\zeta u t^2, \frac{u}{\zeta}[1-t]^2\right),$$

from which it follows by a simple computation that

$$2\int_0^1 u^{1/2}\frac{\partial}{\partial u}\left\{u^{1/2}\chi_{nm}\left(\zeta ut^2, \frac{u}{\zeta}[1-t]^2\right)\right\} dt = u^n\zeta^m. \qquad (2.2.17)$$

Formally integrating $\chi(\zeta ut^2, (u/\zeta)(1-t)^2)$ termwise etc., with respect to t, we have

$$\begin{aligned}
&2\int_0^1 u^{1/2}\frac{\partial}{\partial u}\left\{u^{1/2}\chi\left(\zeta ut^2, \frac{u}{\zeta}(1-t)^2\right)\right\} dt \\
&\quad = 2\sum_{n=0}^{\infty}\sum_{m=-n}^{+n} a_{nm}\int_0^1 u^{1/2}\frac{\partial}{\partial u}\left\{u^{1/2}\chi_{nm}\left(\zeta ut^2, \frac{u}{\zeta}(1-t)^2\right)\right\} dt \\
&\quad = \sum_{n=0}^{\infty}\sum_{m=-n}^{+n} a_{nm}u^n\zeta^m \equiv f(u,\zeta). \qquad (2.2.18)
\end{aligned}$$

Clearly, we may, using the binomial formula, write

$$\begin{aligned}
|\zeta|^m\left|\chi_{nm}\left(\zeta ut^2, \frac{u}{\zeta}(1-t)^2\right)\right| &\le |(\zeta^2ut^2)^{1/2} + (u\zeta^{-2}(1-t)^2)^{1/2}|^{2n} \\
&\le |u|^n\left[|\zeta t| + \left|\frac{1-t}{\zeta}\right|\right]^{2n}.
\end{aligned}$$

For $|\zeta| = 1$, and $t \in [0, 1]$ we may obtain further

$$\left|\chi_{nm}\left(\zeta ut^2, \frac{u}{\zeta}(1-t)^2\right)\right| \le |u|^n;$$

by an earlier estimate this becomes

$$\left|\sum_{n=0}^{\infty}\sum_{m=-n}^{+n} a_{nm}\chi_{nm}\right| \le \sum_{n=0}^{\infty}\sum_{m=-n}^{+n}|a_{nm}|\cdot|u|^n \le M\left(\sum_{n=0}^{\infty}(2n+1)^2\left|\frac{2u}{r_0}\right|^{2n}\right), \qquad (2.2.19)$$

where $r_0 < \rho$, and ρ is the radius of a sphere about the origin in which $H(\mathbf{X})$ is harmonic regular, and $M = \max_{r=r_0}|H(\mathbf{X})|$. This estimate shows us that the series converges uniformly for, say, $|u| \le \rho/3$, and hence it may be differentiated and integrated termwise. This verifies our integral representation (2.2.18), and we summarize the previous discussion by the next theorem.

Theorem 2.2.2 (Bergman) *Let $H(\mathbf{X}) = \mathbf{B}_3 f$ be a harmonic function regular about the origin in a sphere of radius ρ. Then the $\mathbf{B}_3$-associate of $H(\mathbf{X})$ is related to $\tilde{H}(x, z, z^*) \equiv H(z - z^*, -i(z + z^*), x)$ by the integral representation*

$$f(u, \zeta) = \mathbf{B}_3^{-1}\tilde{H} \equiv 2\int_0^1 u^{1/2} \frac{\partial}{\partial u}\{\chi(\zeta u t^2, u\zeta^{-1}(1-t)^2)\}\, dt,$$

where the function $\chi(z, z^*)$ is the restriction of $\tilde{H}(x, z, z^*)$ to the characteristic space $\mathfrak{C}^2$. The integral operator $\mathbf{B}_3^{-1}$ is called the inverse $\mathbf{B}_3$-operator of the first kind. (See also the proof of this result by Kreyszig [K.6].)

Occasionally it is convenient to consider alternate continuations of the arguments of $H(\mathbf{X})$ to complex values. For instance, by introducing, as a particular continuation, the complex spherical coordinates

$$r = +({x_1}^2 + {x_2}^2 + {x_3}^2)^{1/2},$$

$$\eta = \left(\frac{x_1 + ix_2}{x_1 - ix_2}\right)^{1/2} = \left(-\frac{z}{z^*}\right)^{1/2}, \qquad \text{and} \qquad \xi = \frac{x_3}{r},$$

which reduce to $\eta = e^{i\varphi}$, $\xi = \cos\theta$, when x_1, x_2, x_3 are real, we are able to obtain a different inverse operator for $\mathbf{B}_3$. (See [G.6,7].) To this end we introduce as a kernel the formal sum

$$B^{(-)}\left(\frac{r}{s}, \xi, \frac{\zeta}{\eta}\right) \equiv \sum_{n=0}^{\infty}\sum_{m=-n}^{+n} \frac{(2n+1)}{(n+m)!}\, n!\left(\frac{r}{s}\right)^{n+1} P_n^m(\xi)\left(\frac{i\zeta}{\eta}\right)^m; \tag{2.2.20}$$

clearly from our discussion of the kernel $B^{(+)}(r/s, \xi, e^{i\varphi}/\zeta)$. [See (2.1.10), (2.1.11)], we realize that for $(r/s, \xi, i\zeta/\eta) \in \mathfrak{D}(\varepsilon, \delta)$ this sum converges uniformly. Indeed in $\mathfrak{D}(\varepsilon, \delta)$ we may obtain an explicit form for this kernel by the following simple computational device,

$$B^{(-)}\left(\frac{r}{s}, \xi, \frac{\zeta}{\eta}\right) = \frac{r}{s}\left(1 - 2s\frac{\partial}{\partial s}\right)\sum_{n=0}^{\infty}\left(\frac{u}{s}\right)^n = r\frac{s+u}{(s-u)^2} \tag{2.2.21}$$

where u is the auxiliary variable introduced before. As before we may invoke Hartogs' theorem to show that $B^{(-)}(t, \xi, \zeta)$ is holomorphic in $\tilde{\mathfrak{D}}(\varepsilon_1, \varepsilon_2, \varepsilon_3) \equiv \{|t| \le 1 - \varepsilon_1\} \times \{|1 - \xi| + |1 + \xi| \le 2 + \varepsilon_2; \xi \not\ge 1, \xi \not\le -1\} \times \{1 - \varepsilon_3 \le |\zeta| \le 1 + \varepsilon_3\}$ $(\varepsilon_k > 0, k = 1, 2, 3)$ and $\varepsilon_2, \varepsilon_3$ are suitably small. Consequently, we may integrate (2.2.20) termwise, and obtain [see (2.2.2)]

$$s^{-n-1}\zeta^m = \frac{1}{4\pi i}\int_{-1}^{+1} d\xi \int_{|\eta|=1} \frac{d\eta}{\eta} B^{(-)}\left(\frac{r}{s}, \xi, \frac{\zeta}{\eta}\right)\left\{\left(\frac{\eta}{i}\right)^m \frac{(n+m)!}{n!} r^{-n-1} P_n^m(\xi)\right\}. \tag{2.2.22}$$

The harmonic functions regular at infinity have a Taylor series expansion of the form

$$H^{\infty}(\mathbf{X}) = \sum_{j,k,l=0}^{\infty} A_{jkl}\, x_1^{-j} x_2^{-k} x_3^{-l} \tag{2.2.23}$$

which converges for all $\mathbf{X} \in \{\mathbf{X} \mid \|\mathbf{X}\| > 1/\varepsilon_1\} \subset \mathbb{R}^3$, where $\varepsilon_1 > 0$ is taken suitably small. By introducing the complexification of $\mathbb{R}^3$, $\mathbb{C}^3 \equiv \mathbb{R}^3 + i\mathbb{R}^3$, with the coordinates $z_k = x_k + iy_k$ $(k = 1, 2, 3)$, the series representation (2.2.23) is seen to be valid for those $\mathbf{Z} \equiv (z_1, z_2, z_3) \in \mathbb{C}^3$ such that $x_1^2 + x_2^2 + x_3^2 > 1/2\varepsilon_1^2$ and $y_1^2 + y_2^2 + y_3^2 > 1/2\varepsilon_1^2$. Considered as a function of the complex variables $\mathbf{Z}$, $H^{\infty}(\mathbf{Z})$ is holomorphic in a neighborhood of the ideal point, $(1/z_1, 1/z_2, 1/z_3) = (0, 0, 0)$, and hence the harmonic function $U(r, \xi, \eta)$ obtained by replacing $\mathbf{Z}$ in $H^{\infty}(\mathbf{Z})$ by

$$\begin{aligned} z_1 &= \frac{r}{2i}\left(\eta - \frac{1}{\eta}\right)(1 - \xi^2)^{1/2} \\ z_2 &= \frac{r}{2}\left(\eta + \frac{1}{\eta}\right)(1 - \xi^2)^{1/2} \\ z_3 &= r\xi, \end{aligned} \tag{2.2.24}$$

is a holomorphic function of r, ξ, η in a region of the form

$$\mathfrak{H}(\varepsilon_1, \varepsilon_2, \varepsilon_3) \equiv \left\{(r, \xi, \eta) \,\middle|\, |r|^2 > \frac{1}{2\varepsilon_1^{\,2}};\ \xi \not\geq 1,\ \xi \not\leq -1, \right.$$
$$\left. |1 - \xi| + |1 + \xi| \leq 2 + \varepsilon_2;\quad 1 - \varepsilon_3 \leq |\eta| \leq 1 + \varepsilon_3 \right\}, \tag{2.2.25}$$

where ε_1 is given above, and $\varepsilon_2, \varepsilon_3 > 0$ are suitably small.

Let $U(r, \xi, \eta)$ be a harmonic function regular at infinity, whose $\mathbf{B}_3$-associate $g(u, \zeta)$ is given by the Laurent series

$$g(u, \zeta) = \sum_{n=0}^{\infty} \sum_{m=-n}^{+n} a_{nm}\, u^{-n-1} \zeta^m; \tag{2.2.26}$$

then $U(r, \xi, \eta)$ has the series representation†

† The functions $r^{-n-1} P_n^m(\cos\theta)\, e^{im\phi}$ $(n = 0, 1, 2, \ldots)$ $(m = 0, \pm 1, \pm 2, \pm 3, \ldots)$ form a complete system of harmonic functions with respect to infinity.

$$U(r, \xi, \eta) = \sum_{n=0}^{\infty} \sum_{m=-n}^{+n} a_{nm} \frac{(n-m)!}{n!} (-i)^m r^{-n-1} P_n^m(\xi)\eta^m. \qquad (2.2.27)$$

Since, the harmonic function $U(r, \xi, \eta)$ is holomorphic in the region $\mathfrak{H}$, the integral

$$*\mathbf{B}_3^{-1}U \equiv \int_{-1}^{+1} d\xi \int_{|\eta|=1} \frac{d\eta}{\eta} B^{(-)}\left(\frac{r}{s}, \xi, \frac{\zeta}{\eta}\right) U(r, \xi, \eta) \qquad (2.2.28)$$

is a Cauchy integral. (Note that the integration path in the ξ-plane is the real axis from -1 to $+1$.)

We summarize the above discussion of the integral transform $*\mathbf{B}_3^{-1}U$ with the following theorem [G.6,7].

Theorem 2.2.3 (Gilbert) *Let $U(r, \cos\theta, e^{i\varphi}) \equiv H^\infty(\mathbf{X})$ be a harmonic function regular at infinity,* i.e., $U(r, \cos\theta, e^{i\varphi}) = (1/2\pi i) \int_{|\zeta|=1} g(u, \zeta)\, d\zeta/\zeta$, *where $g(u, \zeta)$ is given by* (2.2.23) *above. Then $g(s, \zeta)$ may be generated from $U(r, \cos\theta, e^{i\varphi})$ by the following inverse integral operator,*

$$g(s, \zeta) = *\mathbf{B}_3^{-1}U \equiv \frac{1}{4\pi i} \int_{-1}^{+1} d\xi \int_{|\eta|=1} \frac{r(s+u)}{(s-u)^2} U(r, \xi, \eta) \frac{d\eta}{\eta},$$

where u is the usual auxiliary variable. The integral operator $*\mathbf{B}_3^{-1}U$ is called the inverse $\mathbf{B}_3$-operator of the second kind.

We are now able to formulate a theorem concerning the location of singularities of $\mathbf{B}_3$-associates in terms of the singularities of the harmonic function [G.6,7].

Theorem 2.2.4 (Gilbert) *Let $\mathfrak{S}_1 \equiv \{\mathbf{X} \mid r = \Phi(\xi, \eta)\} \subset \mathbb{C}^3$ be a global representation of the singularities of $U(r, \xi, \eta) \equiv H^\infty(\mathbf{X})$.† The function of two complex variables given by the integral representation, $g(s, \zeta) = *\mathbf{B}_3^{-1}U$, is regular at any point $(s, \zeta) \in \mathbb{C}^2$, providing that this point does not lie on the intersection*

$$\mathfrak{S} \equiv \mathfrak{S}_{2,0} \cap \mathfrak{S}_{2,1} \cap \mathfrak{S}_{2,2}, \qquad (2.2.29)$$

where

$$\mathfrak{S}_{2,0} \equiv \left\{(s, \zeta) \mid S(s, \zeta; \xi, \eta) \equiv \Phi(\xi, \eta)\left[\xi + \frac{i}{2}(1-\xi^2)^{1/2}\left(\frac{\zeta}{\eta} + \frac{\eta}{\zeta}\right)\right] - s = 0\right\},$$

$$\mathfrak{S}_{2,1} \equiv \left\{(s, \zeta) \left| \frac{\partial S}{\partial \xi} = 0\right.\right\}, \qquad \mathfrak{S}_{2,2} \equiv \left\{(s, \zeta) \left| \frac{\partial S}{\partial \eta} = 0\right.\right\}, \qquad (2.2.30)$$

† Here $U(r,\xi,\eta) = H^\infty(\mathbf{X})$ is to mean $U(r,\xi,\eta) = H^\infty(-\frac{1}{2}ir[\eta - 1/\eta](1-\xi^2)^{1/2}, \frac{1}{2}r[\eta + 1/\eta](1-\xi^2)^{1/2}, r\xi)$.

or does not lie on the coordinate planes $s = s_n$ $(n = 1, 2, \ldots)$ *with* $s_{k_\mu} = \pm\,\Phi(\pm 1, \eta_k)$, *and* η_k *a root of* $\Phi_\eta(\pm 1, \eta) = 0$.

Proof The intersection condition follows immediately from a corollary of Theorem 1.3.4. The second condition occurs because of a confluence of a singularity with an endpoint of the integration path in the ξ-plane. To see how this happens we note that the Hadamard argument indicates that the singularities must be contained in the family of analytic surfaces

$$S(s, \zeta; \xi, \eta) \equiv \Phi(\xi, \eta)\left[\xi + \frac{i}{2}(1 - \xi^2)^{1/2}\left(\frac{\zeta}{\eta} + \frac{\eta}{\zeta}\right)\right] - s = 0.$$

However, since the endpoints $\xi = \pm 1$ have the special status that they are fixed, they are possible candidates for singularities. One obtains

$$S(s, \zeta; \pm 1, \eta) \equiv \pm\Phi(\pm 1, \eta) - s = 0 \qquad \text{and} \qquad \frac{\partial S}{\partial \eta} \equiv \pm\frac{\partial \Phi}{\partial \eta}(\pm 1, \eta) = 0,$$

as conditions for possible singular points. We remark, that applying the *envelope method* with respect to the variable η, and then the confluence with the end points $\xi = \pm 1$ yields the same singular points.

It has been most natural, because of the particular choice of the operator $^*\mathbf{B}_3^{-1}$ as a Cauchy integral involving the η- and ξ-variables, that these be the variables eliminated in the computation of the singularities of $g(s, \zeta)$. However, we shall show that, unless one is in the neighborhood of a singular point of the analytic set describing the singularities of $U(r, \xi, \eta)$, it is not necessary to give the variables ξ, and η this distinguished position [G.6,7]. To this end let us assume that the singularities of $U(r, \xi, \eta)$ are described globally in $\mathbb{C}^3$ by the set $\mathfrak{S}_{1,0} \equiv \{A(r, \xi, \eta) = 0\}$, where $A(r, \xi, \eta)$ is holomorphic in $\mathbb{C}^3$. The singularities of the kernel are then given by the equation,

$$\Psi(s, \zeta; r, \xi, \eta) \equiv r\left[\xi + \frac{i}{2}(1 - \xi^2)^{1/2}\left(\frac{\zeta}{\eta} + \frac{\eta}{\zeta}\right)\right] - s = 0.$$

For a point (s, ζ) to be a singular point it is then clear that it must satisfy simultaneously the following four equations:

$$A = 0, \quad \Psi = 0, \quad \frac{\partial A}{\partial r}\frac{\partial \Psi}{\partial \xi} - \frac{\partial A}{\partial \xi}\frac{\partial \Psi}{\partial r} = 0, \quad \frac{\partial A}{\partial r}\frac{\partial \Psi}{\partial \eta} - \frac{\partial A}{\partial \eta}\frac{\partial \Psi}{\partial r} = 0. \quad (2.2.31)$$

Under the mapping $(r, \xi, \eta) \to (z_1, z_2, z_3)$ the first two of these equations become $F(\mathbf{Z}) = 0$ and $\chi(s, \zeta; \mathbf{Z}) \equiv (\zeta/2)(z_1 + iz_2) + z_3 - (1/2\zeta)(z_1 - iz_2) -$

$s = 0$, where $\mathbf{Z} \equiv (z_1, z_2, z_3)$. The second two equations of (2.2.28) imply that for any choice of the differentials $d\xi$ and $d\eta$ one has

$$\left(\frac{\partial A}{\partial r}\frac{\partial \Psi}{\partial \xi} - \frac{\partial A}{\partial \xi}\frac{\partial \Psi}{\partial r}\right) d\xi + \left(\frac{\partial A}{\partial r}\frac{\partial \Psi}{\partial \eta} - \frac{\partial A}{\partial \eta}\frac{\partial \Psi}{\partial r}\right) d\eta \equiv 0. \qquad (2.2.32)$$

On the other hand if (2.2.32) is true for arbitrary choice of $d\xi$ and $d\eta$ it implies both brackets vanish. Equation (2.2.32) is equivalent, however, to the vanishing of the differential

$$d\Psi \equiv \frac{\partial \Psi}{\partial r} dr + \frac{\partial \Psi}{\partial \xi} d\xi + \frac{\partial \Psi}{\partial \eta} d\eta,$$

subject to the auxiliary condition that $A(r, \xi, \eta) = 0$, i.e., $d\Psi$ vanishes for *any* choice of dr, $d\xi$, $d\eta$ subject to the condition that $A = 0$. This is seen to be equivalent to the vanishing of the first differential of χ, i.e.,

$$d\chi \equiv \frac{\partial \chi}{\partial z_1} dz_1 + \frac{\partial \chi}{\partial z_2} dz_2 + \frac{\partial \chi}{\partial z_3} dz_3,$$

subject to the condition $F = 0$. From this we conclude that the singular points of $g(s, \zeta)$ must satisfy simultaneously the following equations,

$$z_3 = P(z_1, z_2) \qquad \text{where} \quad F(z_1, z_2, P) \equiv 0,$$

$$\chi = \frac{\zeta}{2}(z_1 + iz_2) + P(z_1, z_2) - \frac{1}{2\zeta}(z_1 - iz_2) - s = 0,$$

$$\begin{aligned} \frac{\partial \chi}{\partial z_1} &\equiv \frac{1}{2}\left(\zeta - \frac{1}{\zeta}\right) + \frac{\partial P}{\partial z_1} = 0, \\ \frac{\partial \chi}{\partial z_2} &\equiv \frac{i}{2}\left(\zeta + \frac{1}{\zeta}\right) + \frac{\partial P}{\partial z_2} = 0, \end{aligned} \qquad (2.2.33)$$

where $z_3 = P(z_1, z_2)$ is the condition $A(r, \xi, \eta) = 0$ in the z_1, z_2, z_3, coordinates.

3. *Location of Singularities of Harmonic Functions*

The reason for introducing the system (2.2.33) as characterizing the possible singularities of $f(s, \zeta)$ is that this system is better for analytic computations.

We illustrate this result by the following example. Let $g(u, \zeta)\zeta^{-1}$ be a holomorphic function having the particular form $\zeta^{-1}g(u, \zeta) = G(u^{-1}[\zeta - (1/\zeta)])$, where $G(z)$ is an analytic function of a single complex variable having an isolated singularity at $z = \beta$. This choice of $\zeta^{-1}g(u, \zeta)$ generates a harmonic function regular at infinity, $H^{\infty}(\mathbf{X})$, having a simple type of singularity. In this case the singularity manifold of the integrand of the operator $\mathbf{B}_3\, g$ consists of those points which satisfy

$$S(\mathbf{X}; \zeta) \equiv \zeta[\beta(x_1 + ix_2) - 2] + 2\beta x_3 - \frac{1}{\zeta}[\beta(x_1 - ix_2) - 2] = 0. \quad (2.3.1)$$

Eliminating ζ between $S(\mathbf{X}; \zeta) = 0$, and

$$\frac{\partial S}{\partial \zeta} \equiv [\beta(x_1 + ix_2) - 2] + \frac{1}{\zeta^2}[\beta(x_1 - ix_2) - 2] = 0\,, \qquad (2.3.2)$$

we obtain the following locus as the possible singularities of $H^{\infty}(\mathbf{X})$:

$$\mathfrak{S} \equiv \left\{\mathbf{X} \,\middle|\, \left(x_1 - \frac{2}{\beta}\right)^2 + x_2{}^2 + x_3{}^2 = 0\right\} \subset \mathbb{C}^3. \qquad (2.3.3)$$

If we consider the restrictions of $\mathfrak{S}$ to $\mathbb{R}^3$ we have the following two cases. (1) If $\beta \neq 0$ is real, then $\mathfrak{S}$ reduces to a point $\mathbf{X} \equiv (2/\beta, 0, 0) \in \mathbb{R}^3$. (2) If $\beta \neq 0$ is complex then $\mathfrak{S} \cap \mathbb{R}^3$ becomes a circle, given by $x_1 = (2/|\beta|^2)\ \mathrm{Re}\ \beta$, $x_2{}^2 + x_3{}^2 = (4/|\beta|^4)(\mathrm{Im}\ \bar{\beta})^2$. We note that these points contain all possible singularities of this particular $H^{\infty}(\mathbf{X})$; however, these points are only *possible* singularities, since Theorem 2.2.1 just prescribes what points must be regular points. In order to determine whether a particular point $\mathbf{X}_0 \in \mathfrak{S}$ is an *actual* singularity we must see whether this point corresponds under the inverse operator $^*\mathbf{B}_3^{-1}$ to a singular point of $g(u, \zeta)\zeta^{-1}$. Any *possible* singular point which generates under the inverse mapping, $\mathbf{B}_3^{-1}\ H^{\infty} = g$, an actual (i.e., given) singularity of $g(s, \zeta)$ is indeed a true singularity of $H^{\infty}(\mathbf{X})$. To illustrate this idea we consider those points $\mathbf{X} \in \mathfrak{S} \cap \mathbb{R}^3$. In this case ($\beta \neq 0$) singular points of $g(s, \zeta) = {}^*\mathbf{B}_3^{-1}\ H^{\infty}$ must satisfy simultaneously†

$$\chi(s, u; x_3) \equiv 2\frac{\mathrm{Re}\ \beta}{|\beta|^2}\left[\zeta - \frac{1}{\zeta}\right]$$
$$\pm \frac{i}{2}\left(\frac{4}{|\beta|^4}(\mathrm{Im}\ \bar{\beta})^2 - x_3{}^2\right)^{1/2}\left[\zeta + \frac{1}{\zeta}\right] + x_3 - s = 0, \qquad (2.3.4)$$

† Here we have already eliminated x_1 and x_2 from $u - s = 0$.

and

$$\frac{\partial\chi}{\partial x_3} \equiv \pm \frac{ix_3}{2}\left[\zeta + \frac{1}{\zeta}\right]\left(\frac{4}{|\beta|^4}(\operatorname{Im}\bar{\beta})^2 - x_3{}^2\right)^{-1/2} + 1 = 0.$$

(The endpoint singularities are of the form $s = \pm 2i/\beta$.) Eliminating x_3 between the above equations yields

$$\pm\left\{\mp i(\operatorname{Im}\beta)\left[\zeta + \frac{1}{\zeta}\right]^2 + (\operatorname{Re}\beta)\left[\zeta - \frac{1}{\zeta}\right]^2 + 4i\operatorname{Im}\beta\right\} = s\,|\beta|^2\left[\zeta - \frac{1}{\zeta}\right]; \quad (2.3.5)$$

by making a suitable choice of signs this is recognized readily as $[\zeta - (1/\zeta)] = \beta s$, which are the given singularities of $g(s, \zeta)\zeta^{-1}$. We conclude from this that the points $\mathbf{X} \in \mathfrak{S} \cap \mathbb{R}^3$ and indeed singular points of $H^\infty(\mathbf{X}) = \mathbf{B}_3\, g$, $g(s, \zeta) \equiv \zeta G(u^{-1}[\zeta - (1/\zeta)])$. It is interesting that the intersection of $\mathfrak{S}$ with the real space is sufficient to determine all of the given singularities of $g(u, \zeta)$ in the present case. Whether this condition is sufficient in all cases which occur for harmonic functions defined over $\mathbb{C}^3$ is at this time an open question.

Bergman [B.23–27] has obtained results concerning the location of singularities for certain special cases of harmonic functions in terms of the Fourier coefficients of (2.1.13). These results are generalizations of the Hadamard and Mandelbrojt theorems from classical function theory. We reproduce these theorems for the case of generalized axially symmetric potential theory for which the author has developed a complete theory (Chapter IV). For a discussion of the Hadamard coefficient problem for harmonic functions of three variables see [B.22].

The present author [G.11] has found the introduction of complex homogeneous coordinates and the use of the complex projective geometry an important method for characterizing geometrically the locus of singularities given by (2.2.10). As representatives of points in (complex) projective three-spaces, $\mathbb{P}^3$, we consider the system of four complex variables $\{Z_1, Z_2, Z_3, Z_4\}$, where not all of the Z_i are zero. We introduce equivalence classes in $\mathbb{P}^3$ by saying two systems $\{Z_1, Z_2, Z_3, Z_4\}$ and $\{\tilde{Z}_1, \tilde{Z}_2, \tilde{Z}_3, \tilde{Z}_4\}$ are equivalent if there exists a nonzero complex number λ such that $Z_i = \lambda\tilde{Z}_i$ $(i = 1, 2, 3, 4)$. A representative of such an equivalence class is referred to as a point of $\mathbb{P}^3$. The finite points of $\mathbb{P}^3$ are those representatives which may be identified with the points of $\mathbb{C}^3$ by the relations $z_1 = Z_1/Z_4$, $z_2 = Z_2/Z_4$, $z_3 = Z_3/Z_4$. A topology may be introduced on $\mathbb{P}^3$, which makes $\mathbb{P}^3$ a complex analytic manifold. Since at least one of the $Z_i \neq 0$, say $i = k$, we may introduce the local parameters, $t_i = Z_i/Z_k$ $(i \neq k, 1 \leq i \leq 3)$ which provide a local analytic mapping (T: $\mathbf{Z} \to \mathbf{t}$) from $\mathbb{P}^3$ into $\mathbb{C}^3$. A neighborhood of a point $\mathbf{Z} \equiv \{Z_1, Z_2, Z_3, Z_4\}$ is then the set of points $\mathcal{N}(\mathbf{Z}) = \{\mathbf{Z} \mid (\tilde{\imath}_1, \tilde{\imath}_2, \tilde{\imath}_3) \in U(\mathbf{t})\}$, i.e., the set of representatives which are mapped into a neighborhood of $\mathbf{t} = T$: $\mathbf{Z}$.

We wish to consider the special case of Eq. (2.2.10) where $S(\mathbf{X}; \zeta)$ has the special form

$$S(\mathbf{X}; \zeta) \equiv h(u, \zeta) \equiv u\zeta + \varphi(\zeta). \tag{2.3.6}$$

To this end we introduce the two sets of homogeneous plane coordinates

$$u_1 = -\tfrac{1}{2}[1 - \zeta^2], \qquad u_2 = \frac{i}{2}[1 + \zeta^2], \qquad u_3 = \zeta, \qquad u_4 = \varphi(\zeta), \tag{2.3.7}$$

and

$$w_1 = \zeta, \qquad w_2 = i\zeta, \qquad w_3 = 1, \qquad w_4 = \varphi'(\zeta). \tag{2.3.8}$$

Equations (2.2.10) may now be written in the form

$$Z_1 u_1 + Z_2 u_2 + Z_3 u_3 + Z_4 u_4 = 0, \tag{2.3.9a}$$

$$Z_1 w_1 + Z_2 w_2 + Z_3 w_3 + Z_4 w_4 = 0; \tag{2.3.9b}$$

for a fixed value of $\zeta \in \mathbb{C}^1$, each of these represents a projective subspace of complex dimension two, or a plane $\pi^2(\zeta)$ in $\mathbb{P}^3$. The intersection of these planes is a subspace of complex dimension one, that is a complex line $\Lambda^1(\zeta)$ in $\mathbb{P}^3$.

The intersection $\Lambda^1(\zeta)$ of the projective planes $\pi_a{}^2(\zeta)$ and $\pi_b{}^2(\zeta)$ given by (2.3.9) may be represented parametrically as

$$\begin{aligned} Z_1 &= (\mu/2)[\zeta - 1/\zeta] + \lambda(\varphi - \tfrac{1}{2}[\zeta + 1/\zeta]\varphi'), \\ Z_2 &= (i\mu/2)[\zeta + 1/\zeta] + i\lambda(\varphi - \tfrac{1}{2}[\zeta - 1/\zeta]\varphi'), \\ Z_3 &= \mu, \\ Z_4 &= \lambda, \end{aligned} \tag{2.3.10}$$

where $(\mu, \lambda) \in \mathbb{C}^2$. The intersection of $\bigcup_\zeta \Lambda^1(\zeta)$ with real projective space we will denote by $\Lambda/\mathbb{R}$, and refer to as the *restriction* of $\bigcup_\zeta \Lambda^1$ to $\Lambda/\mathbb{R}$.

Theorem 2.3.1 (Gilbert) *Let the defining function for the set of singularities of* $f(u, \zeta)\zeta^{-1}$ *be a global defining function in* $\mathbb{C}^2$ *of the form*

$S(\mathbf{X};\zeta) \equiv h(u,\zeta) = \zeta u + \varphi(\zeta)$. Then the harmonic function $H(\mathbf{X}) = \mathbf{B}_3 f$ is singular (on the first Riemann-space sheet) only if $\mathbf{X}$ is a point of $\Lambda/\mathbb{R}$; that is,

$$
\begin{aligned}
x_1 &= \frac{\operatorname{Re}\{\varphi - \frac{1}{2}[\zeta - 1/\zeta]\varphi'\}}{\operatorname{Re}\{\zeta + 1/\zeta\}} [\zeta - 1/\zeta] + (\varphi - \tfrac{1}{2}[\zeta + 1/\zeta]\varphi'),\\
x_2 &= \frac{-i \operatorname{Re}\{\varphi - \frac{1}{2}[\zeta - 1/\zeta]\varphi'\}}{\operatorname{Re}\{\zeta + 1/\zeta\}} [\zeta + 1/\zeta] + i(\varphi - \tfrac{1}{2}[\zeta - 1/\zeta]\varphi'),\\
x_3 &= \frac{-2 \operatorname{Re}\{\varphi - \frac{1}{2}[\zeta - 1/\zeta]\varphi'\}}{\operatorname{Re}\{\zeta + 1/\zeta\}},
\end{aligned}
\tag{2.3.11}
$$

where ζ is restricted to the curve $\mathcal{Q}$ given by

$$
\begin{aligned}
0 = {} & \operatorname{Re}\{\varphi - \tfrac{1}{2}[\zeta - 1/\zeta]\varphi'\} \operatorname{Im}\{\zeta - 1/\zeta\}\\
& - \operatorname{Im}\{\varphi - \tfrac{1}{2}[\zeta + 1/\zeta]\varphi'\} \operatorname{Re}\{\zeta + 1/\zeta\}.
\end{aligned}
\tag{2.3.12}
$$

$\Lambda/\mathbb{R}$, in general, will be a space curve in $\mathbb{P}^3/\mathbb{R}$.

Proof This result follows immediately by noticing that if $\mathbf{Z} \in \Lambda/\mathbb{R}$, then the ratios Z_i/Z_4 $(i = 1, 2, 3)$ must all be real.

In Eqs. (2.3.9a, b) we considered the Z_k as point coordinates and the u_k, w_k as plane coordinates; however, in a dualistic manner, we might have considered the u_k, w_k as point coordinates and the Z_k as plane coordinates. The Grassmann coordinates, or line coordinates, of two points $\{u_k\}$, $\{w_k\}$ of the subspace $\Lambda^1(\zeta)$ are defined as

$$\omega_{ik} = u_i w_k - u_k w_i \qquad (i, k = 1, 2, 3, 4). \tag{2.3.13}$$

There are only five independent coordinates because of the following identities [W. 18, p. 155]

$$
\begin{aligned}
\omega_{ik} \equiv -\omega_{ki}, \qquad \omega_{ii} \equiv 0,\\
\Omega \equiv \omega_{12}\omega_{34} + \omega_{13}\omega_{42} + \omega_{14}\omega_{23} = 0.
\end{aligned}
\tag{2.3.14}
$$

On the other hand, instead of specifying the pairs of points that lie on $\Lambda^1(\zeta)$, we may specify the pairs of planes intersecting in $\Lambda^1(\zeta)$ i.e., $\pi_a{}^2(\zeta)$ and $\pi_b{}^2(\zeta)$. To this end we define the *axial coordinates* of $\Lambda^1(\zeta)$ as

$$\sigma_{ik} = \tilde{u}_i \tilde{v}_k - \tilde{u}_k \tilde{v}_i \qquad (i, k = 1, 2, 3, 4), \tag{2.3.15}$$

where $\tilde{u}_i$, $\tilde{v}_i$ are plane coordinates. The σ_{ik} are proportional to the ω_{mn}, where i, k and m, n are complementary indices; the σ_{ik} also satisfy the same identities as the ω_{ik}.

Lemma 2.3.2 *The axial coordinates for* $\Lambda^1(\zeta)$ (2.3.10) *are*

$$\sigma_{12} = -i\zeta, \qquad \sigma_{13} = -\tfrac{1}{2}[1+\zeta^2], \qquad \sigma_{14} = -\tfrac{1}{2}\varphi'[1-\zeta^2] - \zeta\varphi(\zeta),$$

$$\sigma_{23} = \tfrac{1}{2}i[1-\zeta^2], \qquad \sigma_{24} = \tfrac{1}{2}i\varphi'(\zeta)[1+\zeta^2] - i\zeta\varphi(\zeta),$$

$$\sigma_{34} = \zeta\varphi'(\zeta) - \varphi(\zeta).$$

These coordinates satisfy, for arbitrary $\varphi(\zeta)$ *and arbitrary* $\varphi'(\zeta)$, *the identity*

$$\sigma_{12}^2 + \sigma_{13}^2 + \sigma_{23}^2 = 0, \tag{2.3.16}$$

and hence $\Lambda^1(\zeta)$ *must be contained in a line complex.*

Lemma 2.3.3 *If* $\varphi(\zeta)$ *is analytic then* $\bigcup_\zeta \Lambda^1(\zeta)$ *lies on a ruled surface in* $\mathbb{P}^3$.

Proofs The σ_{ik} and the quadratic identity $\sigma_{12}^2 + \sigma_{13}^2 + \sigma_{23}^2 = 0$ are obtained be direct computation. If $\varphi(\zeta)$ and $\varphi'(\zeta)$ are, at first, considered as unrelated functions an (apparently new) identity is seen to follow by making use of $\sigma_{24} - i\sigma_{14} = i\varphi'$, $\sigma_{24} + i\sigma_{14} = i\zeta^2\varphi' - 2i\zeta\varphi$, $\zeta = -\sigma_{12}(\sigma_{13} + i\sigma_{23})^{-1}$, and $\sigma_{34} = \zeta\varphi' - \varphi$. This identity has the form of a cubic relationship, namely

$$(\sigma_{24} + i\sigma_{14})(\sigma_{13} + i\sigma_{23})^2 = \sigma_{12}^2(\sigma_{24} - i\sigma_{14}) + 2\sigma_{12}\sigma_{34}(\sigma_{13} + i\sigma_{23}), \tag{2.3.17}$$

and is the only other identity which may be found by considering $\varphi(\zeta)$ and $\varphi'(\zeta)$ to be both arbitrary. However, by factoring and using the relation (2.3.14) this reduces to

$$(\sigma_{13} + i\sigma_{23})(-\sigma_{13}\sigma_{24} + \sigma_{14}\sigma_{23} + i\sigma_{23}\sigma_{24} + i\sigma_{13}\sigma_{14}) = \sigma_{12}^2(\sigma_{24} - i\sigma_{14}),$$

which again may be factored into

$$i(\sigma_{23} - i\sigma_{13})(\sigma_{23} + i\sigma_{13})(\sigma_{14} + i\sigma_{24}) = \sigma_{12}^2(\sigma_{24} - i\sigma_{14}).$$

The left-hand side reduces now by way of (2.3.16) to exactly the right-hand side. Therefore we have just *one* homogeneous relation in addition to the Cayley condition (2.3.14), and hence (2.3.9) represents a *line complex* in $\mathbb{P}^3$. If $\varphi(\zeta)$ is an analytic function of ζ, then $\varphi'(\zeta)$ is also analytic and we may obtain two additional (independent) identities by using $\zeta = -\sigma_{12}(\sigma_{13} + i\sigma_{23})^{-1}$

in $\varphi(\zeta)$ and $\varphi'(\zeta)$. In this case (2.3.9) represents a *ruled surface* in $\mathbb{P}^3$ [W.18, p. 158].

One may study a space curve in $\mathbb{P}^n$ by studying an $(n+1)$th degree, an ordinary differential equation having the homogeneous coordinates of the space curve as its set of independent solutions [W.18, p. 51]. To illustrate this let us consider the space curve $\Gamma(u_k) \subset \mathbb{P}^3$, where the $u_k(\zeta)$ $(k = 1, 2, 3, 4)$ are analytic, linearly independent functions for all ζ in some domain $\mathfrak{D} \subset \mathbb{C}^1$. In this case their Wronskian does not vanish in $\mathfrak{D}$, i.e.,

$$\Delta(u_k) \equiv \begin{vmatrix} u_1 & u_2 & u_3 & u_4 \\ u_1' & u_2' & u_3' & u_4' \\ u_1'' & u_2'' & u_3'' & u_4'' \\ u_1^{\text{iii}} & u_2^{\text{iii}} & u_3^{\text{iii}} & u_4^{\text{iii}} \end{vmatrix} \neq 0, \qquad \zeta \in \mathfrak{D}.$$

If $\Delta(u_k) \neq 0$, then $\Gamma(u_k)$ does not lie in a projective subspace π^2 but in $\mathbb{P}^3$; furthermore, the osculating subspace to $\Gamma(u_k)$, has only first order contact with this space curve. The osculating subspace, $P_\alpha{}^2(\zeta)$, is defined by the system

$$\begin{aligned} \alpha_1 u_1 + \alpha_2 u_2 + \alpha_3 u_3 + \alpha_4 u_4 &= 0, \\ \alpha_1 u_1' + \alpha_2 u_2' + \alpha_3 u_3' + \alpha_4 u_4' &= 0, \\ \alpha_1 u_1'' + \alpha_2 u_2'' + \alpha_3 u_3'' + \alpha_4 u_4'' &= 0, \\ \alpha_1 u_1^{\text{iii}} + \alpha_2 u_2^{\text{iii}} + \alpha_3 u_3^{\text{iii}} + \alpha_4 u_4^{\text{iii}} &= 1. \end{aligned}$$

If $\alpha_1 u_1^{\text{iii}} + \alpha_2 u_2^{\text{iii}} + \alpha_3 u_3^{\text{iii}} + \alpha_4 u_4^{\text{iii}} = 0$ for some ζ, then the osculating subspace has more than first order contact, and of course if follows that $\Delta(u_k) = 0$.

Let us now consider the homogeneous plane coordinates $u_k(\zeta)$ of (2.3.9a); these $u_k(\zeta)$ are solutions of the ordinary differential equation

$$\mathbf{L}_1[u] \equiv \varphi^{\text{iii}} u^{\text{iv}} - \varphi^{\text{iv}} u^{\text{iii}} = 0. \tag{2.3.18}$$

The corresponding point coordinates Z_k of (2.3.9a) are solutions to the Lagrange adjoint differential equation of (2.3.18), namely,

$$\mathbf{M}_1[Z] \equiv (\varphi^{\text{iii}}(\zeta)Z)^{\text{iv}} + (\varphi^{\text{iv}}(\zeta)Z)^{\text{iii}} = 0. \tag{2.3.19}$$

Any projective transformation over the complex field transforms the fundamental set of solutions $\{Z_k\}$ to $\mathbf{M}_1[Z] = 0$ into some linear combination of the solutions, hence an integral curve, $\mathscr{C}(Z_k)$, is determined only up to a projective transformation by this method. However, the above approach does permit a *classification* of the types of integral curves to $\mathbf{M}_1[Z]=0$ that may arise and correlates them to the singularities of the $\mathbf{B}_3$-associate $f(u,\zeta)$. Such a classification of singularities is an important step in developing a function theory for harmonic functions of more than two variables. To this end we compute a set of solutions to $\mathbf{M}_1[Z]$ which are projectively equivalent to a solution of Eqs. (2.3.17) i.e., $\alpha_k=\varphi^{\text{iii}}(\zeta)\tilde{Z}_k$ $(k=1,2,3,4)$; these solutions are given by

$$\begin{aligned}
\tilde{Z}_1 &= \{\tfrac{1}{2}[\zeta^2-1]\varphi''(\zeta)-[\zeta\varphi'(\zeta)-\varphi(\zeta)]\}[\varphi^{\text{iii}}(\zeta)]^{-2},\\
\tilde{Z}_2 &= \{i/2[1+\zeta^2]\varphi''(\zeta)-i[\zeta\varphi'(\zeta)-\varphi(\zeta)]\}[\varphi^{\text{iii}}(\zeta)]^{-2},\\
\tilde{Z}_3 &= \{\zeta\varphi''(\zeta)-\varphi'(\zeta)\}[\varphi^{\text{iii}}(\zeta)]^{-2},\\
\tilde{Z}_4 &= [\varphi^{\text{iii}}(\zeta)]^{-2}.
\end{aligned} \tag{2.3.20}$$

The $\tilde{Z}_k$ may be thought of as coordinates of a point on the plane $\pi_a^2(\zeta)$, or dualistically as the plane coordinates of the osculating subspace $P_a^2(\zeta)$ to $\Gamma(u_k)$.

In the case of (2.3.9b) the homogeneous plane coordinates w_k are dependent regardless of the choice of $\varphi(\zeta)$; the Wronskian vanishes identically and the osculating subspace, to $\gamma(w_k)$, $P_b^a(\zeta)$, has more than first order contact. $P_b^2(\zeta)$ is determined by the system $\sum_{k=1}^4 w_k^{(n)}\beta_k=0$, $w_k^{(0)}\equiv w_k$ $(n=0,1,2,3)$, which has as a nontrivial solution $\beta_1=i\beta_2=\Psi(\zeta)$ $(\beta_3=\beta_4=0)$ where $\Psi(\zeta)$ is an arbitrary analytic function of ζ.

Since the point $\{\tilde{Z}_k\}$ given by (2.3.20) satisfies equations (2.3.17) it must be a point on both the planes $\pi_a^2(\zeta)$ and $\pi_b^2(\zeta)$, and hence it lies on $\Lambda^1(\zeta)=\pi_a^2(\zeta)\cap\pi_b^2(\zeta)$. The point $\{\beta_k\}$ (given above), on the other hand, does *not* lie on $\pi_a^2(\zeta)$.

$\Lambda^1(\zeta)$ may be represented by Eqs. (2.3.10) or we may write it as $Z_k=\nu(p_k-q_k)+q_k$ $(k=1,2,3,4)$ where $\{p_k\}$, $\{q_k\}$ are two points on $\Lambda^1(\zeta)$ and $\nu\in\mathbb{C}^1$. To this end we choose $p_k=[\varphi^{\text{iii}}(\zeta)]^2\tilde{z}_k$, and take $\{q_k\}$ to be the point obtained from the representation (2.3.10) by setting $\mu=\zeta\varphi''(\zeta)$, and $\lambda=0$. We obtain $q_1=\frac{1}{2}\varphi''[\zeta^2-1]$, $q_2=\frac{1}{2}i\varphi''[\zeta^2+1]$, $q_3=\zeta\varphi''$, and $q_4=0$, which in turn gives us the following characterization of $\Lambda^1(\zeta)$,

$$\begin{aligned}
Z_1 &= -\nu[\zeta\varphi'-\varphi]+\tfrac{1}{2}\varphi''[\zeta^2-1],\\
Z_2 &= -i\nu[\zeta\varphi'-\varphi]+\tfrac{1}{2}i\varphi''[\zeta^2+1],\\
Z_3 &= -\nu\varphi'+\zeta\varphi'',\\
Z_4 &= \nu, \qquad \text{where} \quad \nu\in\mathbb{C}^1.
\end{aligned} \tag{2.3.21}$$

As ζ varies along a curve $\mathcal{Q}$, the points $\{p_k\}$, $\{q_k\}$ describe two curves, $\mathscr{C}_p$ and $\mathscr{C}_q$, and the locus $\Lambda^1(\zeta)$ is the complex line joining a point of $\mathscr{C}_p$ to the corresponding point of $\mathscr{C}_q$ with the same value of ζ. The complex line $\Lambda^1(\zeta)$ (2.3.21) is seen to be a *generator* of the ruled surface in $\mathbb{P}^3$, and the two curves $\mathscr{C}_p$, $\mathscr{C}_q$ are said to be *integral curves* of a system [W.18, p. 126]

$$\begin{aligned} p'' + a_{11}p' + a_{12}q' + b_{11}p + b_{12}q = 0, \\ q'' + a_{21}p' + a_{22}q' + b_{21}p + b_{22}q = 0, \end{aligned} \tag{2.3.22}$$

if and only if the determinant

$$D \equiv \begin{vmatrix} p_1' & p_2' & p_3' & p_4' \\ q_1' & q_2' & q_3' & q_4' \\ p_1 & p_2 & p_3 & p_4 \\ q_1 & q_2 & q_3 & q_4 \end{vmatrix} \not\equiv 0. \tag{2.3.23}$$

The geometric significance of this fact is that for the curves $\mathscr{C}_p$, $\mathscr{C}_q$ to be integral curves of this system it is necessary and sufficient that the tangents to $\mathscr{C}_p$ and $\mathscr{C}_q$ at corresponding points do not intersect; if $D \equiv 0$, then the ruled surface reduces to a *developable*.

Theorem 2.3.4 *Let $H(\mathbf{Z})$ be a harmonic function given by $H(\mathbf{Z}) = \mathbf{B}_3 f$, where the singularities of $f(u, \zeta)$ have a global representation, $h(u, \zeta) \equiv \zeta u - \varphi(\zeta) = 0$. Then the possible singularities of $H(\mathbf{Z})$ must lie on a developable in $\mathbb{P}^3$.*

Proof By direct computation one shows that the determinant given by (2.3.23) is identically zero.

Theorem 2.3.5 *Let the conditions of Theorem 2.3.4 hold, and let $\varphi(\zeta)$ be a polynomial. Then a necessary and sufficient condition for the possible singularities of $H(\mathbf{Z})$ to lie on a cone in $\mathbb{P}^3$ is that $\varphi(\zeta)$ be of degree less than or equal to 2.*

Proof We consider first the case $\varphi(\zeta) \equiv a\zeta^2 + b\zeta + c$; however, here the $u_k(\zeta)$ will not be solutions of a differential equation (2.3.18). We are, however, able to define the homogeneous point coordinates from the *algebraic* system (2.3.17), and these solutions are projectively equivalent to (2.3.21). Substituting $\varphi(\zeta)$ in (2.3.21), and setting $v = 1$ we find that for all $\zeta \in \mathbb{C}^1$, $\{p_k\}$ is a single point, namely $p_1 = a - c$, $p_2 = i(a + c)$, $p_3 = -b$, $p_4 = 1$. Thus our developable has the property that for each ζ there exists a complex line passing through $\{p_k\}$; such a locus is known as a *cone* [W. 18, p. 130].

To show that this situation does not hold for $\varphi = a_0\zeta^n + a_1\zeta^{n-1} + \ldots + a_n$

($n > 2$) it is merely necessary to perform the above computation for the first homogeneous coordinate. We obtain from (2.3.21)

$$p_1 = a_0\left(v(n-1) - \frac{n(n-1)}{2}\right)\zeta^n + a_1\left(v(n-2) - \frac{(n-1)(n-2)}{2}\right)\zeta^{n-1} + \cdots.$$

Now $\{p_k\}$ is an arbitrary point on the complex line, $\Lambda^1(\zeta)$, and we seek a point on this line which remains fixed as ζ varies. For this to happen the coefficients of ζ^n and ζ^{n-1} must vanish. However, it is impossible to choose v such that they both vanish.

Corollary 2.3.6 *Let the conditions of Theorem* 2.3.4 *hold, and* $\varphi(\zeta)$ *be a polynomial of degree* n, $n > 2$. *Then the singularities of* $H(\mathbf{Z}) = \mathbf{B}_3 f$ *lie on a ruled surface in* $\mathbb{P}^3$ *whose integral curves are twisted* nth *degree (complex) space curves.*

Theorem 2.3.7 *If* $\varphi(\zeta)$ *is a cubic then the integral curves on the above ruled surface are self-dual.*

Proof The integral curve associated with the differential equation

$$\mathbf{M}^*[Z] \equiv Z^{\text{iv}} + f_1 Z^{\text{iii}} + f_2 Z'' + f_3 Z' + f_4 Z = 0$$

is identically self-dual *if and only if* the invariant

$$\Theta_3 \equiv \tfrac{1}{4}(f_3 - f_1'' - \tfrac{1}{2} f_1 f_2 + \tfrac{1}{8} f_1{}^3) - \tfrac{3}{4}(\tfrac{1}{3} f_2{}' - \tfrac{1}{2} f_1'' - \tfrac{1}{4} f_1 f_1{}'),$$

vanishes [W.18, p. 243]. That this is the case here, follows immediately by comparison with Eq. (2.3.19).

Remark One may further characterize the singularities of $H(\mathbf{Z})$ and $H(\mathbf{X})$ by considering in addition to the invariants of $\mathbf{M}^*[Z]$ also the covariants.

4. *Other Operators Generating Harmonic Functions in Three Variables*

In this section we shall construct another operator which transforms holomorphic functions of two complex variables into harmonic functions (see [G.19]). We do this as before by introducing a formal sum for the kernel; for instance, let

$$K^{(+)}\left(\frac{r}{s}, \xi, \frac{\eta}{\zeta}\right) \equiv \sum_{n=0}^{\infty} \sum_{m=0}^{n} \frac{2^m m!}{(2m)!} \left(\frac{r}{s}\right)^n P_n^m(\xi) \left(\frac{\eta}{\zeta}\right)^m, \tag{2.4.1}$$

and let $f(s, \zeta)$ be defined in the bicylinder $\{|s| \leq 1, |\zeta| \leq 1\}$ as

$$f(s, \zeta) \equiv \sum_{n=0}^{\infty} \sum_{m=0}^{n} a_{nm}\, s^n \zeta^m. \tag{2.4.2}$$

Then by a simple computation using the Cauchy formula for two variables we have that the harmonic function

$$U(r, \cos\theta, e^{i\varphi}) \equiv \sum_{n=0}^{\infty} \sum_{m=0}^{n} a_{nm} \frac{2^m m!}{(2m)!} r^n P_n^m(\cos\theta) e^{im\varphi}, \tag{2.4.3}$$

has the integral representation

$$U(r, \cos\theta, e^{i\varphi}) = \frac{-1}{4\pi^2} \int_{|s|=1} \frac{ds}{s} \int_{|\zeta|=1} K^{(+)}\left(\frac{r}{s}, \cos\theta, \frac{e^{i\varphi}}{\zeta}\right) f(s, \zeta) \frac{d\zeta}{\zeta}. \tag{2.4.4}$$

In order to sum $K^{(+)}(r/s, \cos\theta, e^{i\varphi}/\zeta)$ we consider the generating function for Legendre polynomials

$$(1 - 2r\xi + r^2)^{-1/2} = \sum_{n=0}^{\infty} P_n(\xi) r^n, \qquad |r| < 1,$$

and differentiate m times with respect to ξ; we obtain

$$\begin{aligned} \frac{1 \cdot 3 \cdot 5 \cdot \cdots \cdot (2m-1) r^m}{(1 - 2r\xi + r^2)^{m+\frac{1}{2}}} &= \sum_{n=m}^{\infty} r^n \frac{d^m}{d\xi^m} P_n(\xi) \\ &= \sum_{n=m}^{\infty} (-1)^m (1-\xi^2)^{-m/2} P_n^m(\xi) r^n, \end{aligned} \tag{2.4.5}$$

since $P_n^m(\xi) = (-1)^m (1-\xi^2)^{m/2} (d^m/d\xi^m) P_n(\xi)$. Now if we multiply both sides by $(\eta/\zeta)^m$, and sum from 0 to ∞ over m, (replacing r by r/s) we have†

$$\begin{aligned} \left[1 - 2\frac{r}{s}\xi + \frac{r^2}{s^2}\right]^{-1/2} \sum_{m=0}^{\infty} \left(\frac{-\eta r s (1-\xi^2)^{1/2}}{\zeta[s^2 - 2rs\xi + r^2]}\right)^m &= \sum_{m=0}^{\infty} \sum_{n=m}^{\infty} \frac{2^m m!}{(2m)!} \left(\frac{r}{s}\right)^n P_n^m(\xi) \left(\frac{\eta}{\zeta}\right)^m \\ &= \sum_{n=0}^{\infty} \sum_{m=0}^{n} \frac{2^m m!}{(2m)!} \left(\frac{r}{s}\right)^n P_n^m(\xi) \left(\frac{\eta}{\zeta}\right)^m. \end{aligned} \tag{2.4.6}$$

† We may rearrange the orders of summation since the series is absolutely convergent.

Consequently,

$$K^{(+)}\left(\frac{r}{s}, \xi, \frac{\eta}{\zeta}\right) = \frac{s}{[s^2 - 2rs\xi + r^2]^{1/2}}\left[1 + \frac{\eta rs(1-\xi^2)^{1/2}}{\zeta[s^2 - 2rs\xi + r^2]}\right]^{-1}$$
$$= \frac{\zeta s[s^2 - 2rs\xi + r^2]^{1/2}}{\zeta(s^2 - 2rs\xi + r^2) + \eta rs(1-\xi^2)^{1/2}}, \tag{2.4.7}$$

providing

$$\left|\frac{\eta rs(1-\xi^2)^{1/2}}{\zeta(s^2 - 2rs\xi + r^2)}\right| < 1,$$

which is satisfied for $r < \frac{1}{3}$, when $|\eta| = |\zeta| = |s| = 1$. For values of r such that $|r| \geq \frac{1}{3}$ one analytically continues $K^{(+)}(r/s, \xi, \eta/\zeta)$ in the complex r-plane starting at some initial point in the disk $|r| < \frac{1}{3}$.

By introducing Cartesian coordinates as before by the transformation (2.2.24), i.e., $\xi = z_3/r$, $\eta = [(z_1 + iz_2)/(z_1 - iz_2)]^{1/2}$ $r = +(z_1{}^2 + z_2{}^2 + z_3{}^2)$, we obtain for $H(\mathbf{Z}) \equiv U(r, \xi, \eta)$,

$$H(\mathbf{Z}) = \mathbf{G}_3{}^*f$$
$$\equiv \frac{-1}{4\pi^2}\int_{|\zeta|=1}\frac{d\zeta}{\zeta}\int_{|s|=1}\frac{ds\, f(s,\zeta)[z_1{}^2 + z_2{}^2 + (z_3 - s)^2]^{1/2}}{\left(z_1 + \dfrac{s}{2\zeta}\right)^2 + \left(z_2 + \dfrac{is}{2\zeta}\right)^2 + (z_3 + s)^2}. \tag{2.4.8}$$

It is possible to obtain an alternate integral operator, which also generates the harmonic function (2.4.3) from the holomorphic function (2.4.2). We return to (2.4.5), multiply by η^m, replace r by r/s, and then perform a contour integration over $|s| = 1$:

$$\frac{2^m m!}{(2m)!} r^k P_k^m(\xi)\eta^m = \frac{1}{2\pi i}\int_{|s|=1}\left[\frac{-\eta r(1-\xi^2)^{1/2}}{s\left(1 - 2\dfrac{r}{s}\xi + \dfrac{r^2}{s^2}\right)}\right]^m \frac{s^k\, ds}{(s^2 - 2rs\xi + r^2)^{1/2}}$$

for $k \geq m$. This suggests that we consider the mapping of functions of two complex variables $f(s, \sigma) = \sum_{n=0}^{\infty}\sum_{m=0}^{n} a_{nm} s^n \sigma^m$, where σ is the auxiliary variable

$$\sigma = \frac{-\eta r(1-\xi^2)^{1/2}}{s\left(1 - 2\dfrac{r}{s}\xi + \dfrac{r^2}{s^2}\right)} = \frac{-s(x_1 + ix_2)}{x_1{}^2 + x_2{}^2 + (x_3 - s)^2} \qquad \text{and} \qquad \mathbf{Z} = \mathbf{X} \in \mathbb{R}^3$$

We then have formally (the operation of termwise integration may be justified as before by suitable restrictions on the range of $\mathbf{X}$ and the coefficients a_{nm}), that

$$H(\mathbf{X}) = \mathbf{G}_3 f \equiv \frac{1}{2\pi i} \int_{|s|=1} \frac{f(s, \sigma)\, ds}{[x_1{}^2 + x_2{}^2 + (x_3 - s)^2]^{1/2}}, \qquad (2.4.9)$$

where σ is defined as above.

Remark One interesting application of the integral operator method is that we may transplant certain properties of analytic functions into properties concerning solutions of partial differential equations. Bergman has made an extensive study of this method in regard to the operator $\mathbf{B}_3$ and several others, which we shall mention later [B.22–29]. It is of interest to have different operators available for the study of the same partial differential equation, the reason being that these operators may preserve different analytic properties. The operator $\mathbf{G}_3$ for instance, associates a different class of singular solutions for Laplace's equation than the operator $\mathbf{B}_3$. Results concerning these singularities may be found in [G.19, p. 145]. An inverse operator for $\mathbf{G}_3$ is also developed in [G.19, pp. 146–149]; it has the form

$$f(t, \zeta) = \mathbf{G}_3^{-1} U \equiv \frac{1}{4\pi i} \int_{-1}^{+1} d\xi \int_{|\eta|=1} K^{(-)}(t/r, \xi, \zeta/\eta) U(r, \xi, \eta)\, d\xi, \qquad (2.4.10)$$

where the kernel is defined by the formal sum

$$K^{(-)}\left(\frac{t}{r}, \xi, \frac{\zeta}{\eta}\right) \equiv \sum_{n=0}^{\infty} \sum_{m=0}^{n} (2n+1) \frac{(n-m)!\,(2m)!}{(n+m)!\, 2^m m!} \left(\frac{t}{r}\right)^n P_n^m(\xi) \left(\frac{\zeta}{\eta}\right)^m. \qquad (2.4.11)$$

The kernel may be found in closed form, after rather involved manipulation, to be

$$K^{(-)}\left(\frac{t}{r}, \xi, \frac{\zeta}{n}\right) = \frac{r(r^2 - t^2)}{(r^2 - 2tr\xi + t^2)^{3/2}} + \frac{12t^2r^2}{\eta} \zeta(1 - \xi^2)^{1/2} I\left(\frac{t}{r}, \xi, \frac{\zeta}{\eta}\right) \qquad (2.4.12)$$

where

$$I\left(\frac{t}{r}, \xi, \frac{\xi}{\eta}\right) \equiv \left[\frac{1}{a^3 T^{3/2}} \left(-a^2\rho^2 + \frac{a^2 - ab}{2}\rho - \frac{1}{6}[4ac - b^2 - ab] + \frac{r^2a^2}{3t^2}\right) + \frac{1}{6} \frac{(a\rho + b)}{(ac - b^2)} \left(2a^2 \frac{r^2}{t^2}(a + b) - b(4ac - b^2) - ab^2\right)\right]_{\rho=0}^{\rho=1}$$

$$+\left[\frac{1}{3a^2T^{1/2}}\left(2a^2\frac{r^2}{t^2}(a+b)-b(4ac-b^2)-ab^2\right)\right.$$

$$\left.\times\frac{(a\rho+b)}{(ac-b^2)^2}\right]_{\rho=0}^{\rho=1}, \qquad (2.4.13)$$

with $T = a\rho^2 + b\rho + c, a = t + (r/\eta)(1-\xi^2)^{1/2}, b = -2tr[\xi + (1/\eta)(1-\xi^2)^{1/2}]$, and $c = r^2 + (tr/\eta)(1-\xi^2)^{1/2}$. The details of this computation are omitted with an aim toward conciseness of presentation; the reader who is interested in this aspect is referred to the original paper [G.19].

Finally, we mention an operator which maps functions of a single complex variable onto harmonic functions of three variables, the Bergman–Sommerfeld operator, defined by

$$H(\mathbf{X}) = \mathbf{S}_3 f,$$

$$\mathbf{S}_3 f \equiv \int_{\mathcal{Q}} \frac{f(\zeta)\,d\zeta}{([x_1-u_1(\zeta)]^2+[x_2-u_2(\zeta)]^2+[x_3-u_3(\zeta)]^2)^{1/2}} \qquad (2.4.14)$$

where $\mathcal{Q}$ is either an open or closed curve in the ζ-plane and the $u_k(\zeta)$ are real functions of ζ. This type of operator is suggested by the study of Newtonian potentials. Bergman has made an extensive study of harmonic functions generated by the operator $\mathbf{S}_3$. See, for instance, his book [B.22, pp. 57–63] for some of these results and for a complete list of references; in particular also see [B.20].

5. *Harmonic Functions in Four Variables*

In this section we shall construct an operator which may be considered as a generalization of the Bergman–Whittaker operator $\mathbf{B}_3$ to four variables. This new operator, which generates solutions to the four-dimensional Laplace equations, was first introduced by the present author in [G.6,8]. It was later further investigated by Kreyszig in [K.7], and also by the author in [G.15,17, 23,25].

We begin as in the three-variable case by introducing a suitable auxiliary variable $\tau = N_\mu x_\mu$, $N_\mu \equiv N_\mu(\eta, \xi)$ such that $N_\mu N_\mu \equiv 0$. In this way τ^n is a solution of Laplace's equation,

$$\Box H(\mathbf{X}) \equiv \frac{\partial^2 H}{\partial x_\mu\,\partial x_\mu} = 0, \qquad \mathbf{X} \equiv (x_1, x_2, x_3, x_4),$$

and hence serves as a generating function for a system of homogeneous, harmonic polynomials. As our choice of an auxiliary variable we take

$$\begin{aligned}\tau \equiv \tau[\mathbf{X}; \eta, \xi] &= x_\mu N_\mu(\eta, \xi)\\ &= x_1\left(1 + \frac{1}{\eta\xi}\right) + ix_2\left(1 - \frac{1}{\eta\xi}\right) + x_3\left(\frac{1}{\xi} - \frac{1}{\eta}\right) + ix_4\left(\frac{1}{\xi} + \frac{1}{\eta}\right),\end{aligned} \tag{2.5.1}$$

and consider the following class of polynomials $H_n^{k,l}(\mathbf{X})$ $(n = 0, 1, 2, \ldots)$ $(0 \le k, l \le n)$ defined by the generating function expansion

$$\tau^n = \sum_{k=0}^{n} \sum_{l=0}^{n} H_n^{k,l}(\mathbf{X})\eta^{-k}\xi^{-l}, \qquad \mathbf{X} \equiv (x_1, x_2, x_3, x_4). \tag{2.5.2}$$

It is clear from our definition (2.5.1) that $N_\mu N_\mu \equiv 0$, and hence the integral powers of τ are by definition solid, hyperspherical harmonics. Likewise, it is also clear that the polynomials are homogeneous, harmonic polynomials of degree n. (Actually these harmonic polynomials form a complete, linearly independent system of solutions [G.6,8,15].) Kreyszig noticed by introducing the complex coordinates

$$\begin{aligned} y &= x_1 + ix_2, & z &= x_3 + ix_4,\\ y^* &= x_1 - ix_2, & z^* &= -(x_3 - ix_4),\end{aligned} \tag{2.5.3}$$

that these harmonic polynomials, $\hat{H}_n^{k,l}(\mathbf{Y}) \equiv H_n^{k,l}(\mathbf{X})$ $\mathbf{Y} \equiv (y, y^*, z, z^*)$, may be expressed in terms of certain well-known classical polynomials [K.7]. Introducing the above coordinates in our definition of τ yields $\tau \equiv \tau[\mathbf{Y}; \eta, \xi] = (1/\eta\xi)(y\eta\xi + z\eta + z^*\xi + y^*)$; inserting this expression for τ in the following representation for the $\hat{H}_n^{k,l}(\mathbf{Y})$ (which follows from (2.5.2) after applying Cauchy's formula),

$$\hat{H}_n^{k,l}(\mathbf{Y}) = -\frac{1}{4\pi^2}\int_{|\xi|=1} \xi^{l-1}\, d\xi\left\{\int_{|\eta|=1} \eta^{k-1}\tau^n\, d\eta\right\}, \tag{2.5.4}$$

yields the following integral representation:

$$\begin{aligned}\hat{H}_n^{k,l}(\mathbf{Y}) &= -\frac{1}{4\pi^2}\int_{|\xi|=1} \xi^{l-1}\, d\xi\left\{\int_{|\eta|=1} \eta^{k-1}\left[\left(y + \frac{z}{\xi}\right) + \left(z^* + \frac{y^*}{\xi}\right)\eta^{-1}\right]^n d\eta\right\}\\ &= \frac{1}{2\pi i}\binom{n}{k}\int_{|\xi|=1}\left(z^* + \frac{y^*}{\xi}\right)^k\left(y + \frac{z}{\xi}\right)^{n-k}\xi^{l-1}\, d\xi,\end{aligned} \tag{2.5.5a}$$

$$\hat{H}_n^{k,l}(\mathbf{Y}) = \frac{\binom{n}{l}}{2\pi i} \int_{|\eta|=1} [y + z^*\eta^{-1}]^{n-1}[z + y^*\eta^{-1}]^l \eta^{k-1}\, d\eta. \tag{2.5.5b}$$

This becomes, upon introducing a new integration parameter, $t = (2T^2/R^2) \times (\eta^{-1} + S^2/2T^2)$ (with $R^2 \equiv yy^* - zz^*$, $S^2 \equiv yy^* + zz^*$, and $T^2 = y^*z^*$),

$$\hat{H}_n^{k,l}(\mathbf{Y}) = (-1)^l \binom{n}{l} 2^{k-n} R^{2n-2k} y^{*k+l-n} z^{*k-l} \frac{1}{2\pi i} \int_C \frac{(1-t)^l (1+t)^{n-l}\, dt}{(t - t_0)^{k+1}}$$

$$= \frac{(-1)^l}{k!} \binom{n}{l} 2^{k-n} R^{2n-2k} y^{*k+l-n} z^{*k-l} \frac{d^k}{dt_0{}^k} [(1-t_0)^l (1+t_0)^{n-l}],$$

which by Rodrigues' formula for the Jacobi polynomials [E.6, Vol. II, p. 169],

$$P_n^{(\alpha,\beta)}(t_0) = \frac{(-1)^n}{2^n n!} (1-t_0)^{-\alpha}(1+t_0)^{-\beta} \frac{d^n}{dt_0{}^n} [(1-t_0)^{\alpha+n}(1+t_0)^{\beta+n}] \tag{2.5.6}$$

yields

$$\hat{H}_n^{k,l}(\mathbf{Y}) = \binom{n}{l} R^{2k} z^{l-k} y^{n-k-l} P_k^{(l-k,\, n-k-l)}(S^2/R^2), \tag{2.5.7}$$

upon making the replacement, $(1 - t_0)/z^* = -2z/R^2$, $(1 - t_0)/y^* = 2y/R^2$.

Motivated by the example of Bergman's operator $\mathbf{B}_3$ one now considers the following generalization [G.8],

$$H(\mathbf{X}) = \mathbf{G}_4 f \equiv -\frac{1}{4\pi^2} \int_{|\xi|=1} \frac{d\xi}{\xi} \int_{|\eta|=1} \frac{d\eta}{\eta} f(\tau, \eta, \xi); \tag{2.5.8}$$

here $f(\tau, \eta, \xi)$ is a holomorphic function of three complex variables. If $f(\tau, \eta, \xi)$ has the following Taylor series expansion,

$$f(\tau, \eta, \xi) = \sum_{n=0}^{\infty} \sum_{k,l=0}^{n} a_{nkl} \tau^n \eta^k \xi^l, \tag{2.5.9}$$

then the operator $\mathbf{G}_4$ maps it onto the formal sum

$$H(\mathbf{X}) \equiv \sum_{n=0}^{\infty} \sum_{k,l=0}^{n} a_{nkl} H_n^{k,l}(\mathbf{X})$$

$$= \hat{H}(\mathbf{Y}) \equiv \sum_{n=0}^{\infty} \sum_{k,l=0}^{n} a_{nkl} \binom{n}{l} R^{2k} z^{l-k} y^{n-k-l} P_k^{(l-k,\, n-k-l)}(S^2/R^2). \tag{2.5.10}$$

It should be noted that, as in the case of the Bergman–Whittaker operator, the holomorphic function $f(\tau, \eta, \xi)$ which corresponds to the harmonic function (2.5.10) is determined only up to a *null associate*; if

$$g(\tau, \eta, \xi) \equiv \sum_{n=0}^{\infty} \sum_{k, l=0}^{\infty} a_{nkl} \tau^n \eta^k \xi^l,$$

where the coefficients are the same as those of $f(\tau, u, \eta)$ for $k, l \leq n$, then both $g(\tau, \eta, \xi)$ and $f(\tau, \eta, \xi)$ correspond to the same harmonic function (2.5.10). We agree therefore to call (2.5.9) the *normalized associate.*

Kreyszig has also made the important discovery of an inverse integral operator for $\mathbf{G}_4$, which is a generalization of the Bergman inverse operator for $\mathbf{B}_3$, i.e., an *inverse operator of the first kind.* Shortly afterwards, the present author gave another inverse operator for $\mathbf{G}_4$ that generalized his inverse operator of the second kind for $\mathbf{B}_3$ [G.15]. We present both inverse integral operators below.

Theorem 2.5.1 (Kreyszig) *Let $\tilde{H}(Y) \equiv \tilde{H}(y, y^*, z, z^*)$ be a harmonic function regular in a neighborhood of the origin. Then its normalized associate function may be obtained by the following integral operator,*

$$\mathbf{G}_4^{-1}\tilde{H} \equiv \int_0^1 \int_0^1 \frac{\partial}{\partial u}\left\{u \frac{\partial}{\partial u}[u\chi(u[1-\alpha][1-\beta], u\xi\beta[1-\alpha], u\eta\alpha[1-\beta])]\right\} d\alpha\, d\beta,$$

$$f(u, \eta, \xi) = \mathbf{G}_4^{-1}\tilde{H}, \qquad (2.5.11)$$

where the function $\chi(y, z, z^*)$ is the restriction of $\hat{H}(\mathbf{Y})$ to the characteristic space, $\mathfrak{C}^3 \equiv \{\mathbf{X} \mid R^2 \equiv x_1{}^2 + x_2{}^2 + x_3{}^2 + x_4{}^2 = 0\}$.

Proof The restriction of $\hat{H}_n^{l,k}(\mathbf{Y})$ to the characteristic space $\mathfrak{C}^3 \subset \mathbb{C}^4$ (i.e, by setting $yy^* = zz^*$) may be computed easily from the integral representation (2.5.4). For $\mathbf{Y} \in \mathfrak{C}^3$ $\tau = (1/\eta\xi)[y(\eta + z^*/y)(\xi + z/y) + R^2/y]$, hence if $\chi_n^{l,k}$ is the restriction of $\hat{H}_n^{l,k}$ then we have [K.7, p. 199],

$$\begin{aligned}\chi_n^{l,k}(y, z, z^*) &= -\frac{y^n}{4\pi^2}\int_{|\eta|=1}\left(\eta + \frac{z^*}{y}\right)^n \eta^{l-n-1}\, d\eta \int_{|\xi|=1}\left(\xi + \frac{z}{y}\right)^n \xi^{k-n-1}\, d\xi \\ &= \binom{n}{n-l}\binom{n}{n-k} y^{n-l-k} z^{*l} z^k. \qquad (2.5.12)\end{aligned}$$

From this we have, for $\chi(y, z, z^*) \equiv \hat{H}(\mathbf{Y})|_{\mathbf{Y} \in \mathfrak{C}^3}$

$$\chi(u[1-\alpha][1-\beta], u\xi\beta[1-\alpha], u\eta\alpha[1-\beta])$$
$$= \sum_{n=0}^{\infty} \sum_{l,k=0}^{n} a_{nlk} \binom{n}{n-l} \binom{n}{n-k} u^n \xi^l \eta^k \beta^l \alpha^k (1-\alpha)^{n-k} (1-\beta)^{n-l} \qquad (2.5.13)$$

which implies

$$\frac{\partial}{\partial u}\left\{u \frac{\partial}{\partial u}(u\chi)\right\} = \sum_{n=0}^{\infty} \sum_{l,k=0}^{n} a_{nlk}(n+1)^2 \chi_n^{l,k}. \qquad (2.5.14)$$

Using the identity $\int_0^1 \alpha^t(1-\alpha)^{s-t}\, d\alpha = [(s+1)(s/t)]^{-1}$ (for $s - t \geq 0$, s and t positive integers) in (2.5.13) and (2.5.14) yields the desired result (2.5.11).

In the original paper on the operator $\mathbf{G}_4$ a slightly different form of the auxiliary variable τ was used [G.8], which is related to the present one by the following rotation plus a reflection of the **X**-coordinates,

$$x_1 \to \tilde{x}_4, \qquad x_2 \to \tilde{x}_1, \qquad x_3 \to \tilde{x}_3, \qquad x_4 \to -\tilde{x}_2. \qquad (2.5.15)$$

The coordinates $\tilde{\mathbf{X}} \equiv (\tilde{x}_1, \tilde{x}_2, \tilde{x}_3, \tilde{x}_4)$ were originally used because the harmonic polynomials obtained by expanding the powers of this auxiliary variable gave rise to well-known, orthogonal, hyperspherical harmonics [E.6, p. 253]. However, since these orthogonality properties are invariant under the above coordinate transformation we shall retain our present notation.†

As in the original paper [G.8] we introduce surface harmonics $S_n^{k,l}(\theta_1, \theta_2, \varphi)$ by relating them to the homogeneous, harmonic polynomials $H_n^{k,l}(\mathbf{X})$ by the formula

$$\binom{n}{k} \rho^n S_n^{k,l}(\theta_1, \theta_2, \varphi) \equiv H_n^{k,l}(\mathbf{X}), \qquad (2.5.16)$$

where the **X**-coordinates are replaced by the hyperspherical coordinates

$$x_1 = \rho \cos \theta_1, \qquad x_2 = \rho \sin \theta_1 \cos \theta_2,$$
$$x_3 = \rho \sin \theta_1 \sin \theta_2 \cos \varphi, \qquad x_4 = \rho \sin \theta_1 \sin \theta_2 \sin \varphi, \qquad (2.5.17)$$

where $\rho \geq 0$, $0 \leq \theta_j \leq \pi$ $(j = 1, 2)$, $0 \leq \varphi \leq 2\pi$. Since the orthogonality condition on the unit-hypersphere in the $\tilde{\mathbf{X}}$-coordinates is invariant under rotations and reflections we have for these surface harmonics also that [E.6, p. 253]

† The present variation of the auxiliary variable τ is the same as in [K.7]; it was written in this form for the purpose of obtaining an inverse operator of the first kind for $\mathbf{G}_4$.

$$\frac{1}{2\pi^2}\int_\Omega S_n^{k,l}\overline{S_n^{m,p}}\,d\Omega = \frac{\delta_{km}\,\delta_{lp}}{n+1}\frac{\binom{n}{l}}{\binom{n}{k}} \tag{2.5.18}$$

where $d\Omega = \sin^2\theta_1 \sin\theta_2\, d\theta_1\, d\theta_2\, d\varphi$ is the surface area differential.

We remark that the solid harmonics (2.5.16) [and hence also the functions (2.5.7)] are known to form a complete, linearly independent system with respect to Laplace's equation, [E.6, Vol. II, Ch. 11]. Hence, any harmonic function $H(\mathbf{X})$ regular about the origin in a sphere, say, $\|\mathbf{X}\| \le r_0$, may be expanded in terms of them, i.e.,

$$H(\mathbf{X}) \equiv V(\rho, \theta_1, \theta_2, \varphi) = \sum_{n=0}^{\infty}\sum_{k,l=0}^{n} a_{nkl}\binom{n}{k}\rho^n S_n^{k,l}(\theta_1, \theta_2, \varphi). \tag{2.5.19}$$

The series (2.5.19) converges uniformly inside and on the boundary of this sphere, and hence the Fourier coefficients may be found by integrating termwise and employing the conditions (2.5.18). One may show as before in the case of three variables, that for each such harmonic function, regular in the sphere of radius r_0, there exists a holomorphic function $f(\tau, \eta, \xi)$ given by a Taylor series (2.5.9) that converges in the polydisk $\mathfrak{F}(\varepsilon_1, \varepsilon_2, \varepsilon_3) \equiv \{|\tau| \le \varepsilon_1;\ |\eta| \le 1 + \varepsilon_2;\ |\xi| \le 1 + \varepsilon_3\}$ where the $\varepsilon_k > 0$ $(k = 1, 2, 3)$ are chosen suitably small.

If $|\eta| = |\xi| = 1$, then

$$\begin{aligned}|\tau| &= |y\eta\xi + z\eta + z^*\xi + y^*| \le |y| + |z| + |y^*| + |z^*|\\ &\le 2(|z| + |y|) \le 2^{3/2}\|\mathbf{X}\|\end{aligned}$$

by Schwarz's inequality. Hence, if $f(\tau, \eta, \xi)$ is holomorphic and has a convergent Taylor series in $\mathfrak{F}(r_0, \varepsilon_2, \varepsilon_3)$ then $H(\mathbf{X})$ has a convergent Fourier expansion in the sphere $\|\mathbf{X}\| \le r_0/2^{3/2}$. This follows from the fact that under these conditions we may integrate $\mathbf{G}_4 f$ termwise and obtain a uniformly convergent series of the form (2.5.19).

Let us assume $H(\mathbf{X})$ is harmonic-regular in the sphere $\|\mathbf{X}\| \le r_0$, and let us introduce, as in the case of three variables as a kernel, a formal sum

$$B^{(-)}\left(\frac{\sigma}{\rho}, \eta, \xi; \theta_1, \theta_2, \varphi\right) \equiv \sum_{n=0}^{\infty}\sum_{k,l=0}^{n} \frac{(n+1)}{\binom{n}{l}}\left(\frac{\sigma}{\rho}\right)^n S_n^{k,l}\eta^k\xi^l. \tag{2.5.20}$$

Clearly, we may obtain the following result,

$$\sigma^n \eta^m \xi^p = \frac{1}{2\pi^2} \int_\Omega \binom{n}{m} \rho^n \overline{S_n^{m,p}(\theta_j; \varphi)} B^{(-)}\left(\frac{\sigma}{\rho}, \eta, \xi; \theta_1, \theta_2, \varphi\right) d\Omega, \quad (2.5.21)$$

providing termwise integration is permissible. Actually the series (2.5.20) may be seen to converge to an analytic function as follows. Using the identity

$$1 \Big/ \binom{n}{l} = (n+1) \frac{\Gamma(n-l-1)\Gamma(l+1)}{\Gamma(n+2)} = \int_0^1 \alpha^{n-l}(1-\alpha)^l \, d\alpha$$

we have

$$\begin{aligned} B^{(-)} &= \sum_{n=0}^{\infty} \sum_{k,l=0}^{n} \binom{n}{k} (n+1)^2 \left(\frac{\rho}{\sigma}\right)^n \eta^k S_n^{k,l}(\theta_1, \theta_2, \varphi) \int_0^1 \alpha^n \left[\frac{\xi(1-\alpha)}{\alpha}\right]^l d\alpha \\ &= \sum_{n=0}^{\infty} (n+1)^2 \int_0^1 \left[\sum_{k,l=0}^{n} \left(\frac{\rho\alpha}{\sigma}\right)^n \binom{n}{k} S_n^{k,l}(\theta_1, \theta_2, \varphi) \left[\frac{\alpha}{\xi(1-\alpha)}\right]^{-l} \left(\frac{1}{\eta}\right)^{-k}\right] d\alpha \\ &= \sum_{n=0}^{\infty} (n+1)^2 \int_0^1 \left\{\frac{\alpha}{\sigma} \tau\left[\mathbf{X}; \eta^{-1}, \frac{\alpha}{\xi(1-\alpha)}\right]\right\}^n d\alpha, \end{aligned} \quad (2.5.22)$$

where $\tau[\mathbf{X}; \eta, \xi] \equiv \tau$. If $|\eta| = |\xi| = 1$, then

$$\left|\alpha\tau\left[\mathbf{X}; \eta^{-1}, \frac{\alpha}{\xi(1-\alpha)}\right]\right| \le |y| + |z| \le \sqrt{2}\, \|\mathbf{X}\|;$$

consequently, for $\|\mathbf{X}\|$ sufficiently small, say, $\|\mathbf{X}\| \le \frac{1}{2}|\sigma|$, the series (2.5.22) converges uniformly and termwise integration is valid. Hence, one obtains

$$\begin{aligned} B^{(-)} &= \int_0^1 \sum_{n=0}^{\infty} (n+1)^2 \left\{\frac{\alpha}{\sigma} \tau\left[\mathbf{X}; \eta^{-1}, \frac{\alpha}{\xi(1-\alpha)}\right]\right\}^n d\alpha \\ &= \int_0^1 \frac{1 + \alpha\tau/\sigma}{[1 - \alpha\tau/\sigma]^3} \, d\alpha \\ &= \frac{\delta[\mathbf{X}](2\sigma^{-1} - \beta[\mathbf{X}] - 2\delta[\mathbf{X}])}{\sigma^2(\sigma^{-1} - \delta[\mathbf{X}])^2(\sigma^{-1} - \delta[\mathbf{X}] - \beta[\mathbf{X}])^2} \end{aligned} \quad (2.5.23)$$

where

$$\beta[\mathbf{X}] \equiv x_1(1 - \eta\xi) + ix_2(1 + \eta\xi) - x_3(\xi + \eta) + ix_4(\eta - \xi), \quad (2.5.24)$$

$$\delta[\mathbf{X}] \equiv \xi([x_1 - ix_2]\eta + x_3 + ix_4). \tag{2.5.25}$$

We summarize our above discussion by the following theorem.

Theorem 2.5.2 (Gilbert) *Let $H(\mathbf{X})$ be a harmonic function regular at the origin, and let $V(\rho, \theta_1, \theta_2, \varphi)$ be the function obtained by replacing x_1, x_2, x_3, x_4, by the hyperspherical polar coordinates. Then for ρ sufficiently small we have the following integral representation for the $\mathbf{G}_4$-associates of $H(\mathbf{X})$,*

$$f(\sigma, r, \xi) = \mathbf{G}_4^{-1}H \equiv \frac{1}{2\pi^2}\int_\Omega \frac{\overline{V(\rho, \theta_1, \theta_2, \varphi)}\,\delta(2\sigma^{-1} - \beta - 2\delta)\,d\Omega}{\sigma^2(\sigma^{-1} - \delta)^2(\sigma^{-1} - \delta - \beta)^2}$$

where the integration is over the sphere of radius ρ.

This type of inverse operator is useful for formulating necessary and sufficient criteria for singularities (as we did earlier for the three-variable case) and also for obtaining growth theorems for harmonic functions. Growth theorems may be obtained by using the same arguments as are found in Gilbert [G.21] and Gilbert and Howard [G.H.2,3].

Remark Lo [L.10] has investigated, using integral operator methods, the analytic properties of a special class of harmonic functions of four variables. He considers those solutions which may be represented as a series of zonal hyperspherical harmonics; using the properties of the Didon polynomials he obtains an operator, which maps analytic functions of two complex variables onto these solutions, and also the inverse of this operator.

6. *Harmonic Functions in N ≥ 5 Variables*

In this section we shall present two generalizations of the Bergman–Whittaker operator to the case of $N \geq 5$ variables. The first operator was discovered by Bergman in 1928 [B.4] and is actually an immediate extension of the idea used to construct the original auxiliary variable. For instance, let us introduce the variable $v = N_\mu(\zeta_1, \ldots, \zeta_p)x_\mu \equiv \mathbf{N} \cdot \mathbf{X}$ $(\mu = 1, 2, \ldots, p+2)$ where

$$\begin{aligned} N_1 &\equiv \frac{i}{2}\left(\zeta_1 + \frac{1}{\zeta_1}\right), \qquad N_2 \equiv \frac{1}{4}\left(\zeta_1 - \frac{1}{\zeta_1}\right)\left(\zeta_2 + \frac{1}{\zeta_2}\right), \ldots, \\ N_{p+1} &\equiv \left(\frac{-i}{2}\right)^p i\left(\zeta_1 - \frac{1}{\zeta_1}\right)\left(\zeta_2 - \frac{1}{\zeta_2}\right)\cdots\left(\zeta_{p-1} - \frac{1}{\zeta_{p-1}}\right)\left(\zeta_p + \frac{1}{\zeta_p}\right), \\ N_{p+2} &\equiv \left(\frac{-i}{2}\right)^{p+1}\left(\zeta_1 - \frac{1}{\zeta_1}\right)\left(\zeta_2 - \frac{1}{\zeta_2}\right)\cdots\left(\zeta_{p-1} - \frac{1}{\zeta_{p-1}}\right)\left(\zeta_p - \frac{1}{\zeta_p}\right). \end{aligned} \tag{2.6.1}$$

One realizes that as before $\mathbf{N}$ is an isotropic vector, i.e., $N_\mu N_\mu \equiv 0$, and hence if $F(v; \zeta)$ is an analytic function of $(v; \zeta) \equiv (v, \zeta_1, \ldots, \zeta_p)$ in some polycylindrical region $\{|v| \leq \rho_0\} \times [\Pi_{k=1}^p \{1 - \varepsilon_k \leq |\zeta_k| \leq 1 + \varepsilon_k\}]$ for $\rho_0 > 0$, $\varepsilon_k > 0\ (k = 1, \ldots, p)$ then clearly $\partial^2 F(v; \zeta)/(\partial x_\mu\, \partial x_\mu) \equiv 0$ there. Consequently, this suggests the introduction of the integral operator†

$$\mathbf{B}_{p+2} F \equiv \left(\frac{1}{2\pi i}\right)^p \int_{\mathfrak{D}^p} F(v; \zeta) \frac{d\zeta}{\zeta}. \tag{2.6.2}$$

$H(\mathbf{X}) = \mathbf{B}_{p+2} F$, where the domain of integration is a product $\mathfrak{D}^p \equiv \Pi_{k=1}^p \mathscr{L}_k$ of regular contours $\mathscr{L}_k$ in the ζ_k-planes not passing through the origins, and $\|\mathbf{X} - \mathbf{X}^0\| < \varepsilon$ is sufficiently small. In order to realize how the operator $\mathbf{B}_{p+2} F$ transforms the functions $F(v; \zeta)$ into harmonic functions it is useful to consider, as before, v^n as the generating function for a class of harmonic polynomials. We do this by introducing the set of homogeneous, harmonic polynomials of degree n, $h_n(\mathbf{X}; m) \equiv h_n(x_1, \ldots, x_{p+2}; m_1, \ldots, m_p)$ by the relation

$$v^n = \sum_{m=-n}^{+n} h_n(\mathbf{X}; m) \zeta^m \equiv \sum_{m_1=-n}^{+n} \cdots \sum_{m_p=-n}^{+n} h_n(\mathbf{X}; m) \zeta_1^{m_1} \cdots \zeta_p^{m_p}. \tag{2.6.3}$$

Then, by using the several-variable Cauchy formula, we have for $\|\mathbf{X}\| < \varepsilon$, $\varepsilon > 0$ sufficiently small, that the functions of $(p + 1)$ complex variables,

$$F(v; \zeta) = \sum_{n=0}^{\infty} \sum_{m=-n}^{+n} a_n(m) v^n \zeta^m, \tag{2.6.4}$$

map onto the harmonic functions

$$H(\mathbf{X}) = \mathbf{B}_{p+2} F = \sum_{n=0}^{\infty} \sum_{m=-n}^{+n} a_n(-m) h_n(\mathbf{X}; m). \tag{2.6.5}$$

We see then that the operator $\mathbf{B}_{p+2}$ is the natural extension of the Bergman–Whittaker operator $\mathbf{B}_3$; however, there is a major disadvantage in using this operator in that v^n does not generate linearly independent polynomials. As may be readily seen from (2.6.3) we have constructed $(2n + 1)^2$ harmonic polynomials of degree n, but it is well known that there are only $(2n + p) \times (n + p - 1)!/p!n!$ linearly independent harmonic polynomials of degree n.

† $\dfrac{d\zeta}{\zeta} = \dfrac{d\zeta_1}{\zeta_1} \cdots \dfrac{d\zeta_p}{\zeta_p}$.

A concise proof of this may be found in [E.6], Vol. II, p. 237. Because of this fact we are forced to construct a new operator which will enable us to construct a complete system of *linearly independent* harmonic polynomials. This was done by the present author in [G. 10] and is given below.

We introduce the operator

$$\mathbf{G}_{p+2} F \equiv A \int_{\mathfrak{B}} F(\tau)\left[\frac{1}{2i}\left(\zeta - \frac{1}{\zeta}\right)\right]^m \frac{d\zeta}{\zeta} \qquad (m_k = p - k\,;\, k = 1, 2, \ldots, p), \tag{2.6.6}$$

where $\|\mathbf{X} - \mathbf{X}^0\| < \varepsilon$, $\varepsilon > 0$ is sufficiently small, and

$$\tau_k = -\frac{1}{4}\frac{t_{k+1}}{t_k}\left(\zeta_k - \frac{1}{\zeta_k}\right)^2 \sin\theta_k \qquad (k = 1, 2, \ldots, p-1),$$

$$\tau_0 = t_1 r, \qquad \text{and} \qquad \tau_p = -\frac{1}{4}\frac{e^{\pm i\varphi}}{t_p}\left(\zeta_p - \frac{1}{\zeta}\right)\sin\theta_p, \tag{2.6.7}$$

$$t_k = \cos\theta_k + \frac{i}{2}\sin\theta_k\left(\zeta_k + \frac{1}{\zeta_k}\right) \qquad (k = 1, 2, \ldots, p),$$

and $\mathfrak{B}^p \equiv \prod_{k=1}^{p} \mathcal{Q}_k$ is a product of regular contours $\mathcal{Q}_k$ in the ζ_k-plane joining $+1$ to -1 and not passing through the origin. The variables r, θ_j $(j = 1, \ldots, p)$ and φ are hyperspherical polar coordinates defined by [E.6], [G.10],

$$\begin{aligned} x_1 &= r\cos\theta_1 \\ x_2 &= r\sin\theta_1\cos\theta_2 \\ x_3 &= r\sin\theta_1\sin\theta_2\cos\theta_3 \\ &\vdots \\ x_{p+2} &= r\sin\theta_1\sin\theta_2\cdots\sin\theta_p\sin\varphi \end{aligned} \tag{2.6.8}$$

where $0 \le \theta_j \le \pi$ $(j = 1, \ldots, p)$ and $0 \le \varphi \le 2\pi$. The constant A is defined to be

$$A \equiv \prod_{k=0}^{p-1} A_k = \prod_{k=0}^{p-1} \frac{\Gamma(m_{k+1} + m_k + p - k)}{(m_k - m_{k+1})!\left[\Gamma\left(m_{k+1} + \frac{p}{2} - \frac{k}{2}\right)\right]^2}. \tag{2.6.9}$$

This operator is suggested by considering the following set of linearly independent harmonic polynomials of degree n,

$$H(m_k\,;\,\pm\,;\mathbf{X}) \equiv \left(\frac{x_{p+1}}{r_p} + i\,\frac{x_{p+2}}{r_p}\right)^{\pm m_p} r_p^{m_p} \prod_{k=1}^{p} r_{k-1}^{\nu_k} C_{\nu_k}^{\mu_k}\left(\frac{x_k}{r_{k-1}}\right) \tag{2.6.10}$$

$$\left(\mu_k = m_k + \frac{p}{2} + \frac{1}{2} - \frac{k}{2}\right)$$

$$(\nu_k = m_{k-1} - m_k)$$

$$\equiv r^n Y(m_k\,;\,\theta_k\,;\,\varphi) = r^n \exp(\pm m_p \varphi) \prod_{k=1}^{p} (\sin\theta_k)^{m_k} C_{\nu_k}^{\mu_k}(\cos\theta_k),$$

with $r_k = x_{k+1}^2 + x_{k+2}^2 + \cdots + x_{p+2}^2)^{1/2}$, $r = r_0$, $k = 0, 1, \ldots, p$, and $n = m_0 \geq m_1 \geq \cdots \geq m_p \geq 0$, and where the $C_\nu^\lambda(\cos\theta_k)$ are Gegenbauer polynomials.

It is well known that a harmonic function regular in a neighborhood of the origin may be expanded in terms of a series

$$H(\mathbf{X}) = \sum_{n=0}^{\infty} \sum_{m=0}^{m'} \beta_n(m) r^n Y(m;\,\theta;\,\pm\varphi)$$

$$\equiv \sum_{n=0}^{\infty} \sum_{m_1=0}^{m_0} \sum_{m_2=0}^{m_1} \cdots \sum_{m_p=0}^{m_{p-1}} \beta_n(m) r^n Y(m;\,\theta;\,\pm\varphi). \tag{2.6.11}$$

Indeed, this series converges within the largest hypersphere inside of which there is no singularity of $H(\mathbf{X})$.

The operator $\mathbf{G}_{p+2}$ is then seen to be constructed by making use of the following classical integral representation:

$$C_\nu^\lambda(\cos\theta) = \frac{\pi^{-1/2}\Gamma(\nu + 2\lambda)\Gamma(\nu + \frac{1}{2})}{\Gamma(\lambda)\Gamma(2\lambda)\Gamma(\nu + 1)} \times \int_0^\pi [\cos\theta + i\sin\theta\cos t]^\nu [\sin t]^{2\lambda - 1}\, dt, \tag{2.6.12}$$

and expressing the $H(m_k;\,\pm\,;\mathbf{X})$ as suitable combinations of these.

We may obtain an inverse operator (of the second kind) for $\mathbf{G}_{p+2}$ by making use of the orthogonality properties of the hyperspherical harmonics on the unit hypersphere [E.6], namely

$$\int_\Omega H(m_k\,;\,\pm\,;\mathbf{X}/r)\overline{H(n_k\,;\,\pm\,;\mathbf{X}/r)}\, d\Omega = (2\pi) \prod_{k=1}^{p} \delta_{m_k}^{n_k} E_k(m_{k-1}, m_k), \tag{2.6.13}$$

where the integration is taken over the unit hypersphere Ω, and where

$$E_k(m_{k-1}, m_k) = \frac{\pi 2^{k-2m_k-p}\Gamma(m_{k-1}+m_k+p+1-k)}{\left(m_{k-1}+\frac{p}{2}+\frac{1}{2}-\frac{k}{2}\right)(m_{k-1}-m_k)!\,\Gamma\left(m_k+\frac{p}{2}+\frac{1}{2}-\frac{k}{2}\right)^2}.$$

As we did in the earlier sections, we define a kernel for the inverse operator as a formal Fourier series,

$$K(\tau\,|\,\theta;\,\pm\varphi) = \sum_{n=0}^{\infty}\sum_{m=0}^{m'} \exp(\pm im_p\varphi)[(\bar{\tau}\sin\theta)^m\mu C_\nu^\mu(\cos\theta)] \quad (2.6.14)$$

($\mu_k = m_k + p/2 + \frac{1}{2} - k/2$, $\nu_k = m_{k-1} - m_k$, and $k = 1, 2, \ldots, p$) which may be shown to converge, uniformly in θ_k, and φ for $|\tau| \le \rho_0 < 1$, by the standard arguments. By making use of the orthogonality properties (2.6.13), and noticing that

$$E_k(m_{k-1}, m_k) = \frac{\pi A_{k-1}}{\left(m_{k-1}+\frac{p}{2}+\frac{1}{2}-\frac{k}{2}\right)},$$

one observes by termwise integration that if

$$F(\tau) = \sum_{n=0}^{\infty}\sum_{m=0}^{m'} \alpha_n(m) f(m;\tau)$$

with

$$f(m;\tau) \equiv \prod_{k=0}^{p} \tau_k^{m_k},$$

and

$$H(\mathbf{X}) \equiv \sum_{n=0}^{\infty}\sum_{m=0}^{m'} \alpha_n(m) r^n Y(m;\theta;\,\pm\varphi),$$

then

$$F(\tau) = \mathbf{G}_{p+2}^{-1} H \equiv \frac{1}{2\pi^{p+1}} \int_\Omega H(\tilde{X}/r)\overline{K(\tau\,|\,\theta;\,\pm\varphi)}\,d\Omega. \quad (2.6.15)$$

7. *The Elliptic Operator* $\mathbf{T}_{p+2}$

In this section we shall show how the integral operator methods of Bergman which were discussed in the previous sections allow us to construct solutions to the following class of elliptic differential equations,

$$\mathbf{T}_{p+2}[\Psi] \equiv \frac{\partial^2 \Psi}{\partial x_\mu \, \partial x_\mu} + A(r^2) x_\mu \frac{\partial \Psi}{\partial x_\mu} + C(r^2)\Psi = 0, \qquad (2.7.1)$$

where $A(r^2)$ and $C(r^2)$ are analytic functions of r^2. The case where $p = 0$, and 1, have been extensively studied by Bergman and others [B.22,5,6]. The case where $p = 2$ has been investigated by Gilbert [G.24,25] and the case of general $p \geq 0$ by Gilbert and Howard [G.H.1].

Our approach is to construct an analogue of Bergman's operator $\mathbf{\Omega}_{p+2}$ ($p = 0$, 1) which generates solutions to $\mathbf{T}_{p+2}[\Psi] = 0$. The following theorem is the natural extension of Bergman's result for $p = 0$, 1 to the case of integral $p \geq 1$; our proof parallels his except for certain modifications in the convergence argument. (We direct the reader to Bergman's book for these details [B.22, p. 13] and also the paper by Gilbert and Howard [G.H.1] where the proof for the case $p \geq 2$ first was given.)

Theorem 2.7.1 (Bergman) *Let $\tilde{H}(r, t)$, $|t| \leq 1$ be a solution of*

$$(1 - t^2)\tilde{H}_{rt} - t^{-1}(t^2 + 1)\tilde{H}_r + rt\left\{\tilde{H}_{rr} + \frac{(p-1)}{r}\tilde{H}_r + B\tilde{H}\right\} = 0, \qquad (2.7.2)$$

where

$$B = -\frac{r}{2}A_r - \frac{(p+2)}{2}A - \frac{r^2 A^2}{4} + C \qquad (2.7.3)$$

and $\tilde{H}_r/rt$ is continuous at $r = t = 0$. Then,

$$\Psi(\mathbf{X}) = \mathbf{\Omega}_{p+2} f \equiv \left(\frac{1}{2\pi i}\right)^p \int_{\mathfrak{D}^p} \frac{d\zeta}{\zeta} \int_{t=-1}^{+1} E(r, t) f(v[1 - t^2]; \zeta)\, dt \qquad (2.7.4)$$

where $E(r, t) = \exp\{-\frac{1}{2}\int_0^r rA\, dr\}\tilde{H}(r, t)$, is a solution of $\mathbf{T}_{p+2}[\Psi] = 0$. Here $f(v, \zeta)$ is a function of $(p + 1)$ variables, $v = N_\mu x_\mu$ is the auxiliary variable given by (2.6.1), *and $\mathfrak{D}^p \equiv \prod_{k=1}^p \mathscr{L}_k$ is a product of regular contours $\mathscr{L}_k$ in the ζ_k-planes, which do not pass through their respective origins.*

Proof We first remark that the representation (2.7.4) may be arrived at by formally substituting it into the differential equation $\mathbf{T}_{p+2}[\Psi] = 0$, and noting the following elementary relationships which exist between the variables:

$$\frac{\partial u}{\partial x_\mu}\frac{\partial u}{\partial x_\mu} \equiv N_\mu N_\mu = 0,$$

$$\frac{\partial u}{\partial x_\mu}\frac{\partial E}{\partial x_\mu} = \frac{\partial E}{\partial r}\frac{\partial r}{\partial x_\mu}\frac{\partial u}{\partial x_\mu} = \frac{\partial u}{\partial r}\frac{\partial E}{\partial r} \qquad (r^2 \equiv x_\mu x_\mu)$$

$$x_\mu \frac{\partial E}{\partial x_\mu} = x_\mu \frac{\partial r}{\partial x_\mu}\frac{\partial E}{\partial r} = r\frac{\partial E}{\partial r}, \tag{2.7.5}$$

$$x_\mu \frac{\partial u}{\partial x_\mu} = u,$$

$$\frac{\partial}{\partial x_\mu} f([1-t^2]u;\zeta) = \frac{1}{2u}\frac{\partial u}{\partial x_\mu}\left(t - \frac{1}{t}\right) f_t .$$

Using these relations, we may formally compute

$$\frac{\partial^2 \Psi}{\partial x_\mu \partial x_\mu} = \mathbf{B}_{p+2}\int_{-1}^{+1} f\left\{\frac{\partial^2 E}{\partial x_\mu \partial x_\mu} - \frac{1}{r}\frac{\partial}{\partial t}\left(E_r\left[t - \frac{1}{t}\right]\right)\right\} dt \tag{2.7.6}$$

and furthermore,

$$\mathbf{T}_{p+2}[\Psi] = \mathbf{B}_{p+2}\int_{-1}^{+1} f(u[1-t^2];\zeta)\left\{\frac{\partial^2 E}{\partial x_\mu \partial x_\mu} - \frac{1}{r}\frac{\partial}{\partial t}\left(E_r\left[t - \frac{1}{t}\right]\right)\right.$$
$$\left. + rAE_r - \frac{A}{2}\frac{\partial}{\partial t}\left(E\left[t - \frac{1}{t}\right]\right) + CE\right\} dt. \tag{2.7.7}$$

We verify that Ψ is a solution of (2.7.1) by showing that the brace of (2.7.7) vanishes if $E = \tilde{H}(r,t)\exp(-\frac{1}{2}\int_0^r Ar\,dr)$, and $\tilde{H}(r,t)$ satisfies (2.7.2). Making this substitution one obtains the desired result, namely, that the bracket becomes

$$\left\{(1-t^2)\tilde{H}_{rt} - \left(t + \frac{1}{t}\right)\tilde{H}_r + rt\tilde{H}_{rr} + rt\left[\tilde{H}\left(-\frac{(p+2)}{2}A\right.\right.\right.$$
$$\left.\left.\left. - \frac{r^2A^2}{4} - \frac{r}{2}A_r + C\right) + \frac{(p+1)}{r}\tilde{H}_r\right]\right\}\exp\left(-\frac{1}{2}\int_0^r Ar\,dr\right). \tag{2.7.8}$$

Following Bergman [B.22] we write

$$\tilde{H}(r,t) = 1 + \sum_{n=1}^{\infty} b^{(n)}(r)t^{2n} \tag{2.7.9}$$

and find by substitution in (2.7.2) that the coefficients satisfy the system of equations

$$\begin{aligned} &b_r^{(1)} + rB = 0, \\ &(2n-1)b_r^{(n)} + rb_{rr}^{(n-1)} - (2n-2-p)b_r^{(n-1)} + rBb^{(n-1)} = 0 \\ &\qquad\qquad (n = 2, 3, \ldots), \\ &b^{(n)}(0) = 0 \qquad (n = 1, 2, \ldots). \end{aligned} \tag{2.7.10}$$

We introduce coefficients $P^{(n)}(r^2) \equiv r^{1-2n}b_r^{(n)}$ to reduce (2.7.10) to the form

$$\begin{aligned} &P^{(1)} + B = 0, \\ &(2n-1)P^{(n)} + 2\frac{d}{d(r^2)}P^{(n-1)} + \frac{p-1}{r^2}P^{(n-1)} \\ &\quad + r^{2-2n}\frac{B}{2}\int_0^{r^2} r^{2n-4}P^{(n-1)}(r^2)\,d(r^2) = 0 \qquad (n = 2, 3, \ldots). \end{aligned} \tag{2.7.11}$$

Let us assume that A and C are regular functions of r^2 for $0 \le r^2 < \rho^2$; thus, by (2.7.3), B is also regular for the same range of values for r^2. From (2.7.11) we see that, in general $P^{(n)}$ is composed of a power series in r^2, plus a polynomial of degree $(n-1)$ in $(1/r^2)$. It is clear also from (2.7.11) that the $Q^{(n)}$ defined by

$$\begin{aligned} &Q^{(1)}(r^2) = a(1 - r^2/\rho^2)^{-1}, \qquad a > 0 \\ &(2n-1)Q^{(n)}(r^2) = R_1^{(n-1)}(r^2) + R_2^{(n-1)}(r^2) + R_3^{(n-1)}(r^2) \qquad (n = 2, 3, \ldots) \end{aligned} \tag{2.7.12}$$

will be dominants for the $P^{(n)}$, in symbols $P^{(n)} \ll Q^{(n)}$, and

$$-2\frac{dP^{(n-1)}}{dr^2} \ll R_1^{(n-1)}, \qquad -\frac{(p-1)}{r^2}P^{(n-1)} \ll R_2^{(n-1)}, \tag{2.7.13}$$

and

$$-\frac{B}{2}\left[(r^2)^{1-n}\int_0^{r^2}(r^2)^{n-2}P^{(n-1)}(r^2)\,d(r^2)\right] \ll R_3^{(n-1)}.$$

The word "dominants" is used here in the sense usually encountered in convergence and existence proofs, that is $P \ll Q$ if and only if $|p_n| \le q_n$ where $P \equiv \sum p_n(r^2)^n$, $Q \equiv \sum q_n(r^2)^n$; in our context n may assume negative as well as positive integer values. $Q^{(1)}$ is clearly a dominant for $P^{(1)}$ since the assumption that B is regular in $(0, \rho^2)$ means there exists a positive constant a such that $B \ll a(1 - r^2/\rho^2)^{-1}$, $0 \le r^2 < \rho_0^2 < \rho^2$.

It will be convenient to find appraisals for $(r^2)^{n-1}Q^{(n)}$ rather than $Q^{(n)}$. To that end we shall prove by induction that

$$(2k-1)\cdots 3\cdot 1(r^2)^{k-1}Q^{(k)} \ll a^{(k)}(1 - r^2/\rho^2)^{-k} \tag{2.7.14}$$

where the $a^{(k)}$ are constants. Clearly (2.7.14) is true for $k = 1$ (with $a^{(1)} = a$). Suppose (2.7.14) is true for $k = n$. Then

$$(2n-1)\cdots 3\cdot 1Q^{(n)} \ll \frac{a^{(n)}}{(n-1)!}\sum_0^\infty \frac{(i+n-1)!}{i!}\frac{(r^2)^{i-n+1}}{(\rho^2)^i}$$

so

$$\frac{dQ^{(n)}}{dr^2} \ll \frac{1}{(2n-1)\cdots 3\cdot 1}\frac{a^{(n)}}{(n-1)!}\sum_0^\infty \frac{(i+n-1)!}{i!}\frac{|i-n+1|(r^2)^{i-n}}{(\rho^2)^i}$$

and

$$(r^2)^n\frac{dQ^{(n)}}{dr^2} \ll \frac{1}{(2n-1)\cdots 3\cdot 1}\frac{a^{(n)}}{(n-1)!}\sum_0^\infty \frac{(i+n-1)!|i-n+1|}{(i)!}\left(\frac{r^2}{\rho^2}\right)^i.$$

Now consider

$$\frac{a^{(n)}}{(2n-1)\cdots 3\cdot 1}(1 - r^2/\rho^2)^{-(n+1)} \equiv \frac{a^{(n)}}{(2n-1)\cdots 3\cdot 1n!}\sum_0^\infty \frac{(i+n)!}{i!}\left(\frac{r^2}{\rho^2}\right)^i.$$

But for $\varepsilon > 0$ and sufficiently small we have

$$(1-\varepsilon)(i+n) \ge |i-n+1| \qquad (i = 0, 1, \ldots) \qquad (n = 1, 2, \ldots). \tag{2.7.15}$$

Hence

$$(r^2)^n\frac{dQ^{(n)}}{dr^2} \ll \frac{n(1-\varepsilon)a^{(n)}}{(2n-1)\cdots 3\cdot 1}(1 - r^2/\rho^2)^{-(n+1)}$$

by use of inequality (2.7.15). Thus

$$-2(r^2)^n\frac{dP^{(n)}}{dr^2} \ll \frac{2n(1-\varepsilon)a^{(n)}}{(2n-1)\cdots 3\cdot 1}(1 - r^2/\rho^2)^{-(n+1)} \equiv (r^2)^n R_1^{(n)}.$$

Moreover

$$(2n-1)\cdots 3\cdot 1\,\frac{|p-1|}{r^2}(r^2)^n Q^{(n)} \ll a^{(n)}|p-1|(1-r^2/\rho^2)^{-(n)},$$

so

$$-\frac{|p-1|}{r^2}(r^2)^n P^{(n)} \ll \frac{a^{(n)}}{(2n-1)\cdots 3\cdot 1}|p-1|(1-r^2/\rho^2)^{-n}$$
$$\ll \frac{a^{(n)}}{(2n-1)\cdots 3\cdot 1}|p-1|(1-r^2/\rho^2)^{-(n+1)}$$
$$\equiv (r^2)^n R_2^{(n)}.$$

Finally, by a computation similar to the one indicated in [B.17, p. 426], one shows

$$\left[(r^2)^{-n}\int_0^{r^2}(r^2)^{n-1}P^{(n)}(r^2)\,d(r^2)\right] \ll Q^{(n)}.$$

Thus we have

$$\frac{a}{2}(1-r^2/\rho^2)^{-1}(r^2)^n Q^{(n)}$$
$$\ll \frac{a}{2}\frac{a^{(n)}}{(2n-1)\cdots 3\cdot 1}(r^2)(1-r^2/\rho^2)^{-(n+1)}$$
$$\ll \frac{a}{2}\rho^2\frac{a^{(n)}}{(2n-1)\cdots 3\cdot 1}(1-r^2/\rho^2)^{-(n+1)}$$
$$\equiv (r^2)^n R_3^{(n)}.$$

Thus from (2.7.12) we get

$$(2n+1)(2n-1)\cdots 3\cdot 1(r^2)^n Q^{(n+1)} \ll a^{(n)}\left[2n(1-\varepsilon)+|p-1|+\frac{a}{2}\rho^2\right]$$
$$\times (1-r^2/\rho^2)^{-(n+1)}$$
$$\equiv a^{(n+1)}(1-r^2/\rho^2)^{-(n+1)}.$$

This completes the proof by induction.

But a dominant series for $r^{-1}\tilde{H}_r = \sum_1^\infty (b_r^{(n)}/r)t^{2n}$ is the series $\sum_1^\infty (r)^{n-1}Q^{(n)}$. By use of the ratio test we conclude we have convergence for r^2 such that

$$\limsup_{n\to\infty}\left(\frac{2n(1-\varepsilon)+|p-1|+(a/2)\rho^2}{(2n+1)(1-r^2/\rho^2)}\right)<1,$$

that is, $r^2 < \varepsilon\rho^2$. Thus the dominant series convergence for $0 \le r^2 < \varepsilon\rho^2$, $\varepsilon > 0$ and sufficiently small, and $\tilde{H}(r, t)$ exists for $0 \le r^2 < \varepsilon\rho^2$, $\varepsilon \le 1$, $|t| \le 1$. Hence $\tilde{H}(r, t)$ with the properties of Theorem 2.7.1 exists.

We note at this point that because of the uniform convergence of the above series we may also represent $\mathbf{\Omega}_{p+2}f$ in the following form, when $r^2 < \varepsilon\rho^2$ and $\varepsilon > 0$ is sufficiently small:

$$\begin{aligned}\Psi(\mathbf{X}) = \mathbf{\Omega}_{p+2}f \equiv \mathbf{B}_{p+2}\int_{-1}^{+1} E(r, t)f(v[1-t^2]; \zeta)\,dt \\ = \int_{-1}^{+1} \mathbf{B}_{p+2}f(v[1-t^2]; \zeta)E(r, t)\,dt \\ = \int_{-1}^{+1} E(r, t)H(\mathbf{X}[1-t^2])\,dt, \qquad (2.7.16)\end{aligned}$$

where $H(\mathbf{X})$ is a harmonic function generated by the Bergman operator $\mathbf{B}_{p+2}$.

Gilbert and Howard [G.H.1] introduced a class of harmonic vectors in $(p+2)$ variables and also certain related vector solutions to $\mathbf{T}_{p+2}[\Psi] = 0$. For instance, if one defines the components of the harmonic vector $\mathbf{H}(\mathbf{X}) \equiv \{H_1(\mathbf{X}), \ldots, H_{p+2}(\mathbf{X})\}$ as

$$H_\mu(\mathbf{X}) = \mathbf{B}_{p+2}[F(v; \zeta)N_\mu(\zeta)], \qquad (2.7.17)$$

it is clear that $\mathbf{H}(\mathbf{X})$ satisfies the following tensor equations (these equations form a generalization of the vanishing of the curl and divergence in two and three variables, and also the Cauchy–Riemann equations in two variables):

$$\frac{\partial H_\mu(\mathbf{X})}{\partial x_\mu} = 0, \quad \text{and} \quad \varepsilon_{mn\mu\nu}\frac{\partial H_\mu(\mathbf{X})}{\partial x_\nu} = 0, \qquad (2.7.18)$$

where $\varepsilon_{mn\mu\nu}$ is a permutation symbol. In the same way it is possible to introduce vector solutions to $\mathbf{T}_{p+2}[\Psi] = 0$, by setting

$$\Psi_\mu(\mathbf{X}) = \left(\frac{1}{2\pi i}\right)^p \int_{-1}^{+1} E(r, t) \int_{\mathfrak{D}^p} N_\mu(\zeta) f(v[1 - t^2]; \zeta) \frac{d\zeta}{\zeta}\, dt$$

$$= \int_{-1}^{+1} E(r, t) H_\mu(\mathbf{X}[1 - t^2])\, dt. \tag{2.7.19}$$

The four-variable case of Eq. (2.7.1) is particularly interesting since in that case we may construct solutions by employing the operator $\mathbf{G}_4$ given above [G. 15, 23]. In this case all of the theory developed by Bergman for the three-variable case have natural analogs. For instance, the theory of multiple-valued harmonic functions can be developed here also. For those interested in the three dimensional case see [B.22, p. 50], also [B.3,13,20],

Bergman has considered the case of harmonic functions of three variables with rational, and algebraic $\mathbf{B}_3$-associates. These results depend on the theory of functions of *one* complex variable, and in particular on certain properties of the period functions defined on a Riemann surface. The interested reader is directed to [B. 22, Chapter II, Section 4], where this topic is discussed, and a complete bibliography cited.

The case of harmonic functions of four or more variables presents a much more complicated structure, since we must consider associates which are functions of *several* complex variables. To illustrate this point let us consider the operator $\mathbf{G}_4$ and a rational associate, i.e., let

$$H(\mathbf{X}) = \mathbf{G}_4 f \equiv -\frac{1}{4\pi^2} \int_{\mathscr{L}} \int_{\mathscr{C}} \frac{P(\mathbf{X}; \eta, \xi)}{Q(\mathbf{X}; \eta, \xi)}\, d\xi\, d\eta, \tag{2.7.20}$$

where

$$f = \frac{p(\tau, \eta, \xi)}{q(\tau, \eta, \xi)} \equiv \eta\xi \frac{P(\mathbf{X}; \eta, \xi)}{Q(\mathbf{X}; \eta, \xi)}$$

and $p(\tau, \eta, \xi)$, $q(\tau, \eta, \xi)$, $P(\mathbf{X}; \eta, \xi)$, $Q(\mathbf{X}; \eta, \xi)$ are polynomials. If Q is of degree n in ξ the singularity manifold of the integrand has n branches, i.e., $Q(\mathbf{X}; \eta, \xi) = \phi(\mathbf{X}; \eta) \prod_{\nu=1}^{n} [\xi - A_\nu(\mathbf{X}; \eta)]$. Now let $\mathscr{L}_\mu \subset \mathscr{L}$ be that subset of $\mathscr{L}$ for which the branch $\xi = A_\mu(\mathbf{X}; \eta)$ remains inside $\mathscr{C}$. Furthermore, let $\mathbf{X}_0$ be a point, such that for all $\mathbf{X} \in \mathscr{N}(\mathbf{X}_0)$, ($\mathscr{N}(\mathbf{X}_0)$ is a suitably small neighborhood of $\mathbf{X}_0$), we have

$$\mathscr{C} \cap \{\xi | \xi = A_\mu(\mathbf{X}; \eta); \mathbf{X} \in \mathscr{N}(\mathbf{X}_0); \eta \in \mathscr{L}; \Delta(\mathbf{X}; \eta) = 0\}$$
$$= \varnothing$$

where

$$\Delta(\mathbf{X};\eta) \equiv (-1)^{\frac{1}{2}n(n-1)}\phi(\mathbf{X};\eta)^{2n-1}V(\mathbf{X}:\eta)$$
$$V(\mathbf{X};\eta) \equiv \prod_{0\le\mu<\nu\le\eta} [A_\nu(\mathbf{X};\eta) - A_\mu(\mathbf{X};\eta)]$$

and

$$\mathscr{C} \cap \{\xi \mid \xi = A_\mu(\mathbf{X};\eta);\, \eta \in \mathscr{L}, \mathbf{X} \in \mathscr{N}(\mathbf{X}_0)\} \equiv \{\xi^{(\nu)}\}_{\nu=1}^{N};$$

i.e., in the ξ-plane we have no more than first order poles crossing $\mathscr{C}$, and the intersections of the singularity branches with $\mathscr{C}$ are a finite collection of isolated points. In this case the integrand is absolutely integrable, and one may represent (2.7.20) as an Abelian integral, over segments of a curve on the Riemann surface, $\mathfrak{R}[\mathbf{X}]$, defined by $Q(\mathbf{X};\eta,\zeta) = 0$, [G.15,17]; i.e.,

$$H(\mathbf{X}) = \frac{1}{2\pi i}\sum_{\mu=1}^{n}\int_{\mathscr{L}_\mu} \frac{P(X;\eta,\xi_\mu(\eta))}{\dfrac{\partial Q(X;\eta,\xi_\mu(\eta))}{\partial\xi}}\,d\eta. \tag{2.7.21}$$

We must perform a classification of certain exceptional **X**-points for the case of harmonic functions with *rational* $\mathbf{G}_4$-associates which is analogous to the classifications given by Bergman [B.20–22] and Mitchell [M.5,7] for harmonic functions with *algebraic* $\mathbf{B}_3$-associates. This is done as follows: let the sets $\mathfrak{Q}_k$ $(k = 1, 2, 3)$ and $\mathfrak{Q} \equiv \bigcup_{k=1}^{3}\mathfrak{Q}_k \subset \mathbb{C}^3$ be defined by

$$\begin{aligned}
\mathfrak{Q}_1 &\equiv \left\{\mathbf{X} \mid \phi(\mathbf{X};\eta) \equiv \frac{\partial^n Q(\mathbf{X};\eta,\xi)}{\partial\xi^n} \equiv 0;\, \eta \in \mathbb{C}^1\right\},\\
\mathfrak{Q}_2 &\equiv \{\mathbf{X} \mid V(\mathbf{X};\eta) \equiv 0;\, \eta \in \mathbb{C}^1\}, \qquad\qquad (2.7.22)\\
\mathfrak{Q}_3 &\equiv \left\{\mathbf{X} \mid V(\mathbf{X};\eta) = \frac{\partial V(\mathbf{X};\eta)}{\partial\eta} = 0\right\} \cup \left\{\mathbf{X} \mid \phi(\mathbf{X};\eta) = \frac{\partial\phi(\mathbf{X};\eta)}{\partial\eta} = 0\right\}.
\end{aligned}$$

Then if $\mathscr{N}(\mathbf{X}_0) \cap \mathfrak{Q} = 0$, the genus $(\rho = \rho[\mathbf{X}])$, and also the number of sheets $(m = m[\mathbf{X}])$ of $\mathfrak{R}[\mathbf{X}]$ will be constant for all $\mathbf{X} \in \mathscr{N}(\mathbf{X}_0)$. We remark, if $\mathbf{X} \in \mathfrak{Q}_1$, $\mathfrak{R}[\mathbf{X}]$ has less than m sheets, and if $\mathbf{X} \in \mathfrak{Q}_2$ $Q(\mathbf{X};\eta,\xi)$ has a repeated irreducible factor involving ξ; if $\mathbf{X} \in \mathfrak{Q}_3$, $\Delta(\mathbf{X};\eta)$ or $\phi(\mathbf{X};\eta)$ has a multiple root and two branch points coincide.

The Weierstrass decomposition formula [W.17, p. 264] allows one to represent any algebraic function defined on a Riemann surface in terms of Weierstrass integrands of the first, second, and third kind. For instance if $H_\alpha(\mathbf{X};\eta,\xi)$, $\tilde{H}_\alpha(\mathbf{X};\eta,\xi)$, $H(\mathbf{X};\eta_\nu,\xi_\nu;\eta,\xi)$ are integrands of the first, second, and third kind respectively associated with the Riemann surface $\mathfrak{R}[\mathbf{X}]$, the Weierstrass formula permits us to write

$$\frac{P(\mathbf{X};\eta,\xi)}{Q(\mathbf{X};\eta,\xi)}=\sum_{\nu=1}^{r}c_\nu(\mathbf{X})H(\mathbf{X};\eta_\nu,\xi_\nu;\eta,\xi)-\sum_{\alpha=1}^{\rho}[\tilde{g}_\alpha(\mathbf{X})H_\alpha(\mathbf{X};\eta,\xi)$$
$$-g_\alpha(\mathbf{X})\tilde{H}_\alpha(\mathbf{X};\eta,\xi)]+\frac{d}{d\eta}\left[\sum_{\nu=1}^{r}F_\nu(\mathbf{X};\eta,\xi)\right],\qquad\sum_{\nu=1}^{r}c_\nu(\mathbf{X})=0,$$

where the $F_\nu(\mathbf{X},\eta,\xi)$ are conveniently chosen rational functions of η, ξ that have poles where $Q(\mathbf{X};\eta,\xi)$ vanishes, and the $c_\nu(\mathbf{X})$, $g_\alpha(\mathbf{X})$, $\tilde{g}_\alpha(\mathbf{X})$ are algebraic functions. By using the Weierstrass formula above for algebraic functions defined over a Riemann surface $\mathfrak{R}[\mathbf{X}]$ it is possible to obtain a representation for $H(\mathbf{X})$ in terms of the period system associated with $\mathfrak{R}[\mathbf{X}]$. Indeed in [G.17] it was shown that *if the* $\mathbf{G}_4$*-associate of* $H(\mathbf{X})$ *is rational, then whenever* $\mathbf{X}\notin\mathfrak{Q}$ $H(\mathbf{X})$ *may be represented as*

$$H(\mathbf{X})=\sum_{\mu=1}^{\eta}\sum_{j=1}^{k_\mu}\left\{\sum_{\nu=1}^{r}c_\nu(\mathbf{X})\log\frac{E(\mathbf{X};\eta_\mu^{2j},\xi_\mu^{2j};\eta_\nu,\xi_\nu;\eta_0,\xi_0)}{E(\mathbf{X};\eta_\mu^{2j-1},\xi_\mu^{2j-1};\eta_\nu,\xi_\nu;\eta_0,\xi_0)}\right.$$
$$+\sum_{\alpha=1}^{\rho}\left[\tilde{C}_\alpha(\mathbf{X})\log\frac{E_\alpha(\mathbf{X};\eta_\mu^{2j},\xi_\mu^{2j})}{E_\alpha(\mathbf{X};\eta_\mu^{2j-1},\xi_\mu^{2j-1})}\right.$$
$$\left.-C_\alpha(\mathbf{X})\log\frac{E_\alpha'(\mathbf{X};\eta_\mu^{2j},\xi_\mu^{2j})}{E_\alpha'(\mathbf{X};\eta_\mu^{2j-1},\xi_\mu^{2j-1})}\right]\tag{2.7.23}$$

$$\left.+\sum_{\nu=1}^{r}[F_\nu(\mathbf{X};\eta_\mu^{2j},\xi_\mu^{2j})-F_\nu(\mathbf{X};\eta_\mu^{2j-1},\xi_\mu^{2j-1})]\right\};\tag{2.7.24}$$

here

$$\tilde{C}_\alpha(\mathbf{X})=-\frac{1}{2\pi i}\left(\sum_{\nu=1}^{r}c_\nu\log\frac{E_\alpha'(\mathbf{X};\eta_\nu,\xi_\nu)}{E_\alpha'(\mathbf{X};\eta_0,\xi_0)}\right.$$
$$\left.-2\sum_{\beta=1}^{\rho}[\omega_{\beta\alpha}'(\mathbf{X})\tilde{g}_\beta(\mathbf{X})-\eta_{\beta\alpha}'(\mathbf{X})g_\beta(\mathbf{X})]\right),$$
$$C_\alpha(\mathbf{X})=\frac{1}{2\pi i}\left(\sum_{\nu=1}^{r}c_\nu\log\frac{E_\alpha(\mathbf{X};\eta_\nu,\xi_\nu)}{E_\alpha(\mathbf{X};\eta_0,\xi_0)}\right.\tag{2.7.25}$$
$$\left.-2\sum_{\beta=1}^{\rho}[\omega_{\beta\alpha}(\mathbf{X})\tilde{g}_\beta(\mathbf{X})-\eta_{\beta\alpha}(\mathbf{X})g_\beta(\mathbf{X})]\right).$$

The functions $E_\alpha(\mathbf{X};\eta,\xi)$, $E_\alpha'(\mathbf{X};\eta,\xi)$ and $E(\mathbf{X};\eta,\xi;\eta',\xi';\eta_0,\xi_0)$ are defined in terms of the Weierstrass integrals on $\mathfrak{R}[\mathbf{X}]$, of the first, second, and third kinds respectively, and their respective periods taken over the ρ cycles $K_\beta[\mathbf{X}]$ and ρ conjugate cycles $K_\beta'[X]$,

$$\begin{array}{llll} 2\omega'_{\alpha\beta}(\mathbf{X}), & 2\eta_{\alpha\beta}(\mathbf{X}), & \Omega_\beta(\mathbf{X}; \eta_\nu, \xi_\nu) & (\alpha = 1, 2, \ldots, \rho) \\ 2\omega'_{\alpha\beta}(\mathbf{X}), & 2\eta'_{\alpha\beta}(\mathbf{X}), & \Omega_\beta'(\mathbf{X}; \eta_\nu, \xi_\nu) & (\beta = 1, 2, \ldots, \rho). \end{array} \tag{2.7.26}$$

The functions mentioned above are then defined as [W.17, pp. 373, 374, 398]

$$\begin{aligned} E_\beta(\mathbf{X}; \eta, \xi) &= \exp\{\Omega_\beta(\mathbf{X}; \eta, \xi)\}, \\ E_\beta'(\mathbf{X}; \eta, \xi) &= \exp\{\Omega_\beta'(\mathbf{X}; \eta, \xi)\}, \\ E(\mathbf{X}; \eta, \xi; \eta_\nu, \xi_\nu; \eta_0, \xi_0) &= \exp\{\Omega(\mathbf{X}; \eta, \xi; \eta_\nu, \xi_\nu; \eta_0, \xi_0)\} \\ &= \exp\left\{\int_{(\eta_0, \xi_0)}^{(\eta_\nu, \xi_\nu)} H(\mathbf{X}; \eta, \xi; \eta', \xi')\, d\eta'\right\}. \end{aligned} \tag{2.7.27}$$

In the special case where all of the roots $\xi = A_\mu(\mathbf{X}; \eta)$ $(\mu = 1, 2, \ldots, n)$ lie *inside* $\mathscr{C}$ for *all* $\eta \in \mathscr{L}$, it was shown in [G.17, p. 282] that the representation (2.7.23) for harmonic functions with rational $\mathbf{G}_4$-associates takes on a more simplified form which is analogous to the case of harmonic functions of *three* variables with *algebraic* $\mathbf{B}_3$-associates investigated by Bergman [B.20,21], and Mitchell [M.5,7].

We next consider the case of algebraic $\mathbf{G}_4$-associates which promises to be much more difficult to handle. We consider $\mathbf{G}_4$-associates of the form

$$\eta^{-1}\xi^{-1}f(\tau, \eta, \xi) = \frac{p(\tau, \eta, \xi, s)}{q(\tau, \eta, \xi, s)} \equiv \frac{P(\mathbf{X}; \eta, \xi, s)}{Q(\mathbf{X}; \eta, \xi, s)}, \tag{2.7.28}$$

i.e., a rational function of τ, η, ξ, s, where these variables are connected by the equation

$$\tilde{A}(\tau, \eta, \xi, s) \equiv \sum_{\nu=0}^{n} \tilde{a}_\nu(\tau, \eta, \xi)s^{n-\nu} = 0, \tag{2.7.29}$$

and where the $a_\nu(\tau, \eta, \xi)$ are polynomials. Multiplying $\tilde{A}(\tau, \eta, \xi, s)$ by suitable powers of η, ξ, we may rewrite this condition as $A(\mathbf{X}; \eta, \xi, s) \equiv \sum_{\nu=0}^{n} a_\nu(\mathbf{X}; \eta, \xi)s^{n-\nu} = 0$, where the $a_\nu(\mathbf{X}; \eta, \xi)$ are polynomials in $\mathbf{X}$, η, ξ. For each fixed value of $\mathbf{X}$ the equation $A(\mathbf{X}; \eta, \xi, s) = 0$ defines an *algebraic surface* $\mathscr{A}[\mathbf{X}]$. We choose a fixed value $\mathbf{X}_0$ and a neighborhood $\mathscr{N}(\mathbf{X}_0)$ such that for $\mathbf{X} \in \mathscr{N}(\mathbf{X}_0)$ the algebraic surface $\mathscr{A}[\mathbf{X}]$ has just *ordinary singularities* [P.S.1], [P.3], i.e., there exists a birational transformation which takes

$\mathscr{A}[\mathbf{X}]$ into another algebraic surface whose only singularities are a *double curve* and its *triple points*. In order to introduce the analogues of Weierstrass integrands of the first, second and third kind for the case of double integrals on an algebraic surface it is convenient to rewrite the integrand (2.7.28) as

$$\frac{P(\mathbf{X};\eta,\xi,s)}{Q(\mathbf{X};\eta,\xi,s)} \equiv \frac{R(\mathbf{X};\eta,\xi,s)}{\dfrac{\partial A(\mathbf{X};\eta,\xi,s)}{\partial s}}, \tag{2.7.30}$$

where $R(\mathbf{X};\eta,\xi,s)$ is rational in η, ξ, s. A double integral with integrand (2.7.30) is referred to in [P.S.1] as a *double integral of the first kind* if it is always finite valued on $\mathscr{A}[\mathbf{X}]$, i.e., if it is finite on all sufficiently small analytic 2-cells; it is known that there are exactly $\rho_g[\mathbf{X}] = (n-1)(n-2)(n-3)/6$ linearly independent integrals of the first kind [P.S. 1]. The number $\rho_g[\mathbf{X}]$ is called the *geometric genus* of $\mathscr{A}[\mathbf{X}]$ and it is the number of linearly independent polynomials of degree $(n-4)$ passing through the double curve of $\mathscr{A}[\mathbf{X}]$.

The double integral over the analytic 2-cell $\mathfrak{E}^2$

$$H(\mathbf{X}) = -\frac{1}{4\pi^2}\iint_{\mathfrak{E}^2} \frac{P(\mathbf{X};\eta,\xi,s)}{Q(\mathbf{X};\eta,\xi,s)}\,d\xi\,d\eta, \tag{2.7.31}$$

for a fixed value of $\mathbf{X}$ is a *double integral of the second kind* if for each $(\eta^0,\xi^0,s^0)\in\mathscr{A}[\mathbf{X}]$ there exists an improper integral,

$$J(\mathbf{X}) \equiv -\frac{1}{4\pi^2}\iint_{\mathfrak{E}^2}\left(\frac{\partial U(\mathbf{X};\eta,\xi,s)}{\partial\xi} + \frac{\partial V(\mathbf{X};\eta,\xi,s)}{\partial\eta}\right)d\xi\,d\eta, \tag{2.7.32}$$

such that $H(\mathbf{X}) - J(\mathbf{X})$ remains finite for all sufficiently small analytic 2-cells containing the point (η^0,ξ^0,s^0). There are $\rho_0 = \rho_0[\mathbf{X}] \equiv N - 4p - (n-1) - (\rho - 1)$ distinct double integrals of the second kind, when $\mathscr{A}[\mathbf{X}]$ is simply connected [P.S.1, Vol. 2, p. 407]. Here $N[\mathbf{X}]$ is the *class* of the surface, $p[\mathbf{X}]$ is the *genus* of an arbitrary plane section, $n[\mathbf{X}]$ is the *degree*, and $\rho[\mathbf{X}]$ is the number of particular irreducible algebraic curves $\Gamma_i[\mathbf{X}]$ which may be drawn on $\mathscr{A}[\mathbf{X}]$ (including the curve at ∞) such that there does not exist a *total differential of the third kind having logarithmic* singularities on one or more of the curves $(\bigcup_{i=1}^{\rho}\Gamma_i[\mathbf{X}])$, but if another curve $\gamma[\mathbf{X}]$ should be added to this set there exists an integral having one or more curves from this new set as its *logarithmic curves*, [P.S.1]. The class $N[\mathbf{X}]$ of the surface $\mathscr{A}[\mathbf{X}]$ is the number of values $\xi_i[\mathbf{X}]$ $(i = 1, 2, \ldots, N)$ for which the genus of the

Riemann surface $\mathscr{A}[\mathbf{X}] \cap \{\xi = \xi_i[\mathbf{X}]\}$ is less than $p[\mathbf{X}]$. The genus drops by one when the plane $\xi = \xi_i$ is tangent to $\mathscr{A}[\mathbf{X}]$; such a point is, in general, a double point of the surface. We remark that if the integrand which is the $\mathbf{G}_4$-associate of $H(\mathbf{X})$ is an integrand of the second kind on $\mathscr{A}[\mathbf{X}]$ then $H(\mathbf{X})$ has the representation

$$H(\mathbf{X}) = \sum_{\mu=1}^{p_0} C_\mu(\mathbf{X}) I_\mu(\mathbf{X}) + \frac{1}{4\pi^2} \int_{\mathscr{L}} \int_{\mathscr{C}} \left(\frac{\partial U(\mathbf{X}; \eta, \xi, s)}{\partial \eta} + \frac{\partial V(\mathbf{X}; \eta, \xi, s)}{\partial \xi} \right) d\eta \, d\xi, \tag{2.7.33}$$

where the $I_\mu(\mathbf{X})$ are a unique linearly independent set of integrals of the second kind taken over $\mathscr{L} \times \mathscr{C}$ on $\mathscr{A}(\mathbf{X})$.

The above discussion gives us a classification for the integral representations of harmonic functions by $\mathbf{G}_4$; however, in order to obtain more detailed information we must introduce further algebraic geometric and topological concepts due to Picard [P.S.1], [P.3], Lefschetz [L.6,7] and Zariski [Z.1].

Let $\mathbf{X} \in \mathscr{N}(\mathbf{X}_0)$, then, as we have assumed, $A(\mathbf{X}; \eta, \xi, s)$ is of degree n in s. The n-valued *branch curve*, $D[\mathbf{X}] \equiv \{s = s(X; \eta, \xi\}$, is obtained by eliminating s from $A(\mathbf{X}; \eta, \xi, s) = 0$, $\partial A(X; \eta, \xi, s)/\partial s = 0$, and ignoring the projection of the double curve of $\mathscr{A}[\mathbf{X}]$. We assume as usual, that the point at infinity on the s-axis does not lie on $\mathscr{A}[\mathbf{X}]$, i.e., $a_0(\mathbf{X}; \eta, \xi) \not\equiv 0$. Following the development by Zariski [Z.1, Chapter VI], we assume that the point at ∞ on the η-axis is not on $D[\mathbf{X}]$, that the tangents to $D[\mathbf{X}]$ which are parallel to the η-axis are all simple, and that no principal tangents at any multiple point are parallel to the η-axis. Furthermore, we designate by $\mathfrak{C}_\xi[\mathbf{X}]$ *the pencil of plane sections* cut from $\mathscr{A}[\mathbf{X}]$ by the planes $\xi =$ constant, by $p[\mathbf{X}]$ the genus of a *generic* plane section, by $\{\alpha_i[\mathbf{X}]\}_{i=1}^m$ the ξ-values of the tangents of $D[\mathbf{X}]$ parallel to the η-axis, and by $\{\beta_l[\mathbf{X}]\}$ the ξ-values of the multiple points.

Remark Since the tangents parallel to the η-axis are all simple, two and only two branch points $\{\eta_i\}_{i=1}^m$ coincide for $\xi = \alpha_i[\mathbf{X}]$, hence the genus of $\mathfrak{C}_{\alpha_i}[\mathbf{X}]$ is $p[\mathbf{X}] - 1$.

By fixing a homeomorphism, $\mathbf{T}[\mathbf{X}; a, \xi]$, between the Riemann surfaces associated with $\mathfrak{C}_a[\mathbf{X}]$ and $\mathfrak{C}_\xi[\mathbf{X}]$, ($\mathfrak{C}_a[\mathbf{X}]$ is taken to be a generic plane section), we introduce in the sense of Picard [P.S.1], [P.3], Lefschetz [L.6,7], and Zariski [Z.1] certain cycles $\delta_i[\mathbf{X}; \xi]$ which tend to vanish, i.e., shrink to a double point as $\xi \to \alpha_i[\mathbf{X}]$. The 2-cycles $\Gamma^{(2)}[\mathbf{X}]$ on $\mathscr{A}[\mathbf{X}]$ are constructed by cutting the ξ-plane open along a set of simple arcs $l_i[\mathbf{X}]$, $l_j'[\mathbf{X}]$ connecting the points $\xi = \alpha_i[\mathbf{X}]$, $\beta_j'[\mathbf{X}]$ to the generic point $\xi = \alpha[\mathbf{X}]$, [Z.1, Chapter VI]; every cycle is seen to have the form

$$\Gamma^{(2)}[\mathbf{X}] \sim \sum_{i=1}^{m} \lambda_i \, \Delta_i[\mathbf{X}] + C_a^{(2)}[\mathbf{X}], \tag{2.7.34}$$

where $\Delta_i[\mathbf{X}]$ is taken to be the topological sum, $\Delta_i[\mathbf{X}] = \bigcup_{\xi \in l_i[\mathbf{X}]} \{\delta_i[\mathbf{X}; \xi]\}$, and $C_a^{(2)}[\mathbf{X}]$ is a 2-chain on $\mathfrak{C}_a[\mathbf{X}]$ bounded by

$$\gamma[\mathbf{X}; \xi] \equiv \sum_{i=1}^{m} \lambda_i \, \delta_i[\mathbf{X}; \xi] \sim 0. \tag{2.7.35}$$

Let $P_2(\mathbf{X}; \eta, \xi, s) \equiv \sum_{\nu=0}^{m} p_\nu(\mathbf{X}; \eta, \xi) s^{m-\nu}$. The resultant of A and P_2 with respect to s, $R\{A, P_2\}$, may be expressed as a determinant of the coefficients $a_\mu(\mathbf{X}; \eta, \xi)$, $b_\nu(\mathbf{X}; \eta, \xi)$, using Sylvester's method. We may also write $R\{A, P_2\} = C_1(\mathbf{X}; \eta, \xi, s)A + C_2(\mathbf{X}; \eta, \xi, s)P_2$, where C_1, and C_2 are polynomials. Consequently, on $\mathscr{A}[\mathbf{X}]$ one has the representation

$$\frac{P_1(\mathbf{X}; \eta, \xi, s)}{P_2(\mathbf{X}; \eta, \xi, s)} = \frac{P_1 C_2}{R\{A, P_2\}}, \quad \text{where} \quad s = \frac{\partial R}{\partial a_0} \Big/ \frac{\partial R}{\partial a_1} = \frac{\partial R}{\partial a_1} \Big/ \frac{\partial R}{\partial a_2} = \cdots . \tag{2.7.36}$$

Lefschetz [L.6] showed that for computing the residues of double integrals over an *arbitrary* 2-cycle on an algebraic surface the 2-cycle may be replaced by a sum of *tubular cycles*. Using this fact, we consider the integral (2.7.31) where $\mathfrak{E}^2$ is replaced by $\Gamma^{(2)}[\mathbf{X}] \sim 0$, and express $\Gamma^{(2)}[\mathbf{X}]$ by a sum of *Lefschetz tubular cycles*, $\sum_\mu \Gamma_\mu^{(2)}[\mathbf{X}]$, whose *axes* $\gamma_\mu[\mathbf{X}]$ are the intersections of the *polar curves*

$$D_\mu[\mathbf{X}] \equiv \left\{(\eta, \xi, s) \mid g_\mu(\mathbf{X}; \eta, \xi) = 0; \, s = \frac{\partial R}{\partial a_0} \Big/ \frac{\partial R}{\partial a_1}\right\},$$

and a 3-chain $C^{(3)}[\mathbf{X}]$, with $\partial C^{(3)}[\mathbf{X}] = \Gamma^{(2)}[\mathbf{X}]$. Consequently, the study of multivalued harmonic functions reduces to an investigation of the integrals of the form

$$\begin{aligned} H(\mathbf{X}) &= -\frac{1}{4\pi^2} \iint_{\Gamma^{(2)}[\mathbf{X}]} \frac{P_1(\mathbf{X}; \eta, \xi, s)}{P_2(\mathbf{X}; \eta, \xi, s)} \, d\eta \, d\xi \\ &= -\frac{1}{4\pi^2} \iint_{\Gamma^{(2)}[\mathbf{X}]} \frac{P_1(\mathbf{X}; \eta, \xi, s) C_2(\mathbf{X}; \eta, \xi, s)}{\Phi(\xi) \prod_{\mu=1}^{k} g_\mu(\mathbf{X}; \eta, \xi)^{m_\mu}}, \end{aligned} \tag{2.7.37}$$

where the denominator is a factorization of $R\{A, P_2\}$. A further reduction by partial fractions leads to the consideration of the simpler integrals

$$H(\mathbf{X}) = -\frac{1}{4\pi^2}\sum_{m=1}^{k}\iint_{\Gamma^{(2)}(\mathbf{X})}\frac{Q_\mu(\mathbf{X};\eta,\xi,t)\,d\eta\,d\xi}{g_\mu(\mathbf{X};\eta,\xi)^{m_\mu}}, \tag{2.7.38}$$

where $Q_\mu[\mathbf{X};\eta,\xi,s]$ is a rational function regular on $D_\mu[\mathbf{X}]$. A final reduction of this integral over $\Gamma^{(2)}[\mathbf{X}]$ to a sum of Abelian integrals over the 1-cycles $\gamma_\mu[\mathbf{X}]$ is possible by performing an integration and a simple transformation

$$H(\mathbf{X}) = \frac{1}{2\pi i}\sum_{m=1}^{k}\int_{\gamma_\mu[\mathbf{X}]}\frac{W_\mu(\mathbf{X};\eta,\xi)\,d\eta}{\dfrac{\partial g_\mu(\mathbf{X};\eta,\xi)}{\partial\xi}}, \qquad \gamma_\mu[\mathbf{X}]\subset D_\mu[X],$$

with

$$W_\mu(\mathbf{X};\eta,\xi) = \left[\frac{1}{(m_\mu-1)!}\,\Theta^{m_\mu-1}Q_\mu(\mathbf{X};\eta,\xi,t)\right]_{t=(\partial R/\partial a_0)/(\partial R/\partial a_1)} \tag{2.7.39}$$

and

$$\Theta \equiv \frac{1}{(\partial g_\mu/\partial\eta)}\cdot\frac{\partial}{\partial\eta}.$$

We may now obtain representation formulas for the harmonic functions with algebraic $\mathbf{G}_4$-associates by using the Weierstrass decomposition formula for *each* of the integrands. Each integrand, $W_\mu(\partial g_\mu/\partial\xi)^{-1}$, is an algebraic function defined on the Riemann surface $\mathfrak{R}_\mu[\mathbf{X}]$ (over the η-plane), associated with the polar curve $D_\mu[X]$. One obtains the result [G.23]:

Theorem 2.7.2 (Gilbert) *The harmonic functions defined by $\mathbf{G}_4 f$, where f is a rational function over an algebraic surface $\mathscr{A}[\mathbf{X}]$, where the 2-cycle $\Gamma^{(2)}[\mathbf{X}]$ does not meet the polar curves $D_\mu[\mathbf{X}]$, and where $\mathbf{X}\in\mathscr{N}(\mathbf{X}_0)$, $\mathscr{N}(\mathbf{X}_0)\cap\mathfrak{S}=0$, has a representation of the form*

$$\begin{aligned} H(\mathbf{X}) = \sum_{\mu=1}^{k}\sum_{\beta=1}^{p_\mu}\Bigg\{&\sum_{\nu=1}^{r_\mu} C_\nu^{(\mu)}(\mathbf{X})\Omega_\nu^{(\mu)}(\mathbf{X};\eta_\nu^{(\mu)},\xi_\nu^{(\mu)}) \\ &+ C_\nu'^{(\mu)}(\mathbf{X})\Omega_\nu'^{(\mu)}(\mathbf{X};\eta_\nu^{(\mu)},\xi_\nu^{(\mu)}) - \sum_{\alpha=1}^{p_\mu}(\tilde g_\nu^{(\mu)}(\mathbf{X})\omega_{\alpha\beta}^{(\mu)}(\mathbf{X}) \\ &- \tilde g_\alpha'^{(\mu)}(\mathbf{X})\omega_{\alpha\beta}'^{(\mu)}(\mathbf{X}) - g_\alpha^{(\mu)}(\mathbf{X})\eta_{\alpha\beta}^{(\mu)}(\mathbf{X}) - g_\alpha'^{(\mu)}(\mathbf{X})\eta_{\alpha\beta}'^{(\mu)}(\mathbf{X}))\Bigg\} \\ &+ \operatorname{Res}\left\{\sum_{\mu=1}^{k}\sum_{\nu=1}^{r_\mu}F_\nu^{(\mu)}(\mathbf{X};\eta,\xi)\right\}. \end{aligned} \tag{2.7.40}$$

Here the $F_\nu^{(\mu)}(\mathbf{X};\eta,\xi)$ are conveniently chosen rational functions, and the $(\eta_\nu^{(\mu)},\xi_\nu^{(\mu)})$ are the infinity points of the functions

$$F^{(\mu)}(\mathbf{X};\eta,\xi) \equiv W_\mu(\mathbf{X};\eta,\xi)\left(\frac{\partial g_\mu(\mathbf{X};\eta,\xi)}{\partial\xi}\right)^{-1} \qquad (\mu=1,2,\ldots,k).$$

The functions $\omega_{\alpha\beta}^{(\mu)}(\mathbf{X})$, $\eta_{\alpha\beta}^{(\mu)}(\mathbf{X})$, $\Omega_{\alpha}^{(\mu)}(\mathbf{X}; \eta_{\nu}^{(\mu)}; \xi_{\nu}^{(\mu)})$, *etc., are, as before, period functions associated with the functions* $F^{(\mu)}(\mathbf{X}; \eta, \xi)$ *on the Riemann surface* $\mathfrak{R}_{\mu}[\mathbf{X}]$. *The exceptional* **X**-*sets are defined similarly as* $\mathfrak{S}_{\mu} \equiv \mathfrak{S}_{\mu 1} \cup \mathfrak{S}_{\mu 2} \cup \mathfrak{S}_{\mu 3}$, *where*

$$\mathfrak{S}_{\mu 1} \equiv \{\mathbf{X} \mid g_{\mu 0}[\mathbf{X}; \eta] \equiv 0; \eta \in \mathbb{C}^1\}, \qquad g_{\mu}(\mathbf{X}; \eta, \xi) \equiv \sum_{\nu=0}^{l_{\mu}} g_{\mu\nu}(\mathbf{X}; \eta)\xi^{l_{\mu}-\nu}; \tag{2.7.41}$$

$$\mathfrak{S}_{\mu 2} \equiv \left\{\mathbf{X} \mid R\left\{g_{\mu}, \frac{\partial g_{\mu}}{\partial \xi}\right\} \equiv (-1)^{l_{\mu}(l_{\mu}-1)/2} g_{\mu 0}(\mathbf{X}; \eta)^{2l_{\mu}-1} V_{\mu}(\mathbf{X}; \eta) \equiv 0; \eta \in \mathbb{C}^1\right\}, \tag{2.7.42}$$

where $V_{\mu}(\mathbf{X}; \eta) \equiv \Pi_{0 \le \alpha < \beta \le l_{\mu}}[A_{\beta}^{(\mu)}(\mathbf{X}; \eta) - A_{\alpha}^{(\mu)}(X; \eta)]$ *is the Vandermonde determinant corresponding to* $g_{\mu}(\mathbf{X}; \eta, \xi)$;

$$\mathfrak{S}_{\mu 3} \equiv \left\{\mathbf{X} \mid R\left\{V_{\mu}, \frac{\partial V_{\mu}}{\partial \eta}\right\} = 0\right\} \cup \left\{\mathbf{X} \mid R\left\{g_{\mu 0}, \frac{\partial g_{\mu 0}}{\partial \eta}\right\} = 0\right\}. \tag{2.7.43}$$

The case where the bounding, 2-cycle $\Gamma^{(2)}(\mathbf{X})$ meets some of the discontinuity curves the situation is much more complicated and the reader is referred to [G.23, pp. 320–322], for further details. Nevertheless, we state this result below, and remark that the functions introduced on $\mathfrak{R}_{\mu}[\mathbf{X}]$ ($\mu = 1, 2, \ldots, k$) are analogs of those used previously for the case of rational $\mathbf{G}_4$-associates where there was but a single Riemann surface to consider.

Theorem 2.7.3 (Gilbert) *If* $H(\mathbf{X})$ *is a harmonic function in four variables whose* $\mathbf{G}_4$-*associate is a rational function on an algebraic surface, and if* $\Gamma^{(2)}(\mathbf{X})$ *is a bounding, 2-cycle which meets each* $D_{\mu}[\mathbf{X}]$ *in just two points, i.e., such that* $\gamma_{\mu}[\mathbf{X}] \cap D_{\mu}[\mathbf{X}] \equiv \{(\eta_1^{(\mu)}, \xi_1^{(\mu)}), (\eta_2^{(\mu)}, \xi_2^{(\mu)})\}$, *then* $H(\mathbf{X})$ *has a representation of the form*

$$\begin{aligned} H(\mathbf{X}) = \sum_{\mu=1}^{k} \Bigg[& \sum_{\nu=1}^{r_{\mu}} c_{\nu}^{(\mu)}(\mathbf{X}) \log \frac{E_{\mu}(\mathbf{X}; \eta_2^{(\mu)}, \xi_2^{(\mu)}; \eta_{\nu}^{(\mu)}, \xi_{\nu}^{(\mu)}; \eta_0^{(\mu)}, \xi_0^{(\mu)})}{E_{\mu}(\mathbf{X}; \eta_1^{(\mu)}, \xi_1^{(\mu)}; \eta_{\nu}^{(\mu)}, \xi_{\nu}^{(\mu)}; \eta_0^{(\mu)}, \xi_0^{(\mu)})} \\ & + \sum_{\alpha=1}^{p_{\mu}} \left(C_{\nu}^{\prime(\mu)}(\mathbf{X}) \log \frac{E_{\alpha}^{(\mu)}(\mathbf{X}; \eta_2^{(\mu)}, \xi_2^{(\mu)})}{E_{\alpha}^{(\mu)}(\mathbf{X}; \eta_1^{(\mu)}, \xi_1^{(\mu)})} \right. \\ & \left. - C_{\nu}^{(\mu)}(\mathbf{X}) \log \frac{E_{\alpha}^{\prime(\mu)}(\mathbf{X}; \eta_2^{(\mu)}, \xi_2^{(\mu)})}{E_{\alpha}^{\prime(\mu)}(\mathbf{X}; \eta_1^{(\mu)}, \xi_1^{(\mu)})} \right) \\ & + \sum_{\nu=1}^{r_{\mu}} (F_{\nu}^{(\mu)}(\mathbf{X}; \eta_2^{(\mu)}, \xi_2^{(\mu)}) - F_{\nu}^{(\mu)}(\mathbf{X}; \eta_1^{(\mu)}, \xi_1^{(\mu)})) \Bigg]. \end{aligned} \tag{2.7.44}$$

We return now to consider the differential equation (2.7.1) with $p = 2$; in this case it is more convenient to generate (vector) solutions, using the relation (2.7.17), with the operator $\mathbf{G}_4$ instead of $\mathbf{B}_4$, i.e.,

$$\Psi_\mu(\mathbf{X}) = \int_{-1}^{+1} E(r, t) H_\mu(\mathbf{X}[1 - t^2])\, dt,$$

with

$$H_\mu(\mathbf{X}) = \mathbf{G}_4\, f(\tau, \eta, \xi) N_\mu(\eta, \xi).$$

As before, $\mathbf{H}(\mathbf{X})$ satisfies the tensor equations (2.7.18). With the aid of Theorems 2.7.2 and 2.7.3 it is possible for us to develop residue type theorems for line integrals in $\mathbb{R}^4$,

$$\int_{\mathfrak{T}} \Psi_\mu(\mathbf{X})\, dx_\mu = 2 \int_{\mathfrak{T}} dx_\mu \int_0^1 E(r, t) H_\mu(\mathbf{X}[1 - t^2])\, dt, \tag{2.7.45}$$

when the $\mathbf{G}_4$-associate of $H_\mu(\mathbf{X})$ is rational. Bergman [B.20–22] investigated this problem for the case of rational $\mathbf{B}_3$-associates, and Mitchell [M.5,7] investigated this result for algebraic $\mathbf{B}_3$-associates. The study of the analogous problems for the case of harmonic functions of *four* variables, as is already quite apparent, is a much more formidable task; in order to approach this problem we must use the structure of algebraic geometry and topology.

We consider integrals (2.7.45) where $\mathfrak{T}$ lies on the hypersphere $\|\mathbf{X}\| = R$; then, interchanging orders of integration,

$$\begin{aligned} \int_{\mathfrak{T}} \Psi_\mu(\mathbf{X})\, dx_\mu &= 2 \int_0^1 E(R, t) \left\{ \int_{\mathfrak{T}} H_\mu(\mathbf{X}[1 - t^2])\, dx_\mu \right\} dt \\ &= 2 \int_0^1 \frac{E(R, t)}{1 - t^2} \left\{ \int_{\mathfrak{F}} H_\mu(\mathbf{Y})\, dy_\mu \right\} dt, \end{aligned} \tag{2.7.46}$$

where $\mathfrak{F} = \{\mathbf{Y} \mid y_\mu = [1 - t^2] x_\mu;\ \mathbf{X} \in \mathfrak{T}\}$. Furthermore, one has

$$H_\mu(\mathbf{X}[1 - t^2]) = \frac{-1}{4\pi^2} \int_{\mathscr{L}} \int_{\mathscr{C}} \frac{\eta\xi P(\mathbf{X}[1 - t^2]; \eta, \xi)}{Q(\mathbf{X}[1 - t^2]; \eta, \xi)} N_\mu(\eta, \xi) \frac{d\eta\, d\xi}{\eta\xi}, \tag{2.7.47}$$

which we have shown before may be evaluated by integrating first with respect to ξ,†

† $\mathscr{L}_\sigma(t)$ is for each fixed t, $t \in [0, 1]$, that subset of $\mathscr{L}$ for which the branch $\xi = A_\sigma(\mathbf{X}[1 - t^2])$ lies inside $\mathscr{C}$; $\xi = A_\sigma(\mathbf{X}; \eta)$ $(\sigma = 1, 2, \ldots, n)$ are the roots of $\xi Q(\mathbf{X}; \eta, \xi) = 0$.

$$H_\mu(\mathbf{X}[1-t^2]) = \frac{1}{2\pi i}\sum_{\sigma=0}^{n}\int_{\mathscr{L}_\sigma(t)} \frac{\xi_\sigma P(\mathbf{X}[1-t^2];\eta,\xi_\sigma)N_\mu(\eta,\xi_\sigma)}{(\partial/\partial\xi)\{\xi Q(\mathbf{X}[1-t^2];\eta,\xi)\}_{\xi=\xi_\sigma}}\,d\eta, \qquad (2.7.48)$$

and then by integrating with respect to η over $\mathscr{L}_\sigma(t)$ on the Riemann surface $\mathfrak{R}[\mathbf{X}(1-t^2)]$, associated with $\xi Q_2(\mathbf{X}[1-t^2];\eta,\xi)=0$. For each $t\in[0,1]$ and $\mathbf{X}\notin\mathfrak{S}(t)$, one obtains as before a representation [G.24, pp. 1228, 1229] of the form (here $\mathfrak{S}(t)$ is an exceptional set of $\mathbf{X}$-points depending on the parameter t, and is defined analogously to the previous cases discussed),

$$\begin{aligned} H_\mu(\mathbf{X}[1-t^2]) = \sum_{\sigma=1}^{n}\sum_{\lambda=1}^{k_\delta}\Bigg\{&\sum_{\nu=1}^{r} c_{\mu\nu}(\mathbf{X}[1-t^2]) \\ &\times\log\frac{E_\mu(\mathbf{X}[1-t^2];\eta_\sigma^{(2\lambda)},\xi_\sigma^{(2\lambda)};\eta_\nu,\xi_\nu;\eta_0,\xi_0)}{E_\mu(\mathbf{X}[1-t^2];\eta_\sigma^{(2\lambda-1)},\xi_\sigma^{(2\lambda-1)};\eta_\nu,\xi_\nu;\eta_0,\xi_0)} \\ &+\sum_{\alpha=1}^{p}\Bigg(C'_{\mu\alpha}(\mathbf{X}[1-t^2])\log\frac{E_{\mu\alpha}(\mathbf{X}[1-t^2];\eta_\mu^{(2\lambda)},\xi_\mu^{(2\lambda)})}{E_{\mu\alpha}(\mathbf{X}[1-t^2];\eta_\mu^{(2\lambda-1)},\xi_\mu^{(2\lambda-1)})} \\ &-C_{\mu\alpha}(\mathbf{X}[1-t^2])\log\frac{E'_{\mu\alpha}(\mathbf{X}[1-t^2];\eta_\mu^{(2\lambda)},\xi_\mu^{(2\lambda)})}{E'_{\mu\alpha}(\mathbf{X}[1-t^2];\eta_\mu^{(2\lambda-1)},\xi_\mu^{(2\lambda-1)})}\Bigg) \\ &+\sum_{\nu=1}^{r}(F_{\mu\nu}(\mathbf{X}[1-t^2];\eta_\mu^{(2\lambda)},\xi_\mu^{(2\lambda)}) \\ &-F_{\mu\nu}(\mathbf{X}[1-t^2];\eta_\mu^{(2\lambda-1)},\xi_\mu^{(2\lambda-1)}))\Bigg\}. \end{aligned} \qquad (2.7.49)$$

Here $p=p[\mathbf{X}(1-t^2)]$ and $r=r[\mathbf{X}(1-t^2)]$ are the genus of the Riemann surface and the number of infinity points of the integrand; the points $(\eta_\sigma^{(2\lambda)},\xi_\sigma^{(2\lambda)})$, $(\eta_\sigma^{(2\lambda-1)},\xi_\sigma^{(2\lambda-1)})$ are where the root $\xi=A_\sigma(\mathbf{X}[1-t^2])$ crosses over $\mathscr{C}$.

In order to perform the t-integration it is useful to introduce the families of $\mathbf{X}$-sets, for all $t\in[0,1]$,

$$\begin{aligned}\mathfrak{M}(t)&\equiv\{\mathbf{X}\mid V(\mathbf{X}[1-t^2];\eta)=0;\,\eta\in\mathscr{L}\}\\ \mathfrak{N}(t)&\equiv\{\mathbf{X}\mid \phi(\mathbf{X}[1-t^2];\eta)=0;\,\eta\in\mathscr{L}\}.\end{aligned} \qquad (2.7.50)$$

By a proper choice of $\mathscr{L}$ for each fixed $\mathbf{X}\notin\mathfrak{S}(t)$ for $\forall t\in[0.\ 1]$, there exists only a finite set of t-values, $\{t_k\}$ $(k=1,2,\ldots,N[\mathbf{X}])$ such that $\mathbf{X}\in\mathfrak{M}(t_k)\cup\mathfrak{N}(t_k)$.† If $\mathrm{t}_k[\mathbf{X}]\equiv\{t\mid t_{k-1}<t<t_k\}$ $(t_0=0;\ t_n=1,\ n=N[\mathbf{X}]+1)$, then for $\mathbf{X}\notin\bigcup_{\mathrm{t}_k[\mathbf{X}]}\mathfrak{M}(t)$ the number of poles, $r_k[\mathbf{X}]$, inside $\mathscr{L}$ remains constant for $t\in\mathrm{t}_k[\mathbf{X}]$; likewise, for $\mathbf{X}\notin\bigcup_{\mathrm{t}_k[\mathbf{X}]}\mathfrak{N}(t)$ the genus of the Riemann surface, $\mathfrak{R}[\mathbf{X}(1-t^2)]$, remains constant for $t\in\mathrm{t}_k[\mathbf{X}]$. Consequently, the integral for

† In general, $\bigcup_{0\le u\le 1}\mathfrak{S}(t)|_{\mathbb{R}}$ is a finite set of truncated cones.

$\Psi_\mu(\mathbf{X})$ may be completed by computing the t-integration for each $\mathfrak{t}_k[\mathbf{X}]$ interval. In order to perform the line integration (2.7.46) we make use of a device introduced for the case of harmonic functions with algebraic $\mathbf{B}_3$-associates [M.5, p. 445]; we decompose the $\mathbf{X}$-integration along the contour $\mathfrak{T}$ into a finite number of segments with the end points $\{\mathbf{X}_k(t)\}_{k=1}^m$. These end points are chosen for each fixed t as the (assumed) finite set of points $\mathfrak{T} \cap \{\mathfrak{M}(t) \cup \mathfrak{N}(t)\}$.

If $\mathfrak{T}_k$ is the open interval on $\mathfrak{T}$ between $\mathbf{X}_k(t)$ and $\mathbf{X}_{k+1}(t)$, then for $(t, \mathbf{X}) \in \mathfrak{t}_j[\mathbf{X}] \times \mathfrak{T}_k$ the number of poles $r(j; k)$ and the genus $p(j; k)$ remain constant; hence the line integral (2.7.45) may be evaluated as a sum of integrals,

$$\sum_{\alpha=1}^{m} \sum_{k=1}^{N_\alpha} \int_{\mathfrak{T}_\alpha} \left\{ \int_{\mathfrak{t}_k} E(r, t) H_\mu^{(\alpha)}(\mathbf{X}[1 - t^2])\, dt \right\} dx_\mu, \tag{2.7.51}$$

where the superscript α in the integrand indicates that for each α a different Weierstrass decomposition must be accomplished [G.24, p. 1231].

The integral (2.7.46) may be rewritten as [G.24]

$$\int_{\mathfrak{T}} \Psi_\mu(\mathbf{X})\, dx_\mu = \frac{-1}{2\pi^2} \int_0^1 \frac{E(r, t)}{1 - t^2} \int_{\mathscr{L}} \frac{d\eta}{\eta} \int_{\mathscr{C}} \frac{d\xi}{\xi} \int_{\mathfrak{C}} \frac{p(\sigma, \eta, \xi)}{q(\sigma, \eta, \xi)}\, d\sigma, \tag{2.7.52}$$

where $\mathfrak{C} \equiv \{\sigma \mid \sigma = \tau(1 - t^2); \mathbf{X} \in \mathfrak{T}; \eta, \xi \text{ are fixed}\}$, and $p(\tau, \eta, \xi)/q(\tau, \eta, \xi) = P(\mathbf{X}; \eta, \xi)/Q(\mathbf{X}; \eta, \xi)$. Using the methods of algebraic geometry developed for harmonic functions with $\mathbf{G}_4$-associates in [G.23] we may show that (2.7.52) may be evaluated in terms of Weierstrass functions on the Riemann surfaces $\mathfrak{R}^{(\nu)}$, associated with the polar curves of $p(\tau, \eta, \xi)/R\{q, \partial q/\partial\tau\}$ on the algebraic surface $\mathscr{A}$ (defined by $p(\tau, \eta, \xi) = 0$) [G.24]; one obtains representations of the form

$$\begin{aligned}
&-\frac{1}{2\pi i} \sum_{\lambda=0}^{N} \sum_{\mu=0}^{N_\lambda} \sum_{k \in I(\mathfrak{T}, \lambda, \mu)} \int_{t_{k-1}}^{t_k} \frac{E(R, t)}{(1 - t^2)} \\
&\left\{ \sum_{\nu=1}^{M} \sum_{i=1}^{m_\mu} \left[\sum_{\alpha=1}^{r_\nu} d_\alpha^{(\nu)} \log \frac{E_\nu(\eta_{2i+1}^{(\nu)}, \xi_{2i+1}^{(\nu)}; \eta_\alpha^{(\nu)}, \xi_\alpha^{(\nu)}; \eta_0^{(\nu)}, \xi_0^{(\nu)})}{E_\nu(\eta_{2i}^{(\nu)}, \xi_{2i}^{(\nu)}; \eta_\alpha^{(\nu)}, \xi_\alpha^{(\nu)}; \eta_0^{(\nu)}, \xi_0^{(\nu)})} \right.\right. \\
&+ \sum_{\beta=1}^{p_\nu} \left(C_\beta'^{(\nu)} \log \frac{E_\beta^{(\nu)}(\eta_{2i+1}^{(\nu)}, \xi_{2i+1}^{(\nu)})}{E_\beta^{(\nu)}(\eta_{2i}^{(\nu)}, \xi_{2i}^{(\nu)})} + C_\beta^{(\nu)} \log \frac{E_\beta'^{(\nu)}(\eta_{2i+1}^{(\nu)}, \xi_{2i+1}^{(\nu)})}{E_\beta(\eta_{2i}^{(\nu)}, \xi_{2i}^{(\nu)})} \right) \\
&\left.\left. + \sum_{\alpha=1}^{r_\nu} \left\{ (F_\alpha^{(\nu)}(\eta_{2i+1}^{(\nu)}, \xi_{2i+1}^{(\nu)}) - F_\alpha^{(\nu)}(\eta_{2i}^{(\nu)}, \xi_{2i}^{(\nu)})) \right\} \right] \right\}.
\end{aligned} \tag{2.7.53}$$

The symbol $I(\mathfrak{T}; \lambda, \mu)$ denotes an index set which depends on $\mathfrak{T}$, λ, and μ; the specification of this set depends on providing several composite decompositions of the integration intervals as was done above, and is quite detailed in construction. The reader wishing further information on this point is referred to the original work [G.24, pp. 1231–1235].

References and Additional Reading

[B.1]
[B.2]
[B.3]
[B.4]
[B.13]
[B.17]
[B.20]
[B.21]
[B.22]
[B.24]
[B.25]
[B.26]
[B.27]
[B.29]
[C.H.1]
[D.6]
[E.6]
[G.6]
[G.7]
[G.8]
[G.10]
[G.11]
[G.12]
[G.15]
[G.17]
[G.19]
[G.23]
[G.24]
[G.25]
[G.H.1]
[G.K.L.1]
[H.3]
[H.10]
[K.4]
[K.5]
[K.6]
[K.7]
[L.6]
[L.7]
[L.8]
[L.9]
[L.10]
[L.11]
[M.2]
[M.4]
[M.5]
[M.6]
[M.7]
[M.F.1]
[P.2]
[P.S.1]

3

Elliptic differential equations in two variables with analytic coefficients

Introduction

In this chapter we shall study how to construct integral operators which associate in a one-to-one manner the solutions of linear, elliptic partial differential equations,

$$\mathbf{e}[u] \equiv \frac{\partial^2 u}{\partial x^2} + \frac{\partial^2 u}{\partial y^2} + a(x, y)\frac{\partial u}{\partial x} + b(x, y)\frac{\partial u}{\partial y} + c(x, y)u = 0, \quad (3.0.1)$$

with analytic functions of a complex variable. The coefficients a, b, c may be taken to be entire in the space $\mathbb{C}^2$ or in certain instances the less restrictive assumption will be made that they possess a certain analytic continuation described below. Let us introduce formally the linear transformation of $\mathbb{C}^2$ into itself,

$$\begin{aligned} z &= x + iy \\ z^* &= x - iy \end{aligned} \qquad (x, y) \in \mathbb{C}^2, \qquad (3.0.2)$$

where the variables z and z^* are complex conjugates if and only if x and y are real. Let us define the "continued" coefficients

$$\tilde{a}(z, z^*) \equiv a\left(\frac{z + z^*}{2}, \frac{z - z^*}{2i}\right), \qquad \tilde{c}(z, z^*) \equiv c\left(\frac{z + z^*}{2}, \frac{z - z^*}{2i}\right), \qquad (3.0.3)$$
$$\tilde{b}(z, z^*) \equiv b\left(\frac{z + z^*}{2}, \frac{z - z^*}{2i}\right),$$

and let us suppose that the coefficients a, b, c are real analytic functions of the variables x and y in a common domain, $\mathfrak{S}$, i.e., for $z = x + iy \in \mathfrak{S}$. We then shall say that the coefficients a, b, c have an analytic continuation to the bicylinder $\mathfrak{S} \times \mathfrak{S}^*$, providing that the functions $\tilde{a}$, $\tilde{b}$, $\tilde{c}$ are analytic regular (holomorphic) for $(z, z^*) \in \mathfrak{S}^{(2)} \equiv \mathfrak{S} \times \mathfrak{S}^*$.

1. Bergman's Integral Operator of the First Kind

Bergman in a series of papers [B.5–12] has investigated the differential equation (3.0.1) and obtained methods for constructing solutions. Bergman usually assumes in his investigations that the coefficients of (3.0.1) have a continuation to the bicylinder $\mathfrak{S}^{(2)} \equiv \mathfrak{S} \times \mathfrak{S}^*$. (Such a domain $\mathfrak{S}$ has been referred to by Vekua as a *fundamental domain* [V.3], [H.6].)

We consider (3.0.1) under the transformation (3.0.2) and obtain

$$\mathbf{E}[U] = U_{zz^*} + A(z, z^*)U_z + B(z, z^*)U_{z^*} + C(z, z^*)U = 0, \qquad (3.1.1)$$

where

$$A(z, z^*) = \tfrac{1}{4}(\tilde{a}(z, z^*) + i\tilde{b}(z, z^*)),$$
$$B(z, z^*) = \tfrac{1}{4}(\tilde{a}(z, z^*) - i\tilde{b}(z, z^*)),$$
$$C(z, z^*) = \tfrac{1}{4}\tilde{c}(z, z^*),$$

and

$$U(z, z^*) = u\left(\frac{z + z^*}{2}, \frac{z - z^*}{2i}\right) \qquad (z, z^*) \in \mathfrak{S} \times \mathfrak{S}^*.$$

Remark If, as is assumed, the coefficients of (3.0.1) are real, then for real x and y, $A(z, \bar{z}) = \overline{B(z, \bar{z})}$ and $C(z, \bar{z})$ is real. If the function $V(z, z^*)$ is defined in the bicylinder, $\mathfrak{S}^{(2)}$, by the relation

$$V(z, z^*) = U(z, z^*) \exp\left\{\int_0^{z^*} A(z, \zeta^*)\, d\zeta^* - n(z)\right\}, \qquad (3.1.2)$$

where $n(z)$ is an arbitrary analytic function of z, following Bergman we notice that Eq. (3.1.1) may be reduced to the canonical form

$$\mathbf{L}[V] \equiv V_{zz^*} + D(z, z^*)V_{z^*} + F(z, z^*)V = 0, \qquad (3.1.3)$$

where

$$F(z, z^*) = -(A_z + AB - C)$$

and

$$D(z, z^*) = n'(z) - \int_0^{z^*} A_z(z, \zeta^*)\, d\zeta^* + B(z, z^*).$$

This may be seen by direct substitution of (3.1.2) in (3.1.1), taking into account that these coefficients are at least in $\mathscr{C}^{(1)}[\mathfrak{S}^{(2)}]$ and the solutions $U(z, z^*)$ are assumed to be of class $\mathscr{C}^{(2)}[\mathfrak{S}^{(2)}]$.

Bergman's method is then concerned with obtaining an integral representation of solutions for Eq. (3.1.3) in the form

$$V(z, z^*) = \mathbf{b}_2{}'f, \tag{3.1.4}$$

where

$$\mathbf{b}_2{}'f \equiv \int_{\mathscr{L}} \tilde{E}(z, z^*, t) f\left(\frac{z}{2}[1 - t^2]\right) \frac{dt}{(1 - t^2)^{1/2}}, \tag{3.1.5}$$

where $\tilde{E}(z, z^*, t)$ is a suitably chosen kernel, or as Bergman calls it, *generating function*, and $\mathscr{L}$ is a rectifiable arc from -1 to $+1$ which usually is taken not to pass through the origin. From the above notation it is intended that $\mathbf{b}_2{}'f$ be considered as an integral operator that maps analytic functions onto complex solutions of the partial differential equation (3.1.3).

By formally substituting the expression for $V(z, z^*)$ as an integral into Eq. (3.1.3) and integrating by parts one has

$$\mathbf{L}[V] = -\left[\tilde{E}_{z^*} \frac{(1 - t^2)^{1/2}}{2zt} f\right]_{t=-1}^{+1} + \int_{\mathscr{L}} \left\{ \frac{\tilde{E}_{zz^*}}{(1 - t^2)^{1/2}} + \left(\tilde{E}_{z^*} \frac{(1 - t^2)^{1/2}}{2zt}\right)_t + \frac{D\tilde{E}_{z^*}}{(1 - t^2)^{1/2}} + F \frac{\tilde{E}}{(1 - t^2)^{1/2}} \right\} f\, dt. \tag{3.1.6}$$

If we further restrict $\tilde{E}(z, z^*, t)$ so that $\tilde{E}_{z^*}(z, z^*, t)t^{-1}$ is continuous in $\mathfrak{S} \times \Delta$, where

$$\Delta \equiv \{t \mid |t| \le 1\},$$

and if f is an arbitrary analytic function, then for each fixed $(z, z^*) \in \mathfrak{S}^{(2)}$ the integrand of (3.1.6) must vanish everywhere on $\mathscr{L}$. If $V(z, z^*) \in \mathscr{C}^{(2)}[\mathfrak{S}^{(2)}]$ it follows that the integrand vanishes, or in other words the generating function must satisfy the following partial differential equation:

$$(1 - t^2)\tilde{E}_{z^*t} - t^{-1}\tilde{E}_{z^*} + 2tz(\tilde{E}_{zz^*} + D\tilde{E}_{z^*} + F\tilde{E}) = 0. \tag{3.1.7}$$

Bergman refers to the function

$$E(z, z^*, t) \equiv \tilde{E}(z, z^*, t) \exp\left\{-\int_0^{z^*} A(z, \zeta^*)\, d\zeta^* + n(z)\right\} \tag{3.1.8}$$

as the generating function for the differential equation (3.1.1) where $\tilde{E}(z, z^*, t)$ is a solution of (3.1.7) that satisfies the above continuity condition.

A necessary and sufficient condition for $z^* = \bar{z}$ is for x and y to be real. If the coefficients of (3.0.1) are real analytic then one obtains real solutions, $\Psi(z, \bar{z})$, to this equation with the representation [B.22, p. 11]

$$\Psi(z, \bar{z}) = \int_{\mathscr{L}} \left[E(z, \bar{z}, t) f\left(\frac{z}{2}[1 - t^2]\right) + \bar{E}(\bar{z}, z, \bar{t}) \bar{f}\left(\frac{\bar{z}}{2}[1 - \bar{t}^2]\right)\right] \frac{dt}{(1 - t^2)^{1/2}}.$$

At first glance it might appear that the problem of representing solutions of (3.1.1) as integrals of the form

$$U(z, z^*) = \mathbf{b}_2 f \equiv \int_{\mathscr{L}} E(z, z^*, t) f\left(\frac{z}{2}[1 - t^2]\right) \frac{dt}{(1 - t^2)^{1/2}}, \tag{3.1.9}$$

has been made more difficult in that one must now solve a partial differential equation in three variables instead of two. However, this is misleading since only a single solution of Eq. (3.1.7), which is of class $\mathscr{C}^{(0)}[\mathfrak{S}^{(2)}, \Delta]$ with $\tilde{E}_{z^*} t^{-1} \in \mathscr{C}^{(0)}$, is needed in order to obtain a continuous operator of the form (3.1.9). If $\mathfrak{S}$ is a simply connected fundamental domain, then since $\mathbf{B}_2 f \equiv \operatorname{Re} \mathbf{b}_2 f$ is continuous we may generate a complete system of real solutions for (3.0.1) by the mapping of the powers of z onto solutions, i.e.,

$$\Psi_n(z, z^*) \equiv \mathbf{B}_2 z^n \qquad (n = 1, 2, 3, \ldots). \tag{3.1.10}$$

This follows from the well-known fact that the powers of z form a complete system of analytic functions for any simply connected region: if the $\{\Psi_n\}$ were not complete then the $\{z_n\}$ would not be complete.

If the set of functions $f_n(z)$ ($n = 1, 2, 3, \ldots$) is another complete system of analytic functions an alternate complete system of solutions is given by

$$\tilde{\Psi}_n(z, z^*) \equiv \mathbf{B}_2 f_n(z) \qquad (n = 1, 2, 3, \ldots).$$

If $\mathfrak{S}$ is an m-fold multiply connected domain, i.e., suppose it is bounded by the set of simple closed curves $\Gamma_0, \Gamma_1, \ldots, \Gamma_m$, where Γ_0 contains the other curves, and the curves Γ_j contain the points z_j ($j = 1, \ldots, m$), then the following system of rational functions,

$$(z - z_0)^n, \qquad (z - z_j)^{-n-1}, \qquad (n = 0, 1, 2, \ldots) \qquad (j = 1, 2, \ldots, m)$$

form a complete system with respect to the class of functions analytic in $\mathfrak{S}$. However, in this case the complete system of real solutions to (3.0.1) defined by

$$\Psi_{-n, j}(z, z^*) \equiv \mathbf{B}_2[(z - z_j)^{-n-1}], \qquad (n = 0, 1, 2, \ldots) \qquad (j = 1, 2, \ldots, m), \tag{3.1.11}$$

may not be single-valued. In order to obtain single-valued solutions in a multiply connected domain, one must choose as associate functions multi-valued analytic functions in $\mathfrak{S}$. This aspect has been discussed in Vekua [V.3, pp. 45–54], to which the reader is directed.

We summarize our above discussion of Bergman's operator method with the following theorem.

Theorem 3.1.1 (Bergman) *Let the coefficients of the differential equation* (3.1.1) *be real analytic regular in the bicylinder* $\mathfrak{S}^{(2)}$, *and let the functions* $D(z, z^*)$ $F(z, z^*)$ *be defined in* $\mathfrak{S}^{(2)}$ *by* (3.1.3). *Then if* $\tilde{E}(z, z^*, t)$ *is of class* $\mathscr{C}^{(2)}[\mathfrak{S}^{(2)}, \Delta]$ (*where* Δ *is the unit disk*) *and satisfies Eq.* (3.1.7), *and the "characteristic condition"* (3.1.6), $\Psi(z, z^*) = \mathbf{B}_2 f$ *is a real solution of Eq.* (3.1.1).

From the above it is realized that what is needed for a practical method for solving equations of the form (3.0.1) is a means to construct solutions for the generating function equation (3.1.7). Once this is done we are able to find a complete system of solutions by the scheme illustrated before, construct the Bergman kernel function for the domain $\mathfrak{S}$, and thereby be in a position to solve the usual boundary value problems associated with elliptic equations [B.19], [B.S.1]. See also Garabedian [G.4, Chap. 7, Sect. III]. Bergman has given such a constructive method for obtaining solutions for the generating function equation (3.1.7). For instance, if we seek a solution $E(z, z^*, t)$ which has the form

$$\tilde{E}(z, z^*, t) = 1 + \sum_{n=1}^{\infty} t^{2n} z^n \int_0^{z^*} P^{(2n)}(z, \zeta^*)\, d\zeta^*, \tag{3.1.12}$$

for $(z, z^*) \in [|z| \leq a,\ |z^*| \leq a] \subset \mathfrak{S} \times \mathfrak{S}^*$, then we find that the $P^{(2n)}(z, z^*)$ satisfy the following equations:

$$P^{(2n)}(z, z^*) = -2F(z, z^*),$$

$$(2n+1)P^{(2n+2)}(z, z^*) = -2P_z^{(2n)} + DP^{(2n)} + F\int_0^{z^*} P^{(2n)}\, d\zeta^*, \tag{3.1.13}$$

$$(n = 1, 2, \ldots).$$

Bergman shows by using the method of dominants that the series (3.1.12) converges to an analytic function of the three complex variables z, z^*, t in the region $\mathfrak{D}^{(3)} \equiv [|z| \leq a,\ |z^*| \leq a,\ |t| \leq 1]$. Furthermore, the system (3.1.12), (3.1.13) yields a method (in view of Bergman's proof of the uniform convergence of (3.1.12)), of constructing the kernel $\tilde{E}(z, z^*, t)$ by successive approximations. He also gives an alternate method for successively approximating $\tilde{E}(z, z^*, t)$ which we shall discuss in the following section (3.2).

We reproduce now, with modification, Bergman's proof of the existence of a kernel $E(z, z^*, t) = \tilde{E}(z, z^*, t)\exp\{-\int_0^{z^*} A(z, \zeta^*)\, d\zeta^* + n(z)\}$. First we note that the functions $P^{(2n)}(z, z^*)$ defined recursively above in (3.1.13) are holomorphic in the bicylinder $\mathfrak{S} \times \mathfrak{S}^*$ if $\mathfrak{S}$ is a fundamental domain for $\mathbf{E}[U] = 0$. Secondly, if $\{|z| \leq r,\ |z^*| \leq r\} \subset \mathfrak{S} \times \mathfrak{S}^*$, then we may use the following dominants for $D(z, z^*)$ and $F(z, z^*)$:

$$D(z, z^*) \ll M\left(1 - \frac{z}{r}\right)^{-1}\left(1 - \frac{z^*}{r}\right)^{-1},$$

$$F(z, z^*) \ll M\left(1 - \frac{z}{r}\right)^{-1}\left(1 - \frac{z^*}{r}\right)^{-1},$$

where M is a suitably chosen constant. Dominants for the $P^{(2n)}(z, z^*)$, i.e., functions $\tilde{P}^{(2n)}(z, z^*) \gg P^{(2n)}(z, z^*)$, may be introduced as follows:

$$\tilde{P}^{(0)}(z, z^*) = 1, \qquad \tilde{P}^{(2)}(z, z^*) = \frac{2C}{\left(1 - \dfrac{z}{r}\right)\left(1 - \dfrac{z^*}{r}\right)}, \qquad C \geq M,$$

$$(2n+1)\tilde{P}^{(2n+2)}(z, z^*) =$$
$$2\left[\tilde{P}_z^{(2n)}(z, z^*) + \frac{C}{\left(1-\frac{z}{r}\right)\left(1-\frac{z^*}{r}\right)}\tilde{P}^{(2n)}(z, z^*)\right.$$
$$\left. + \frac{C}{\left(1-\frac{z}{r}\right)\left(1-\frac{z^*}{r}\right)}\int_0^{z^*}\tilde{P}^{(2n)}(z, z^*)\,dz^*\right]$$
$$(n = 1, 2, \ldots).$$

By inspection of the above formulas, which define the majorants $\tilde{P}^{(2n+2)}(z, z^*)$, we realize that we may rewrite this system of equations by setting

$$\tilde{P}^{(0)}(z, z^*) = Q^{(0)}(z, z^*) = 1, \qquad \tilde{P}^{(2)}(z, z^*) = \frac{Q^{(2)}(z^*)}{1-\frac{z}{r}},$$

$$\tilde{P}^{(2n)}(z, z^*) = \frac{2^{n-1}Q^{(2n)}(z^*)}{\left(1-\frac{z}{r}\right)^n 1\cdot 3\cdot 5\cdot\cdots\cdot(2n-1)} \qquad (n = 2, 3, \ldots).$$

We obtain the following reduced system for the functions, $Q^{(2n)}(z^*)$ (which only depend on the variable z^*):

$$Q^{(2)}(z^*) = \frac{2C}{\left(1-\frac{z^*}{r}\right)},$$

$$Q^{(2n+2)}(z^*) = Q^{(2n)}(z^*)\left[\frac{n}{r} + \frac{C}{1-\frac{z^*}{r}}\right] + \frac{C}{1-\frac{z^*}{r}}\int_0^{z^*}Q^{(2n)}(z^*)\,dz^*.$$

This last equation, since $\int_0^{z^*}Q^{(2n)}(z^*)\,dz^* \ll Q^{(2n)}(z^*)$, yields the following majorization,

$$Q^{(2n+2)}(z^*) \ll Q^{(2n)}(z^*)\frac{2(n+Cr)}{r\left(1-\frac{z^*}{r}\right)},$$

from which we have

$$\tilde{p}^{(2n)}(z, z^*) \ll \frac{2^{(2n-2)}(n-1+Cr)(n-2+Cr)\cdots(1+Cr)C}{\left(1-\frac{z}{r}\right)^n r^{n-1}\left(1-\frac{z^*}{r}\right)^{n-1} 1\cdot 3\cdots(2n-1)}.$$

Consequently, the majorant series for $\tilde{E}(z, z^*, t)$, i.e.,

$$1 + \frac{|t|^2 2C}{\left(1-\frac{|z|}{r}\right)} + 4Cr^2\left(1-\frac{|z^*|}{r}\right)\sum_{n=2}^{\infty}|t|^{2n}\left|\frac{4z}{r}\right|^n \times \frac{(n-1+Cr)\cdots(1+Cr)}{\left(1-\frac{|z|}{r}\right)^n\left(1-\frac{|z^*|}{r}\right)^n 1\cdot 3\cdots(2n-1)},$$

is seen by comparison with the series,

$$\sum_{n=2}^{\infty}\frac{(n+\alpha)(n+\alpha-1)\cdots(\alpha+1)}{(2n-1)(2n-3)\cdots 3\cdot 1}|\chi|^{2n}, \qquad \alpha > 0,$$

(which converges for $|\chi| < \sqrt{2}$) to represent a holomorphic function of the three complex variables z, z^*, and t in some neighborhood of the polycylinder $\{|z| < 2 - \sqrt{3}\} \times \{|z^*| < 2 - \sqrt{3}\} \times \{|t| \leq 1\}$. This verifies the existence of Bergman's E-function and hence also the existence of the integral operator of the first kind as a linear operator which maps the class of analytic functions onto a class of solutions regular in a neighborhood of the origin.

2. *Analytic Computations of the Bergman E-Function*

Bergman [B.11,22] has given the following alternate method for constructing the generating function of the operator $\mathbf{b}_2 f$. He does this by introducing an auxiliary function $g(z)$ that is related to $f(z/2)$ by a pair of reciprocal integral transforms.

Let us assume that $g(z)$ and $f(z)$ have the following Taylor series developments about the origin:

$$g(z) = \sum_{n=0}^{\infty} A_n z^n, \qquad f(z) = \sum_{n=0}^{\infty} a_n z^n, \tag{3.2.1}$$

where

$$a_n \equiv \frac{\Gamma(n+1)A_n 2^n}{\Gamma(\frac{1}{2})\Gamma(n+\frac{1}{2})};$$

then by using the identity

$$\int_{-1}^{+1} (1 - t^2)^{p-1/2}\, dt = \frac{\Gamma(p + \frac{1}{2})\Gamma(\frac{1}{2})}{\Gamma(p + 1)}, \qquad \operatorname{Re} p > -\tfrac{1}{2},$$

we have

$$\begin{aligned} g(z) \equiv \sum_{n=0}^{\infty} A_n z^n &= \sum_{n=0}^{\infty} \frac{a_n}{2^n} z^n \int_{-1}^{+1} (1 - t^2)^{n-\frac{1}{2}}\, dt \\ &= \sum_{n=0}^{\infty} a_n \frac{\Gamma(n + \frac{1}{2})\Gamma(\frac{1}{2})}{\Gamma(n + 1)} \left(\frac{z}{2}\right)^n \\ &= \int_{-1}^{+1} f\left(\frac{z}{2}[1 - t^2]\right) \frac{dt}{(1 - t^2)^{1/2}}. \end{aligned} \tag{3.2.2}$$

Likewise we may show that an inverse integral relation holds between these functions by considering the integral identity

$$\frac{1}{2\pi} \int_{\mathscr{L}-1}^{+1} (1 - t^2)^n \frac{dt}{t^2} = \frac{\Gamma(n + 1)}{\Gamma(\frac{1}{2})\Gamma(n + \frac{1}{2})},$$

where $\mathscr{L}$ does not pass through the origin. It follows then as Bergman has shown [B.22] that

$$f\left(\frac{z}{2}\right) = \frac{1}{2\pi} \int_{-1}^{+1} g(z[1 - t^2]) \frac{dt}{t^2}. \tag{3.2.3}$$

In what follows we shall assume the coefficients of (3.1.1) are entire and hence that $\mathfrak{S} \equiv \mathbb{C}^1$. The function $g(z)$ will be seen to play an interesting role in the construction of integral operators. For instance, let us assume the E-function has a representation of the form (3.1.12), namely

$$E(z, z^*, t) = \left[\exp\left\{-\int_0^{z^*} A(z, \zeta^*)\, d\zeta^*\right\}\right]\left[1 + \sum_{n=1}^{\infty} z^n t^{2n} Q^{(n)}(z, z^*)\right] \tag{3.2.4}$$

where $Q^{(n)}(z, z^*) \equiv \int_0^{z^*} P^{(2n)}(z, \zeta^*)\, d\zeta^*$, and the $P^{(2n)}(z, z^*)$ are the functions introduced in the scheme (3.1.13), and let us consider the general term corresponding to $t^{2n} f(\frac{1}{2}z[1 - t^2])$ which occurs in the series representation

$$\int_{-1}^{+1} \left[1 + \sum_{n=1}^{\infty} z^n t^{2n} \int_0^{z^*} P^{(2n)}(z, \zeta^*)\, d\zeta^*\right] \frac{f(\frac{1}{2}z[1 - t^2])}{(1 - t^2)^{1/2}}\, dt$$

for $\mathbf{b}_2 f$. It may be seen from the following expression, where we have exchanged orders of summation and integration,

$$\int_{-1}^{+1} t^{2n} f\left(\frac{z}{2}[1-t^2]\right)\frac{dt}{(1-t^2)^{1/2}}$$

$$= \sum_{m=0}^{\infty} a_m \left(\frac{z}{2}\right)^m \int_{-1}^{+1} (1-t^2)^{m-\frac{1}{2}} t^{2n}\, dt$$

$$= \sum_{m=0}^{\infty} a_m \left(\frac{z}{2}\right)^m \frac{\Gamma(m+\frac{1}{2})\Gamma(n+\frac{1}{2})}{\Gamma(m+n+1)}$$

$$= \frac{1}{2}\cdot\frac{3}{2}\cdots\left(\frac{2n+1}{2}\right) z^{-n} \int_0^z\int_0^{z_1}\cdots\int_0^{z_{n-1}} g(z_n)\, dz_n \ldots dz_1, \qquad (3.2.5)$$

that the integral operator $\mathbf{b}_2$ also may be written in the form

$$\mathbf{b}_2 f \equiv \exp\left\{-\int_0^z A(z,\zeta^*)\, d\zeta^*\right\}\left[g(z) + \sum_{n=1}^{\infty} \frac{Q^{(n)}(z,z^*)(2n+1)!}{2^n(n+1)!}\right.$$

$$\left.\times \int_0^z\int_0^{z_1}\cdots\int_0^{z_{n-1}} g(z_n)\, dz_n \cdots dz_1\right] = \mathbf{c}_2\{z, z^*; g\}. \qquad (3.2.6)$$

If in addition we have $g(0) = 0$, then by successively integrating by parts we may show that

$$\int_0^z\int_0^{z_1}\cdots\int_0^{z_{n-1}} g(z_n)\, dz_n \cdots dz_1 = \frac{1}{n!}\int_0^z (z-z_1)^{n-1} g(z_1)\, dz_1, \qquad (3.2.7)$$

and hence obtain the alternate expression

$$\mathbf{c}_2[z, z^*; g] \equiv \exp\left\{-\int_0^z A(z,\zeta^*)\, d\zeta^*\right\}$$

$$\times \left[g(z) + \sum_{n=1}^{\infty} \frac{Q^{(n)}(z,z^*)}{B(n, n+1)} \int_0^z (z-\zeta)^{n-1} g(\zeta)\, d\zeta\right]. \qquad (3.2.8)$$

The form of (3.2.8) suggests its use in successive approximations of solutions $U(z, z^*)$ by the functions $U_N(z, z^*)$, defined by

$$U_N(z, z^*) \equiv \exp\left\{-\int_0^z A(z,\zeta^*)\, d\zeta^*\right\}$$

$$\times \left[g(z) + \sum_{n=1}^{N} \frac{Q^{(n)}(z,z^*)}{B(n, n+1)} \int_0^z (z-\zeta)^{n-1} g(\zeta)\, d\zeta\right]. \qquad (3.2.9)$$

Estimates for the functions $Q^{(n)}(z, z^*)$ may be found in Bergman's book from which one may approximate the difference, $|U(z, z^*) - U_N(z\, z^*)|$.

In the special case where the differential equation (3.0.1) takes the form

$$\mathbf{T}_2[u] \equiv \frac{\partial^2 u}{\partial x^2} + \frac{\partial^2 u}{\partial y^2} + a(r^2)\left\{x \frac{\partial u}{\partial x} + y \frac{\partial u}{\partial y}\right\} + c(r^2)u = 0, \qquad (3.2.10)$$

the generating function $E(z, z^*, t)$ is simply a function of $r^2 = z\, z^*$ and t.

The particular case where $a(r^2) \equiv 1$ has also been treated by Avila and Gilbert [A.G.1] using an approach similar to that discussed in Chapter 4. The reader is directed to Bergman's book [B.22, pp. 27–30], and the author's paper with Avila for further details concerning the function theoretic treatment of this particular equation.

As the reader will recall, the approach discussed above can be generalized to the case of elliptic partial differential equations in $(p + 2)$ independent variables,

$$\mathbf{T}_{p+2}[\Psi] \equiv \frac{\partial^2 \Psi}{\partial x_\mu\, \partial x_\mu} + A(r^2)x_\mu \frac{\partial \Psi}{\partial x_\mu} + C(r^2)\Psi = 0, \qquad (3.2.11)$$

which was accomplished in Chapter 2.

Another approach for obtaining the generating function suggests itself since $f(\frac{1}{2}z[1 - t^2])$ is analytic in a neighborhood of the origin and can be expanded as a power series. In this case one obtains by formally exchanging integration and summation processes that

$$V(z, z^*) = \sum_{n=0}^{\infty} a_n \left(\frac{z}{2}\right)^n \int_{\mathscr{L}} \tilde{E}(z, z^*, t)(1 - t^2)^{n-\frac{1}{2}}\, dt. \qquad (3.2.12)$$

Furthermore, if we assume that $t^{-1}\tilde{E}_{z^*}$ is continuous for $t = 0$, as we have done earlier, then we may write

$$V(z, z^*) = \sum_{n=0}^{\infty} a_n \left(\frac{z}{2}\right)^n \int_{-1}^{1} \tilde{E}(z, z^*, t)(1 - t^2)^{n-\frac{1}{2}}\, dt. \qquad (3.2.13)$$

By setting $u = -\ln(1 - t^2)$ we obtain the following integral representation,

$$V(z, z^*) = \sum_{n=0}^{\infty} a_n \left(\frac{z}{2}\right)^n \int_0^{\infty} \{\hat{G}(z, z^*, u) + \hat{G}(z, z^*, ue^{-2\pi i})\}e^{-nu}\, du \qquad (3.2.14)$$

where

$$\hat{G}(z, z^*, u) \equiv \frac{\tilde{E}(z, z^*, (1 - e^{-u})^{1/2})}{2(e^u - 1)^{1/2}},$$

which we may rewrite formally as

$$V(z, z^*) = \sum_{n=0}^{\infty} a_n \left(\frac{z}{2}\right)^n \{G_1(z, z^*; n) + G_0(z, z^*; n)\}. \tag{3.2.15}$$

Here $G_k(z, z^*; n) \equiv \mathscr{L}\{\hat{G}(z, z^*; ue^{2\pi ik})\}$ $(k = 0, 1)$ is the Laplace transform of $\hat{G}$ with respect to the variable u. We see from this that knowledge of the function $\hat{G}(z, z^*; u)$ allows us to construct solutions of the differential equation (3.1.3) or (3.1.1).

In order to see how we can construct the functions $\hat{G}(z, z^*; u)$ we return to the original differential equation for the kernel, namely

$$(1 - t^2)\tilde{E}_{z^*t} - \frac{\tilde{E}_{z^*}}{t} + 2tz\mathbf{L}[\tilde{E}] = 0,$$

and we notice the following results obtained by multiplying the various terms by $(1 - t^2)^\alpha$ and integrating by parts. For instance let $\alpha > 0$, and let us take as our path of integration, $\mathscr{L}' \equiv [-1, -\varepsilon] \cup \gamma_\varepsilon \cup [\varepsilon, 1]$, where γ_ε is a semicircle from $-\varepsilon$ to ε in the lower half plane. Then since $\lim_{t \to \pm 1}(1 - t^2)^{1/2} \times \tilde{E}(z, z^*, t) = 0$,

$$\int_{\mathscr{L}'} (1 - t^2)^{\alpha+1} \frac{\tilde{E}_{z^*t}}{t}\, dt = 2(\alpha + 1)\int_{\mathscr{L}'} (1 - t^2)^\alpha \tilde{E}_{z^*}\, dt + \int_{\mathscr{L}'} t^{-2}\tilde{E}_{z^*}(1 - t^2)^{\alpha+1}\, dt.$$

Consequently, by summing the various terms in the differential equation as shown below we obtain

$$\begin{aligned}\int_{\mathscr{L}'} (1 - t^2)^{\alpha+1} \frac{\tilde{E}_{z^*t}}{t}\, dt - \int_{\mathscr{L}'} (1 - t^2)^\alpha \frac{\tilde{E}_{z^*}}{t^2}\, dt + 2z \int_{\mathscr{L}'} (1 - t^2)^\alpha \mathbf{L}[\tilde{E}]\, dt \\ = 2(\alpha + \tfrac{1}{2})\int_{\mathscr{L}'} (1 - t^2)^\alpha \tilde{E}_{z^*}\, dt + 2z \int_{\mathscr{L}'} (1 - t^2)^\alpha \mathbf{L}[\tilde{E}]\, dt \\ = 0.\end{aligned}$$

Hence, taking the limit as $\varepsilon \to 0$, and $\mathscr{L}' \to [-1, +1]$, we obtain

$$\int_{-1}^{+1} \{2(\alpha + 1)\tilde{E}_{z^*} + \mathbf{L}[\tilde{E}]\}(1 - t^2)^\alpha\, dt = 0. \tag{3.2.16}$$

Since $\tilde{E}(z, z^*, t) \in \mathscr{C}^2[\mathfrak{S}^{(2)} \times \Delta]$, and $\lim_{t\to\pm 1}(1-t^2)^{1/2}\tilde{E}(z, z^*, t) = 0$, the auxiliary function $K(z, z^*; \alpha)$, defined by the integral

$$K(z, z^*; \alpha) \equiv \int_{-1}^{1} \tilde{E}(z, z^*, t)(1-t^2)^{\alpha}\, dt, \qquad \alpha > 0 \tag{3.2.17}$$

must satisfy a certain partial differential equation in the two independent variables z, z^*, with an independent parameter α, namely

$$\mathbf{L}[K] + 2(\alpha+1)K_{z^*} \equiv K_{zz^*} + [D + 2(\alpha+1)]K_{z^*} + FK = 0. \tag{3.2.18}$$

If α is a half integer $(n - \frac{1}{2})$ $(n \geq 1)$, then clearly

$$\begin{aligned} K(z, z^*; n - \tfrac{1}{2}) &= G_1(z, z^*; n) + G_0(z, z^*; n) \\ &= \int_{-1}^{+1} \tilde{E}(z, z^*, t)(1-t^2)^{n-\frac{1}{2}}\, dt. \end{aligned}$$

The development (3.1.12) for $\tilde{E}(z, z^*, t)$ implies, also certain conditions on $K(z, z^*; \alpha)$ in addition to the differential equation (3.2.18). Since $\tilde{E}(z, 0, t) = \tilde{E}(0, z^*, t) = 1$, we have that

$$\begin{aligned} K(z, 0; \alpha) = K(0, z^*; \alpha) &= \int_{-1}^{+1} (1-t^2)^{\alpha}\, dt \\ &= \frac{\pi\Gamma(2\alpha+2)}{2^{2\alpha+1}\Gamma(\alpha+\frac{3}{2})^2}. \end{aligned} \tag{3.2.19}$$

Hence $K(z, z^*; \alpha)$ satisfies a rather simple Goursat problem which depends on the parameter α. Indeed if one introduces the function $J(z, z^*; \alpha) = K(z, z^*; \alpha)e^{2z(\alpha+1)}$, $J(z, z^*; \alpha - \frac{1}{2})$ satisfies the original (normalized) differential equation (3.1.3) with the altered Goursat conditions:

$$\begin{aligned} J(z, 0; \alpha - \tfrac{1}{2}) &= \frac{\pi\Gamma(2\alpha+1)}{2^{2\alpha}\Gamma(\alpha+1)^2}\, e^{z(2\alpha+1)}, \\ J(0, z^*; \alpha - \tfrac{1}{2}) &= \frac{\pi\Gamma(2\alpha+1)}{2^{2\alpha}\Gamma(\alpha+1)^2}. \end{aligned} \tag{3.2.20}$$

We summarize the above discussion by the following theorem.

Theorem 3.2.1 *For each fixed* $(z, z^*) \in \mathfrak{S}^{(2)}$ *let* $J(z, z^*; \alpha - \frac{1}{2})$ *be a solution to Eq.* (3.1.3) *which satisfies the Goursat conditions* (3.2.20). *Furthermore,* *let $J(z, z^*; \alpha - \frac{1}{2})$ be a Laplace transform defined in the half plane* $\operatorname{Re} \alpha \geq 0$. *Then Bergman's generating function may be obtained in the form*

$$\tilde{E}(z, z^*; t) = \frac{e^{-z}}{2\pi i} \frac{t}{(1 - t^2)^{1/2}} \int_{c-i\infty}^{c+i\infty} ([1 - t^2]e^{2z})^{-\alpha} J(z, z^*; \alpha - \tfrac{1}{2})\, d\alpha, \tag{3.2.21}$$

where $c > 0$.

As a special case of the above equation we consider the differential equation

$$\frac{\partial^2 u}{\partial x^2} + \frac{\partial^2 u}{\partial y^2} + C(r^2)u = 0, \tag{3.2.22}$$

where $C(r^2)$ is analytic in r^2. Introducing the z, and z^* variables as before we rewrite this as

$$\frac{\partial^2 U}{\partial z\, \partial z^*} + \tfrac{1}{4}C(zz^*)U = 0.$$

Our equation for $E(z, z^*, t) \equiv E(r, t)$ becomes

$$E_{z^*t}(1 - t^2) - t^{-1}E_{z^*} + 2tz(E_{zz^*} + \tfrac{1}{4}CE) = 0.$$

Since

$$\frac{\partial E}{\partial z^*} = \frac{\partial r}{\partial z^*} \frac{\partial E}{\partial r} = \tfrac{1}{2}e^{i\theta} \frac{\partial E}{\partial r}, \qquad \text{and} \qquad \frac{\partial E}{\partial z} = \tfrac{1}{2}e^{-i\theta} \frac{\partial E}{\partial r},$$

when $z = re^{i\theta}$, we obtain

$$\tfrac{1}{2}e^{i\theta}E_{rt}(1 - t^2) - \tfrac{1}{2}t^{-1}e^{i\theta}E_r + 2tre^{i\theta}\left(\tfrac{1}{4}E_{rr} + \tfrac{1}{4}(zz^*)^{-\frac{1}{2}}E_r + \frac{C}{4}E\right) = 0,$$

or

$$(1 - t^2)E_{rt} - t^{-1}(t^2 + 1)E_r + tr\left(E_{rr} + \frac{2}{r}E_r + CE\right) = 0. \tag{3.2.23}$$

By setting, as before,

$$R(r, \alpha) = \int_{-1}^{+1} E(r, t)(1 - t^2)^{\alpha}\, dt,$$

one obtains an equation for $R(r, \alpha)$, namely

$$\frac{d^2R}{dr^2} + \frac{2(\alpha+1)}{r}\frac{dR}{dr} + C(r^2)R = 0, \tag{3.2.24}$$

along with the initial conditions

$$R(0, \alpha) = \frac{\pi\Gamma(2\alpha+2)}{2^{2\alpha+1}\Gamma(\alpha+\frac{3}{2})^2}, \qquad R'(0, \alpha) = 0. \tag{3.2.25}$$

As an illustration let us consider the special case where $C(r^2) \equiv k^2$. Then a solution to (3.2.24)–(3.2.25) is seen to be

$$R(r, \alpha) = \sqrt{\pi}(2/kr)^{\alpha+\frac{1}{2}}\Gamma(\alpha+1)J_{\alpha+\frac{1}{2}}(kr)$$

where $J_{\alpha+\frac{1}{2}}(z)$ is a Bessel function of the first kind. Now if $E(r, t) = E(r, -t)$ we have that

$$R(r, \alpha) = 2\int_0^1 E(r, t)(1-t^2)^\alpha\, dt = \int_0^\infty \left\{\frac{E(r, (1-e^{-u})^{1/2})}{(e^u-1)^{1/2}}\, e^{-u/2}\right\} e^{-\alpha u}\, du;$$

hence,

$$R(r, \alpha - \tfrac{1}{2}) = \mathscr{L}_u\left\{\frac{E(r, (1-e^{-u})^{1/2})}{(e^u-1)^{1/2}}\right\},$$

where $\mathscr{L}_u\{\ \}$ is to mean the Laplace transform with respect to u.

One has from [E.5, Vol. I, p. 274] that

$$\mathscr{L}_\alpha^{-1}\left\{\left(\frac{2}{kr}\right)^\alpha \sqrt{\pi}\Gamma(\alpha+\tfrac{1}{2})J_\alpha(kr)\right\} = (e^u-1)^{-1/2}\cos[kr(1-e^{-u})^{1/2}]$$

$$= \frac{E(r, (1-e^{-u})^{1/2})}{(e^u-1)^{1/2}},$$

from which we have $E(r, t) = \cos krt$. (Compare with Bergman [B.22, p. 28] where this is obtained by successive approximations.)

Bergman [B.11,12,14,22,28,29] (also see Stark [S.5]) investigates the following special case of partial differential equations of mixed type:

$$\mathbf{M}[U] \equiv U_{xx} + l(x)U_{yy} = 0, \qquad l(x) = \sum_{n=1}^\infty a_n(-x)^n \qquad (a_1 > 0),$$

where $l(x) > 0$ for $x < 0$, and $l(x) < 0$ for $x > 0$. These equations have been investigated in connection with the theory of compressible flows; see the above references, and also [B.9,10,28], [B.G.1], [B.E.1], [B.B.1], [D.R.1], [V.M.1], [V.M.S.1] and Bers [B.30,31,35].

Bergman reduces this equation to the form $U_{\lambda\lambda} + U_{yy} + 4N(\lambda)U_\lambda = 0$, $N = \frac{1}{8}l^{-3/2}l_x$, by the change of variables $\lambda(x) = \int_0^x l(t)^{1/2}\,dt$. Another change of (dependent) variables by setting $U^* = U/H$, $H = \exp(-\int_{-\infty}^{\lambda} N(t)\,dt)$, yields the new equation

$$U^*_{\lambda\lambda} + U^*_{yy} + 4FU^* = 0,$$

where F has the following development about $\lambda = 0$,

$$F = s^{-3}(a_0 + a_1 s + a_2 s^2 + \cdots), \qquad s = (-\lambda)^{2/3},$$

with $a_0 = 5/144$ ($a_1 = 0$). Bergman has developed an integral operator approach to this equation in a series of papers. For further details see [B.22, pp. 106–131], and a number of the above cited references.

3. *Fundamental Solutions, Initial Value, and Boundary Value Problems*

From (3.1.12) we note that $\tilde{E}(z, 0, t) = 1$ and $\tilde{E}(0, z^*, t) = 1$, and hence from (3.1.8) we have

$$E(z, 0, t) = e^{-n(z)} \qquad \text{and} \qquad E(0, z^*, t) = \exp\left\{-\int_0^{z^*} A(0, \zeta^*)\,d\zeta^*\right\}.$$

Using this in the representation (3.1.9) yields certain "initial conditions" that the solution $U(z, z^*)$ must satisfy, namely,

$$U(z, 0) = e^{-n(z)} \int_{-1}^{+1} f\left(\frac{z}{2}[1 - t^2]\right) \frac{dt}{(1 - t^2)^{1/2}} = e^{-n(z)} g(z), \qquad (3.3.1)$$

and

$$U(0, z^*) = \exp\left\{-\int_0^{z^*} A(0, \zeta^*)\,d\zeta^*\right\} g(0). \qquad (3.3.2)$$

Since the differential equation (3.1.1) is formally "hyperbolic," the functions $e^{-n(z)}g(z)$ and $\exp\{-\int_0^{z^*} A(0, \zeta^*)\,d\zeta^*\}g(0)$ may be considered as the initial value of $U(z, z^*)$ at $z^* = 0$ and $z = 0$, respectively. The two conditions, (3.3.1), (3.3.2) are sufficient to uniquely determine a solution to (3.1.1), however, which may be shown by the method of successive approximations. We consider first, for purposes of demonstration, a special case of (3.1.1), namely the equation,

$$V_{zz^*} + Q(z, z^*)V = 0, \tag{3.3.3}$$

where $Q(z, z^*)$ is holomorphic in $\mathfrak{S} \times \mathfrak{S}^*$.

Equation (3.3.3) may be replaced by the integral equation,

$$V(z, z^*) = g(z) + \int_0^z d\zeta \int_0^{z^*} d\zeta^* \, Q(\zeta, \zeta^*)V(\zeta, \zeta^*), \tag{3.3.4}$$

from which one obtains by successive approximations (i.e., the Riemann–Picard method) the solution

$$V(z, z^*) = g(z) + \int_0^z d\zeta_1 \int_0^{z^*} d\zeta_1^* \, Q(\zeta_1, \zeta_1^*)g(\zeta_1)$$
$$+ \int_0^z d\zeta_1 \int_0^{z^*} d\zeta_1^* \, Q(\zeta_1, \zeta_1^*) \int_0^{\zeta_1} d\zeta_2 \int_0^{\zeta_1^*} d\zeta_2^* \, Q(\zeta_2, \zeta_2^*)g(\zeta_2) + \cdots. \tag{3.3.5}$$

Since for special case (3.3.3) one has $A(z, z^*) \equiv 0$, and $F(z, z^*) \equiv Q(z, z^*)$, the conditions $V(z, 0) = g(z)$ and $V(0, z^*) = g(0)$ are exactly the conditions (3.3.1) and (3.3.2). Hence, the solution (3.3.5) as obtained by the successive approximations method is the same solution as (3.1.9), where $E(z, z^*, t)$ was determined by the system (3.1.13). One may interpret the series representation (3.3.5) as a linear operator which maps the class of functions $\{g(z)\}$ analytic in $\mathfrak{S}$, onto solutions $V(z, z^*)$ which are holomorphic in $\mathfrak{S} \times \mathfrak{S}^*$.

The Riemann–Picard method used above may also be used to obtain a series representation for fundamental singular solutions defined in the bicylinder $\mathfrak{S} \times \mathfrak{S}^*$ [B.S.1, pp. 292–294]. (See also [G.4], Chap. 5, Sect. 1, and Chap. 16.) To this end we seek a solution of the form

$$S(z, z^*; \zeta, \zeta^*) = \tfrac{1}{2}R(\zeta, \zeta^*; z, z^*)\{\log(z - \zeta) + \log(z^* - \zeta^*)\}$$
$$+ H(z, z^*; \zeta, \zeta^*). \tag{3.3.6}$$

The purpose of reversing the order of z, ζ variables as shown in $R(\zeta, \zeta^*; z, z^*)$ will become apparent in Section 5 of this chapter when we discuss the complex Riemann function. By substituting this directly into (3.3.3) we obtain

$$\tfrac{1}{2}\{\log(z-\zeta)+\log(z^*-\zeta^*)\}\{R_{zz^*}+Q(z,z^*)R\}$$

$$+\frac{1}{2}\frac{R_{z^*}}{z-\zeta}+\frac{1}{2}\frac{R_z}{z^*-\zeta^*}+H_{zz^*}+Q(z,z^*)H=0. \tag{3.3.7}$$

If we first choose $R(\zeta, \zeta^*; z, z^*)$ to satisfy the partial differential equation $R_{zz^*}+QR=0$, then $H(z, z^*; \zeta, \zeta^*)$ must satisfy $H_{zz^*}+QH=M$, where

$$M(z, z^*; \zeta, \zeta^*) \equiv \frac{1}{2}\left\{\frac{R_{z^*}}{z-\zeta}+\frac{R_z}{z^*-\zeta^*}\right\}. \tag{3.3.8}$$

Using the Riemann–Picard method we may formally obtain a particular solution to the equation for $R(z, z^*; \zeta, \zeta^*)$. Such a solution, which satisfies also the conditions $R(\zeta, \zeta^*; \zeta, z^*)=1$, $R(\zeta, \zeta^*; z, \zeta^*)=1$, $R(\zeta, \zeta^*; \zeta, \zeta^*)=1$, is given by

$$\begin{aligned} R(\zeta, \zeta^*; z, z^*) = 1 &- \int_\zeta^z dt_1 \int_{\zeta^*}^{z^*} dt_1{}^*\, Q(t_1, t_1{}^*) \\ &+ \int_\zeta^z dt_1 \int_{\zeta^*}^{z^*} dt_1{}^*\, Q(t_1, t_1{}^*) \\ &\times \int_\zeta^{t_1} dt_2 \int_{\zeta^*}^{t_1^*} dt_2{}^*\, Q(t_2, t_2{}^*) - \cdots; \end{aligned} \tag{3.3.9}$$

this solution is the analog for the case of the classical Riemann function which occurs in the theory of real hyperbolic equations. (We note, however, that for our particular equation (3.3.3), which is self-adjoint, $R(z, z^*; \zeta, \zeta^*) = R(\zeta, \zeta^*; z, z^*)$.) A solution to the equation for $H(z, z^*; \zeta, \zeta^*)$ can then be found in the form, $[M(t_1, t_2) \equiv M(t_1, t_2; \zeta_1, \zeta_2)]$,

$$\begin{aligned} H(z, z^*; \zeta, \zeta^*) = &\int_\zeta^z dt_1 \int_{\zeta^*}^{z^*} dt_1{}^*\, M(t_1, t_1{}^*) \\ &- \int_\zeta^z dt_1 \int_{\zeta^*}^{z^*} dt_1{}^*\, Q(t_1, t_1{}^*) \int_\zeta^{t_1} dt_2 \int_{\zeta^*}^{t_1^*} dt_2{}^*\, M(t_2, t_2{}^*) \\ &+ \int_\zeta^z dt_1 \int_{\zeta^*}^{z^*} dt_1{}^*\, Q(t_1, t_1{}^*) \int_\zeta^{t_1} dt_2 \int_{\zeta^*}^{t_1^*} dt_2{}^*\, Q(t_2, t_2{}^*) \\ &\times \int_\zeta^{t_2} dt_3 \int_{\zeta^*}^{t_2^*} dt_3{}^*\, M(t_3, t_3{}^*) - \cdots. \end{aligned} \tag{3.3.10}$$

We must still show that the only singularity of $S(z, z^*; \zeta, \zeta^*)$ in $\mathfrak{S} \times \mathfrak{S}^*$ is the logarithmic singularity at $z = \zeta$, and $z^* = \zeta^*$. Clearly if $Q(z, z^*)$ is holomorphic in $\mathfrak{S} \times \mathfrak{S}^*$, then by the method of majorants we may show $R(\zeta, \zeta^*; z, z^*)$ as represented by the series (3.3.9) converges uniformly, in any compact bidisk $\{|z - \zeta| \leq a\} \times \{|z^* - \zeta^*| \leq a\} \subset \mathfrak{S} \times \mathfrak{S}^*$, to a holomorphic function. By analytic continuation we can extend its domain of definition to $\mathfrak{S} \times \mathfrak{S}^*$. (See also in this regard Sect. 4 of this chapter.) If we are able to show that the function $M(z, z^*; \zeta, \zeta^*)$ is also holomorphic in a bidisk $\{|z - \zeta| \leq a\} \times \{|z^* - \zeta^*| \leq a\} \subset \mathfrak{S} \times \mathfrak{S}^*$, then by the same argument used above we may show that $H(z, z^*; \zeta, \zeta^*)$ is holomorphic in $\mathfrak{S} \times \mathfrak{S}^*$. To this end we compute

$$\frac{\partial R}{\partial z} = -\int_{\zeta^*}^{z^*} dt_1^* \, Q(z, t_1^*)$$

$$+ \int_{\zeta^*}^{z^*} dt_1^* \, Q(z, t_1^*) \int_{\zeta}^{t_1} dt_2 \int_{\zeta^*}^{t_1^*} dt_2^* \, Q(t_2, t_2^*) - \cdots.$$

Now, since $Q(z, z^*)$ is holomorphic in $\mathfrak{S} \times \mathfrak{S}^*$ it can be developed as a power series about any point interior to $\mathfrak{S} \times \mathfrak{S}^*$, say (ζ, ζ^*); hence, we obtain

$$Q(z, z^*) = \sum_{m=0}^{\infty} \sum_{n=0}^{\infty} a_{mn}(z - \zeta)^m (z^* - \zeta^*)^n,$$

and

$$\int_{\zeta^*}^{z^*} dt_1^* \, Q(z, t_1^*) = \sum_{m=0}^{\infty} \sum_{n=0}^{\infty} \frac{a_{mn}}{n+1} (z - \zeta)^m (z^* - \zeta^*)^{n+1}.$$

Clearly, it is then seen that $1/(z^* - \zeta^*) \, \partial R/\partial z$ is regular in $\{|z - \zeta| \leq a\} \times \{|z^* - \zeta^*| \leq a\}$; likewise, we may show $1/(z - \zeta) \, \partial R/\partial z^*$ is regular in this same bidisk. Our representation (3.3.10) for $H(z, z^*; \zeta, \zeta^*)$ may then be verified by the method of majorants.

We consider next the general, normalized equation,

$$\mathbf{L}[V] \equiv V_{zz^*} + D(z, z^*)V_{z^*} + F(z, z^*)V = 0,$$

and seek a solution $V(z, z^*)$ which satisfies as before the initial conditions, $V(z, 0) = g(z)$, $V(0, z^*) = g(0)$. Clearly, we may then replace $\mathbf{L}[V] = 0$ by the integral equation

$$V(z, z^*) = g(z) - \int_0^z d\zeta \int_0^{z^*} d\zeta^* \, D(\zeta, \zeta^*) \frac{\partial V}{\partial \zeta^*}(\zeta, \zeta^*)$$

$$- \int_0^z d\zeta \int_0^{z^*} d\zeta^* \, F(\zeta, \zeta^*) V(\zeta, \zeta^*). \tag{3.3.11}$$

A solution to (3.3.11) may be obtained by the Riemann–Picard method in the form [B.22, pp. 17–18]

$$V(z, z^*) = g(z) + \sum_{\mu=1}^{\infty} (-1)^\mu \mathbf{J}_\mu(g), \tag{3.3.12}$$

where the symbol $\mathbf{J}_\mu(g)$ is defined as follows: the $\mathbf{J}_\mu(g)$ are the sums of the $2^{\mu-1}$ expressions $\mathbf{T}(F_\mu, D_{\mu-1}, \ldots, F_1; g)$, where

$$\mathbf{T}(F_\mu, D_{\mu-1}, \ldots, F_1; g)$$

$$\equiv \int_0^z dz_\mu \int_0^{z^*} dz^*_{\mu-j} F_\mu \int_0^{z_\mu} dz_{\mu-1} \int_0^{z^*_{\mu-j}} dz^*_{\mu-j-1} \, D_{\mu-1}$$

$$\times \int_0^{z_{\mu-1}} dz_{\mu-2} \, D_{\mu-2} \cdots \int_0^{z_3} dz_2 \int_0^{z_3^*} dz_2^* \, F_2 \int_0^{z_2} dz_1 \int_0^{z_2^*} dz_1^* \, F_1 g, \tag{3.3.13}$$

and

$$F_\nu \equiv F(z_\nu, z^*_{\nu+p}), \qquad D_{\nu-1} \equiv D(z_{\nu-1}, z^*_{\nu+p-1}), \tag{3.3.14}$$

where reading from *left to right* in (3.3.13) we have *after* each term F_ν a double integration, and *after* each term D_ν, a single integration. The integer j is the number of terms D_ν appearing in $\mathbf{T}(F_\mu, D_{\mu-1}, \ldots, F_1; g)$, and p is the number of D_ν terms to the *right* of the integration over the z_ν-variable. Finally, in forming the sum $\mathbf{J}_\mu(g)$, all combinations of F_ν and D_p terms are considered as entries in the $\mathbf{T}$-terms composing this sum, with the exception that a D_1-term never appears in the last place.

Bergman shows by a majorization argument that the representation (3.3.12) converges and indeed is holomorphic in a bicylinder $\{|z| \le a\} \times \{|z^*| \le a\} \subset \mathfrak{S} \times \mathfrak{S}^*$. The reader is directed to [B.22, pp. 17–19] for further details.

We now attempt to obtain a fundamental, singular solution, $S = \frac{1}{2}R \times \{\log(z - \zeta) + \log(z^* - \zeta^*)\} + H$, for the general equation $\mathbf{L}[V] = 0$. As before, upon substituting $S(z, z^*; \zeta, \zeta^*)$ into our differential equation, we obtain

$$\tfrac{1}{2}\{\log(z-\zeta)+\log(z^*-\zeta^*)\}\{R_{zz^*}+D(z,z^*)R_{z^*}+F(z,z^*)R\}$$
$$+\frac{1}{2}\left\{\frac{R_{z^*}}{z-\zeta}+\frac{R_z}{z^*-\zeta^*}+\frac{D(z,z^*)R}{z^*-\zeta^*}\right\}$$
$$+H_{zz^*}+D(z,z^*)H_{z^*}+F(z,z^*)H=0. \tag{3.3.15}$$

If we choose $R(\zeta,\zeta^*;z,z^*)$ such that $\mathbf{L}_{(z)}[R]=0$, and such that the initial conditions, $R(\zeta,\zeta^*;\zeta,z^*)=1$, $R(\zeta,\zeta^*;z,\zeta^*)=\exp\{-\int_\zeta^z D(t,\zeta^*)\,dt\}$ and $R(\zeta,\zeta^*;\zeta,\zeta^*)=1$ hold (which is automatically satisfied if the previous two conditions are) then we obtain as our solution the series

$$R(\zeta,\zeta^*;z,z^*)=\exp\left\{-\int_\zeta^z D(t,\zeta^*)\,dt\right\}$$
$$+\sum_{\mu=1}^{\infty}(-1)^\mu \mathbf{J}_\mu\left(\exp\left\{-\int_\zeta^z D(t,\zeta^*)\,dt\right\}\right), \tag{3.3.16}$$

where here the expressions $\mathbf{T}(F_\mu, D_{\mu-1},\ldots,F_1;\exp\{-\int_\zeta^z D(t,\zeta^*)\,dt\})$ are taken as

$$\mathbf{T}\left(F_\mu, D_{\mu-1},\ldots,F_1;\exp\left\{-\int_\zeta^z D(t,\zeta^*)\,dt\right\}\right)$$
$$\equiv\int_\zeta^z dz_\mu\int_{\zeta^*}^{z^*} dz^*_{\mu-j}\,F_\mu\int_\zeta^{z_\mu} dz_{\mu-1}\int_{\zeta^*}^{z^*_{\mu-j}} dz^*_{\mu-j-1}\,D_{\mu-1}\int_\zeta^{z_{\mu-1}} dz_{\mu-2}\,D_{\mu-2}$$
$$\cdots\int_\zeta^{z_3} dz_2\int_{\zeta^*}^{z_3^*} dz_2^*\,F_2\int_\zeta^{z_2} dz_1\int_{\zeta^*}^{z_2^*} dz_1^*\,F_1\exp\left\{-\int_\zeta^{z_1} D(t,\zeta^*)\,dt\right\}. \tag{3.3.17}$$

As before, we choose $H(z,z^*)\equiv H(z,z^*;\zeta,\zeta^*)$ to be a solution of

$$H_{zz^*}+D(z,z^*)H_{z^*}+F(z,z^*)H=L, \tag{3.3.18}$$

where†

$$L(z,z^*;\zeta,\zeta^*)\equiv\frac{1}{2}\left\{\frac{R_{z^*}}{z-\zeta}+\frac{R_z}{z^*-\zeta^*}+\frac{D(z,z^*)R}{z^*-\zeta^*}\right\};$$

† Here we choose $z^*=\zeta^*$ instead of the origin as our initial point, and define

$$D(z,z^*)=n'(z;\zeta^*)-\int_{\zeta^*}^{z^*} A_z(z,t^*)\,dt^*+B(z,z^*).$$

If $n'(z,\zeta^*)=B(z,\zeta^*)$, then $D(z,z^*)=(z^*-\zeta^*)D_1(z,z^*)$, where $D_1(z,z^*)$ is regular at (ζ,ζ^*).

then $H(z, z^*; \zeta, \zeta^*)$ is seen to satisfy the integral equation

$$H(z, z^*) = H(z, \zeta^*) - \int_\zeta^z dt \int_{\zeta^*}^{z^*} dt^* \, D(t, t^*) \frac{\partial H(t, t^*)}{\partial t^*} - \int_\zeta^z dt \int_{\zeta^*}^{z^*} dt^* \, F(t, t^*) H(t, t^*) + \int_\zeta^z dt \int_{\zeta^*}^{z^*} dt^* \, L(t, t^*; \zeta, \zeta^*), \tag{3.3.19}$$

where $H(z, \zeta^*)$ is the initial value of $H(z, z^*)$ on $z^* = \zeta^*$. In this case we may obtain a solution by the Riemann–Picard method having the representation

$$H(z, z^*) = H(z, \zeta^*) + \sum_{\mu=1}^{\infty} (-1)^\mu \mathbf{J}_\mu(H(z, \zeta^*)) + \sum_{\mu=1}^{\infty} (-1)^\mu \mathbf{J}_\mu^* \left(\int_\zeta^z dt \int_{\zeta^*}^{z^*} dt^* \, L(t, t^*; \zeta, \zeta^*) \right); \tag{3.3.20}$$

here the terms $\mathbf{J}_\mu(H)$ are defined as sums of the $\mathbf{T}(F_\mu, D_{\mu-1}, \ldots, F_1; H)$ as given in (3.3.17). The terms $\mathbf{J}_\mu^*(\int_\zeta^z dt \int_{\zeta^*}^{z^*} dt^* \, L)$ are different, however, in that for these terms we *may allow* a D_1 to appear in the last place of $\mathbf{T}$, i.e., $\mathbf{T}(F_\mu, D_{\mu-1}, \ldots, D_1; \int_\zeta^z dt \int_{\zeta^*}^{z^*} dt^* \, L)$. If we take $H(z, \zeta^*) = 0$, then a particular solution of (3.3.18) is

$$H(z, z^*; \zeta, \zeta^*) = \sum_{\mu=1}^{\infty} (-1)^\mu \mathbf{J}_\mu^* \left(\int_\zeta^z dt \int_{\zeta^*}^{z^*} dt^* \, L(t, t^*; \zeta, \zeta^*) \right). \tag{3.3.21}$$

The use of the fundamental singular solutions to represent solutions of the elliptic, partial differential equations (3.0.1) in terms of one value of the solution and the normal derivative on the boundary are well known. For instance, if $S(z, z^*; \zeta, \zeta^*)$ is such a fundamental solution, and $\mathfrak{S}$ is a simply-connected, fundamental domain for (3.0.1), i.e., for (3.1.1), then we may represent a solution $U(z, \bar{z}) = u(x, y)$, ($z^* = \bar{z}$, when x and y are real), in the form

$$U(z, \bar{z}) = \frac{1}{2\pi} \int_{\partial\mathfrak{S}} \left[U(\zeta, \bar{\zeta}) \frac{\partial S(z, \bar{z}; \zeta, \bar{\zeta})}{\partial \eta_\zeta} - \frac{\partial U(\zeta, \bar{\zeta})}{\partial \eta_\zeta} S(z, \bar{z}; \zeta, \bar{\zeta}) \right] ds_\zeta, \tag{3.3.22}$$

where η_ζ is an interior normal, and ds_ζ is a differential arc length along the boundary $\partial\mathfrak{S}$ of $\mathfrak{S}$. We remark at this point that the representation (3.3.22) actually provides an analytic continuation of $U(z, \bar{z})$ where $(z, \bar{z}) \in \mathfrak{S}$ to $U(z, z^*)$ with $(z, z^*) \in \mathfrak{S} \times \mathfrak{S}^*$, by simply replacing the $\bar{z}$ in (3.3.22) by z^*.

This may be done, since as we have seen, the only singularities of $S(z, z^*; \zeta, \bar{\zeta})$ are the logarithmic singularities on the analytic planes $z = \zeta$, and $z^* = \bar{\zeta}$.

As we have remarked earlier, the function $R(\zeta, \zeta^*; z, z^*)$, which we introduced as the coefficient of the logarithmic singularity, is the complex Riemann function. In the next section, when we discuss Vekua's function theoretic approach to Eq. (3.0.1), we shall develop many of the properties of this function which are analogous to those of the real Riemann function. Indeed, among other things that we will show, will be a representation for the solution of the complex Goursat problem in terms of $R(\zeta, \zeta^*; z, z^*)$. Actually, some of this information is already at hand; if we will accept the fact that the representation (3.3.16) is convergent in our fundamental domain $\mathfrak{S}$. The proof of this for bidisks, $\{|z| \leq a\} \times \{|z^*| \leq a\} \subset \mathfrak{S} \times \mathfrak{S}^*$, follows immediately from Bergman's proof of the convergence of (3.3.16) by majorants [B.22, pp. 17–19]. In the next section we obtain a representation for $R(\zeta, \zeta^*; z, z^*)$, which shows that it is a holomorphic function of the four complex variables $(\zeta, \zeta^*; z, z^*) \in \mathfrak{S} \times \mathfrak{S}^* \times \mathfrak{S} \times \mathfrak{S}^*$. For the purposes of exposition we ask the reader to accept this fact, and proceed to discuss the complex Goursat problem for the differential equation

$$\mathbf{L}[V] \equiv V_{zz^*} + D(z, z^*)V_{z^*} + F(z, z^*)V = 0.$$

Goursat data for $\mathbf{L}[V] = 0$, consists of prescribing in a fundamental bicylinder, $\mathfrak{S} \times \mathfrak{S}^*$, initial data of the form $V(z, \zeta^*) = \varphi(z)$, $V(\zeta, z^*) = \varphi^*(z^*)$, where $(\zeta, \zeta^*) \in \mathfrak{S} \times \mathfrak{S}^*$ is an arbitrary but fixed point; consistency requires that $\varphi(\zeta) = \varphi^*(\zeta^*)$. Since it does not affect the generality of our approach, we furthermore take the point $(\zeta, \zeta^*) = (0, 0)$. Then a solution to $\mathbf{L}[V] = 0$, which is holomorphic in $\mathfrak{S} \times \mathfrak{S}^*$ and satisfies the above Goursat data is given by [see Eqs. (3.4.26)–(3.4.28)]

$$V(z, z^*) = \Phi(0)R(0, 0; z, z^*) + \int_0^z \Phi'(t)R(t, 0; z, z^*)\, dt$$
$$+ \int_0^{z^*} \Phi^{*\prime}(t^*)R(0, t^*; z, z^*)\, dt^*, \tag{3.3.23}$$

where

$$\Phi(z) = \varphi(z) + \int_0^z D(t, 0)\varphi(t)\, dt \qquad \text{and} \qquad \Phi^*(z^*) = \varphi^*(z^*).$$

If we now seek a solution $V(z, z^*)$ satisfying, as before, the special Goursat data $V(z, 0) = g(z)$, $V(0, z^*) = g(0)$, then our representation (3.3.23) simplifies to the form

$$V(z, z^*) = g(0)R(0, 0; z, z^*) + \int_0^z \{g'(t) + g(t)D(t, 0)\}R(t, 0; z, z^*)\, dt. \qquad (3.3.24)$$

The expression (3.3.24) is then the same solution to the differential equation $\mathbf{L}[V] = 0$, as Bergman has obtained using his E-function. We obtain then still another expression for Bergman's operator of the first kind, $\mathbf{C}_2 g = \operatorname{Re} \mathbf{c}_2 g$,

$$\mathbf{c}_2 g = \exp\left\{-\int_0^z A(z, \zeta^*)\, d\zeta^*\right\}\left[g(0)R(0, 0; z, z^*) + \int_0^z D(t, 0)g(t)R(t, 0; z, z^*)\, dt + \int_0^z g'(t)R(t, 0; z, z^*)\, dt\right] \quad (3.3.25)$$

with

$$g(z) = \int_{-1}^{+1} f\left(\frac{z}{2}[1 - t^2]\right) \frac{dt}{(1 - t^2)^{1/2}}.$$

Combining this result with the expression (3.2.8) one obtains the following identity concerning the functions $Q^{(n)}(z, z^*)$,

$$\sum_{n=1}^{\infty} \frac{Q^{(n)}(z, z^*)(z - \zeta)^{n-1}}{2^{2n}B(n, n+1)} = D(\zeta, 0)R(\zeta, 0; z, z^*) - \frac{\partial R}{\partial \zeta}(\zeta, 0; z, z^*).$$

It has been shown by Bergman that the operator $\mathbf{C}_2 g$ is a continuous linear operator, and that it generates a complete set of solutions to the differential equation (3.0.1) in the following sense: every real solution $U(z, z^*) = u(x, y)$ which is regular in the open disk $\{x^2 + y^2 > \rho\}$ may be represented there in the form $u(x, y) = \operatorname{Re}[\sum_{\nu=0}^{\infty} a_\nu \varphi_\nu(x, y)]$, where $\varphi_\nu(x, y) \equiv \mathbf{c}_2[z^\nu]$ [B.22, pp. 22–24]. Because of this we consider the problem of determining functions $g(z)$, which give rise to solutions with prescribed properties.

Bergman has shown how the integral operator method may be combined with his kernel function approach to provide feasible methods for the numerical solution of boundary value problems for elliptic partial differential equations: see in particular, [B.19,23,28,29], [B.G.1], [B.H.1]. Recently, Deeter and Springer [D.S.1] also have shown how one may use a discreet analog of Bergman's kernel function for the numerical solution of these boundary value problems.

In a series of papers Diaz and Ludford [D.L.1–5] noticed that Bergman's operator $\mathbf{B}_2$ could be written in another form. Their ideas went back to the work of LeRoux who had considered *real* hyperbolic equations of the form (3.1.1). In the case where $\mathfrak{S}$ is a fundamental domain for $\mathbf{E}[U]=0$, the method of Diaz and Ludford has an obvious modification; hence we shall present their ideas here for this case.

It is easily verified that if $W(z, z^*; \alpha)$ is an arbitrary solution of $\mathbf{E}[U]=0$, which depends on a complex parameter α, for all α contained on a smooth curve $\mathscr{L}$, and $f(\alpha) \in \mathscr{C}^{(0)}[\mathscr{L}]$,

$$U(z, z^*) = \int_{\mathscr{L}} f(\alpha) W(z, z^*; \alpha)\, d\alpha \tag{3.3.26}$$

is also a solution of this differential equation. LeRoux's result (restated in complex form) is that if $(z, z^*) \in \mathfrak{S}^{(2)} \equiv \mathfrak{S} \times \mathfrak{S}^*$, and $W(z, z^*; \alpha)$ is a solution of $\mathbf{E}[U]=0$, that is, chosen to satisfy the "characteristic condition"

$$\frac{\partial W(\alpha, z^*; \alpha)}{\partial z^*} + A(\alpha, z^*) W(\alpha, z^*; \alpha) = 0 \qquad (\text{at } z = \alpha), \tag{3.3.27}$$

then the function

$$U_1(z, z^*) = \int_{\substack{z_0 \\ \mathscr{L}_1}}^{z} f(\alpha) W(z, z^*; \alpha)\, d\alpha, \tag{3.3.28}$$

where $\mathscr{L}_1$ is a rectifiable curve in the α-plane from $\alpha = z_0$ to $\alpha = z$, is also a solution of the above differential equation. Likewise, if $W(z, z^*; \alpha^*)$ is chosen to satisfy (on $z^* = \alpha^*$)

$$\frac{\partial W(z, \alpha^*; \alpha^*)}{\partial z} + B(z, \alpha^*) W(z, \alpha^*; \alpha^*) = 0, \tag{3.3.29}$$

then

$$U_2(z, z^*) = \int_{\substack{z_0^* \\ \mathscr{L}_2}}^{z^*} f(\alpha^*) W(z, z^*; \alpha^*)\, d\alpha^* \tag{3.3.30}$$

(where $\mathscr{L}_2 \subset \mathscr{L}$ terminates at $\alpha^* = z^*$) is again a solution. Diaz and Ludford remark, furthermore, that since both of these characteristic conditions are satisfied by the Riemann function [i.e., $R(\alpha, \zeta^*; z, z^*)$ satisfies (3.3.26) on the analytic plane $z = \alpha$, whereas $R(\zeta, \alpha^*; z, z^*)$ satisfies (3.3.28) on the analytic plane $z^* = \alpha^*$] for arbitrary $f(\alpha)$, the following indefinite integrals represent solutions of $\mathbf{E}[U]=0$:

$$U_1(z, z^*) \equiv \int_{\substack{\beta_0 \\ \gamma_1}}^{z} f(\beta) R(\beta, \zeta^*; z, z^*) \, d\beta$$

(where $\gamma_1 \subset \mathfrak{S}$ is a rectifiable curve from $\beta = \beta_0$ to $\beta = z$),

$$U_2(z, z^*) \equiv \int_{\substack{\beta_0^* \\ \gamma_2}}^{z^*} f(\beta) R(\zeta, \beta; z, z^*) \, d\beta$$

(where $\gamma_2 \subset \mathfrak{S}$ is a rectifiable curve from $\beta = \beta_0$ to $\beta = z^*$), and

$$U_3(z, z^*) \equiv \int_{\substack{z \\ \gamma_3}}^{z^*} f(\beta) R(\beta, \beta; z, z^*) \, d\beta$$

(where $\gamma_3 \subset \mathfrak{S} \cap \mathfrak{S}^*$ is a rectifiable curve from z to z^*).

The main result of Diaz and Ludford [D.L.1] is that they show it is possible to represent Bergman's generating function $E(z, z^*, t)$ in terms of a solution $W(z, z^*; \alpha)$ of (3.1.1) which depends on the parameter α, and satisfies the characteristic condition (3.3.27). In particular, if the function $U(z, z^*; \alpha)$ is defined by

$$U(z, z^*; \alpha) \equiv \frac{E\left(z, z^*, \left(\dfrac{z - \alpha}{z}\right)^{1/2}\right)}{[\alpha(z - \alpha)]^{1/2}}, \tag{3.3.31}$$

then it may be shown that $U(z, z^*; \alpha)$ satisfies (3.3.27) and is a solution of $\mathbf{E}[U] = 0$. The operator $\mathbf{b}_2$ is then seen to have the alternate representation

$$U(z, z^*) = \mathbf{b}_2 f \equiv \int_0^z W(z, z^*; \alpha) f(\alpha/2) \, d\alpha, \tag{3.3.32}$$

when we are able to take the contour of integration of (3.1.9) as the straight line from -1 to $+1$.

4. *The Complex Riemann Function: Vekua's Approach*

The approach we shall outline below was initiated by the Russian mathematician Vekua at about the same time that Bergman was developing his own integral operator method. Vekua's contribution to the analytic theory of partial differential equations is summarized in his book, "New Methods for

Solving Elliptic Boundary Value Problems" [V.3] which has just recently been translated into English. Fortunately, there has been in existence an excellent survey article by Henrici [H.6], who has also added to and helped develop this theory [H.4–8].

The method of Vekua depends on the introduction of a special solution of (3.1.1),

$$\mathbf{E}[U] \equiv U_{zz^*} + AU_z + BU_{z^*} + CU = 0, \tag{3.4.1}$$

which we shall refer to as the Riemann function because of its formal analogy with the classical function of that name from the theory of real hyperbolic equations. In order to show it is always possible to construct this function we proceed by first introducing the adjoint equation of (3.4.1),

$$\begin{aligned}\hat{\mathbf{E}}[U] &\equiv U_{zz^*} - (AU)_z - (BU)_{z^*} + CU \\ &= U_{zz^*} + \hat{A}U_z + \hat{B}U_{z^*} + \hat{C}U = 0.\end{aligned} \tag{3.4.2}$$

Now if $\mathfrak{S}$ is a simply connected fundamental domain of (3.4.1), and hence also of (3.4.2), then we may write an equivalent (complex) integral equation for (3.4.2) when $(z, z^*, \zeta, \zeta^*) \in \mathfrak{S}^{(4)} \equiv \mathfrak{S}^{(2)} \times \mathfrak{S}^{(2)}$, namely,

$$\begin{aligned}U(z, z^*) &- \int_\zeta^z B(s, z^*)U(s, z^*)\,ds - \int_{\zeta^*}^{z^*} A(z, s^*)U(z, s^*)\,ds^* \\ &+ \int_\zeta^z ds \int_{\zeta^*}^{z^*} C(s, s^*)U(s, s^*)\,ds^* = F(z, z^*),\end{aligned} \tag{3.4.3}$$

where

$$\begin{aligned}F(z, z^*) \equiv &- \int_\zeta^z B(s, \zeta^*)U(s, \zeta^*)\,ds - \int_{\zeta^*}^{z^*} A(\zeta, s^*)U(\zeta, s^*)\,ds^* \\ &+ U(\zeta, z^*) + U(z, \zeta^*) - U(\zeta, \zeta^*) = \Phi(z) + \Psi(z^*).\end{aligned} \tag{3.4.4}$$

It is clear that if $U(z, z^*) \in \mathscr{C}^{(2)}[\mathfrak{S}^{(2)}]$ is a solution of (3.4.3), then it also satisfies the adjoint equation (3.4.2). If we consider the special class of solutions which satisfy

$$U(z, \zeta^*) = U(\zeta, \zeta^*) + \int_\zeta^z B(s, \zeta^*)U(s, \zeta^*)\,ds, \tag{3.4.5a}$$

$$U(\zeta, z^*) = U(\zeta, \zeta^*) + \int_{\zeta^*}^{z^*} A(\zeta, s^*)U(\zeta, s^*)\,ds^*, \tag{3.4.5b}$$

the right-hand side becomes a constant (which we further specify by taking $U(\zeta, \zeta^*)$ equal to one). In this case, if $R(z, z^*, \zeta, \zeta^*)$ is a solution of (3.4.3) satisfying the above conditions it is seen to obey the following five relations for all points $(z, \zeta; z^*, \zeta^*) \in \mathfrak{S}^{(4)}$. The first three of these relations are obvious:

$$R(\zeta, \zeta^*; \zeta, \zeta^*) = 1, \tag{3.4.6}$$

$$\frac{\partial R}{\partial z}(z, \zeta^*; \zeta, \zeta^*) = B(z, \zeta^*)R(z, \zeta^*; \zeta, \zeta^*), \tag{3.4.7}$$

$$\frac{\partial R}{\partial z^*}(\zeta, z^*; \zeta, \zeta^*) = A(\zeta, z^*)R(\zeta, z^*; \zeta, \zeta^*). \tag{3.4.8}$$

Integrating (3.4.5a) and (3.4.5b) yields respectively the following identities,

$$R(z, z^*; \zeta, z^*) = \exp\left\{\int_\zeta^z B(s, z^*)\, ds\right\},$$

$$R(z, z^*; z, \zeta^*) = \exp\left\{\int_{\zeta^*}^{z^*} A(z, s^*)\, ds^*\right\},$$

from which one may obtain the fourth and fifth relations referred to above,

$$\frac{\partial R}{\partial \zeta}(z, z^*; \zeta, z^*) = -B(\zeta, z^*)R(z, z^*; \zeta, z^*), \tag{3.4.9}$$

$$\frac{\partial R}{\partial \zeta^*}(z, z^*; z, \zeta^*) = -A(z, \zeta^*)R(z, z^*; z, \zeta^*). \tag{3.4.10}$$

The integral equation that $R(z, z^*; \zeta, \zeta^*)$ satisfies is clearly

$$\begin{aligned} R(z, z^*; \zeta, \zeta^*) &- \int_\zeta^z B(s, z^*)R(s, z^*; \zeta, \zeta^*)\, ds \\ &- \int_{\zeta^*}^{z^*} A(z, s^*)R(z, s^*; \zeta, \zeta^*)\, ds^* \\ &+ \int_\zeta^z \int_{\zeta^*}^{z^*} C(s, s^*)R(s, s^*; \zeta, \zeta^*)\, ds^*\, ds = 1. \end{aligned} \tag{3.4.11}$$

In order to investigate the existence of solutions to (3.4.11) we next turn our attention to complex Volterra equations of the type (3.4.3) where the coefficients A, B, C, F are holomorphic (analytic regular) in $\mathfrak{S}^{(2)}$. We shall show that for such prescribed coefficients A, B, C, and F there exists a unique solution, holomorphic in $\mathfrak{S}^{(2)}$. Our proof parallels that given originally by Vekua in his book [V.3, pp. 11–18] and summarized later by Henrici in his survey article [H.6]. Once we have shown this we will have the existence of a unique holomorphic solution of (3.4.11) for arbitrary $(z, z^*, \zeta, \zeta^*) \in \mathfrak{S}^{(4)}$. This particular solution $R(z, z^*; \zeta, \zeta^*)$ of the adjoint equation (3.4.2) is called the Riemann function. We shall show later that it possesses analogous properties to the classical function and plays a similar role in constructing solutions of (3.4.1).

In order to facilitate the proof of the existence of a unique holomorphic function to (3.4.3) (and hence also (3.4.11)) we first consider the following Volterra integral equation in the complex domain $\mathfrak{S}$,

$$W(z) - \int_\zeta^z W(s)K(z, s)\, ds = f(z), \tag{3.4.12}$$

where $\zeta, z \in \mathfrak{S}, f(z)$ is holomorphic in $\mathfrak{S}$ and $K(z, s)$ is holomorphic in the closure $\overline{\mathfrak{S} \times \mathfrak{S}}$. By using the method of successive approximations we can show that a unique, analytic solution exists. To this end let us introduce the sequence of iterated functions, defined for $(z, \zeta) \in \mathcal{N}(\mathfrak{S}^{(2)})$ (a neighborhood of $\mathfrak{S} \times \mathfrak{S}$), $W^{(0)}(z) = f(z)$,

$$W^{(n)}(z) = f(z) + \int_\zeta^z W^{(n-1)}(s)K(z, s)\, ds \qquad (n = 1, 2, \ldots).$$

Then by direct computation we see that

$$W^{(1)}(z) = f(z) + \int_\zeta^z f(s)K(z, s)\, ds,$$

$$W^{(2)}(z) = f(z) + \int_\zeta^z f(s)K(z, s)\, ds + \int_\zeta^z ds \int_\zeta^s K(z, s)K(s, t)f(t)\, dt,$$

and, because of the holomorphy of the kernel in $\mathfrak{S} \times \mathfrak{S}$, we may rewrite the double integral as

$$\int_\zeta^z f(t)\left\{\int_t^z K(z, s)K(s, t)\, ds\right\} dt = \int_\zeta^z f(t)K^{(2)}(z, t)\, dt,$$

$$K^{(2)}(z, t) \equiv \int_t^z K(z, s)K(s, t)\, ds,$$

and hence we have

$$W^{(2)}(z) = f(z) + \int_\zeta^z f(s)K(z, s)\, ds + \int_\zeta^z f(s)K^{(2)}(z, s)\, ds.$$

Likewise we may obtain

$$W^{(3)}(z) = f(z) + \int_\zeta^z f(s)K(z, s)\, ds + \int_\zeta^z f(s)K^{(2)}(z, s)\, ds + \int_\zeta^z f(s)K^{(3)}(z, s)\, ds,$$

where

$$K^{(3)}(z, s) \equiv \int_s^z K(z, t)K^{(2)}(t, s)\, dt;$$

continuing successively in this manner we have

$$W^{(n)}(z) = f(z) + \int_\zeta^z \Gamma^{(n)}(z, s)f(s)\, ds,$$

where

$$\Gamma^{(n)}(z, s) \equiv \sum_{l=1}^{n} K^{(l)}(z, s),$$

and

$$K^{(l+1)}(z, s) \equiv \int_s^z K(z, t)K^{(l)}(t, s)\, dt \qquad (l = 1, 2, \ldots),$$

$$K^{(1)}(z, s) \equiv K(z, s).$$

We next show that the sequence of holomorphic functions $\Gamma^{(n)}(z, s)$ ($n = 1, 2, \ldots$) converges uniformly to a holomorphic function in $\mathfrak{S}^{(2)} \equiv \mathfrak{S} \times \mathfrak{S}$. This is done by first estimating $|K^{(n)}(z, s)|$. We proceed by first noting that

$$\begin{aligned} K^{(l+1)}(z, s) &= \int_s^z K(z, t) \int_s^t K(t, t_1)K^{(l-1)}(t_1, s)\, dt_1\, dt \\ &= \int_s^z K(z, t) \int_s^t K(t, t_1) \int_s^{t_1} K(t_1, t_2) \int_s^{t_2} \cdots \\ &\quad \times \int_s^{t_{l-1}} K(t_{l-1}, s)\, dt_{l-1}\, dt_{l-2} \cdots dt_2\, dt_1\, dt. \end{aligned}$$

Since the kernels $K(t_i, t_{i+1})$ are holomorphic in $\mathcal{N}(\mathfrak{S}^{(2)})$ they are bounded in $\mathfrak{S}^{(2)}$; furthermore, since the $K(t_i, t_{i+1})$ are holomorphic in $\mathcal{N}(\mathfrak{S}^{(2)})$ by Cauchy's theorem, we may use as our domain of integration the product of the rays from s to z, $t_1, \ldots,$ and t_{l-1}. Hence, if $|K(t_i, t_{i+1})| \leq M$ for $(t_i, t_{i+1}) \in \mathfrak{S}^{(2)}$, we have

$$|K^{(l+1)}(z, s)| \leq \frac{M^l}{l!} |z - s|^l,$$

from which it follows that

$$|\Gamma^{(l+1)}(z, s)| \leq \sum_{n=1}^{l+1} \frac{M^{n-1} |z - s|^{n-1}}{(n-1)!} \leq \exp(M |z - s|)$$

for $(z, s) \in \mathfrak{S}^{(2)}$. We conclude that the sequence of holomorphic functions $\Gamma^{(n)}(z, s)$ are uniformly bounded in the closure of $\mathfrak{S}^{(2)}$. Since this sequence constitutes a normal family we can always extract a convergent subsequence that converges to a holomorphic function. However, this may be seen by directly considering the series

$$\Gamma(z, s) = \sum_{n=1}^{\infty} K^{(n)}(z, s),$$

which we have just shown converges uniformly and absolutely in $\mathfrak{S}^{(2)}$, and hence represents a holomorphic function of (z, ζ) in $\mathfrak{S}^{(2)}$. Hence, the solution of (3.4.12) may be written in the form

$$W(z) = f(z) + \int_{\zeta}^{z} \Gamma(z, s) f(s)\, ds,$$

which clearly is seen to be holomorphic in $\mathfrak{S}$. That this solution is unique may be shown in the usual way for real Volterra equations. The reader may easily supply the proof for this last remark.

In his survey article Henrici lists several corollaries to this result, which we list below as lemmas. The proof of these corollaries may be established in the same way as the result above, with a few additional remarks needed for the second lemma.

Lemma 3.4.1 *The solution $W(z, \zeta) \equiv W(z)$ of the Volterra equation* (3.4.12) *is also a holomorphic function of the point $\zeta \in \mathfrak{S}$.*

Lemma 3.4.2 *If for the Volterra integral equation*

$$W(z, t) = \int_{\zeta}^{z} K(z, s, t)W(s, t)\, ds + f(z, t),$$

the kernel $K(z, s, t)$ *is holomorphic for* $(z, s, t) \in \mathfrak{S}^{(2)} \times \mathfrak{H}$ *and* $f(z, t)$ *is holomorphic for* $(z, t) \in \mathfrak{S} \times \mathfrak{H}$, *then the resolving kernel* $\Gamma(z, s, t)$ *is holomorphic for* $(z, s, t) \in \mathfrak{S}^{(2)} \times \mathfrak{H}$.

Proof We add a few lines of proof (of our own) for the last lemma. Clearly for each fixed value of $t^0 \in \mathfrak{H}$ we may show the resolving kernel $\Gamma(z, s, t^0)$ is holomorphic in $\mathfrak{S}^{(2)} \equiv \mathfrak{S} \times \mathfrak{S}$ by simply repeating our previous argument concerning the uniform convergence of the series,

$$\Gamma(z, s, t^0) = \sum_{n=1}^{\infty} \Gamma^{(n)}(z, s, t^0).$$

Since

$$\Gamma^{(n)}(z, s, t) \equiv \sum_{l=1}^{n} K^{(l)}(z, s, t),$$

we realize that for each $(z, s) \in \mathfrak{S}^{(2)}$, $\Gamma^{(n)}(z, s, t)$ and hence (because of convergence) $\Gamma(z, s, t)$ must be a holomorphic function of $t \in \mathfrak{H}$. By Hartogs' theorem we then see that $\Gamma(z, s, t)$ is holomorphic in the product space $\mathfrak{S}^{(2)} \times \mathfrak{H}$.

Lemma 3.4.3 *The kernel and resolving kernel corresponding to the Volterra equation* (3.4.12) *obey the following identity*:

$$\Gamma(z, t) - \int_{t}^{z} K(z, s)\Gamma(s, t)\, ds = K(z, t).$$

Proof Since $\Gamma^{(n)}(z, t) = \sum_{l=1}^{n} K^{(l)}(z, t)$, we have

$$\Gamma^{(n)}(z, t) - \sum_{l=2}^{n} K^{(l)}(z, t) = K^{(1)}(z, t) \equiv K(z, t);$$

hence,

$$\Gamma^{(n)}(z, t) - \int_{t}^{z} K(z, s)\Gamma^{(n-1)}(s, t)\, ds = K(z, t).$$

Since we have shown that the convergence of $\lim_{n\to\infty} \Gamma^{(n)}(z, t)$ is uniform we may pass to the limit under the integral sign and obtain

$$\Gamma(z, t) = \lim_{n\to\infty} \Gamma^{(n)}(z, t) = \lim_{n\to\infty} \int_t^z K(z, s)\Gamma^{(n-1)}(s, t)\, ds + K(z, t)$$

$$= \int_t^z K(z, s)\Gamma(s, t)\, ds + K(z, t).$$

We now return to our double Volterra equation (3.4.3) and consider the terms $A(z, s^*)$, $B(s, z^*)$ to be the kernels of equations of the form (3.4.12), namely

$$W_1(z, z^*) - \int_{\zeta^*}^{z^*} A(z, s^*)W_1(z, s^*)\, ds^* = f_1(z, z^*) \tag{3.4.13}$$

$$W_2(z, z^*) - \int_{\zeta}^{z} B(s, z^*)W_2(s, z^*)\, ds = f_2(z, z^*), \tag{3.4.14}$$

where in (3.4.13) we assume z is a parameter $\in \mathfrak{S}$, and in (3.4.14) z^* is a parameter $\in \mathfrak{S}^*$. By the preceding lemma there exists a relationship between the kernels of (3.4.13), (3.4.14) and their resolving kernels, which is independent of the functions $f_k(z, z^*)$ $(k = 1, 2)$. Let $\Gamma_A(z, z^*, \zeta^*)$, $\Gamma_B(z, z^*, \zeta)$ be the resolving kernels of (3.4.13), (3.4.14), respectively; then we have

$$\Gamma_A(z, z^*, \zeta^*) - \int_{\zeta^*}^{z^*} A(z, s^*)\Gamma_A(z, s^*, \zeta^*)\, ds^* = A(z, \zeta^*), \tag{3.4.15}$$

$$\Gamma_B(z, z^*, \zeta) - \int_{\zeta}^{z} B(s, z^*)\Gamma_B(s, z^*, \zeta)\, ds = B(\zeta, z^*). \tag{3.4.16}$$

Combining the results of Lemmas 3.4.1 and 3.4.3 the functions Γ_A and Γ_B are seen to be holomorphic in $\mathfrak{S}^{(2)} \times \mathfrak{H}^*$ and $\mathfrak{S}^{(2)} \times \mathfrak{H}$, respectively.

If we now seek a solution of (3.4.3) of the form

$$U(z, z^*) = U_0(z, z^*) + \int_{\zeta^*}^{z^*} \Gamma_A(z, z^*, s^*)U_0(z, s^*)\, ds^*$$

$$+ \int_{\zeta}^{z} \Gamma_B(z, z^*, s)U_0(s, z^*)\, ds, \tag{3.4.17}$$

then by directly substituting this into (3.4.3) we obtain

$$
\begin{aligned}
U_0(z, z^*) &+ \int_{\zeta^*}^{z^*} \Gamma_A(z, z^*, s^*) U_0(z, s^*)\, ds^* + \int_{\zeta}^{z} \Gamma_B(z, z^*, s) U_0(s, z^*)\, ds \\
&- \int_{\zeta}^{z} B(s, z^*) U_0(s, z^*)\, ds \\
&- \int_{\zeta}^{z} ds\, B(s, z^*) \int_{\zeta^*}^{z^*} \Gamma_A(s, z^*, s^*) U_0(s, s^*)\, ds^* \\
&- \int_{\zeta}^{z} ds\, B(s, z^*) \int_{\zeta}^{s} \Gamma_B(s, z^*, t) U_0(t, z^*)\, dt \\
&- \int_{\zeta^*}^{z^*} A(z, s^*) U_0(z, s^*)\, ds^* \\
&- \int_{\zeta^*}^{z^*} ds^* A(z, s^*) \int_{\zeta^*}^{s^*} \Gamma_A(z, s^*, t^*) U_0(z, t^*)\, dt^* \\
&- \int_{\zeta}^{z} ds \int_{\zeta^*}^{z^*} A(z, s^*) \Gamma_B(z, s^*, s) U_0(s, s^*)\, ds^* \\
&+ \int_{\zeta}^{z} ds \int_{\zeta^*}^{z^*} C(s, s^*) U_0(s, s^*)\, ds^* \\
&+ \int_{\zeta}^{z} ds \int_{\zeta^*}^{z^*} ds^* C(s, s^*) \int_{\zeta^*}^{s^*} \Gamma_A(s, s^*, t^*) U_0(s, t^*)\, dt^* \\
&+ \int_{\zeta}^{z} ds \int_{\zeta^*}^{z^*} ds^*\, C(s, s^*) \int_{\zeta}^{s} \Gamma_B(s, s^*, t) U_0(t, s^*)\, dt = F(z, z^*).
\end{aligned}
$$

Recombining these terms, and reordering several integrations we have

$$
\begin{aligned}
U_0(z, z^*) &+ \int_{\zeta^*}^{z^*} ds^*\, U_0(z, s^*) \Big\{ \Gamma_A(z, z^*, s^*) \\
&\quad - \int_{s^*}^{z^*} \Gamma_A(z, t^*, s^*) A(z, t^*)\, dt^* - A(z, s^*) \Big\} \\
&+ \int_{\zeta}^{z} ds\, U_0(s, z^*) \Big\{ \Gamma_B(z, z^*, s) \\
&\quad - \int_{s}^{z} \Gamma_B(t, z^*, s) B(t, z^*)\, dt - B(s, z^*) \Big\} \\
&+ \int_{\zeta}^{z} ds \int_{\zeta^*}^{z^*} ds^*\, U_0(s, s^*) \Big\{ C(s, s^*) - B(s, z^*) \Gamma_A(s, z^*, s^*) \\
&\quad - A(z, s^*) \Gamma_B(z, s^*, s) + \int_{s^*}^{z^*} C(s, t^*) \Gamma_A(s, t^*, s^*)\, dt^* \\
&\quad + \int_{s}^{z} C(t, s^*) \Gamma_B(t, s^*, s)\, dt \Big\} = F(z, z^*).
\end{aligned}
$$

The first two integrals vanish identically by virtue of (3.4.15) and (3.4.16), respectively. Consequently, if we define

$$\begin{aligned} K(z, z^*; s, s^*) \equiv C(s, s^*) &- B(s, z^*)\Gamma_A(s, z^*, s^*) \\ &- A(z, s^*)\Gamma_B(z, s^*, s) \\ &+ \int_{s^*}^{z^*} C(s, t^*)\Gamma_A(s, t^*, s^*)\, dt^* \\ &+ \int_{s}^{z} C(t, s^*)\Gamma_B(t, s^*, s)\, dt, \end{aligned} \tag{3.4.18}$$

then we may rewrite (3.4.3) in the simpler form

$$U_0(z, z^*) - \int_\zeta^z ds \int_{\zeta^*}^{z^*} ds^*\, K(z, z^*; s, s^*)U_0(s, s^*) = F(z, z^*). \tag{3.4.19}$$

We may solve this double Volterra equation by successive approximations just as we did in the previous case for the single variable Volterra equation. We introduce the sequence of successive approximations for

$$(z, z^*) \in (\mathfrak{S} \times \mathfrak{S}^*) \equiv \mathfrak{S}^{(2)}$$

$$U_0^{(n+1)}(z, z^*) \equiv F(z, z^*) + \int_\zeta^z ds \int_{\zeta^*}^{z^*} K(z, z^*; s, s^*)U_0^{(n)}(s, s^*)\, ds^*$$
$$(n = 0, 1, 2, \ldots,) \quad (3.4.20)$$

$$U_0^{(0)}(z, z^*) \equiv F(z, z^*);$$

the resolving kernel,

$$\Gamma(z, z^*; s, s^*) = \lim_{N \to \infty} \sum_{n=1}^{N} K^{(n)}(z, z^*; s, s^*),$$

where

$$K^{(n+1)}(z, z^*; s, s^*) \equiv \int_s^z dt \int_{s^*}^{z^*} dt^* K(z, z^*; t, t^*)K^{(n)}(t, t^*; s, s^*)$$
$$(n = 1, 2, \ldots)$$

$$K^{(1)}(z, z^*; s, s^*) \equiv K(z, z^*; s, s^*),$$

may be seen to converge uniformly and absolutely to a holomorphic function in $\mathfrak{S}^{(2)} \times \mathfrak{S}^{(2)} \equiv \mathfrak{S}^{(4)}$.

From the above discussion we realize that the Riemann function which we defined as a solution of (3.4.11) is uniquely determined as a holomorphic function in any fundamental domain of the partial differential equation (3.4.1).

In order to see how the function $R(z, z^*; t, t^*)$ may be used to construct solutions of the equation

$$\mathbf{E}[u] = f(z, z^*),$$

we shall derive the "classical" Riemann representation formula,

$$\begin{aligned} U(z, z^*) &= U(t, t^*)R(t, t^*; z, z^*) \\ &\quad + \int_t^z R(s, t^*; z, z^*)[U_s(s, t^*) + B(s, t^*)U(s, t^*)]\, ds \\ &\quad + \int_{t^*}^{z^*} R(t, s^*; z, z^*)[U_{s^*}(t, s^*) + A(t, s^*)U(t, s^*)]\, ds^* \\ &\quad + \int_{t^*}^{z^*} ds^* \int_{t^*}^{z^*} R(s, s^*; z, z^*)f(s, s^*)\, ds, \end{aligned} \tag{3.4.21}$$

where (t, t^*) is an arbitrary point in the bicylinder $\mathfrak{S}^{(2)}$. Let $U(z, z^*)$, $V(z, z^*)$ be arbitrary functions holomorphic in $\mathfrak{S}^{(2)}$, then we have the identity

$$V\mathbf{E}[U] - U\hat{\mathbf{E}}[V] \equiv (VU_z + BUV)_{z^*} - (UV_{z^*} - AUV)_z. \tag{3.4.22}$$

If we choose $V(z, z^*) \equiv R(z, z^*; \zeta, \zeta^*)$, then with respect to its first two variables, R is a solution of the adjoint equation, $\hat{\mathbf{E}}[R] = 0$; hence,

$$\begin{aligned} \mathbf{E}[U]R(z, z^*; \zeta, \zeta^*) &= (RU_z + BUR)_{z^*} - (UR_{z^*} - AUR)_z \\ &= -(U[R_z - BR])_{z^*} - (U[R_{z^*} - AR])_z + (RU)_{zz^*}. \end{aligned} \tag{3.4.23}$$

Reordering and integrating with respect to the first two arguments (z, z^*) from t to ζ and t^* to ζ^* where (ζ, ζ^*) is a fixed point in $\mathfrak{S}^{(2)}$, we have

$$\begin{aligned} &\int_{t^*}^{\zeta^*} ds^* \int_t^{\zeta} [R(s, s^*; \zeta, \zeta^*)U(s, s^*)]_{ss^*}\, ds \\ &\quad = \int_{t^*}^{\zeta^*} ds^* \int_t^{\zeta} R(s, s^*; \zeta, \zeta^*)\mathbf{E}[U(s, s^*)]\, ds \\ &\qquad + \int_t^{\zeta} ds\{U(s, \zeta^*)[R_s(s, \zeta^*; \zeta, \zeta^*) - B(s, \zeta^*)R(s, \zeta^*; \zeta, \zeta^*)] \\ &\qquad - U(s, t^*)[R_s(s, t^*; \zeta, \zeta^*) - B(s, t^*)R(s, t^*; \zeta, \zeta^*)]\} \\ &\qquad + \int_{t^*}^{\zeta^*} ds^*\{U(\zeta, s^*)[R_{s^*}(\zeta, s^*; \zeta, \zeta^*) - A(\zeta, s^*)R(\zeta, s^*; \zeta, \zeta^*)] \\ &\qquad - U(t, s^*)[R_{s^*}(t, s^*; \zeta, \zeta^*) - A(t, s^*)R(t, s^*; \zeta, \zeta^*)]\}, \end{aligned}$$

which because of the characteristic conditions (3.4.7) and (3.4.8) can be simplified by cancelling certain terms to become

$$\begin{aligned}
&U(\zeta, \zeta^*)R(\zeta, \zeta^*; \zeta, \zeta^*) - U(\zeta, t^*)R(\zeta, t^*; \zeta, \zeta^*) \\
&\qquad - U(t, \zeta^*)R(t, \zeta^*; \zeta, \zeta^*) + U(t, t^*)R(t, t^*; \zeta, \zeta^*) \\
&\qquad = \int_{t^*}^{\zeta^*} ds^* \int_t^{\zeta} R(s, s^*; \zeta, \zeta^*)\mathbf{E}[U(s, s^*)]\, ds \\
&\qquad\quad - \int_t^{\zeta} U(s, t^*)[R_s(s, t^*; \zeta, \zeta^*) - B(s, t^*)R(s, t^*; \zeta, \zeta^*)]\, ds \\
&\qquad\quad - \int_{t^*}^{\zeta^*} U(t, s^*)[R_{s^*}(t, s^*; \zeta, \zeta^*) - A(t, s^*)R(t, s^*; \zeta, \zeta^*)]\, ds^* \\
&\qquad = \int_{t^*}^{\zeta^*} ds^* \int_t^{\zeta} R(s, s^*; \zeta, \zeta^*)\mathbf{E}[U(s, s^*)]\, ds \\
&\qquad\quad + \int_t^{\zeta} R(s, t^*; \zeta, \zeta^*)[U_s(s, t^*) + B(s, t^*)U(s, t^*)]\, ds \\
&\qquad\quad + \int_{t^*}^{\zeta^*} R(t, s^*; \zeta, \zeta^*)[U_{s^*}(t, s^*) + A(t, s^*)U(t, s^*)]\, ds^* \\
&\qquad\quad - U(\zeta, t^*)R(\zeta, t^*; \zeta, \zeta^*) + U(\ , t^*)R(t, t^*; \zeta, \zeta^*) \\
&\qquad\quad - U(t, \zeta^*)R(t, \zeta^*; \zeta, \zeta^*) + U(t, t^*)R(t, t^*; \zeta, \zeta^*).
\end{aligned}$$

Rearranging the order of these terms, and taking into account $R(\zeta, \zeta^*; \zeta, \zeta^*) = 1$, yields the following expression:

$$\begin{aligned}
U(\zeta, \zeta^*) = {} & U(t, t^*)R(t, t^*; \zeta, \zeta^*) \\
& + \int_t^{\zeta} R(s, t^*; \zeta, \zeta^*)[U_s(s, t^*) + B(s, t^*)U(s, t^*)]\, ds \\
& + \int_{t^*}^{\zeta^*} R(t, s^*; \zeta, \zeta^*)[U_{s^*}(t, s^*) + A(t, s^*)U(t, s^*)]\, ds^* \\
& + \int_{t^*}^{\zeta^*} ds^* \int_t^{\zeta} R(s, s^*; \zeta, \zeta^*)\mathbf{E}[U(s, s^*)]\, ds.
\end{aligned} \tag{3.4.24}$$

Putting $\mathbf{E}[U] = f(s, s^*)$ in the above expression gives us a complex analogue of Riemann's classical result.

We are now in a position to prove an interesting result concerning the Riemann function of the adjoint equation $\hat{\mathbf{E}}[U]=0$. We follow the usual proof as, say, given in Courant–Hilbert [Vol. II, Chapter 1, pp. 454–455] and in Garabedian [G.4, Chapter 4, p. 132], or as also given by Henrici for the complex case above [H.6, p. 179].

Lemma 3.4.4 (Symmetry of the Riemann Function.) *The Riemann function* $\hat{R}(z, z^*; t, t^*)$ *of the adjoint equation* $\hat{\mathbf{E}}[U]=0$ *is related to the Riemann function* $R(z, z^*; t, t^*)$ *of* (3.1.1) *by the rule*

$$R(z, z^*; t, t^*) = \hat{R}(t, t^*; z, z^*).$$

Proof We wish to show that

$$\hat{R}(z, z^*; t, t^*) = R(t, t^*; z, z^*);$$

hence we must show that $R(t, t^*; z, z^*)$ is a solution to Eq. (3.4.1) in the z, z^* variables and that it satisfies certain characteristic conditions. We show the latter first by noting that the characteristic conditions (3.4.7) and (3.4.8) for $R(z, z^*; t, t^*)$ are the analogues of (3.4.9) and (3.4.10) for $R(t, t^*; z, z^*)$. To show that $R(t, t^*; z, z^*)$ is a solution of (3.4.1) we set $U(z, z^*) \equiv R(t, t^*; z, z^*)$ in (3.4.24) which then becomes

$$\begin{aligned} R(t, t^*; \zeta, \zeta^*) = {} & R(t, t^*; t, t^*)R(t, t^*; \zeta, \zeta^*) \\ & + \int_t^{\zeta} R(s, t^*; \zeta, \zeta^*)[R_s(t, t^*; s, t^*) + B(s, t^*)R(t, t^*; s, t^*)]\, ds \\ & + \int_{t^*}^{\zeta^*} R(t, s^*; \zeta, \zeta^*)[R_{s^*}(t, t^*; t, s^*) \\ & \qquad + A(t, s^*)R(t, t^*; t, s^*)]\, ds^* \\ & + \int_{t^*}^{\zeta^*} ds^* \int_t^{\zeta} R(s, s^*; \zeta, \zeta^*)\mathbf{E}[R(t, t^*; s, s^*)]\, ds, \end{aligned}$$

which simplifies to

$$\int_{t^*}^{\zeta^*} ds^* \int_t^{\zeta} R(s, s^*; \zeta, \zeta^*)\mathbf{E}[R(t, t^*; s, s^*)]\, ds = 0 \tag{3.4.25}$$

in view of the above conditions. Since $R(t, t^*; s, s^*)$ is holomorphic in $\mathfrak{S}^{(4)} \equiv \mathfrak{S}^{(2)} \times \mathfrak{S}^{(2)}$ our result follows.

We conclude this section with a discussion of how Vekua introduces an operator which constructs a complete system of solutions. To do this we shall pose what by a formal analogy to the real case could be called a Goursat problem. We wish to remark, however, that if we should make a restriction of the z, z^* space to the xy plane this problem would not correspond to either an initial value or a boundary value problem. The purpose of including a discussion of this problem is that we shall obtain an integral operator which can be used to construct a complete system of solutions, from which we can form an approximation to Bergman's kernel function. Vekua, on the other hand [V.3, Chap. III], uses these solutions combined with his and Muskhelishvili's theory of singular integral equations in order to solve the boundary value problems of mathematical physics. The reader interested in this approach is directed to the above work which also lists a detailed bibliography.

Definition *We shall call a holomorphic solution to the equation* (3.4.1) *a solution of a formal Goursat problem in the fundamental domain* $\mathfrak{S}^{(2)} \equiv \mathfrak{S} \times \mathfrak{S}^*$ *if the following conditions are met*:

(1) *There exist two functions* $\phi(z)$, $\phi^*(z^*)$ *that are holomorphic in* $\mathfrak{S}$ *and* $\mathfrak{S}^*$ *respectively.*

(2) *For a fixed point* $\zeta \in \mathfrak{S}$ *and all* $z^* \in \mathfrak{S}^*$ *we have* $U(\zeta, z^*) = \phi^*(z^*)$.

(3) *For a fixed point* $\zeta^* \in \mathfrak{S}^*$ *and all* $z \in \mathfrak{S}$ *we have* $U(z, \zeta^*) = \phi(z)$.

(4) $\phi(\zeta) = \phi^*(\zeta^*)$.

Proof We now consider the proof of the existence and uniqueness of a solution to a formal Goursat problem. Let $R(z, z^*; t, t^*)$ be the Riemann function of $\mathbf{E}[U] = 0$ in the z, z^* variables; consequently, the function defined by

$$U(z, z^*) \equiv \Phi(\zeta)R(\zeta, \zeta^*; z, z^*) + \int_\zeta^z \Phi'(t)R(t, \zeta^*; z, z^*)\, dt + \int_{\zeta^*}^{z^*} \Phi^{*\prime}(t^*)R(\zeta, t^*; z, z^*)\, dt^*, \tag{3.4.26}$$

where $\Phi(\zeta)$, and $\Phi^*(\zeta^*)$ are arbitrary holomorphic functions in $\mathfrak{S}$ and $\mathfrak{S}^*$ respectively is also a solution of $\mathbf{E}[U] = 0$. Furthermore, if we specify the functions $\Phi(\zeta)$, $\Phi^*(\zeta^*)$ so that they satisfy

$$\Phi(z) \equiv \phi(z) - \int_\zeta^z \hat{B}(t, \zeta^*)\phi(t)\, dt, \tag{3.4.27}$$

$$\Phi^*(z^*) \equiv \phi^*(z^*) - \int_{\zeta^*}^{z^*} \hat{A}(\zeta, t^*)\phi^*(t^*)\,dt^*, \tag{3.4.28}$$

we have the following equality:

$$\begin{aligned} U(z, \zeta^*) &= \Phi(\zeta)R(\zeta, \zeta^*; z, \zeta^*) \\ &\quad + \int_{\zeta}^{z} \{\phi'(t) - \hat{B}(t, \zeta^*)\phi(t)\}R(t, \zeta^*; z, \zeta^*)\,dt \\ &= \phi(z)R(z, \zeta^*; z, \zeta^*) \\ &\quad - \int_{\zeta}^{z} \{R_t(t, \zeta^*; z, \zeta^*) + \hat{B}(t, \zeta^*)R(t, \zeta^*; z, \zeta^*)\}\phi(t)\,dt \\ &= \phi(z). \end{aligned}$$

Likewise we may show that

$$\begin{aligned} U(\zeta, z^*) &= \Phi(\zeta)R(\zeta, \zeta^*; \zeta, z^*) \\ &\quad + \int_{\zeta^*}^{z^*} \{\phi^{*\prime}(t^*) - \hat{A}(\zeta, t^*)\phi^*(t^*)\}R(\zeta, t^*; \zeta, z^*)\,dt^* \\ &= \phi^*(z^*)R(\zeta, z^*; \zeta, z^*) \\ &\quad - \int_{\zeta^*}^{z^*} \{R_{t^*}(\zeta, t^*; \zeta, z^*) \\ &\quad + \hat{A}(\zeta, t^*)R(\zeta, t^*; \zeta, z^*)\}\phi^*(t^*)\,dt^* \\ &= \phi^*(z^*). \end{aligned}$$

Hence, our representation (3.4.26) with the auxiliary conditions (3.4.27), (3.4.28), is a solution of our Goursat problem. That this representation is unique follows from the fact that each solution to our Goursat problem must satisfy the equivalent integral equation

$$\begin{aligned} U(z, z^*) &- \int_{\zeta}^{z} \hat{B}(t, z^*)U(t, z^*)\,dt - \int_{\zeta^*}^{z^*} \hat{A}(z, t^*)U(z, t^*)\,dt^* \\ &+ \int_{\zeta}^{z} dt \int_{\zeta^*}^{z^*} \hat{C}(t, t^*)U(t, t^*)\,dt^* \\ &= \Phi(z) + \Phi^*(z^*) - \Phi(\zeta), \end{aligned}$$

whose solution we have already seen is uniquely determined by our previous iteration scheme.

It is clear from the representation (3.4.26), that actually any solution holomorphic in the bicylinder $\mathfrak{S}^{(2)}$ can be expressed in this form, where we determine $\phi(z)$ and $\phi^*(z^*)$ so that

$$\phi(z) \equiv U(z, \zeta^*), \qquad \phi^*(z^*) \equiv U(\zeta, z^*);$$

the condition $\phi^*(\zeta^*) = \phi(\zeta)$ obviously is satisfied by this definition.

We wish to stress at this time that a formal Goursat problem for the equation $\mathbf{E}[U] = 0$ does not correspond to either an initial value problem or a boundary value problem for the real, elliptic partial differential equation $\mathbf{e}[u] = 0$. This is evident by rewriting our Goursat data for the real case, i.e., for $z^* = \bar{z}$, $\zeta^* = \bar{\zeta}$, as

$$u\left(\frac{z+\bar{\zeta}}{2}, \frac{z-\bar{\zeta}}{2i}\right) = \phi(z), \qquad u\left(\frac{\zeta+\bar{z}}{2}, \frac{\zeta-\bar{z}}{2i}\right) = \phi^*(\bar{z}), \qquad \phi(\zeta) = \phi^*(\bar{\zeta}),$$

which is essentially an analytic continuation problem. Vekua has solved various boundary value problems for elliptic equations [V.3–6]; however, these methods are based on either the theory of singular integral equations, or for the case of differential equations with nonanalytic coefficients, on his theory of generalized analytic functions. These topics will not be discussed here. The author with Aziz and Howard [A.G.2], [A.G.H.2] has investigated the possibility of using representations similar to (3.4.26) to show the existence of solutions for the equation $\mathbf{e}[u] = 0$ which satisfy "generalized" Goursat data on intersecting analytic surfaces in $\mathbb{C}^2$. These will be discussed later in this chapter.

Since each solution holomorphic in $\mathfrak{S}^{(2)}$ has a representation (3.4.26) this suggests the introduction of the following integral operator

$$\begin{aligned} U(z, z^*) &= \mathbf{V}_2[\{\phi(z), \phi^*(z^*)\}] \\ &\equiv \Phi(\zeta)R(\zeta, \zeta^*; z, z^*) \\ &\quad + \int_\zeta^z \Phi'(t)R(t, \zeta^*; z, z^*)\, dt + \int_{\zeta^*}^{z^*} \Phi^{*\prime}(t^*)R(\zeta, t^*; z, z^*)\, dt^*, \quad (3.4.29) \end{aligned}$$

where $\Phi(z)$ and $\Phi^*(z^*)$ are defined by (3.4.27), (3.4.28), and $\phi^*(\zeta^*) = \phi(\zeta)$. We shall use the terminology of Henrici [H.6] and refer to a pair of functions $\phi(z)$, $\phi^*(z^*)$ satisfying the latter condition as being *admissible*. The operator $\mathbf{V}_2[\{\phi(z), \phi^*(z^*)\}]$, defined above, maps each admissible pair $\{\phi, \phi^*\}$ onto a solution of some Goursat problem, since each such solution that is generated by an admissible pair must satisfy $U(z, \zeta^*) = \phi(z)$, and $U(\zeta, z^*) = \phi^*(z^*)$, with $\phi(z) = \phi^*(z^*)$.

Because the Riemann function is holomorphic in $\mathfrak{S}^{(4)}$ the operator $\mathbf{V}_2[\{\phi, \phi^*\}]$ is continuous. Hence, using this operator we may construct complete systems of solutions in $\mathfrak{S}^{(2)} = \mathfrak{S} \times \mathfrak{S}^*$ by mapping a pair of complete systems of holomorphic functions, defined in $\mathfrak{S}$ and in $\mathfrak{S}^*$ respectively, into the linear space of solutions for $\mathbf{E}[U] = 0$. As before, if the fundamental domain $\mathfrak{S}$ contains the origin, we may take as a complete system of functions in $\mathfrak{S}$ the powers z^n $(n = 0, 1, 2, \ldots,)$. In this case, since $U(z, z^*)$ is holomorphic in $\mathfrak{S}^{(2)}$ we may represent it as a Taylor series in any set $\{|z| < \rho\} \times \{|z^*| < \rho\} \subset \mathfrak{S}^{(2)}$,

$$U(z, z^*) = \sum_{n, m=0}^{\infty} a_{nm} z^n z^{*m}.$$

Because one has

$$\phi(z) = U(z, 0) = \sum_{n=0}^{\infty} a_{n0} z^n, \qquad \phi^*(z^*) = U(0, z^*) = \sum_{m=0}^{\infty} a_{0m} z^{*m},$$

this suggests the following system of admissible pairs $F_\nu \equiv \{\phi_\nu, \phi_\nu^*\}$:

$$F_0 = \{1, 1\}, \qquad F_{2n} = \{z^n, 0\}, \qquad F_{2n+1} = \{0, z^{*n}\}. \tag{3.4.30}$$

On the other hand, an admissible pair, $F = \{\phi(z), \phi^*(z^*)\}$ defined in $\{|z| \le \rho\} \times \{|z^*| \le \rho\} \subset \mathfrak{S}^{(2)}$ has a representation

$$F = \{\phi, \phi^*\} = \sum_{n=0}^{\infty} b_n F_n = \sum_{n=1}^{\infty} b_{2n}\{z^n, 0\} + b_0 + \sum_{n=1}^{\infty} b_{2n-1}\{0, z^{*n}\},$$

which generates the following solution when it is operated on by $\mathbf{V}_2$:

$$U(z, z^*) = \mathbf{V}_2[F] = \sum_{n=1}^{\infty} b_{2n} \mathbf{V}_2[\{z^n, 0\}] + \mathbf{V}_2[\{0, 1\}] b_0 + \sum_{n=1}^{\infty} b_{2n-1} \mathbf{V}_2[\{0, z^{*n}\}].$$

Henrici [H.6] gives a general form for a complete set of admissible pairs, namely if $f_n(z)$ $(n = 0, 1, 2, \ldots)$ is a complete set for $\mathfrak{S}$, then $f_n(z) = f_n(\bar{z})$ is a complete set with respect to $\mathfrak{S}^*$. Hence, one may introduce as a complete system of admissible pairs,

$$F_0 = \{1, 1\}, \qquad F_{2n} = \{(z - \zeta) f_{n-1}(z), 0\},$$
$$F_{2n-1} = \{0, (z^* - \zeta^*) \bar{f}_{n-1}(z^*)\} \qquad (n = 1, 2, \ldots).$$

Clearly for $(\zeta, \zeta^*) \in \mathfrak{S}^{(2)}$ we have

$$\phi(z) = U(z, \zeta^*) = U(\zeta, \zeta^*) + (z - \zeta) \sum_{n=1}^{\infty} b_{2n} f_{n-1}(z),$$

$$\phi^*(z^*) = U(\zeta, z^*) = U(\zeta, \zeta^*) + (z^* - \zeta) \sum_{n=1}^{\infty} b_{2n-1} \bar{f}_{n-1}(z^*),$$

which yields the following general expansion for an arbitrary admissible pair:

$$\begin{aligned} F \equiv \{\phi, \phi^*\} &= \sum_{n=0}^{\infty} b_n F_n \\ &\equiv \{U(\zeta, \zeta^*), U(\zeta, \zeta^*)\} + \sum_{n=1}^{\infty} b_{2n}\{(z - \zeta) f_{n-1}(z), 0\} \\ &\quad + \sum_{n=1}^{\infty} b_{2n-1}\{0, (z^* - \zeta^*) \bar{f}_{n-1}(z^*)\}. \end{aligned}$$

We now consider a generalization of the previously discussed Goursat problem. We consider, as before, the complex, hyperbolic equation,

$$\mathbf{E}[U] = f(z, z^*);$$

however, we now seek a solution which simultaneously satisfies the conditions

$$U_z(z, z^*) = \alpha_0(z) U(z, z^*) + \alpha_1(z) U_{z^*}(z, z^*) + g(z) \qquad \text{on } \Gamma_1 \qquad (3.4.30a)$$

$$U_{z^*}(z, z^*) = \beta_0(z^*) U(z, z^*) + \beta_1(z^*) U_z(z, z^*) + h(z^*) \qquad \text{on } \Gamma_2, \qquad (3.4.30b)$$

with $U(0, 0) = \gamma$. Here Γ_1 and Γ_2 are analytic surfaces, which are represented globally in the domain $\mathfrak{S} \times \mathfrak{S}^*$ by $z^* = F_1(z)$, and $z = F_2(z^*)$. Furthermore, one assumes that $\Gamma_1 \cap \Gamma_2 \cap \{\mathfrak{S} \times \mathfrak{S}^*\} = \{(0, 0)\}$, and that the coefficients of the Goursat data (3.4.30) are to be holomorphic in the holomorphic domain $\mathfrak{S}$, or its conjugate domain, $\mathfrak{S}^*$, as the case may be.

Now, if $R(\xi, \xi^*; z, z^*)$ is the Riemann function associated with the homogeneous equation, $\mathbf{E}[U] = 0$, then from (3.4.21) we have that a solution of the nonhomogeneous equation is given by

$$U(z, z^*) = P(z, z^*) + \int_0^z \varphi(\xi)R(\xi, 0; z, z^*)\, d\xi + \int_0^{z^*} \psi(\xi^*)R(0, \xi^*; z, z^*)\, d\xi^*, \tag{3.4.31}$$

where

$$\begin{aligned} \varphi(z) &= U_z(z, 0) + B(z, 0)U(z, 0), \\ \psi(z^*) &= U_{z^*}(0, z^*) + A(0, z^*)U(0, z^*), \\ P(z, z^*) &= \gamma R(0, 0; z, z^*) + \int_0^z \int_0^{z^*} f(\xi, \xi^*)R(\xi, \xi^*; z, z^*)\, d\xi^*\, d\xi. \end{aligned} \tag{3.4.32}$$

By substituting (3.4.31), (3.4.32) into (3.4.30a) and (3.4.30b) one obtains a system of integral equations for $\varphi(z)$ and $\psi(z^*)$, namely

$$\begin{aligned} \varphi(z) = G(z) + S(z)\psi(F_1(z)) &+ \int_0^z K_1(\xi, 0; z)\varphi(\xi)\, d\xi \\ &+ \int_0^{F_1(z)} K_1(0, \xi^*; z)\psi(\xi^*)\, d\xi^*, \end{aligned} \tag{3.4.33}$$

$$\begin{aligned} \psi(z^*) = H(z^*) + T(z^*)\varphi(F_2(z^*)) &+ \int_0^{F_2(z)} K_2(\xi, 0; z^*)\varphi(\xi)\, d\xi \\ &+ \int_0^z K_2(0, \xi^*; z^*)\psi(\xi^*)\, d\xi^*, \end{aligned} \tag{3.4.34}$$

where

$$\begin{aligned} K_1(\xi, \xi^*; z) = [R(\xi, \xi^*; z, F_1(z)]^{-1}\{&\alpha_0(z)R(\xi, \xi^*; z, F_1(z)) \\ &- R_z(\xi, \xi^*; z, F_1(z)) + \alpha_1(z)R_{z^*}(\xi, \xi^*; z, F_1(z))\}, \end{aligned} \tag{3.4.35}$$

$$\begin{aligned} K_2(\xi, \xi^*; z^*) = [R(\xi, \xi^*; F_2(z^*), z^*)]^{-1}\{&\beta_0(z^*)R(\xi, \xi^*; F_2(z^*), z^*) \\ &+ \beta_1(z^*)R_z(\xi, \xi^*; F_2(z^*), z^*) - R_{z^*}(\xi, \xi^*; F_2(z^*), z^*)\}, \end{aligned} \tag{3.4.36}$$

$$\begin{aligned} G(z) = [R(z, 0; z, F_1(z))]^{-1}\{&g(z) + \alpha_0(z)P(z, F_1(z)) - P_z(z, F_1(z)) \\ &+ \alpha_1(z)P_{z^*}(z, F_1(z))\}, \end{aligned} \tag{3.4.37}$$

$$H(z^*) = [R(0, z^*; F_2(z^*), z^*)]^{-1}\{h(z^*) + \beta_0(z^*)P(F_2(z^*), z^*)$$
$$+\beta_1(z^*)P_z(F_2(z^*), z^*) - P_{z^*}(F_2(z^*), z^*)\}, \tag{3.4.38}$$

$$S(z) = \frac{\alpha_1(z)R(0, F_1(z); z, F_1(z))}{R(z, 0; z, F_1(z))}, \tag{3.4.39}$$

$$T(z^*) = \frac{\beta_1(z^*)R(F_2(z^*), 0; F_2(z^*), z^*)}{R(0, z^*; F_2(z^*), z^*)}. \tag{3.4.40}$$

The coefficients of the Goursat conditions are all holomorphic in the fundamental domain of the partial differential equation; furthermore, as we have seen, the Riemann function $R(z, z^*; \zeta, \zeta^*)$ is holomorphic in $\mathfrak{S}^{(4)} = \mathfrak{S} \times \mathfrak{S}^* \times \mathfrak{S} \times \mathfrak{S}^*$. From this one concludes that the functions $G(z)$, $S(z)$ and $H(z^*)$, $T(z^*)$ will be holomorphic in $\mathfrak{S}$ and $\mathfrak{S}^*$ respectively, save at the zeros of their denominators. Recalling from before that

$$R(z, 0; z, z^*) = \exp\left\{-\int_0^{z^*} A(z, s)\, ds\right\},$$

$$R(0, z^*; z, z^*) = \exp\left\{-\int_0^{z} B(t, z^*)\, dt\right\},$$

one realizes that the denominators of $G(z)$, $S(z)$, $H(z^*)$, $T(z^*)$ do not vanish in their respective domains, and hence these functions are holomorphic there. We next turn to consider the functions, $K_1(z, 0; z)$, $K_1(0, z^*; z)$, $K_2(z, 0; z^*)$, and $K_2(0, z^*; z^*)$. The functions $K_1(z, 0; z)$ and $K_2(0, z^*; z^*)$ are seen by the above reasoning to be holomorphic in $\mathfrak{S} \times \mathfrak{S}$ and $\mathfrak{S}^* \times \mathfrak{S}^*$ respectively. The functions $K_1(0, z^*; z)$ and $K_2(z, 0; z^*)$ present a different problem; however, since $R(0, 0; 0, 0) = 1$, we realize that in a sufficiently small polycylindrical neighborhood of the origin, $\mathcal{N}^4(0)$, in $\mathbb{C}^4$, $R(z, z^*; \zeta, \zeta^*) \neq 0$. Consequently, in $\mathcal{N}^4(0) \cap \mathbb{C}^2$, $K_1(0, z^*; z)$ and $K_2(z, 0; z^*)$ are holomorphic also. We are now in a position to establish the following (see [A.G.1]):

Theorem 3.4.5 *Let $\mathfrak{S}$ be the fundamental domain of the equation, $\mathbf{E}[U] = f(z, z^*)$, and let Γ_k $(k = 1, 2)$ be analytic surfaces with the above described properties, and such that the functions F_1, F_2 are injective maps in $\mathfrak{S}$ and $\mathfrak{S}^*$ respectively. Furthermore, let us assume that the additional condition holds,*

$$\tilde{M} = \sup_{\mathfrak{S} \times \mathfrak{S}^*} \{|S(z)T(z^*)|\} < 1.$$

Then there exists a unique solution to the initial value problem (3.4.30), *holomorphic in the small of the origin.*

Proof In a sufficiently small neighborhood of $(0, 0) \in \mathbb{C}^2$ the functions $K_1(0, z^*; z)$ and $K_2(z, 0; z^*)$ are bounded, hence there exists a finite, positive constant N, such that

$$N = \max\{ \sup_{\mathfrak{S}\times\mathfrak{S}} |K_1(z, 0; z)|, \sup_{\mathfrak{S}^*\times\mathfrak{S}} |K_1(0, z^*; z)|,$$
$$\sup_{\mathfrak{S}\times\mathfrak{S}^*} |K_2(z, 0; z^*)|, \sup_{\mathfrak{S}^*\times\mathfrak{S}^*} |K_2(0, z^*; z^*)|\}.$$

Also, since $S(z)$ and $T(z^*)$ are holomorphic in $\mathfrak{S}$ and $\mathfrak{S}^*$, there exists a finite positive constant M such that

$$M = \max\{\sup_{\mathfrak{S}}|S(z)|, \sup_{\mathfrak{S}^*}|T(z^*)|\}.$$

In order to simplify our approach we introduce the pair of functions $\chi \equiv [\varphi, \psi]$, where $\varphi \in \mathscr{A}[\mathfrak{S}]$, $\psi \in \mathscr{A}[\mathfrak{S}^*]$, i.e., φ, ψ, belong to the set of all analytic functions defined on $\mathfrak{S}$ and $\mathfrak{S}^*$ respectively. Furthermore, let us define the following operations on these pairs of functions,

$$\mathbf{H}\chi \equiv [S(z)\psi \circ F_1(z), \qquad T(z^*)\varphi \circ F_2(z^*)], \tag{3.4.41}$$

and

$$\mathbf{J}\chi \equiv \left[\int_0^z K_1(\xi, 0; z)\varphi(\xi)\, d\xi + \int_0^{F_1(z)} K_1(0, \xi^*; z)\psi(\xi^*)\, d\xi^*,\right.$$
$$\left.\int_0^{F_2(z^*)} K_2(\xi, 0; z^*)\varphi(\xi)\, d\xi + \int_0^{z^*} K_2(0, \xi^*; z^*)\psi(\xi^*)\, d\xi^*\right]. \tag{3.4.42}$$

In this notation the system of equations (3.4.33) and (3.4.34) may be rewritten as the operator equation

$$\chi = \mathbf{T}\chi \equiv \chi_0 + (\mathbf{H} + \mathbf{J})\chi, \tag{3.4.43}$$

where $\chi_0 \equiv [G(z), H(z^*)]$. Let $\hat{\mathscr{A}}[\mathfrak{S}, \mathfrak{S}^*]$ be the Banach space of pairs of functions holomorphic in $[\mathfrak{S}, \mathfrak{S}^*]$, where our norm is defined as $\| \ \| = \max\{\|\varphi\|, \|\psi\|\}$, and

$$\|\varphi\| = \sup_{\mathfrak{S}}|\varphi(z)|, \qquad \text{and} \qquad \|\psi\| = \sup_{\mathfrak{S}^*}|\psi|.$$

In order to solve (3.4.43) it is sufficient to show that the operator **T** has a fixed point in the Banach space $\hat{\mathscr{A}}[\mathfrak{S}, \mathfrak{S}^*]$. It is evident that **T** is a continuous mapping of $\hat{\mathscr{A}}[\mathfrak{S}, \mathfrak{S}^*]$; hence it suffices to verify that $\mathbf{T}^2$ is a contraction mapping to show **T** has a fixed point. To obtain an estimate for $\|\mathbf{T}^2\chi - \mathbf{T}^2\tilde{\chi}\|$ we proceed to compute the following terms:

$$\begin{aligned}
\mathbf{J}^2\chi = \Bigg[\int_0^z & K_1(\eta, 0; z)\left\{\int_0^\eta K_1(\xi, 0; \eta)\varphi(\xi)\, d\xi + \int_0^{F_1(\eta)} K_1(0, \xi^*; \eta)\psi(\xi^*)\, d\xi^*\right\} d\eta \\
&+ \int_0^{F_1(z)} K_1(0, \eta^*; z) \\
&\times \left\{\int_0^{F_2(\eta^*)} K_2(\xi, 0; \eta^*)\varphi(\xi)\, d\xi + \int_0^{\eta^*} K_2(0, \xi^*; \eta^*)\psi(\xi^*)\, d\xi^*\right\} d\eta^*, \\
\int_0^{F_2(z^*)} & K_2(\eta, 0; z^*)\left\{\int_0^\eta K_1(\xi, 0; \eta)\varphi(\xi)\, d\xi \right.\\
&\left. + \int_0^{F_1(\eta)} K_1(0, \xi^*; \eta)\psi(\xi^*)\, d\xi^*\right\} d\eta \\
&+ \int_0^{z^*} K_2(0, \eta^*; z^*)\left\{\int_0^{F_2(\eta^*)} K_2(\xi, 0; \eta^*)\varphi(\xi)\, d\xi \right.\\
&\left. + \int_0^{\eta^*} K_2(0, \xi^*; \eta^*)\psi(\xi^*)\, d\xi^*\right\} d\eta^*\Bigg].
\end{aligned}$$

Since, as was pointed out earlier, the integrands are holomorphic in a sufficiently small bicylindrical neighborhood of the origin in $\mathbb{C}^2$, the integrals are invariant with respect to deformation of contours (in this bicylinder), and we may replace the integration paths by straight lines. We estimate a typical integral, using the injective property of F_k $(k = 1, 2)$, as follows:

$$\begin{aligned}
&\left|\int_0^{F_1(z)} K_1(0, \eta^*, z)\left\{\int_0^{F_2(\eta^*)} K_2(\xi, 0, \eta^*)\varphi(\xi)\, d\xi\right\} d\eta^*\right| \\
&\quad \le \left|\int_0^{F_1(z)} |K_1(0, \eta^*; z)|\left\{\int_0^{F_2(\eta^*)} |K_2(\xi, 0; \eta^*)|\, |\varphi(\xi)|\, |d\xi|\right\}|d\eta^*|\right| \\
&\quad \le N^2\|\varphi\|\left|\int_0^{F_1(z)}\left\{\int_0^{F_2(\eta^*)} |d\xi|\right\}|d\eta^*|\right| \le N^2\|\varphi\|\left|\int_0^{F_1(z)} |F_2(\eta^*)|\, |d\eta^*|\right| \\
&\quad \le LN^2\|\varphi\|\left|\int_0^{F_1(z)} |d\eta^*|\right| \le L^2N^2\|\varphi\|,
\end{aligned}$$

where $L \equiv \sup_{\mathfrak{S}}\{|z|\}$. The same estimate holds for the other integrals involved, hence

$$\|\mathbf{J}^2\chi\| \leq 4LN^2 \|\chi\|.$$

We next proceed to evaluate $\mathbf{HJ}\chi$:

$$\begin{aligned}\mathbf{HJ}\chi \equiv \Bigg[S(z)\Bigg\{&\int_0^{F_2 \circ F_1(z)} K_2(\xi, 0; F_1(z))\varphi(\xi)\, d\xi \\ &+ \int_0^{F_1(z)} K_2(0, \xi^*; F_1(z))\psi(z^*)\, d\xi^*\Bigg\}, \\ T(z^*)\Bigg\{&\int_0^{F_2(z^*)} K_1(\xi, 0; F_2(z^*))\varphi(\xi)\, d\xi \\ &+ \int_0^{F_1 \circ F_2(z^*)} K_1(0, \xi^*; F_2(z^*))\psi(\xi^*)\, d\xi^*\Bigg\}\Bigg].\end{aligned}$$

Arguing as above, and using the upper bound on the sup norm for $S(z)$ and $T(z^*)$, we have

$$\|\mathbf{HJ}\chi\| \leq 2LMN \cdot \|\chi\|.$$

In a similar computation we obtain

$$\begin{aligned}\mathbf{JH}\chi \equiv \Bigg[&\int_0^z K_1(\xi, 0; z)S(\xi)\psi \circ F_1(\xi)\, d\xi \\ &+ \int_0^{F_1(z)} K_1(0, \xi^*; z)T(\xi^*)\varphi \circ F_2(\xi^*)\, d\xi^*, \\ &\int_0^{F_2(z^*)} K_2(\xi, 0; z)S(\xi)\psi \circ F_1(\xi)\, d\xi \\ &+ \int_0^{z^*} K_2(0, \xi^*; z^*)T(\xi^*)\varphi \circ F_2(z^*)\, d\xi^*\Bigg],\end{aligned}$$

from which we have that $\|\mathbf{JH}\chi\| \leq 2LMN \cdot \|\chi\|$. Finally,

$$\mathbf{H}^2\chi \equiv [S(z)T \circ F_1(z)\varphi \circ F_2 \circ F_1(z),\ T(z^*)S \circ F_2(z^*)\psi \circ F_1 \circ F_2(z^*)]$$

and $\|\mathbf{H}^2\chi\| \leq \tilde{M}\|\chi\|$. From the above, we readily see that if χ and $\tilde{\chi} \in \mathscr{A}[\mathfrak{S}, \mathfrak{S}^*]$, then we have

$$\|\mathbf{T}^2\chi - \mathbf{T}^2\tilde{\chi}\| \leq (\tilde{M} + 4L^2M + 4LMN) \cdot \|\chi - \tilde{\chi}\|$$

which can be made less than 1, by choosing L sufficiently small, since by hypothesis $\tilde{M} < 1$. (Remark: The injective property of F_k $(k = 1, 2)$ holds for disks, whose centers are the origin, and which are contained in $\mathfrak{S}$ or $\mathfrak{S}^*$, as the case may be.) Hence $\mathbf{T}^2$ is a contraction mapping and $\mathbf{T}$ has a fixed point. This proves our result [A.G.2].

5. *Existence Theorems for Nonlinear Equations*

In this section we shall investigate the existence and uniqueness of solutions to the nonlinear (complex) hyperbolic equation,

$$U_{zz^*} = f(z, z^*, U, U_z, U_{z^*}), \tag{3.5.1}$$

which satisfy "generalized" Goursat data of the form

$$U_z(z, z^*) \equiv \alpha_0(z, z^*)U(z, z^*) + \alpha_1(z, z^*)U_{z^*}(z, z^*) + g(z, z^*) \tag{3.5.2}$$

on the analytic surface, $\{z^* = F_1(z)\}$,

$$U_{z^*}(z, z^*) \equiv \beta_0(z, z^*)U(z, z^*) + \beta_1(z, z^*)U_z(z, z^*) + h(z, z^*) \tag{3.5.3}$$

on the analytic surface, $\{z = F_2(z^*)\}$, and

$$U(0, 0) = \gamma. \tag{3.5.4}$$

The function $f(z, z^*, U, P, Q)$ is to be considered a holomorphic function of five complex variables when (z, z^*, U, P, Q) is contained in a suitable product space, $\mathfrak{S}^{(2)} \times \mathfrak{H}^{(3)} \equiv (\mathfrak{S} \times \mathfrak{S}^* \times \mathfrak{H} + \mathfrak{H} \times \mathfrak{H})$, and with $(0, 0) \in \mathfrak{S} \times \mathfrak{S}^*$. The results which follow are due to the author with Aziz and Howard [A.G.H.2] and were generalizations of earlier methods concerning real hyperbolic equations, and the reader is directed to the papers of Aziz, Bogdanowicz, Chu and Diaz for further details [A.B.1], [A.D.1], [C.D.1,2].

Suppose U is a solution of the equation (3.5.1) and let us define a function $s(z, z^*)$ (in the class of functions holomorphic and bounded in $\mathfrak{S} \times \mathfrak{S}^*$) by

$$U_{zz^*} \equiv s. \tag{3.5.5}$$

We then have the following:

$$U(z, z^*) = \int_0^z \int_0^{z^*} s(\xi, \xi^*) \, d\xi^* \, d\xi + \int_0^z \varphi(\xi) \, d\xi + \int_0^{z^*} \psi(\xi^*) \, d\xi^* + U(0, 0), \tag{3.5.6}$$

$$U_z(z, z^*) = \int_0^{z^*} s(z, \xi^*)\, d\xi^* + \varphi(z), \tag{3.5.7}$$

$$U_{z^*}(z, z^*) = \int_0^{z} s(\xi, z^*)\, d\xi + \psi(z^*), \tag{3.5.8}$$

where

$$\varphi(z) = U_z(z, 0) \qquad \text{and} \qquad \psi(z^*) = U_{z^*}(0, z^*). \tag{3.5.9}$$

We note that $s(z, z^*)$ must satisfy the equation,

$$\begin{aligned} s(z, z^*) = f\Bigg(z, z^*, &\int_0^z \int_0^{z^*} s(\xi, \xi^*)\, d\xi^*\, d\xi + \int_0^z \varphi(\xi)\, d\xi \\ &+ \int_0^{z^*} \psi(\xi^*)\, d\xi^* + U(0,0), \int_0^{z^*} s(z, \xi^*)\, d\xi^* + \varphi(z), \\ &\int_0^z s(\xi, z^*)\, d\xi + \psi(z^*)\Bigg). \end{aligned} \tag{3.5.10}$$

Conversely, if s satisfies (3.5.10) then a solution of (3.5.1) is given by (3.5.6). We also find that the initial conditions (3.5.7)–(3.5.10) are equivalent to

$$\begin{aligned} \varphi(z) = \alpha_0(z)\Bigg\{&\int_0^z \varphi(\xi)\, d\xi + \int_0^{F_1(z)} \psi(\xi^*)\, d\xi^* \\ &+ \int_0^z \int_0^{F_1(z)} s(\xi, \xi^*)\, d\xi^*\, d\xi + \gamma\Bigg\} + \alpha_1(z)\Bigg\{\psi(F_1(z)) \\ &+ \int_0^z s(\xi, F_1(z))\, d\xi\Bigg\} - \int_0^{F_1(z)} s(z, \xi^*)\, d\xi^* + g(z) \end{aligned} \tag{3.5.11}$$

and

$$\begin{aligned} \psi(z^*) = \beta_0(z^*)\Bigg\{&\int_0^{z^*} \psi(\xi^*)\, d\xi^* + \int_0^{F_2(z^*)} \varphi(\xi)\, d\xi \\ &+ \int_0^{F_2(z^*)} \int_0^{z^*} s(\xi, \xi^*)\, d\xi^*\, d\xi + \gamma\Bigg\} + \beta_1(z^*)\Bigg\{\varphi(F_2(z^*)) \\ &+ \int_0^{z^*} s(F_2(z^*), \xi^*)\, d\xi^*\Bigg\} - \int_0^{F_2(z^*)} s(\xi, z^*)\, d\xi + h(z^*). \end{aligned} \tag{3.5.12}$$

We conclude that if $U(z, z^*)$ *is a solution of* (3.5.1), *then* $s(z, z^*)$ *as given by*

(3.5.5) *satisfies* (3.5.10) *and conversely. Moreover the initial conditions* (3.5.2)–(3.5.4) *are equivalent to* (3.5.11)–(3.5.12).

Next, we introduce the Banach spaces $\mathscr{A}_1$ and $\mathscr{A}_2$ of functions holomorphic and bounded in $\mathfrak{S}$ and $\mathfrak{S}^*$ with norms given by, respectively,

$$\|\varphi\|_\lambda = \sup\{e^{-\lambda|z|}\,|\varphi(z)|\} \qquad \text{where} \quad z \in \mathfrak{S}, \qquad \lambda > 0,$$

$$\|\psi\|_\lambda = \sup\{e^{-\lambda|z^*|}\,|\psi(z^*)|\} \qquad \text{where} \quad z^* \in \mathfrak{S}^*, \quad \lambda > 0.$$

For convenience let us introduce as before a simplifying notation;

$$\chi = (\varphi, \psi), \qquad \chi_0 = (g(z) + \alpha_0(z)\gamma, h(z^*) + \beta_0(z^*)\gamma), \tag{3.5.13}$$

$$\mathbf{H}\chi = (\alpha_1(z)\psi(F_1(z)), \beta_1(z^*)\varphi(F_2(z^*))), \tag{3.5.14}$$

$$\begin{aligned}\mathbf{J}\chi = \Bigg(&\alpha_0(z)\left\{\int_0^z \varphi(\xi)\,d\xi + \int_0^{F_1(z)} \psi(\xi^*)\,d\xi^*\right\},\\ &\beta_0(z^*)\left\{\int_0^{z^*} \psi(\xi^*)\,d\xi^* + \int_0^{F_2(z^*)} \varphi(\xi)\,d\xi\right\}\Bigg),\end{aligned} \tag{3.5.15}$$

$$\begin{aligned}\mathbf{\Omega}s &= (\mathbf{\Omega}_1 s, \mathbf{\Omega}_2\, s)\\ &= \Bigg(\alpha_0(z)\int_0^z\int_0^{F_1(z)} s(\xi, \xi^*)\,d\xi^* + \alpha_1(z)\int_0^z s(\xi, F_1(z))\,d\xi\\ &\quad - \int_0^{F_1(z)} s(z, \xi^*)\,d\xi^*, \beta_0(z^*)\int_0^{F_2(z^*)}\int_0^{z^*} s(\xi, \xi^*)\,d\xi^*\,d\xi\\ &\quad + \beta_1(z^*)\int_0^{z^*} s(F_2(z^*), \xi^*)\,d\xi^* - \int_0^{F_2(z^*)} s(\xi, z^*)\,d\xi\Bigg).\end{aligned} \tag{3.5.16}$$

We may then write system (3.5.11) symbolically in operator notation as

$$(\mathbf{I} - \mathbf{H} - \mathbf{J})\chi = \chi_0 + \mathbf{\Omega}s \tag{3.5.17}$$

and if the inverse operator $\mathbf{B} = (\mathbf{I} - \mathbf{H} - \mathbf{J})^{-1}$ exists then we shall be able to express the functions φ and ψ as operators on the function s. Note that in the present context we are dealing with couples (φ, ψ), etc., where $\varphi \in \mathscr{A}_1$, $\psi \in \mathscr{A}_2$ and that this set of couples may be itself regarded as a Banach space if one uses as a norm $\|(\varphi, \psi)\| = \max\{\|\varphi\|_\lambda, \|\psi\|_\lambda\}$. Let us denote this Banach space by $\mathscr{A}(\mathfrak{S}, \mathfrak{S}^*)$. We note that the various operators we are considering are from $\mathscr{A}$ into $\mathscr{A}$ if $(F_1(z), F_2(z^*)) \in (\mathfrak{S}, \mathfrak{S}^*)$ for $(z, z^*) \in (\mathfrak{S}, \mathfrak{S}^*)$.

In order to show that the operator **B** exists it is sufficient to show that the equation

$$(\mathbf{I} - \mathbf{H} - \mathbf{J})\chi = G$$

has a unique solution for every $G \in \mathscr{A}$. Now if $(\mathbf{I} - \mathbf{H})^{-1}$ exists we may rewrite this equation as

$$(\mathbf{I} - \mathbf{A})\chi \equiv (\mathbf{I} - (\mathbf{I} - \mathbf{H})^{-1}\mathbf{J})\chi = (\mathbf{I} - \mathbf{H})^{-1}G.$$

Consequently, the question of whether the operator **B** exists can be reduced to a study of first whether $(\mathbf{I} - \mathbf{H})^{-1}$ exists and then whether $(\mathbf{I} - \mathbf{A})^{-1}$ exists. To this end it is shown in [A.G.H.2] that the following result holds, and the reader is directed to that reference for further details.

Lemma 3.5.1 *Let $f(z, z^*, U, P, Q)$ be holomorphic in the polycylinder $\mathfrak{S}^{(2)} \times \mathfrak{H}^{(3)}$, and let $\{\Delta_\rho, \Delta_\rho^*\} \equiv \{|z| \le \rho\} \times \{|z^*| \le \rho\} \subset \mathfrak{S}^{(2)}$. Furthermore, let $F_1(z) = z^*$ be an injective map of Δ_ρ into Δ_ρ^*, and $F_2(z^*) = z$ be an injective map of Δ_ρ^* into Δ_ρ, where $F_1(z)$ and $F_2(z^*)$ are analytic functions which leave the origin fixed and not both of the $F_k(W)$ assume the equality $|F_k(W)| = |W|$ in Δ_ρ. Finally, let $|\alpha_1(0)\beta_1(0)| < 1$. Then the operator $(\mathbf{I} - \mathbf{H})^{-1}$ exists in the Banach space $\mathscr{A}(\Delta_\rho, \Delta_\rho^*)$, and $\|(\mathbf{I} - \mathbf{H})^{-1}\|_\lambda \le K$ for some positive K and all $\lambda > 0$.*

Remark It is clear from the proof of Lemma 3.5.1 that if $\|\alpha_1\|_0 \cdot \|\beta_1\|_0 < 1$, then the F_k $(k = 1, 2)$ may be taken as analytic, bijective maps of Δ_ρ onto Δ_ρ, leaving the origin invariant (i.e., rotations of Δ_ρ).

We consider next the operator,

$$\mathbf{A} \equiv (\mathbf{I} - \mathbf{H})^{-1}\mathbf{J}.$$

One has the λ-norm estimate, $\|\mathbf{A}\|_\lambda \le \|(\mathbf{I} - \mathbf{H})^{-1}\|_\lambda \|\mathbf{J}\|_\lambda$. If we let $\tilde{\chi} = \mathbf{J}\chi = (\tilde{\varphi}, \tilde{\psi})$, then, from the definition of **J**, one has

$$\begin{aligned}
|\tilde{\varphi}(z)| &= \left|\alpha_0(z)\left\{\int_0^z \varphi(\xi)\,d\xi + \int_0^{F_1(z)} \psi(\xi^*)\,d\xi^*\right\}\right| \\
&\le \|\alpha_0\|_0\left\{\left|\int_0^z \varphi(\xi)\,d\xi\right| + \left|\int_0^{F_1(z)} \psi(\xi^*)\,d\xi^*\right|\right\} \\
&\le \|\alpha_0\|_0\left\{\int_0^{|z|} \|\varphi\|_\lambda e^{\lambda|\xi|}|d\xi| + \int_0^{|z|} \|\psi\|_\lambda e^{\lambda|\xi^*|}|d\xi^*|\right\} \\
&\le 2\|\alpha_0\|_0(e^{\lambda|z|}/\lambda)\,\|\chi\|_\lambda,
\end{aligned}$$

where we have assumed that $|F_1(z)| < |z|$, and that φ and ψ are regular in the disks $\Delta\rho$ and $\Delta^*\rho$ so that curvilinear paths of integration may be replaced by straight line paths of integration.

Similarly for $|\tilde{\psi}(z^*)|$ we have

$$|\tilde{\psi}(z^*)| \le 2\,\|\beta_0\|_0(e^{\lambda|z^*|}/\lambda)\,\|\chi\|_\lambda, \qquad \text{so} \quad \|\mathbf{J}\|_\lambda \le M/\lambda$$

for some positive constant M, and $\lambda > 0$. Combining this result with $\|(\mathbf{I}-\mathbf{H})^{-1})\|_\lambda \le K$ we have, for sufficiently large λ, $\|\mathbf{A}\|_\lambda \le KM/\lambda < \frac{1}{2}$. Consequently, for λ sufficiently large one has $\|\mathbf{B}\|_\lambda \le 2K$; we conclude with:

Lemma 3.5.2 *If the hypotheses of Lemma* 3.5.1 *hold, then the operator* $(\mathbf{I}-\mathbf{H}-\mathbf{J})\chi = G$ *has a solution in the Banach space* $\mathscr{A}(\Delta_\rho, \Delta_\rho{}^*)$.

What we have shown is that if $U(z, z^*)$ is a solution of (3.5.1), then we may solve for $\chi \equiv (\varphi, \psi)$ in terms of $s(z, z^*) \equiv U_{zz^*}$. From this conclusion we are now able to investigate our original problem, i.e., the existence of a unique solution to the initial value problem (3.5.1)–(3.5.4). With this object in mind we now introduce the operator

$$\mathbf{T}s(z, z^*) = f(z, z^*, \mathbf{K}_1 s, \mathbf{K}_2 s, \mathbf{K}_3 s)$$

(where the $\mathbf{K}_i$ ($i = 1, 2, 3$) are the right-hand sides of (3.5.6)–(3.5.8), which may be shown to map a closed set in the Banach space $\mathscr{A}(\Delta_\rho, \Delta_\rho{}^*)$ into itself. The $\mathbf{K}_i$ ($i = 1, 2, 3$) are representable in terms of the components of

$$\begin{aligned}\chi \equiv (\varphi, \psi) &= (\mathbf{I}-\mathbf{H}-\mathbf{J})^{-1}(\chi_0 + \mathbf{\Omega} s)\\ &= \mathbf{B}(\chi_0 + \mathbf{\Omega} s) = (\mathbf{B}_1\varphi_0, \mathbf{B}_2\psi_0) + (\mathbf{B}_1\mathbf{\Omega}_1 s, \mathbf{B}_2\mathbf{\Omega}_2 s).\end{aligned}$$

Using the above notation in the formulas (3.5.6)–(3.5.8), we may express $(\mathbf{K}_i s)$ ($i = 1, 2, 3$) as follows:

$$\begin{aligned}\mathbf{K}_1 s &= \tilde{\mathbf{D}} s + \mathbf{j}(\mathbf{B}_1\mathbf{\Omega}_1 s) + \mathbf{j}^*(\mathbf{B}_2\mathbf{\Omega}_2 s) + u_1,\\ \mathbf{K}_2 s &= \mathbf{D}^* s + \mathbf{B}_1\mathbf{\Omega}_1 s + \varphi_1,\\ \mathbf{K}_3 s &= \mathbf{D} s + \mathbf{B}_2\mathbf{\Omega}_2 s + \psi_1,\end{aligned} \tag{3.5.18}$$

where

$$\tilde{\mathbf{D}} s(z, z^*) = \int_0^z \int_0^{z^*} s(\xi, \xi^*)\, d\xi^*\, d\xi,$$

$$\mathbf{D}^* s(z, z^*) = \int_0^{z^*} s(z, \xi^*)\, d\xi^*, \tag{3.5.19}$$

$$\mathbf{D}s(z, z^*) = \int_0^z s(\xi, z^*)\, d\xi,$$

$$\mathbf{j}(\mathbf{B}_1\mathbf{\Omega}_1 s) = \int_0^z (\mathbf{B}_1\mathbf{\Omega}_1 s)(\xi, z^*)\, d\xi,$$

$$\mathbf{j}^*(\mathbf{B}_2\mathbf{\Omega}_2 s) = \int_0^{z^*} (\mathbf{B}_2\mathbf{\Omega}_2 s)(z, \xi^*)\, d\xi^*, \tag{3.5.20}$$

and where

$$u_1 = \gamma + \int_0^z \varphi_1(\xi)\, d\xi + \int_0^{z^*} \psi_1(\xi^*)\, d\xi^*. \tag{3.5.21}$$

As we recall, $f(z, z^*, U, P, Q)$ was assumed to be holomorphic in the polycylinder, $\mathfrak{S}^{(2)} \times \mathfrak{H}^{(3)}$; consequently, using the Schwarz lemma for functions of several complex variables, Theorem 1.4.1, one has for (z, z^*, U_0, P_0, Q_0), $(z, z^*, U, P, Q) \in \mathfrak{S}^{(2)} \times \mathfrak{H}^{(3)}$, that

$$|f(z, z^*, U, P, Q) - f(z, z^*, U_0, P_0, Q_0)| \leq \frac{\|W\|}{R} \max_{\|W\|=R} |f(z, z^*, U, P, Q)| \tag{3.5.22}$$

where $W \equiv (U - U_0, P - P_0, Q - Q_0)$, $\|W\|$ is a suitable norm, and $\{\|W\| = R\} \subset \mathfrak{H}^{(3)}$. If for instance, we take as our norm,

$$\|W\| = |U - U_0| + |P - P_0| + |Q - Q_0|,$$

then one obtains the following Lipschitz condition with a *sharp* inequality,

$$|\mathbf{T}s - \mathbf{T}\tilde{s}| \leq L_0(|\mathbf{K}_1 s - \mathbf{K}_1 \tilde{s}| + |\mathbf{K}_2 s - \mathbf{K}_2 \tilde{s}| + |\mathbf{K}_3 s - \mathbf{K}_3 \tilde{s}|), \tag{3.5.23}$$

where $L_0 = (1/R) \max_{\|W\|=R} |f(z, z^*, U, P, Q)|$. From our definition of the λ-norm we obtain from this,

$$\|\mathbf{T}s - \mathbf{T}\tilde{s}\|_\lambda \leq L_0(\|\mathbf{K}_1 s - \mathbf{K}_1 \tilde{s}\|_\lambda + \|\mathbf{K}_2 s - \mathbf{K}_2 \tilde{s}\|_\lambda + \|\mathbf{K}_3 s - \mathbf{K}_3 \tilde{s}\|_\lambda). \tag{3.5.24}$$

It is easy to show that the various operators appearing in (3.5.18)–(3.5.21) estimated in terms of their λ-norms are of the order $1/\lambda$, for $\lambda > 0$; for instance we obtain

$$
\begin{aligned}
|\tilde{\mathbf{D}}s| &\leq \|s\|_\lambda \int_0^{|z|}\int_0^{|z^*|} \exp[\lambda(|\xi| + |\xi^*|)]\, d\xi^*\, d\xi \\
&\leq (\|s\|_\lambda/\lambda^2) \exp \lambda(|z| + |z^*|),
\end{aligned}
$$

which implies $\|\tilde{\mathbf{D}}\|_\lambda \leq 1/\lambda$ for $\lambda > 1$. Obtaining similar bounds for the other operators we have

$$
\|\mathbf{K}_1 s\|_\lambda \leq \|\tilde{\mathbf{D}}\|_\lambda \|s\|_\lambda + \|\mathbf{j}\mathbf{B}_1 \boldsymbol{\Omega}_1\|_\lambda \|s\|_\lambda + \|\mathbf{j}^*\mathbf{B}_2 \boldsymbol{\Omega}_2\|_\lambda \|s\|_\lambda + \|u_1\|_0,
$$

where all the coefficients of $\|s\|_\lambda$ are $O(1/\lambda)$. Hence, for $\|s\|_\lambda$ bounded, and for λ sufficiently large $\|\mathbf{K}_1 s\| \leq C_1$ if $\|u_1\|_0 < C_1$. Likewise, for $\|s\|_\lambda$ bounded and λ sufficiently large, by completely analogous reasoning, we have if $\|\varphi_1\|_0 < C_2$ and $\|\psi_1\|_0 < C_3$, then $\|\mathbf{K}_2 s\| < C_2$ and $\|\mathbf{K}_3 s\| < C_3$.

Combining the above result with (3.5.24) we have

$$
\|\mathbf{T}s - \mathbf{T}\tilde{s}\|_\lambda \leq L_0[C_1 + C_2 + C_3] = L_1 ;
$$

hence if $\|s - \tilde{s}\|_\lambda \leq L_1$ (for λ sufficiently large) then $\mathbf{T}$ takes a closed ball in $\mathscr{A}(\Delta_\rho, \Delta_\rho^*)$ into itself. To see finally that $\mathbf{T}$ is a contraction mapping, we consider the following estimate (for λ sufficiently large)

$$
\|\mathbf{T}s - \mathbf{T}\tilde{s}\|_\lambda \leq L_0 \left\{ \sum_{i=1}^{3} \|\mathbf{K}_i s - \mathbf{K}_i \tilde{s}\| \right\} \leq L_2/\lambda.
$$

We have then:

Lemma 3.5.3 *There exists a unique solution to the equation* $\mathbf{T}s(z, z^*) = s(z, z^*)$.

The above results have applications to both linear and nonlinear elliptic equations. First let us consider the nonlinear equation,

$$
F(x, y, W, W_x, W_y, W_{xx}, W_{yy}) \equiv \Delta W + \tilde{f}(x, y, W, W_x, W_y) = 0, \tag{3.5.25}
$$

where $W(x, y) = u(x, y) + iv(x, y)$, and let us seek a solution that satisfies the following initial data on the two analytic curves, $y = f_1(x)$, $x = f_2(y)$:

$$
\begin{aligned}
u_x &= \alpha_0^{(1)}u - \alpha_0^{(2)}v + \alpha_1^{(1)}u_y - \alpha_1^{(2)}v_y + g^{(1)} \qquad (\text{on } y = f_1(x)), \\
v_x &= \alpha_0^{(2)}u + \alpha_0^{(1)}v + \alpha_1^{(2)}u_y + \alpha_1^{(1)}v_x + g^{(2)} \qquad (\text{on } y = f_1(x)),
\end{aligned}
\tag{3.5.26}
$$

$$\begin{aligned} u_y &= \beta_0^{(1)}u - \beta_0^{(2)}v + \beta_1^{(1)}u_x - \beta_1^{(2)}v_x + h^{(1)} && (\text{on } x = f_2(y)), \\ v_y &= \beta_0^{(2)}u + \beta_0^{(1)}v + \beta_1^{(2)}u_x + \beta_1^{(1)}v_y + h^{(2)} && (\text{on } x = f_2(y)), \end{aligned} \tag{3.5.27}$$

where

$$\begin{aligned} \tilde{\alpha}_k &= \alpha_k^{(1)} + i\alpha_k^{(2)} \quad (k = 0, 1), \quad \tilde{g} = g^{(1)} + ig^{(2)}, \\ \tilde{\beta}_k &= \beta_k^{(1)} + i\beta_k^{(2)} \quad (k = 0, 1), \quad \tilde{h} = h^{(1)} + ih^{(2)}, \end{aligned} \tag{3.5.28}$$

and

$$u(x_0, y_0) = \gamma^{(1)}, \qquad v(x_0, y_0) = \gamma^{(2)}, \qquad \tilde{\gamma} = \gamma^{(1)} + i\gamma^{(2)}. \tag{3.5.29}$$

Finally, certain analyticity conditions must be imposed on the coefficients of the data and the function $\tilde{f}(x, y, W, W_x, W_y)$. The conditions on the data are essentially the same as for the linear version of (3.5.25), and we state the following theorem which applies to the linear case. We first prove a theorem for the case where the carriers of the Goursat data are two straight lines.

Theorem 3.5.4 [G.K.L.1] *The nonlinear elliptic partial differential equation* (3.5.25) *with initial data*, (3.5.26)–(3.5.29), *given on the two straight lines*, $y = Ax$, $x = By$, with $AB \neq 1$, *has a unique solution in a sufficiently small disk* Δ_ρ, *providing the following conditions hold:*

(1) $\Delta_\rho \subset \mathfrak{S} \cap \mathfrak{S}^*$;

(2) $\tilde{\alpha}_0(\xi_2), \tilde{\alpha}_1(\xi_2)$ $\tilde{g}(\xi_2)$ *are analytic in* $(i\mathfrak{R}^{(2)})$, *and* $\tilde{\beta}_0(\xi_1), \tilde{\beta}_1(\xi_1), \tilde{h}(\xi_1)$ *are analytic in* $\mathfrak{R}^{(2)}$, *where* $(i\mathfrak{R}^{(2)}) \equiv$ *convex hull of* $[\mathfrak{S} \cup \mathfrak{S}^*]$;

(3) $f(z, z^*, W, W_z, W_{z^*}) \equiv \tilde{f}\{(z + z^*)/2, (z - z^*)/2i, W, W_z + W_{z^*}, i[W_z - W_{z^*}]\}$ *with* $W(z, z^*) \equiv \hat{W}(x, y)$ *has a holomorphic continuation to a polycylinder* $\mathfrak{S}^{(2)} \times \mathfrak{H}^{(3)}$; *and*

(4) $$\left| \frac{\tilde{\alpha}_1(0) - i}{\tilde{\alpha}_1(0) + 1} \cdot \frac{\tilde{\beta}_1(0) - i}{\tilde{\beta}_1(0) + i} \right| < 1.$$

Proof We transform the linear partial differential equation (3.5.25) with the initial data (3.5.26)–(3.5.29) to the hyperbolic equation (3.5.1) with the generalized Goursat data (3.5.2)–(3.5.4). Condition (2) implies that the F_k are bijective mappings of Δ_ρ *onto* Δ_ρ; in particular, we have $F_1(z) \equiv ze^{i\alpha}$, and $F_2(z^*) \equiv z^*e^{i\beta}$, where $e^{i\alpha} = (i + A)/(i - A)$ and $e^{i\beta} = (B + i)/(B - i)$. Using this form for the analytic surfaces Γ_k $(k = 1, 2)$ the transformed Goursat data (3.5.2), (3.5.3) becomes,

$$U_z(z, z^*) = \{1 - \alpha_1(z)e^{i\alpha}\}^{-1}[\alpha_0(z)U(z, z^*) + \hat{g}(z)], \tag{3.5.30}$$

and

$$U_{z^*}(z, z^*) = \{1 - \beta_1(z^*)e^{i\beta}\}^{-1}[\beta_0(z^*)U(z, z^*) + \hat{h}(z^*)]. \tag{3.5.31}$$

Introducing the functions $s(z, z^*)$, $\varphi(z)$, and $\psi(z^*)$ as before by (3.5.5)–(3.5.9), we obtain the following altered form of the initial data (3.5.11) and (3.5.12), namely

$$\begin{aligned}\varphi(z) = {} & [a(z)\alpha_0(z)\int_0^z d\xi \int_0^{ze^{i\alpha}} d\xi^*\, s(\xi, \xi^*) - \int_0^{ze^{i\alpha}} s(z, \xi^*)\, d\xi^*] \\ & + a(z)\alpha_0(z)[\int_0^z \varphi(\xi)\, d\xi + \int_0^{ze^{i\alpha}} \psi(\xi^*)\, d\xi^*] + a(z)\alpha_0(z)[\hat{g}(z) + \gamma],\end{aligned} \tag{3.5.32a}$$

where $a(z) \equiv \{1 - \alpha_1(z)e^{i\alpha}\}^{-1}$, and

$$\begin{aligned}\psi(z^*) = {} & [b(z^*)\beta_0(z^*)\int_0^{e^{i\beta}z^*} d\xi \int_0^{z^*} d\xi^*\, s(\xi, \xi^*) - \int_0^{e^{i\beta}z^*} s(\xi, z^*)\, d\xi] \\ & + b(z^*)\beta_0(z^*)[\int_0^{z^*} \psi(\xi^*)\, d\xi^* + \int_0^{e^{i\beta}z^*} \varphi(\xi)\, d\xi] \\ & + b(z^*)\beta_0(z^*)[\hat{h}(z^*) + \gamma],\end{aligned} \tag{3.5.32b}$$

where $b(z^*) \equiv \{1 - \beta_1(z^*)e^{i\beta}\}^{-1}$. With the above formulation, the operator equation (3.5.17) takes on a reduced form,

$$(\mathbf{I} - \mathbf{J}')x = \chi_0 + \Omega' s, \tag{3.5.33}$$

where the definitions of $\mathbf{J}'$ and Ω' are somewhat modified from before; i.e.,

$$\begin{aligned}\mathbf{J}'\chi \equiv {} & (a(z)\alpha_0(z)[\int_0^z \varphi(\xi)\, d\xi + \int_0^{ze^{i\alpha}} \psi(\xi^*)\, d\xi^*], \\ & b(z^*)\beta_0(z^*)[\int_0^{z^*} \psi(\xi^*)\, d\xi^* + \int_0^{z^*e^{i\beta}} \varphi(\xi)\, d\xi]),\end{aligned} \tag{3.5.34}$$

and

$$\Omega'\chi \equiv (a(z)\alpha_0(z) \int_0^z d\xi \int_0^{ze^{i\alpha}} s(\xi, \xi^*)\, d\xi^* - \int_0^{ze^{i\alpha}} s(z, \xi^*)\, d\xi^*,$$

$$b(z^*)\beta_0(z^*) \int_0^{z^*} d\xi^* \int_0^{z^*e^{i\beta}} s(\xi, \xi^*)\, d\xi - \int_0^{z^*e^{i\beta}} s(\xi, z^*)\, d\xi). \quad (3.5.35)$$

The essential difference between this operator equation and (3.5.17) is that no operator of the form **H** appears here. The reader will recall that the approach used to establish Lemma 3.5.2 depended on the existence of the operator $(\mathbf{I} - \mathbf{H})^{-1}$. The existence at this operator was proved in [A.G.H.2] for the case where the F_k were strictly *into* analytic maps $F_k : \Delta_\rho \to \Delta_\rho$. In the present case we have bijective maps of Δ_ρ *onto* Δ_ρ; however, the operator **H** does not appear in (3.5.33). Now, providing the functions $a(z)$ and $b(z^*)$ remain bounded in Δ_ρ and Δ_ρ^* respectively, one may show by using identical arguments, as when bounding $\|\mathbf{J}\|$, that $\|\mathbf{J}'\| < M/\lambda$. If $|\alpha_1(0)\beta_1(0)| < 1$, then by continuity, there will exist a closed disk of radius ρ in which $a(z)$ and $b(z^*)$ are bounded. Condition (4) ensures that this holds for the transformed coefficients.

Finally, we conclude that $(\mathbf{I} - \mathbf{J}')^{-1}$ exists and that (3.5.33) has a solution in the Banach space $\mathscr{A}(\Delta_\rho, \Delta_\rho^*)$. The remainder of the theorem follows identically the proof of Lemma 3.5.3.

Corollary 3.5.5 *The nonlinear elliptic partial differential equation* (3.5.25) *with initial data* (3.5.26)–(3.5.29) *given on two nontangent analytic curves, has a unique solution in a sufficiently small disk* Δ_ρ, *providing conditions* (1)–(4) *of Theorem* (3.5.4) *hold, and in addition, one has:*

(5) $f_1(\xi_1), f_2(\xi_2)$ *are analytic for* $\xi_1 \in \mathfrak{R}^{(2)}$ *and* $\xi_2 \in (i\mathfrak{R}^{(2)})$ *respectively.*

Proof Locally, two analytic surfaces are approximated by their tangent analytic planes. Hence, in a sufficiently small neighborhood of the origin, all nontangent intersecting analytic curves intersect essentially as two straight lines, $y = Ax$, $x = By$ $(AB \neq 1)$. If the above problem did not have a unique solution then this would violate the validity of Theorem 3.5.4.

Remark Corollary 3.5.5 has also been established by entirely analytic arguments by the author and Colton [C.G.2], who by using the methods of conformal mapping are able to present a constructive proof which exhibits the solution.

Remark The condition (4) of (3.5.4) and (3.5.5) implies that the coefficients $\tilde{\alpha}_1(0)$ and $\tilde{\beta}_1(0)$ are complex. This condition appears to be necessary, for if the Goursat data coefficients (3.5.28) and $\tilde{\gamma}$ were real-valued, the validity of (3.5.4) and (3.5.5) would imply the nonuniqueness of the Robin problem. Indeed, if the real data (3.5.26), (3.5.27) for the real solution $u(x, y)$ (i.e., $v(x, y) \equiv 0$) were rewritten in terms of u and its normal derivatives on $\Gamma_1 \equiv \{y = f_1(x)\}$ and $\Gamma_2 \equiv \{x = f_2(y)\}$, then in Δ_ρ one would have Robin data given on the open curve $(\Gamma_1 \cup \Gamma_2) \cap \Delta_\rho$. Such a problem is clearly not well posed and does not have a unique solution, [C.G.2].

References and Additional Reading

[A.B.1]
[A.D.1]
[A.G.2]
[A.G.H.2]
[B.5]
[B.6]
[B.7]
[B.8]
[B.9]
[B.10]
[B.11]
[B.12]
[B.14]
[B.18]
[B.22]
[B.27]
[B.28]
[B.29]
[B.30]
[B.31]
[B.32]
[B.33]
[B.35]
[B.B.1]
[B.E.1],
[B.G.1]
[B.H.1]
[B.S.1]
[C.3]
[C.D.1]
[C.D.2]
[C.G.2]
[C.H.1]
[D.1]
[D.2]
[D.3]
[D.5]
[D.7]
[D.8]
[D.L.1]
[D.L.2]
[D.L.3]
[D.L.4]
[D.L.5]
[D.R.1]
[D.S.1]
[D.S.2]
[D.W.1]
[E.1]
[E.2]
[E.3]
[E.4]
[F.1]
[G.1]
[G.2]
[G.3]
[G.4]
[G.5]
[G.16]
[H.5]
[H.6]
[H.8]
[H.W.1]
[K.3]
[K.F.1]
[L.3]
[L.4]
[L.5]
[N.1]
[N.2]
[N.3]
[N.4]
[N.5]
[R.W.1]
[S.3]
[S.5]
[S.6]
[S.8]
[T.2]
[V.1]
[V.2]
[V.3]
[V.4]
[V.5]
[V.6]
[V.K.1]
[V.K.2]
[V.M.1]
[V.M.S.1]
[W.1]
[W.7]
[W.9]

4

Singular partial differential equations

1. *Integral Operators for Axially Symmetric Potentials*

If one considers the subclass $\mathscr{S}$ of axially symmetric harmonic functions the reader will recall from Chapter 2, that these functions must satisfy the Laplace equation in three variables and be independent of the azimuthal angle about the x_3-axis. In other words if we introduce the polar spherical coordinates r, θ, ϕ, which are related to x_1, x_2, x_3 by

$$x_3 = r\cos\theta, \qquad x_2 = r\sin\theta\cos\phi, \qquad x_1 = r\sin\theta\sin\phi, \tag{4.1.1}$$

then these harmonic functions must satisfy the partial differential equation

$$\frac{\partial^2\Psi}{\partial r^2} + \frac{\partial^2\Psi}{\partial\theta^2} + \frac{2}{r}\frac{\partial\Psi}{\partial r} = 0. \tag{4.1.2}$$

If we consider the operator $\mathbf{B}_3$ it is clear that we may generate solutions to this equation by simply considering integral powers of u, i.e.,

$$r^n P_n(\cos\theta) = \mathbf{B}_3(u^n) \equiv \frac{1}{2\pi i}\int_{\mathscr{L}} u^n \frac{d\zeta}{\zeta}, \tag{4.1.3}$$

where $\mathscr{L} \equiv \{\zeta \mid \zeta = e^{i\alpha}; 0 \le \alpha \le 2\pi\}$. Here $P_n(\xi) \equiv P_n^0(\xi)$, where $P_n^m(\xi)$ is the associated Legendre polynomial defined by (2.1.4). In terms of the r, θ, ϕ coordinates u may be rewritten as

$$u = r\left\{\cos\theta + \frac{i}{2}\sin\theta\left[\frac{e^{i\phi}}{\zeta} + \frac{\zeta}{e^{i\phi}}\right]\right\}. \tag{4.1.4}$$

It may be readily seen that the auxiliary variable u may be replaced by a simpler variable σ,

$$\sigma = r\left\{\cos\theta + \frac{i}{2}\sin\theta\left[\zeta + \frac{1}{\zeta}\right]\right\}, \tag{4.1.5}$$

by noticing that Cauchy's residue formula yields

$$r^n P_n(\cos\theta) = \frac{1}{2\pi i}\int_{\mathscr{L}} \sigma^n \frac{d\zeta}{\zeta}, \tag{4.1.6}$$

(where $\mathscr{L}$ is the unit circle). This follows by expanding σ^n and u^n in powers of ζ, i.e.,

$$\sigma^n = r^n \sum_{m=-n}^{+n} A_{nm}(\theta, \phi)\zeta^m \tag{4.1.7}$$

$$u^n = \sum_{m=-n}^{+n} \frac{n!}{(n-m)!} r^n P_n^m(\cos\theta)e^{-im\phi}\zeta^m, \tag{4.1.8}$$

and computing the integrals (4.1.3) and (4.1.6) above. It is clear that only the coefficient of ζ^0 contributes to the integral; hence,

$$r^n A_{n,0}(\theta, \phi) \equiv r^n P_n(\cos\theta) = \frac{1}{2\pi i}\int_{\mathscr{L}} \sigma^n \frac{d\zeta}{\zeta}.$$

If we introduce as new variables

$$x = r\cos\theta, \qquad y = r\sin\theta,$$

then the axially symmetric Laplacian (4.1.2) becomes

$$\Phi_{xx} + \Phi_{yy} + y^{-1}\Phi_y = 0, \qquad \Phi(x, y) \equiv \Psi(r, \theta). \tag{4.1.9}$$

Hence, we see that a partial differential equation of the form (3.0.1) occurs with singular coefficients when one reduces the number of coordinates of the Laplace equation by setting $x = x_1$, and $y = +(x_2{}^2 + x_3{}^2)^{1/2}$. If one considers instead the n-dimensional Laplace equation

$$\frac{\partial^2\tilde{\Phi}}{\partial x_1{}^2} + \frac{\partial^2\tilde{\Phi}}{\partial x_2{}^2} + \cdots + \frac{\partial\tilde{\Phi}}{\partial x_n{}^2} = 0, \tag{4.1.10}$$

and just those solutions which depend solely on the variables $x = x_1$, $y = +(x_2{}^2 + \cdots + x_n{}^2)^{1/2}$, then those functions $\Phi(x, y) \equiv \tilde{\Phi}$ satisfy the singular equation given below, which is known as the partial differential equation of generalized axially symmetric potential theory (GASPT)†,

$$\mathbf{L}_\mu[\Phi] \equiv \frac{\partial^2 \Phi}{\partial x^2} + \frac{\partial^2 \Phi}{\partial y^2} + \frac{2\mu}{y}\frac{\partial \Phi}{\partial y} = 0, \qquad \text{where} \quad 2\mu = n - 2 \quad \text{(GASPT)}. \tag{4.1.11}$$

By changing to the polar coordinates $x = r\cos\theta$, $y = r\sin\theta$, this becomes $\Phi(r; \theta) \equiv \Phi(r\cos\theta, r\sin\theta)$,

$$\frac{\partial^2 \Phi}{\partial r^2} + \frac{2\mu + 1}{r}\frac{\partial \Phi}{\partial r} + \frac{1}{r^2}\frac{\partial^2 \Phi}{\partial \theta^2} + \frac{2\mu}{r^2}\operatorname{ctn}\theta \frac{\partial \Phi}{\partial \theta} = 0.$$

The standard method of separation of variables yields a system of solutions regular about the origin having the form

$$\Phi_n(r; \theta) \equiv r^n C_n^\mu(\cos\theta) \qquad (n = 0, 1, 2, \ldots), \tag{4.1.12}$$

where the $C_n^\mu(\xi)$ are Gegenbauer (ultraspherical) polynomials [E.6]. The system (4.1.12) is known to form a complete set with respect to functions of the class $L^2[\Delta]$ ($\Delta \equiv \{(x, y) \mid x^2 + y^2 \le 1\}$). This is indeed true for all μ, such that $\operatorname{Re}\mu > 0$.

The well-known classical integral representation for the Gegenbauer polynomials, namely

$$r^n C_n^\mu(\cos\theta) = \frac{2^{1-2\mu}}{n!}\frac{\Gamma(n + 2\mu)}{\Gamma(\mu)^2}\int_0^\pi [x + iy\cos\phi]^n \sin^{2\mu-1}\phi \, d\phi \tag{4.1.13}$$

suggests an integral operator that will generate solutions of (4.1.11) for arbitrary but fixed μ such that $\operatorname{Re}\mu > 0$. For instance, if we use the variable σ introduced in (4.1.5) then it is clear that we may rewrite (4.1.13) by introducing the change of integration parameter, $\zeta = e^{i\phi}$, as

† The theory and application of GASPT has been extensively developed by Weinstein [W.6–15] and his associates at the Institute for Fluid Dynamics and Applied Mathematics. Weinstein was the first to consider fractional dimensional spaces, i.e., for μ not necessarily a positive half-integer, and has shown the usefulness of such a concept in the application to problems in fluid mechanics and other areas of applied mathematics. See also Payne [P.1]

$$\frac{\Gamma(2\mu)\Gamma(n+1)}{\Gamma(n+2\mu)} r^n C_n^\mu(\cos\theta) = \alpha_\mu \int_{\mathscr{L}} \sigma^n(\zeta - \zeta^{-1})^{2\mu-1} \frac{d\zeta}{\zeta}, \tag{4.1.14}$$

where

$$\alpha_\mu \equiv \frac{4\Gamma(2\mu)}{(4i)^{2\mu}\Gamma(\mu)^2}, \qquad \text{and} \qquad \mathscr{L} \equiv \{\zeta \mid \zeta = e^{i\phi}; 0 \le \phi \le \pi\}.$$

The choice of the "normalization constant" a_μ is made so that when $y = 0$ one has

$$\begin{aligned} x^n &= \alpha_\mu \int_{\mathscr{L}} (\sigma|_{y=0})^n(\zeta - \zeta^{-1})^{2\mu-1} \frac{d\zeta}{\zeta} \\ &= x^n \alpha_\mu \int_{\mathscr{L}} (\zeta - \zeta^{-1})^{2\mu-1} \frac{d\zeta}{\zeta}. \end{aligned}$$

We realize then that the auxiliary variable σ plays the same role in this case as for the axially symmetric potentials ($\mu = \frac{1}{2}$), and that the operator

$$\mathbf{A}_\mu f \equiv \alpha_\mu \int_{\mathscr{L}} f(\sigma)(\zeta - \zeta^{-1})^{2\mu-1} \frac{d\zeta}{\zeta} \tag{4.1.15}$$

generates solutions of Eq. (4.1.11) known as the partial differential equation of "generalized" axially symmetric potentials (GASP) [G.9].† For instance, if $f(\sigma)$ has the following Taylor series development about the origin,

$$f(\sigma) = \sum_{n=0}^{\infty} a_n \sigma^n,$$

then the corresponding solution $u(r; \theta) = \mathbf{A}_\mu f$ has the representation‡

$$u(r; \theta) = (2\mu - 1) \sum_{n=0}^{\infty} B(2\mu - 1, n + 1) a_n r^n C_n^\mu(\cos\theta), \qquad \mu > \tfrac{1}{2}; \tag{4.1.16}$$

furthermore, if $u(r; \theta) \equiv u(r\cos\theta, r\sin\theta)$, then on the x-axis ($y = 0$) we have

$$f(x) = \sum_{n=0}^{\infty} a_n x^n = u(x, 0).$$

† For further details concerning axially symmetric potentials we refer the reader to the work of Weinstein [W.6–15], Erdélyi [E.7,9], Henrici [H.4,7,8] and Ranger [R.1,2].

‡ $B(p, q) = \Gamma(p)\Gamma(q)/\Gamma(p + q)$ is the beta function [E.6, Vol. I, p. 9].

Consequently, if we are speaking of real solutions of (4.1.11), then $f(z)$ is real on the x-axis and (4.1.15) gives a "continuation" of the GASP function to either the upper or lower half-plane that has the boundary value $u(x, 0) = f(x)$ on the x-axis. In general, $u(x, y) \neq u(x, -y)$; however, if $u(x, y) \in \mathscr{C}^{(2)}$ and $\partial u(x, 0)/\partial y = 0$, then we have this type of reflection principle.

We now turn our attention to another singular equation that was investigated by the author [G.20] using a similar approach to that given above, namely the equation†

$$\mathbf{L}_{\mu\nu}[\Phi] \equiv \frac{\partial^2 \Phi}{\partial x^2} + \frac{2\mu}{x}\frac{\partial \Phi}{\partial x} + \frac{\partial^2 \Phi}{\partial y^2} + \frac{2\nu}{y}\frac{\partial \Phi}{\partial y} = 0, \tag{4.1.17}$$

$\mu, \nu > 0$. We shall consider just these solutions of (4.1.17) that are even in x and y. In this case for $\Phi(x, y) \in \mathscr{C}^{(2)}$ we must have that $\partial \Phi/\partial x = 0$ on $x = 0$, and $\partial \Phi/\partial y = 0$ on $y = 0$. A complete set of solutions for this equation that are regular about the origin are given by [G.20], [H.6]

$$\Phi_n(x, y) \equiv \Phi_n(r; \theta) = r^{2n} P_n^{(\nu - \frac{1}{2}, \mu - \frac{1}{2})}(\cos 2\theta), \tag{4.1.18}$$

where the $P_n^{(\alpha, \beta)}(\xi)$ are the Jacobi polynomials [E.6] and $\theta = \cos^{-1}(x/r)$. We are able to construct an integral operator for the solutions of (4.1.17) by making use of the Rodrigues formula for the Jacobi polynomials, i.e.,

$$P_n^{(\alpha, \beta)}(\xi) = \frac{(-1)^n}{2^n n!}(1 - \xi)^{-\alpha}(1 + \xi)^{-\beta}\frac{d^n}{d\xi^n}[(1 - \xi)^{\alpha + n}(1 + \xi)^{\beta + n}],$$

which leads to the integral representation for the $P_n^{(\alpha, \beta)}$,

$$P_n^{(\alpha, \beta)}(\xi) = \frac{1}{2\pi i}\int_{|t - \xi| = \varepsilon}\left(\frac{1}{2}\frac{t^2 - 1}{t - \xi}\right)^n\left(\frac{1 - t}{1 - \xi}\right)^\alpha\left(\frac{1 + t}{1 + \xi}\right)^\beta dt, \tag{4.1.19}$$

where the circle about ξ is sufficiently small so as not to include $\xi = \pm 1$. The representation (4.1.19) may be written in a more convenient form if we take the parameter of integration to be $t = \xi + \varepsilon(\xi^2 - 1)^{1/2}e^{i\phi}$; then we have

$$r^{2n} P_n^{(\nu - \frac{1}{2}, \mu - \frac{1}{2})}(\cos 2\theta) = \frac{1}{2\pi i}\int_{|\zeta| = \varepsilon}(x^2 - y^2 + ixy[\zeta + \zeta^{-1}])^n \times \left(1 + \frac{ix}{y}\zeta\right)^{\nu - \frac{1}{2}}\left(1 + \frac{iy}{x}\zeta\right)^{\mu - \frac{1}{2}} d\zeta \tag{4.1.20}$$

† Henrici has given an operator that depends on the variable σ, which generates solutions of (4.1.17). We shall discuss this operator in Section 5 of this chapter.

where $\varepsilon < \min\{|x/y|, |y/x|\}$, $x \neq 0$, $y \neq 0$. This expression suggests the introduction of the following integral operator:

$$\Phi(x, y) = \mathbf{G}_{\mu\nu} f \equiv \frac{1}{2\pi i} \int_{|\zeta|=\varepsilon} f(\tau)\left[1 + \frac{ix}{y}\zeta\right]^{\nu-\frac{1}{2}}\left[1 + \frac{iy}{x}\zeta\right]^{\mu-\frac{1}{2}} d\zeta, \quad (4.1.21)$$

$\tau = x^2 - y^2 + ixy[\zeta + 1/\zeta]$, where $z = (x + iy)$ is a point in a sufficiently small neighborhood $\mathcal{N}(z^0)$ of z^0 (an initial point of definition), which does not meet the x- or y-axes. The operator $\mathbf{G}_{\mu\nu}$ may be seen to map the class of analytic functions regular about the origin $f(z) = \sum_{n=0}^{\infty} a_n z^n$ onto the class of solutions,

$$\Phi(x, y) = \sum_{n=0}^{\infty} a_n r^{2n} P_n^{(\nu-\frac{1}{2}, \mu-\frac{1}{2})}(\cos 2\theta).\dagger \quad (4.1.22)$$

It is possible to introduce another operator which generates solutions of the equation (4.1.17) by making use of the *generating function* for the Jacobi polynomials and the reader is referred to the paper [G.20] by the author for details concerning the construction of such an operator.

Frequently, it is useful in the study of the solutions generated by integral operators to have an inverse operator which maps solutions back onto the analytic function to which they correspond. (This is particularly true for the investigation of singularities and the growth of solutions which will be seen later.) To this end we introduce the kernel

$$K_2(\tau r^{-2}, \xi) \equiv 2^{-\mu-\nu} \sum_{n=0}^{\infty} \frac{(2n + \mu + \nu)n!\,\Gamma(n + \mu + \nu)}{\Gamma(n + \mu + \frac{1}{2})\Gamma(n + \nu + \frac{1}{2})} P_n^{(\mu-\frac{1}{2}, \nu-\frac{1}{2})}(\xi)\left(\frac{\tau}{r^2}\right)^n, \quad (4.1.23)$$

so that by employing the orthogonality criteria for the Jacobi polynomials [E.6],

$$\int_{-1}^{+1} P_n^{(\alpha,\beta)}(\xi) P_m^{(\alpha,\beta)}(\xi)(1 - \xi)^\alpha (1 + \xi)^\beta \, d\xi = \frac{\delta_{nm} 2^{\alpha+\beta+1}\Gamma(n + \alpha + 1)\Gamma(n + \beta + 1)}{(2n + \alpha + \beta + 1)n!\,\Gamma(n + \alpha + \beta + 1)},$$

we have by formally integrating term-by-term that

† We note that even though the series (4.1.22) is defined in a full neighborhood of $z = 0$ the integral representation (4.1.21) is not defined on $\{x = 0\} \cup \{y = 0\}$.

$$f(\tau) \equiv \sum_{n=0}^{\infty} a_n \tau^n = \int_{-1}^{+1} K_2\left(\frac{\tau}{r^2}, \xi\right)\left[\sum_{n=0}^{\infty} a_n r^{2n} P_n^{(\mu-\frac{1}{2}, \nu-\frac{1}{2})}(\xi)\right] d\xi. \quad (4.1.24)$$

This representation suggests the definition of the integral operator,

$$\mathbf{G}_{\mu\nu}^{-1}\Phi \equiv \int_{\mathscr{L}-1}^{+1} K_2(\tau/r^2, \xi)\Phi(r; \xi)\, d\xi,$$

where $\mathscr{L}$ is a simple curve joining -1 to $+1$. The author obtained a closed expression for the kernel $K_2(\tau r^{-2}, \xi)$ by making use of a generating function given by Brafman [B.38], [E.6]. He obtained the expression

$$\frac{\Gamma(\mu+\frac{1}{2})\Gamma(\nu+\frac{1}{2})2^{\mu+\nu}}{\Gamma(\mu+\nu-1)} K\left(\frac{\tau}{r^2}, \xi\right)$$

$$= \Bigg[(\mu+\nu-1)(\mu+\nu)\overset{(0)(0)}{F\,F} - \frac{t}{\omega}(\omega+t-\zeta)\left(\frac{3}{2}(\mu+\nu)\right.$$

$$\left.-\frac{t}{\omega^2}(\omega+t-\zeta)\right)\overset{(1)(0)}{F\,F} + \frac{t}{\omega}(\omega-t+\zeta)\left(\frac{3}{2}(\mu+\nu)\right.$$

$$\left.+\frac{t}{\omega^2}(\omega+t-\zeta)\right)\overset{(0)(1)}{F\,F} - t^2\frac{(1-\zeta^2)}{\omega^2}\overset{(1)(1)}{F\,F} - \frac{t^2}{2\omega^2}(\omega+t-\zeta)^2\overset{(2)(0)}{F\,F}$$

$$+\frac{t^2}{2\omega^2}(\omega-t+\zeta)^2\overset{(0)(2)}{F\,F}\Bigg]_{t=\tau/r^2},$$

where $\overset{(n)}{F}(a, b; c; z) \equiv F(a+n, b+n; c+n; z)$, and the products $\overset{(\alpha)}{F}\overset{(\beta)}{F}$ mean the ordered products,

$$\overset{(\alpha)}{F}(1, \mu+\nu-1; \nu+\tfrac{1}{2}; \tfrac{1}{2}-\tfrac{1}{2}t-\tfrac{1}{2}\omega)\overset{(\beta)}{F}(1, \mu+\nu-1; \mu+\tfrac{1}{2}; \tfrac{1}{2}+\tfrac{1}{2}t+\omega/2),$$

and where $\omega = (1-2\xi t+t^2)^{1/2}$, and

$$F(a, b; c; z) = \sum_{n=0}^{\infty} \frac{(a)_n(b)_n}{(c)_n}\frac{z^n}{n!}$$

is a hypergeometric series. The reader who is interested in the details of this derivation is referred to the original paper by the author [G.20].

The auxiliary variable approach to the construction of integral operators has been used in several cases of partial differential equations of three or more independent variables also. These will be discussed in later sections of this chapter.

2. *Analytic Properties of Generalized Axially Symmetric Potentials*

In this section we shall develop a theory for generalized axially symmetric potentials (GASPT) that mirrors the theory of analytic functions. We shall do this by employing methods similar to those developed by Bergman [B.22] for harmonic functions of three variables. (See Chapter 2 of the present work for this development of the theory.) The reason for this is quite apparent when one compares Bergman's operator $\mathbf{B}_3$ with our $\mathbf{A}_\mu$ introduced in the previous section.† The motivation for developing the present theory is to show how one may formalize a procedure by which analytic functions of a complex variable may be transformed into solutions of a partial differential equation. Clearly, these methods may be extended to a fairly wide class of partial differential equations (and this prospect will be investigated in subsequent sections). However, because the results may be explained in a more concise form for the case of GASPT we shall illustrate the range of our methods here, and merely indicate what may be accomplished with other equations, giving a complete reference to further descriptions that may be found in the literature. The importance of our theory is threefold: (1) to transplant theorems concerning analytic functions into theorems about solutions of partial differential equations, (2) to obtain representation theorems for solutions, and (3) to consider the analytic continuation of solutions. Furthermore, physical applications of results of (1), (2), and (3) will be found in the theory of scattering of elementary particles and in nonrelativistic collision theory. These applications will be considered in the next chapter.

As we have just mentioned, a major use of the integral operator method is to transplant theorems concerning analytic functions into theorems about solutions of partial differential equations. These theorems are usually stated in terms of the $\mathbf{A}_\mu$-associates, and not expressed solely in terms of the solutions. In order to overcome this it is necessary to obtain an inverse operator to $\mathbf{A}_\mu$, which maps solutions of the GASPT equation back onto their $\mathbf{A}_\mu$-associates. This may be done in several ways.

We may obtain an inverse operator of the second kind (in the language of Chapter 2) by using certain orthogonality properties of our solutions on the unit circle. This is done by first choosing a particular continuation of the

† There is no obvious connection, however, between Bergman's integral operator of the first kind and the operators of this section.

variables x, y to complex values by introducing the new (complex) variables $r = +(x^2 + y^2)^{1/2}$, $\xi = x/r$. (When x, y are real, $\xi = \cos\theta$.) Next, we define the kernel

$$K\left(\frac{\sigma}{r}, \xi\right) = \frac{\Gamma(2\mu)^2}{\Gamma(\mu+\frac{1}{2})^2} \frac{(1-\xi^2)^{\mu-\frac{1}{2}}}{2^{2\mu}} \sum_{m=0}^{\infty} (2m+2\mu)\left(\frac{\sigma}{r}\right)^m C_m^\mu(\xi). \quad (4.2.1)$$

Then, from the orthogonality relation for the Gegenbauer polynomials [E.6, Vol. I, p. 177]

$$\int_{-1}^{+1} (1-\xi^2)^{\mu-\frac{1}{2}} C_n^\mu(\xi) C_m^\mu(\xi)\, d\xi = \frac{2^{2\mu-1}\Gamma(2\mu+n)}{(n+\mu)n!} \left(\frac{\Gamma(\mu+\frac{1}{2})}{\Gamma(2\mu)}\right)^2 \delta_{mn}, \quad (4.2.2)$$

it may be seen that

$$\sigma^m = \int_{-1}^{+1} \frac{m!}{\Gamma(m+2\mu)} r^m C_m^\mu(\xi) K\left(\frac{\sigma}{r}, \xi\right) d\xi. \quad (4.2.3)$$

Consequently, if $f(\sigma) = \sum_{n=0}^{\infty} a_n \sigma^n$, and

$$W(r, \xi) = \mathbf{A}_\mu f = \Gamma(2\mu) \sum_{n=0}^{\infty} \frac{a_n n!}{\Gamma(n+2\mu)} r^n C_n^\mu(\xi),$$

then one has

$$f(\sigma) = \sum_{n=0}^{\infty} a_n \sigma^n = \int_{-1}^{+1} W(r, \xi) K\left(\frac{\sigma}{r}, \xi\right) d\xi, \quad (4.2.4)$$

where $W(r, \xi) = u(x, y)$ with x, y replaced by $r\xi$, $r(1-\xi^2)^{1/2}$, respectively. To justify this procedure we note that $K(\sigma/r, \xi)$ may be summed formally, whenever $|\sigma/r| \le \rho < 1$;

$$\begin{aligned} K\left(\frac{\sigma}{r}, \xi\right) &= 2^{-2\mu} \frac{\Gamma(2\mu)^2}{[\Gamma(\mu+\frac{1}{2})]^2} (1-\xi^2)^{\mu-\frac{1}{2}} \\ &\quad \times \left\{ t^{1-2\mu} \frac{\partial}{\partial t} \left[t^{2\mu} \sum_{n=0}^{\infty} t^{2n} C_n^\mu(\xi) \right] \right\}_{t=(\sigma/r)^{1/2}} \\ &= \mu 2^{-2\mu+1} \frac{\Gamma(2\mu)^2}{[\Gamma(\mu+\frac{1}{2})]^2} \frac{(1-\xi^2)^{\mu-\frac{1}{2}}(1-\sigma^2/r^2)}{[1-2\xi(\sigma/r)+\sigma^2/r^2]^{\mu+1}}. \end{aligned} \quad (4.2.5)$$

This follows from the classical identity [E.6, Vol. I, p. 175]

$$\sum_{n=0}^{\infty} t^n C_n^{\mu}(\xi) = (1 - 2\xi t + t^2)^{-\mu}, \qquad \text{for} \quad |t| < 1. \tag{4.2.6}$$

The constant coefficient in (4.2.5) may be reduced by means of the Legendre duplication formula [E.6, Vol. I, p. 5]

$$\frac{\Gamma(2\mu)}{\Gamma(\mu)} = \frac{2^{2\mu-1}}{\pi^{1/2}} \Gamma(\mu + \tfrac{1}{2}),$$

such that one obtains

$$K\left(\frac{\sigma}{r}, \xi\right) = \frac{\beta_\mu (1 - \xi^2)^{\mu - \frac{1}{2}} (1 - \sigma^2/r^2)}{[1 - 2\xi(\sigma/r) + \sigma^2/r^2]^{\mu+1}},$$
$$\beta_\mu = \frac{\mu}{\pi} \Gamma(\mu)^2 2^{2\mu-1}. \tag{4.2.7}$$

Lemma 4.2.1 *Let* $W(r, \cos\theta) = u(x, y)$ *be a* GASPT *function element defined about the origin by the integral operator* $\mathbf{A}_\mu f$, *where* $f(\sigma) = \sum_{n=0}^{\infty} a_n \sigma^n$. *Then there exists an inverse integral operator*

$$\mathbf{A}_\mu^{-1} u \equiv \int_{\mathscr{C}-1}^{+1} W(r, \xi) K(\sigma/r, \xi)\, d\xi,$$

$K(\sigma/r, \xi)$ *is the kernel defined in* (4.2.7) *and* $\mathscr{C}$ *is a smooth curve joining* -1 to $+1$, *which maps* $u(x, y)$ *back onto its* $\mathbf{A}_\mu$*-associate*, $f(\sigma)$.

It is possible to find another inverse operator for $\mathbf{A}_\mu$ by considering $u(x, y)$ on the space $r^2 \equiv zz^* = 0$. We assume as before that

$$f(\sigma) = \sum_{n=0}^{\infty} a_n \sigma^n, \qquad \text{and} \qquad u = \mathbf{A}_\mu f = \sum_{n=0}^{\infty} \frac{a_n \Gamma(2\mu) n!}{\Gamma(n + 2\mu)} r^n C_n^{\mu}(\xi).$$

Since

$$C_n^{\mu}(\xi) = \sum_{m=0}^{n} \frac{(-1)^m \Gamma(\mu + m) \Gamma(n + 2\mu + m)(\frac{1}{2} - \frac{1}{2}\xi)^m}{m!\, \Gamma(\mu) \Gamma(2m + 2\mu)(n - m)!} \qquad \left(\xi = \frac{x}{r}\right); \tag{4.2.8}$$

as $r \to 0$, we have

$$\lim_{r \to 0} r^n C_n^\mu(\xi) = \frac{\Gamma(\mu + n)}{n!\,\Gamma(\mu)} (\tfrac{1}{2}x)^n \qquad \text{on} \quad zz^* = 0; \tag{4.2.9}$$

we may rewrite this as

$$\frac{\Gamma(\mu)^2 n!}{\Gamma(2\mu + n)} (2r)^n C_n^\mu(\xi) \Big|_{zz^*=0} = [B(\mu + n, \mu) x^n] \Big|_{zz^*=0} \tag{4.2.10}$$

for $\mu > 0$, where $B(p, q)$ is the beta function.

Consequently, one has on $\{zz^* = 0\}$,

$$\begin{aligned}\frac{\Gamma(\mu)^2}{\Gamma(2\mu)} W(2r, \xi) &= \Gamma(\mu)^2 \sum_{n=0}^{\infty} \frac{a_n n!}{\Gamma(2\mu + n)} (2r)^n C_n^\mu(\xi) \\ &= \sum_{n=0}^{\infty} B(\mu + n, \mu) a_n x^n \\ &= \sum_{n=0}^{\infty} \int_0^1 t^{n+\mu-1} (1 - t)^{\mu-1} a_n x^n \, dt \\ &= \int_0^1 \sum_{n=0}^{\infty} a_n (xt)^n t^{\mu-1} (1 - t)^{\mu-1} \, dt. \end{aligned} \tag{4.2.11}$$

The inversion of the order of summation and integration is valid for all x, $\ni |x| \le \rho_0 <$ the radius of convergence of $f(\sigma)$; this result follows by considering Hadamard's theorem concerning the multiplication of singularities with respect to the functions

$$\sum_{n=0}^{\infty} a_n x^n, \qquad \sum_{n=0}^{\infty} \frac{\Gamma(2\mu + n)}{n!} x^n, \qquad \sum_{n=0}^{\infty} a_n \frac{\Gamma(2\mu + n)}{n!} x^n.$$

On the set $\mathfrak{C}^{(1)}\{zz^* = 0\}$, we may consider (4.2.11) as an integral equation for $f(xt)$, that is

$$u(2x, 2y)\,|_{\mathfrak{C}^{(1)}} = \frac{\Gamma(2\mu)}{\Gamma(\mu)^2} \int_0^1 f(xt) t^{\mu-1} (1 - t)^{\mu-1} \, dt, \tag{4.2.12}$$

where $u(2x, 2y) = w(2r, \xi)$. If we write $F(x) = u(2x, 2y)$ on $\mathfrak{C}^{(1)}$, then (4.2.12) may be written as

$$F(x) = \frac{\Gamma(2\mu)}{\Gamma(\mu)^2} \int_0^1 f(xt) t^{\mu-1} (1 - t)^{\mu-1} \, dt,$$

and by setting $\tau = xt$, $G(x) = x^{2\mu-1}F(x)$, $g(\tau) = \tau^{\mu-1}f(\tau)$, may be rewritten as a Riemann–Liouville integral [E.9],

$$G(x) = \mathbf{I}_x{}^{\mu} g(x) \equiv \frac{\Gamma(2\mu)}{\Gamma(\mu)^2} \int_0^x g(\tau)(x-\tau)^{\mu-1}\, d\tau. \tag{4.2.13}$$

The formal solution of this equation is given by

$$g(x) = \frac{\Gamma(\mu)\Gamma(2\mu)^{-1}}{\Gamma([\mu]-\mu+1)} \left(\frac{d}{dx}\right)^{[\mu]+1} \int_0^x (x-\tau)^{[\mu]-\mu} G(\tau)\, d\tau,$$

which yields

$$f(x) = \frac{(\mu)\Gamma(2\mu)^{-1}x^{1-\mu}}{\Gamma([\mu]-\mu+1)} \left(\frac{d}{dx}\right)^{[\mu]+1} \int_0^x (x-\tau)^{[\mu]-\mu}\tau^{2\mu-1} u(2\tau, 2\sigma)\,|_{\mathfrak{C}(1)}\, d\tau$$

where $t = \sigma + i\tau$. Sufficient conditions for the validity of this solution are obvious.

Having introduced the operator $\mathbf{A}_\mu$ and its inverse operator of the second kind we are now able to proceed with our investigation of the analytic properties of GASPT functions. We begin by considering the nature of singular points for such functions. To this end let us assume that $f(\sigma)$ is analytic about the origin; then

$$u(x, y) = \alpha_\mu \int_{\mathscr{L}} f\left(x + \frac{iy}{2}[\zeta + \zeta^{-1}]\right)(\zeta - \zeta^{-1})^{2\mu-1} \frac{d\zeta}{\zeta}, \tag{4.2.14}$$

where $\mathscr{L} = \{\zeta \mid \zeta = e^{i\alpha};\ 0 \le \alpha \le \pi\}$ defines a GASPT function element in some neighborhood of the origin, $\mathscr{N}(0)$. The representation (4.2.14) is actually valid for all points $z = x + iy$, which may be reached by continuation along a contour γ, providing that no point of γ corresponds to a singularity of the integrand on the path of integration, $\mathscr{L}$. We refer to this set of points $\mathfrak{D}$ as the initial domain of definition for $u(x, y) = \mathbf{A}_\mu f$. It is possible, however, sometimes to extend this domain of definition by continuously deforming the path of integration $\mathscr{L}$ into $\mathscr{L}'$ in such a manner, that it does not cross over a singularity of the integrand. For instance, as we continue $u(x, y)$ along γ in the z-plane, the singularities of $f(x + \frac{1}{2}(iy)[\zeta + \zeta^{-1}])$ move in the ζ-plane; however, as long as these singularities do not cross over $\mathscr{L}'$ we may continue $u(x, y)$ further.†

† See Chapter 1, Theorem 1.3.1 for a more detailed discussion of this process of continuation.

Let us consider the special case, where the only finite singularity of $f(\sigma)$ is at $\sigma = \alpha$; here we may represent the singularity manifold of $u(x, y)$ in complex two-space $\mathbb{C}^2$ as

$$\mathfrak{S}_0 \equiv \{(x, y) \mid S(x, y; \zeta) \equiv (x - \alpha)\zeta + \zeta\tfrac{1}{2}(iy)(^2 + 1) = 0\}.$$

It has been shown in Chapter 1 (Theorems 1.31. and 1.3.2), that the only possible singularities of a $u(x, y)$ defined by a Cauchy-type integral whose integrand is singular on the set $\mathfrak{S}_0$, must be contained in the union of the sets obtained by the envelope method $\mathfrak{S} \equiv \mathfrak{S}_0 \cap \mathfrak{S}_1$, the endpoint-pinch singularities $\hat{\mathfrak{S}} \equiv \mathfrak{S}_0 \cap \{\zeta = \pm 1\}$, and the Hadamard-pinch singularities $\tilde{\mathfrak{S}} \equiv \mathfrak{S}_0 \cap \{\zeta = 0\}$, where

$$\mathfrak{S}_1 \equiv \left\{(x, y) \,\middle|\, \frac{\partial S(x, y; \zeta)}{\partial \zeta} \equiv (x - \alpha) + iy\zeta = 0\right\}.$$

Eliminating ζ between $S = 0$ and $\partial S/\partial\zeta = 0$, yields

$$\mathfrak{S} \equiv \{(x, y) \mid (x - \alpha)^2 + y^2 = 0\} \equiv \{z \mid (z - \alpha)(z - \bar{\alpha}) = 0\}.$$

We easily compute also that $\hat{\mathfrak{S}} \equiv \mathfrak{S}$, and $\tilde{\mathfrak{S}} \equiv \{(x, y) \mid y = 0\}$. Using a simple majorization argument, one may show that the series expansion for $u(x, y)$ converges for $|z| < |\alpha|$, and is also $\mathscr{C}^{(\infty)}$ there. In order to investigate other points on the x-axis we make use of the fact that the GASPT differential equation is invariant under horizontal translations. If $(x_0, 0)$ is an arbitrary point on the x-axis and $x_0 \neq \alpha$, then we may represent the solution in a neighborhood of x_0 as

$$\tilde{u}(x', y) \equiv u(x' + x_0, y) = \alpha_\mu \int_{\mathscr{L}} f\left(x' + x_0 + \frac{iy}{2}\left[\zeta + \frac{1}{\zeta}\right]\right) (\zeta - \zeta^{-1})^{2\mu} \frac{d\zeta}{\zeta}.$$

In this way we may show that on the first Riemann space sheet of $u(x, y)$ (over the complex ξ-plane), $u(x, y)$ is regular at points on the x-axis providing they correspond to regular points of $f(z)$.
We list this result as a lemma.

Lemma 4.2.2 *If the only finite singularities of the* $\mathbf{A}_\mu$*-associate for a* GASPT-*function element* $u(x, y)$ *is at* α, *then the only possible singularities of* $u(x, y)$, *on its first Riemann sheet, lie at* α, *and* $\bar{\alpha}$.

It is possible for us, however, to show that $z = \alpha, \bar{\alpha}$ are the actual singularities of $u(x, y)$. This may be done by using the inverse operator,

$$f(\sigma) = \mathbf{A}_\mu^{-1}u(x, y) = \beta_\mu(1 - \sigma^2/r^2) \int_{\mathscr{Q}^{-1}}^{+1} \frac{W(r, \xi)(1 - \xi^2)^{\mu - \frac{1}{2}}\, d\xi}{(1 - 2\xi\sigma/r + \sigma^2/r^2)^{\mu+1}} \tag{4.2.15}$$

($W(r, \xi) = u(r\xi, r(1 - \xi^2)^{1/2})$, and considering what are the possible singularities of $f(\sigma)$ if $u(x, y)$ is singular at $z = \alpha, \bar{\alpha}$.

Lemma 4.2.3 *Let $u(x, y) = \mathbf{A}_\mu f$ be a* GASPT-*function element defined in the small of the origin. Furthermore, let $W(r, \xi) = u(r\xi, r(1 - \xi^2)^{1/2})$, and let $\mathfrak{S} \equiv \{(r, \xi) \mid \xi = \Psi(r)\}$ be the singularity manifold of $W(r, \xi)$ in $\mathbb{C}^2$; then the function $f(\sigma) = \mathbf{A}_\mu^{-1}u$ is regular at σ providing this point does not lie on the intersection*

$$\{\sigma \mid \Phi(\sigma; r) \equiv r^2 - 2\sigma r\Psi(r) + \sigma^2 = 0\} \cap \{\sigma \mid \partial\Psi/\partial r = 0\}. \tag{4.2.16}$$

Proof The proof of this result parallels that of Lemma 4.2.2. We notice that the singularities of the integrand of (4.2.15) are of two different kinds; for instance, the singularities of the kernel $K(\sigma/r, \xi)$ move in the ξ-plane as we attempt to continue $f(\sigma)$ in the σ-plane, whereas the singularities of $W(r, \xi)$ remain fixed. We realize then by Theorem 1.3.1 of Chapter I that the only possible singularities of (4.2.15) occur when the singularities of $W(r, \xi)$ and $K(\sigma/r, \xi)$ coincide in the ξ-plane. The endpoint singularities in this case do not lead to actual singularities as may be seen by computing the intersection of the kernel singularities with $\xi = \pm 1$. This concludes our proof.

Theorem 4.2.4 *If $W(r, \xi) = u(r\xi, r(1 - \xi^2)^{1/2}) = \mathbf{A}_\mu f$ has for its only finite singularities the points on the set*

$$\mathfrak{Z}^{(1)} \equiv \{(r, \xi) \mid r^2 - 2\alpha\xi r + \alpha^2 = 0\},$$

then $f(\sigma)$ is singular only at $\sigma = \alpha$.

This may be seen from the fact that the only possible singularities of $f(\sigma)$ must lie on the intersection (4.2.16). However, if $r^2 - 2\alpha\xi r + \alpha^2 = 0$, then $\xi = \Psi(r) \equiv \frac{1}{2}(r/\alpha + \alpha/r)$. Now, eliminating r between

$$\Phi(\sigma; r) \equiv r^2 - \sigma(r^2/\alpha + \alpha) + \sigma^2 = 0, \qquad \text{and} \qquad \partial\Phi/\partial r \equiv 2r(1 - \sigma/\alpha) = 0$$

yields $\sigma = \alpha$ or $\sigma = 0$. We disregard $\sigma = 0$, since $u(x, y)$ [and then consequently $f(\sigma)$] is regular at the origin.

We notice that this result can be rephrased in terms of z, and $\bar{z}$. For instance, since

$$(z-\alpha)(\bar{z}-\alpha) = z\bar{z} - \alpha(\bar{z}+z) + \alpha^2 = x^2 + y^2 - 2\alpha x + \alpha^2 = r^2 - 2\alpha r\xi + \alpha^2,$$

if $u(x, y)$ is singular at $z = \alpha, \bar{\alpha}, f(\sigma)$ may have a singularity at $\sigma = \alpha$. However, one may rewrite the singularity manifold of $u(x, y)$ as

$$(z-\bar{\alpha})(\bar{z}-\bar{\alpha}) = 0, \qquad \text{or as} \quad r^2 - 2\bar{\alpha}r\xi + \bar{\alpha}^2 = 0,$$

which implies $f(\sigma)$ may have a singularity at $\sigma = \bar{\alpha}$. Consequently, we have the following result.

Theorem 4.2.5 *The necessary and sufficient conditions for $u(x, y) = \mathbf{A}_\mu f$ to be singular at $z = \alpha$, on its first Riemann sheet, is that $f(\sigma)$ be singular at $\sigma = \alpha$, or $\bar{\alpha}$.*

The validity of Theorem 4.2.5 is realized as follows: each "possible" singularity of $u(x, y)$ is seen to correspond to an actual singularity of its $\mathbf{A}_\mu$-associate under the inverse mapping $f(\sigma) = \mathbf{A}_\mu^{-1} u$.

In [H.7] Henrici gave by another method necessary and sufficient conditions for a real GASPT function to be regular at a particular point. Our result is developed for complex-valued GASPT functions and has certain features which are unique to the case where the coefficients a_n and the variables x, y are not real. To be specific let us consider the case of Legendre series by setting $\mu = \frac{1}{2}$; then the $C_n^{1/2}(\xi) \equiv P_n(\xi)$. We have the following example due to Nehari [N.6] of a Legendre series

$$g(\xi) \equiv \sum_{n=0}^{\infty} P_n(\xi)\frac{a^{n+1}}{n+1} = \log\left\{\frac{a - \xi + (1 - 2a\xi + a^2)^{1/2}}{1-\xi}\right\}, \qquad 0 < a < 1,$$

which converges in an ellipse with foci at ± 1 and passes through $\xi = \frac{1}{2}(a + a^{-1})$. The associated power series

$$f(z) \equiv \sum_{n=0}^{\infty} \frac{z^n a^{n+1}}{n+1} = \frac{-1}{z}\log(1 - az),$$

has its only finite singularity at $z = 1/a$; however the branch of $g(\xi)$ which corresponds to negative values of the radical (for $\xi = 0$) has a logarithmic branch at $\xi = \pm 1$.

This result has an analogous interpretation for GASPT. For the case of axially symmetric potentials ($\mu = \frac{1}{2}$) the function

$$u(r, \theta) \equiv \sum_{n=0}^{\infty} r^n P_n(\cos\theta)\frac{a^{n+1}}{n+1} = \frac{1}{r}\log\left\{\frac{ar - \cos\theta + (1 - 2ar\cos\theta + a^2r^2)^{1/2}}{1-\cos\theta}\right\}$$

is clearly regular on the *first* Riemann sheet over the complex ξ-plane save for the singularities at $z = 1/a$ and $z^* = 1/a$. In terms of the complex $x - y$ space, u is regular on the first Riemann sheet over cartesian $\mathbb{C}^2$ except for the complex planes $x + iy = 1/a$, $x - iy = 1/a$.

Remark In future theorems of the above type we shall restrict ourselves to the case of the real $x - y$ space.

We are now in a position to transplant certain results of analytic function theory to the case of GASPT. We list some theorems which were proved by the author, and indicate their proofs below [G.9,13,14,18,21].

Theorem 4.2.6 *Let $\Phi(x, y)$, and $\Psi(x, y)$ be two* GASPT-*function elements with the series expansions*

$$\Phi \equiv \sum_{n=0}^{\infty} a_n r^n C_n^{\mu}(\cos\theta), \qquad \Psi \equiv \sum_{n=0}^{\infty} b_n r^n C_n^{\mu}(\cos\theta).$$

Furthermore, let us suppose, that Φ and Ψ have singularities, respectively, at the point pairs $\{\alpha, \bar{\alpha}\}$, and $\{\beta, \bar{\beta}\}$. Then the GASPT-*function element defined by the development*

$$F \equiv \sum_{n=0}^{\infty} a_n b_n r^n C_n^{\mu}(\cos\theta)$$

has singularities at either the point pair $\{\alpha\beta, \bar{\alpha}\bar{\beta}\}$, or at $\{\alpha\bar{\beta}, \bar{\alpha}\beta\}$.

Proof Let $f(\sigma)$, $g(\sigma)$ and $h(\sigma)$ be the $\mathbf{A}_\mu$-associates of Φ, Ψ, and F, respectively. From Hadamard's multiplication of singularities theorem we realize that if $f(\sigma)$, $g(\sigma)$ have singularities at δ, γ, respectively, then $h(\sigma)$ may be singular only at $\sigma = \delta\gamma$. In this case, the corresponding singularities of Φ, Ψ, and F are then at the point pairs $\{\delta, \bar{\delta}\}$, $\{\gamma, \bar{\gamma}\}$, and $\{\delta\gamma, \overline{\delta\gamma}\}$, respectively. This completes the proof.

Theorem 4.2.7 *Let $u(x, y)$ be a* GASPT-*function element with the following series development about the origin,*†

$$u = \sum_{n=0}^{\infty} a_n r^n C_n^{\mu}(\cos\theta).$$

† Erdélyi has also given a similar theorem concerning the disk of convergence for a Gegenbauer series [E.7].

Then, u converges uniformly and absolutely in any compact subset of the disk of convergence $|z| < R$, *where*

$$R^{-1} = \overline{\lim_{n\to\infty}} |a_n|^{1/n}.$$

Proof We first recognize, that the $\mathbf{A}_\mu$-associate for $u(x, y)$ is the function

$$f(\sigma) = \sum_{n=0}^{\infty} \frac{\Gamma(2\mu + n)}{\Gamma(2\mu)n!} a_n \sigma^n,$$

and that the radius of convergence for $f(\sigma)$ may be computed by the Hadamard formula to be

$$\begin{aligned} R &= \left(\overline{\lim_{n\to\infty}} \left|\frac{\Gamma(2\mu + n)}{n!} a_n\right|^{1/n}\right)^{-1} \\ &= \left(\lim_{n\to\infty} \left|\frac{\Gamma(2\mu + n)}{n!}\right|^{1/n} \overline{\lim_{n\to\infty}} |a_n|^{1/n}\right)^{-1} \\ &= \left(\overline{\lim_{n\to\infty}} |a_n|^{1/n}\right)^{-1}. \end{aligned}$$

This may be seen by using the fact, that $\Gamma(2\mu + n)/\Gamma(n + 1) \approx n^{2\mu-1}$ for large n [E.6, Vol. I, p. 47].

Next, since $|\sigma| = |x + iy \cos \alpha| \le |z|$, when $\zeta = e^{i\alpha}$, we have that

$$\begin{aligned} \left|u(x, y) - \sum_{n=0}^{N} a_n r^n C_n^\mu(\cos \theta)\right| &= \left|\sum_{n=N+1}^{\infty} a_n r^n C_n^\mu(\cos \theta)\right| \\ &\le \sum_{n=N+1}^{\infty} |a_n r^n C_n^\mu(\cos \theta)| \le \sum_{n=N+1}^{\infty} \frac{|a_n|\, \Gamma(2\mu + n)}{2^{2\mu-1} n!\, \Gamma(\mu)^2} \int_0^\pi |\sigma|^n \sin^{2\mu-1} \alpha \, d\alpha \\ &< \frac{\pi}{2^{2\mu-1}} \sum_{\nu=0}^{\infty} \frac{\Gamma(N + 1 + 2\mu + \nu)}{(N + 1 + \nu)!} \times |a_{N+1+\nu}| \cdot r^{N+1+\nu} \cdot \left|\frac{z}{r}\right|^{N+1+\nu}, \end{aligned}$$

where $|z| < r \le R$. Since $f(\sigma)$ is analytic-regular in the disk $|\sigma| < R$, the terms $[\Gamma(N + 1 + 2\mu + \nu)/(N + 1 + \nu)!]\ |a_{N+1+\nu}| r^{N+1+\nu}$ are bounded above, say by M. Consequently, we have

$$\left|u(x, y) - \sum_{n=0}^{N} a_n r^n C_n^\mu(\cos \theta)\right| \le \frac{\pi M}{2^{2\mu-1}} \left|\frac{z}{r}\right|^{N+1} \frac{1}{1 - |z/r|},$$

which tends to zero as $N \to \infty$, for $|z| < r \le R$.

It is clear from Lemma 4.2.2 that $u(x, y)$ is regular in the disk $|z| < r \leq R$, and that the first singularity of $u(x, y)$ must occur on the circle $|z| = R$. Finally we obtain a result which is an analog (and a generalization) to the results obtained by Bergman in regard to the "general coefficient problem" for harmonic functions [B.22 24 27]. Because of the existence of the inverse operator for $A_\mu f$ we are able to obtain *both necessary and sufficient* conditions concerning the location, number, and kind of singularities.

Theorem 4.2.8 *Let $u(x, y)$ be a* GASPT-*function element defined about* $z = 0$, *with the series development*

$$u(x, y) = \sum_{n=0}^{\infty} a_n r^n C_n^\mu(\cos\theta).$$

Furthermore, let

$$D_\lambda^{(n)} \equiv \begin{vmatrix} a_\lambda & a_{\lambda+1} & a_{\lambda+n} \\ a_{\lambda+1} & a_{\lambda+2} & a_{\lambda+n+1} \\ \vdots & \vdots & \vdots \\ a_{\lambda+n} & a_{\lambda+n+1} & a_{\lambda+2n} \end{vmatrix}$$

and $l_n \equiv \limsup_{\lambda\to\infty} |D_\lambda^{(n)}|^{1/n}$. *Then we have the following among the possibilities*:

1. If there is a ν such that $l_\nu / l_{\nu-1} = 0$, $u(x, y)$ has 2ν singularities (pole-like or zero-like branch points) in the entire z-plane.
2. If $l_\mu / l_{\mu-1} \to 0$, $u(x, y)$ has just a finite number of singularities in every finite region.
3. If $l_\mu / l_{\mu-1} \to 1/R$, $u(x, y)$ has just a finite number of singularities in the disk $|z| \leq \rho < R$, but an infinite number of singularities in the neighborhood of $|z| = R$.

Proof This result is essentially a transplating of Hadamard's theorem concerning the singularities of meromorphic functions [D.4]. In order to see that it is true we first note, that the $\mathbf{A}_\mu$ associate of $u(x, y)$ is

$$f(\sigma) = \sum_{n=0}^{\infty} \frac{\Gamma(n + 2\mu)}{n!\,\Gamma(2\mu)} a_n \sigma^n.$$

From our fundamental theorem concerning singularities of GASPT functions, we recall that the necessary and sufficient criteria for $u(x, y)$ to be singular at

$z = \alpha, \bar{\alpha}$, is for $f(\sigma)$ to be singular at either $\sigma = \alpha$ or $\bar{\alpha}$. With this in mind we apply the Hadamard criteria to $f(\sigma)$ as given above and consider the determinants

$$\Delta_\lambda^{(n)} \equiv \begin{vmatrix} \frac{\Gamma(2\mu+\lambda)}{\lambda!} a_\lambda, \ldots, & \frac{\Gamma(2\mu+\lambda+\mu)}{(\lambda+\mu)!} a_{\lambda+\mu} \\ \vdots & \\ \frac{\Gamma(2\mu+\lambda+\mu)}{(\lambda+\mu)!} a_{\lambda+\mu}, \ldots, & \frac{\Gamma(2\mu+\lambda+2\mu)}{(\lambda+2\mu)!} a_{\lambda+2\mu} \end{vmatrix}$$

and the limits

$$L_\mu = \limsup_{\lambda\to\infty} |\Delta_\lambda^{(\mu)}|^{1/\lambda}.$$

If $f(\sigma)$ is a meromorphic function (in the case of (3), meromorphic in a disk $|z| < R$) then one of the conditions (1), (2), or (3) must hold.† For real λ sufficiently large we have [E.6, Vol. I, p. 47],

$$\frac{\Gamma(2\mu+\lambda+\nu)}{\Gamma(\lambda+\nu+1)} \approx \lambda^{2\mu-1}\left\{1 + \frac{(2\mu-1)(\mu+\nu)}{\lambda} + O\left(\frac{1}{\lambda^2}\right)\right\};$$

hence we may obtain the estimate for large λ, $\Delta_\lambda^{(n)} \approx \lambda^{2\mu-1} D_\lambda^{(n)}\{1 + O(1/\lambda)\}$. From this we conclude, since $\lim_{\lambda\to\infty}|\lambda^{2\mu-1}|^{1/\lambda} = 1$, that

$$\begin{aligned} L_\mu &= \limsup_{\lambda\to\infty} |\Delta_\lambda^{(n)}|^{1/\lambda} = \limsup_{\lambda\to\infty} |\lambda^{2\mu-1}|^{1/\lambda} |D_\lambda^{(n)}|^{1/\lambda}(1 + O(1/\lambda))^{1/\lambda} \\ &= \limsup_{\lambda\to\infty} |D_\lambda^{(n)}|^{1/\lambda} = l_\mu. \end{aligned}$$

This concludes our proof.

3. *GASPT Functions with Entire and Meromorphic Associates*

Let us consider the case where the $\mathbf{A}_\mu$-associate of $u(x, y)$ is a meromorphic function in the finite σ-plane. Then we may express $f(\sigma)$ in terms of its Mittag–Leffler expansion as [A.1, p. 149]

$$f(\sigma) = \sum_{\nu=1}^{\infty} \left[P_\nu\left(\frac{1}{\sigma - b_\nu}\right) - p_\nu(\sigma)\right] + e(\sigma), \tag{4.3.1}$$

† If $l_\mu/l_{\mu-1} = 1/R$ for all $\mu \geq \nu > 1$ then $f(\sigma)$ has a non-polar singularity on the circle of radius R. See Dienes [D.4, p. 335].

where the b_ν are the poles of $f(\sigma)$, $P_\nu(1/(\sigma - b_\nu))$ the corresponding principal parts, the $p_\nu(\sigma)$ suitably chosen polynomials to ensure convergence, and $e(\sigma)$ an entire function. Since (4.3.1) converges uniformly in every compact subset of the σ-plane which does not contain the b_ν, one may evaluate the integral representation for $u(x, y) = \mathbf{A}_\mu f$ by inverting the orders of summation and integration. One has in this instance

$$\begin{aligned} u(x, y) = \mathbf{A}_\mu f &\equiv \alpha_\mu \int_{\mathscr{L}} f(\sigma)(\zeta - \zeta^{-1})^{2\mu-1} \frac{d\zeta}{\zeta} \\ &= \alpha_\mu \int_{\mathscr{L}} \left\{ \sum_{\nu=1}^{\infty} \left[P_\nu\left(\frac{1}{\sigma - b_\nu}\right) - p_\nu(\sigma)\right] + e(\sigma)\right\}(\zeta - \zeta^{-1})^{2\mu-1} \frac{d\zeta}{\zeta} \\ &= \sum_{\nu=1}^{\infty} [\Phi_\nu(x, y) - \varphi_\nu(x, y)] + E(x, y), \end{aligned} \tag{4.3.2}$$

where $E(x, y)$ is an entire GASPT function, and $\varphi_\nu(x, y)$ is a GASPT polynomial.

If μ is a half-integer, then the integrals

$$\Phi_\nu(x, y) = \alpha_\mu \int_{\mathscr{L}} P_\nu\left(\frac{1}{\sigma - b_\nu}\right)(\zeta - \zeta^{-1})^{2\mu-1} \frac{d\zeta}{\zeta} \tag{4.3.3}$$

may be easily evaluated using the calculus of residues if we replace $\mathscr{L}$ by the unit circle and divide (4.3.3) by 2. For instance, if

$$P_\nu\left(\frac{1}{\sigma - b_\nu}\right) = \sum_{k=1}^{m_\nu} \frac{M_{k\nu}}{(\sigma - b_\nu)^k}, \tag{4.3.4}$$

then

$$\begin{aligned} \Phi_\nu &= \frac{\alpha_\mu}{2} \sum_{k=1}^{m\nu} M_{k\nu} \int_{|\zeta|=1} \frac{(\zeta - \zeta^{-1})^{2\mu-1}}{(\sigma - b_\nu)^k} \frac{d\zeta}{\zeta} \\ &= \frac{\pi i}{2} \alpha_\mu \sum_{k=1}^{m\nu} M_{k\nu} \frac{(-1)^k}{k!} \left(\frac{2}{iy}\right)^{2\mu} \frac{\partial^k}{\partial x^k} [(x - b_\nu)^2 + y^2]^\mu. \end{aligned} \tag{4.3.5}$$

(If $\mu > 0$ is *not* a half-integer, then these terms may be evaluated in terms of Legendre functions) [G.18 p. 582]) Consequently if μ is a half-integer $u(x, y)$ has the representation.

$$u(x, y) = \alpha_\mu \frac{i\pi}{2} \sum_{\nu=1}^{\infty} \left\{ \sum_{k=1}^{m\nu} M_{k\nu} \frac{(-1)^k}{k!} \left(\frac{2}{iy}\right)^{2\mu} \frac{\partial^k}{\partial x^k} ((x - b_\nu)^2 + y^2)^\mu - \varphi_\nu(x, y) \right\} + E(x, y). \tag{4.3.6}$$

It may be shown that this infinite-series representation converges in every compact set in the z-plane which does not contain singularities of the $\Phi_\nu(x, y)$.

It is possible to obtain bounds for GASPT-function elements with meromorphic $\mathbf{A}_\mu$-associates. This problem has already been considered by Bergman [B.24] for harmonic functions in three variables, and been discussed for the case of GASPT by the author [G.20,21].

Let us assume that the $\mathbf{A}_\mu$-associate of $u(x, y)$ may be written as $f(\sigma) \equiv h_1(\sigma)/h_2(\sigma)$, where the $h_k(\sigma)$ $(k = 1, 2)$ are entire functions of order λ. (That is, if $M_k(r)$ is the maximum modulus of $h_k(\sigma)$ $(k = 1, 2)$ on $|\sigma| = r$ we have $\lambda = \lambda_k = \limsup_{r\to\infty} \log\log M_k(r)/\log r$). It is possible for us to obtain a lower bound for the minimum modulus of an entire function from a theorem of Borel [C.6, p. 173]. For instance, if $m(r)$ is the minimum modulus of $h(\sigma)$ and λ the order, then for $\varepsilon > 0$, $m(r) > \exp -r^{\lambda+\varepsilon}$ on circles of arbitrarily large radius for those regions $\mathfrak{R}$ excluding the circles $\{|\sigma - \sigma_n| \le |\sigma_n|^{-h}\}$, where $h > \lambda$.

We may use these results to obtain bounds for GASPT-function elements in their domains of association as follows. Suppose, that the poles of $f(\sigma)$ are located at the set of points $\{b_\nu\}_{\nu=1}^{\infty}$, and that no $b_\nu = 0$. In this case $u(x, y)$ is regular at $z = 0$, and its domain of association is the z-plane less the segments $\{z \mid x = \operatorname{Re} b_\nu, y^2 \ge |\operatorname{Im} b_\nu|;\ \nu = 1, 2, \ldots\}$. After Bergman [B.24], we then consider the z-plane minus strips of thickness $2|b_\nu|^{-h}$ covering the above segments; that is, we are interested in the domain

$$\mathfrak{B} \equiv \left\{ z \,\middle|\, \sum_{\nu=1}^{\infty} [\operatorname{Re} b_\nu + |b_\nu|^{-h} \le x \le \operatorname{Re} b_{\nu+1} - |b_{\nu+1}|^{-h}, y^2 < \infty] \right\}$$
$$\cup \left\{ z \,\middle|\, \sum_{\nu=1}^{\infty} [\operatorname{Re} b_\nu - |b_\nu|^{-h} \le x \le \operatorname{Re} b_\nu + |b_\nu|^{-h}, y^2 < |x - b_\nu|^2 - |b_\nu|^{-2h}] \right\}. \tag{4.3.7}$$

It is clear that if $z \in \mathfrak{B}$ then $\sigma \in \mathfrak{R}$; consequently, we may prove the result.

Theorem 4.3.1 *Let $u(x, y)$ be a* GASPT *function with a meromorphic associate $f(\sigma)$. Furthermore, let $f(\sigma)$ be representable as a quotient of entire functions of order λ, $h(\sigma)/g(\sigma)$, such that $h(\sigma)$ is not of maximum type. Then, in* *the subdomain of the domain of association for* $u(x, y)$, *and for* $|z| = r$ *sufficiently large, one has the inequality*

$$|u(x, y)| \leq \exp(a' r^{\lambda+\varepsilon'}), \tag{4.3.8}$$

where $a' = a + 1 + \varepsilon$, *and* $\varepsilon, \varepsilon' > 0$ *are arbitrarily small, and* $a =$ *type.*

Proof From the integral representation for $u(x, y)$ we have, for r sufficiently large,

$$|u(x, y)| \leq 2^{2\mu-1} |\alpha_\mu| \int_0^\pi |f(x + iy \cos \psi)| \sin^{2\mu-1} \psi \, d\psi$$
$$\leq |\alpha_\mu| \frac{\Gamma(2\mu)}{[\Gamma(\mu + \frac{1}{2})]^2} \int_0^\pi \left\{ \max_{0 \leq \psi \leq \pi} |f| \right\} d\psi = \max_{0 \leq \psi \leq \pi} |f(\sigma)|,$$

hence

$$|u(x, y)| \leq \frac{\exp[(a + \varepsilon) r^\lambda]}{\exp(-r^{\lambda+\varepsilon'})} = \exp\{r^{\lambda+\varepsilon'}[(a + \varepsilon) r^{-\varepsilon'} + 1]\} \equiv \exp[a' r^{\lambda+\varepsilon'}],$$

where $a' \equiv [(a + \varepsilon) r^{-\varepsilon'} + 1]$, and $a < \infty$ (since $h(\sigma)$ is not of maximum type), and $\varepsilon, \varepsilon'$ are arbitrarily small.

We shall call a GASPT function entire if it is without singularities in the finite z-plane. Because of Theorems 4.2.5 and 4.2.7, we realize that a GASPT function is entire if and only if its $\mathbf{A}_\mu$-associate is entire; consequently, we have the following result.

Theorem 4.3.2 *A* GASPT *function, regular about the origin, and defined by a series development*

$$u(x, y) = \sum_{n=0}^{\infty} a_n (x^2 + y^2)^{n/2} C_n^\mu \left(\frac{x}{(x^2 + y^2)^{1/2}} \right) \tag{4.3.9}$$

is an entire GASPT *function if and only if* $\lim_{n=\infty} |a_n|^{1/n} = 0$.

It is possible also to characterize entire GASPT functions by their order and type in a similar manner as is done for entire analytic functions. With this in mind we shall establish the following:

Theorem 4.3.3 *Let* $u(x, y)$ *be a* GASPT *function with a series development* (4.3.9); *then there exists a number* λ *(its order), such that for* R *sufficiently* *large and any* $\varepsilon > 0$ *the maximum modulus* $M(R)$ *of* $u(x, y)$ *is bounded above and below by*†

$$\exp(R^{\lambda-\varepsilon}) < M(R) < \exp(R^{\lambda+\varepsilon}). \tag{4.3.10}$$

Proof If $u(x, y)$ is entire, its associate $f(\sigma)$ is entire, and since $|f(\sigma)| < \exp R^{\lambda+\varepsilon}$ for some λ and all $\varepsilon > 0$, if R is sufficiently large, we obtain a similar bound for $u(x, y)$. To attempt a lower bound for $|u(x, y)|$ we consider the inverse operator $\mathbf{A}_\mu^{-1}u$, which may be written as

$$f(\sigma) = \mathbf{A}_\mu^{-1}u \equiv \left(\frac{i}{2}\right)^{2\mu} \beta_\mu(z\bar{z} - \sigma^2) \int_{\substack{0\\|z|=R}}^{\pi} \frac{V(z, \bar{z})(z - \bar{z})^{2\mu}}{[(z-\sigma)(\bar{z} - \sigma)]^{\mu+1}}\, d\theta$$

$$|\sigma| \le \rho < R = z\bar{z}, \qquad \text{where} \quad V(z, \bar{z}) = u\left(\frac{z + \bar{z}}{2}, \frac{z - \bar{z}}{2i}\right).$$

From this it follows that if $|u(x, y)| \le M^*(R)$, for $|z| \le R$ we have

$$|f(\sigma)| \le \mu 2^{2\mu}\Gamma(\mu)^2 R^{2\mu} M^*(R) \frac{R^2 + \rho^2}{(R - \rho)^{2\mu+2}}, \qquad |\sigma| \le \rho < R. \tag{4.3.11}$$

If $M(\rho)$ is the maximum modulus of $f(\sigma)$ for $|\sigma| \le \rho < R$ then we have

$$\exp(\rho^{\lambda-\varepsilon'}) < M(\rho) \le \mu 2^{2\mu} \frac{\Gamma(\mu)^2 R^{2\mu}}{(R - \rho)^{2\mu+2}} (R^2 + \rho^2) M^*(R), \qquad \text{for all} \quad \varepsilon' > 0. \tag{4.3.12}$$

Now for $\rho = \rho_0 \equiv R\theta$, where θ is fixed and $0 < \theta < 1$, there exists for large R an $\varepsilon > 0$, such that

$$\exp R^{\lambda-\varepsilon} \equiv \exp \rho_0^{\lambda-\varepsilon'} \frac{(R - \rho_0)^{2(\mu+1)}}{\mu 2^{2\mu}\Gamma(\mu)^2 R^{2\mu}(R^2 + \rho_0{}^2)} < M^*(R), \tag{4.3.13}$$

then

$$\begin{aligned} R^{\lambda-\varepsilon} = \rho_0^{\lambda-\varepsilon'} &+ 2(\mu + 1)\log(R - \rho_0) \\ &- \log \mu 2^{2\mu}\Gamma(\mu)^2 - 2\mu \log R - \log(R^2 + \rho_0{}^2), \end{aligned}$$

† Lo [L.11] has recently extended this result to the case of harmonic functions of three variables by adapting the Gol'dberg inequalities [F.4], for entire functions of several complex variables, to the function theoretic approach. He does this by using the Bergman–Whittaker operator, and its inverse integral operator of the second kind.

and

$$R^{-\varepsilon} = \frac{\rho_0^{\lambda-\varepsilon'}}{R^\lambda} + 2(\mu+1)\frac{\log(R-\rho_0)}{R^\lambda}$$
$$- \frac{\log \mu 2^{2\mu}\Gamma(\mu)^2}{R^\lambda} - \frac{2\mu \log R}{R^\lambda} - \frac{\log(R^2+\rho_0{}^2)}{R^\lambda}.$$

As $R \to \infty$, and $\rho_0/R \equiv \theta < 1$ remains fixed, one has approximately

$$R^\varepsilon \approx \theta^{-\lambda}\rho_0^{\varepsilon'},$$

or

$$\varepsilon \approx -\lambda\frac{\log\theta}{\log R} + \varepsilon'\frac{\log\rho_0}{\log R}$$
$$= \varepsilon' + (\varepsilon'-\lambda)\frac{\log\theta}{\log R}. \tag{4.3.14}$$

Consequently, for R sufficiently large ε is of the same order of magnitude as ε' (which is arbitrarily small); hence, we conclude that $\exp R^{\lambda-\varepsilon} < M^*(R)$, for arbitrary $\varepsilon > 0$, and R sufficiently large. This proves our theorem.

Theorem 4.3.4 *If $u(x, y)$ is an entire* GASPT *function of order λ, then we may distinguish the type, α, of $u(x, y)$ from its series development* (4.3.9) *by the formula*

$$\limsup_{n\to\infty} n^{1/\lambda}|a_n|^{1/n} = (\lambda e\alpha)^{1/\lambda}. \tag{4.3.15}$$

Proof From the hypothesis we realized that the $\mathbf{A}_\mu$-associate of $u(x, y)$ is

$$f(\sigma) = \sum a_n \frac{\Gamma(2\mu+n)}{\Gamma(2\mu)n!}\sigma^n,$$

and from the above discussion we realize that its order is also λ. The type α, of an entire (analytic) function may be obtained (once we know the order) by considering the limit [D.4, p. 293]

$$\limsup_{n\to\infty} n^{1/\lambda}\left|a_n\frac{\Gamma(2\mu+n)}{n!}\right|^{1/n} = (\lambda e\alpha)^{1/\lambda}.$$

However, one has

$$\begin{aligned}\limsup_{n\to\infty} n^{1/\lambda}\left| a_n \frac{\Gamma(2\mu+n)}{n!}\right|^{1/n} &= \limsup_{n\to\infty}(n^{1/\lambda}|a_n|^{1/n}) \lim_{n\to\infty}\left|\frac{\Gamma(2\mu+n)}{n!}\right|^{1/2n} \\ &= \limsup_{n\to\infty}(n^{1/\lambda}|a_n|^{1/n}) \\ &=(\lambda e\alpha)^{1/\lambda}. \end{aligned} \tag{4.3.16}$$

We shall now show that it is also possible to obtain an analog of the residue calculus for GASPT functions. To this end we note that the GASPT equation may be rewritten in the form

$$\frac{\partial}{\partial x}\left(y^{2\mu}\frac{\partial u}{\partial x}\right) + \frac{\partial}{\partial y}\left(y^{2\mu}\frac{\partial u}{\partial y}\right) = 0, \tag{4.3.17}$$

and in this form it implies the existence of a stream function $v(x, y)$, which satisfies the Stokes–Beltrami equations

$$y^{2\mu}\frac{\partial u}{\partial x} = \frac{\partial v}{\partial y}, \qquad y^{2\mu}\frac{\partial u}{\partial y} = -\frac{\partial v}{\partial x}. \tag{4.3.18}$$

It is possible to introduce an integral operator $\mathbf{A}_\mu{}^*f$ which generates the stream function $v(x, y)$. For instance, if $u(x, y)$ is a GASPT function, then $f(\sigma) = \mathbf{A}_\mu^{-1}u$, and

$$v(x, y) = \mathbf{A}_\mu{}^*f \equiv \tfrac{1}{2}iy^{2\mu}\mathbf{A}_\mu[(\zeta + \zeta^{-1})f(\sigma)]. \tag{4.3.19}$$

It is convenient in what follows that the functions $u(x, y)$, $v(x, y)$ be real. This may be done by choosing $f(\sigma)$ so that it is real on the real axis; in the remainder of this section we shall assume that $u(x, y)$, $v(x, y)$ are real.

We now introduce a complex combination of the real potential and stream functions,

$$\begin{aligned} w(x, y) &= u(x, y) + iy^{-2\mu}v(x, y) \\ &\equiv \mathbf{A}_\mu[f(\sigma)\{1 - \tfrac{1}{2}(\zeta + \zeta^{-1})\}] \\ &= -\tfrac{1}{2}\mathbf{A}_\mu[f(\sigma)(\zeta - 1)^2\zeta^{-1}]. \end{aligned} \tag{4.3.20}$$

Consider its domain of association, and the various function elements related to this domain of association. To simplify our discussion we consider the case where $f(\sigma) = h(\sigma)/(\sigma - \alpha)$, and $h(\sigma)$ is entire. Then, in order to understand the connection between the different function elements we must consider the singularity manifold for $f(\sigma)(\zeta - \zeta^{-1})^{2\mu-1}$, which we represent as

$$\mathfrak{S}_0 \equiv \{\zeta \mid \zeta_\nu = (i/y)[(x-\alpha) + (-1)^\nu((x-\alpha)^2 + y^2)^{1/2}];\ \nu = 1, 2\}. \quad (4.3.21)$$

Now, unless $(x-\alpha)^2 + y^2 \equiv (z-\alpha)(\bar{z}-\alpha) = 0$, the singularity manifold has two branches, which is particularly interesting in terms of the Theorem 4.2.5.

Let us assume that the representation (4.3.20) is defined in the neighborhood of an initial point z^0. It is possible for us to extend this initial domain of definition by continuing $w(x, y)$ along a contour γ, starting at z^0, providing that no point of γ corresponds to a singularity of the integrand on the path of integration. We recall, however, that σ depends on both z and ζ, and hence as we continue $w(x, y)$ along γ in the z-plane, the singularities of the integrand move in the ζ-plane. For instance the points $\zeta = \zeta_\nu(z)$ $(\nu = 1, 2)$ [Eq. (4.3.21)] move and may cross over the path of integration $\mathscr{L}$. If this should happen, the integral will have a jump in value equal to a branch of $w(x, y)$. If $\zeta_\nu \in \mathscr{L}$ $(\nu = 1, 2)$ the corresponding "singular" points in the z-plane are given by

$$\begin{aligned} x &= \mathrm{Re}[\alpha] - \mathrm{Im}[\alpha][(|\zeta|^2 - 1)/(|\zeta|^2 + 1)]\tan\psi, \\ y &= 2\,\mathrm{Im}[\alpha][|\zeta|/(|\zeta|^2 + 1)]\sec\psi, \qquad \psi = \arg[\zeta]. \end{aligned} \quad (4.3.22)$$

Equations (4.3.22) may be interpreted as a one-to-two mapping of the ζ-plane onto the z-plane $z = \mathbf{T}\zeta$. For instance, the arcs $\mathscr{L}_k \equiv \{\zeta \mid |\zeta| = 1, (k-1)\frac{1}{2}\pi \le \arg\zeta \le \pi k/2\}$ $(k = 1, 2, 3, 4)$ map onto the half-lines (when $\mathrm{Im}[\alpha] > 0$),

$$\Lambda_j = \{z \mid x = \mathrm{Re}[\alpha];\ (y/\mathrm{Im}[\alpha])^{(-1)^j} \le (-1)^{j+1}\} \qquad (j = 1, 2) \quad (4.3.23)$$

in the following manner:

$$\mathscr{L}_1 \to \Lambda_1, \qquad \mathscr{L}_2 \to \Lambda_2, \qquad \mathscr{L}_3 \to \Lambda_2, \qquad \mathscr{L}_4 \to \Lambda_1;$$

the point at infinity of the z-plane serves as a "double" branch point.

By a simple computation it can be shown that when z crosses Λ_1 from the right, $\zeta_1(z)$ leaves the unit disk by crossing $\mathscr{L}_4$, whereas $\zeta_2(z)$ enters over $\mathscr{L}_1$. On the other hand, as z crosses Λ_2 from the right, $\zeta_1(z)$ leaves the unit disk by passing over $\mathscr{L}_2$, and $\zeta_2(z)$ enters over $\mathscr{L}_3$. We are now able to consider the continuation of $w(x, y)$ along γ, which originates at a point $z^0 \notin \Lambda_1 \cup \Lambda_2$. If $\gamma \cap \{\Lambda_1 \cup \Lambda_2\} = 0$, then $w(x, y)$ may be continued to any point z which is the terminal point of γ. On the other hand if $\gamma \cap \{\Lambda_1 \cup \Lambda_2\} = z^1$, then $w(x, y)$ has a jump in value at z^1, as we cross over Λ_1 or Λ_2, which is equal to a branch of $w(x, y)$. Because of this property associated with the lines Λ_1, Λ_2, we refer to them as the *lines of separation* for $w(x, y)$.

To clarify this point we consider as an illustration the associate $f(\sigma) = h(\sigma)/(\sigma - \alpha)$, where $h(\sigma)$ is entire and nonzero at $\sigma = \alpha$. Then

$$w(x, y) = \alpha_\mu \int_{\mathscr{L}+1}^{-1} \frac{h(\sigma)}{\sigma - \alpha} (\zeta - \zeta^{-1})^{2\mu+1}\, d\zeta$$

$$= \frac{2\alpha_\mu}{iy} \int_{\mathscr{L}} \frac{h(\sigma)(\zeta - \zeta^{-1})^{2\mu+1}}{[\zeta - \zeta_1(z)][\zeta - \zeta_2(z)]} \zeta\, d\zeta, \tag{4.3.24}$$

where $\zeta(z)$ is given by (4.3.21). When z crosses Λ_1 from the left, $w(x, y)$ goes through a jump in value equal to

$$[-4\pi/\Gamma(\mu)^2]h(\alpha)([x-\alpha]^2 + y^2)^{\mu-1}(-1/2y)^{2\mu}(y + i[x - \alpha]). \tag{4.3.25}$$

We are now in a position to consider integrals of the following type:

$$\int_{\mathscr{I}} (u\, dx - y^{-2\mu} v\, dy) = \operatorname{Re}\left\{\int_{\mathscr{I}} w(x, y)\, dz\right\} \tag{4.3.26}$$

where $\mathscr{I} \cap \{y \le 0\} = 0$, and $\mathscr{I}$ is a smooth Jordan curve. It is possible to rewrite the integral (4.3.26) by making use of the identity

$$u\, dx - y^{-2\mu} v\, dy = \alpha_\mu \int_{\mathscr{L}+1}^{-1} f(\sigma)\left[dx + \frac{i}{2} dy\, (\zeta + \zeta^{-1})\right](\zeta - \zeta^{-1})^{2\mu-1} \frac{d\zeta}{\zeta}$$

$$= \alpha_\mu \int_{\mathscr{L}+1}^{-1} [f(\sigma)\, d\sigma](\zeta - \zeta^{-1})^{2\mu-1} \frac{d\zeta}{\zeta}, \tag{4.3.27}$$

where z is contained in a sufficiently small neighborhood of z^0, $\mathscr{N}(z^0)$, such that $\mathscr{N}(z^0) \cap [\Lambda_1 \cup \Lambda_2] = 0$. Then, if $\mathscr{I}$ does not intersect $\Lambda_1 \cup \Lambda_2$, one has clearly, since the integrand is absolutely integrable, that

$$\operatorname{Re}\left\{\int_{\mathscr{I}} w(x, y)\, dz\right\}$$

$$= \alpha_\mu \int_{\mathscr{I}} \left[\int_{\mathscr{L}+1}^{-1} f(\sigma)\left(dx + \frac{i}{2} dy\, (\zeta + \zeta^{-1})\right)(\zeta - \zeta^{-1})^{2\mu-1} \frac{d\zeta}{\zeta}\right.$$

$$= \alpha_\mu \int_{\mathscr{L}+1}^{-1} \frac{d\zeta}{\zeta} (\zeta - \zeta^{-1})^{2\mu-1} \int_{\mathscr{C}_\sigma} f(\sigma)\, d\sigma, \tag{4.3.28}$$

where $\mathscr{C}_\sigma$ is the image of $\mathscr{I}$ under the mapping $z \to \sigma$ (ζ fixed).

Theorem 4.3.5 *Let $w_0(x, y)$ be the* GASPT-*function element defined in a neighborhood of z_0 by means of $\mathbf{A}_\mu f$, where $f(\sigma) = h(\sigma)/(\sigma - \alpha)$, $h(\sigma)$ is entire, and $h(\alpha) \neq 0$. Furthermore, let $\mathscr{J}$ be a smooth Jordan curve, which originates at a point $z_0 \notin \Lambda_k$ $(k = 1, 2)$, and which intersects Λ_1 at just one point z_1. Then*

$$\begin{aligned}\operatorname{Re}\left\{\int_{\mathscr{J}} w(x, y)\, dz\right\} &\equiv \int_{\mathscr{J}} (u\, dx - y^{-2\mu}\, v\, dy)\\ &= \operatorname{Re}\left\{\int_{\mathscr{J}} w_0(x, y)\, dz\right\} + (-\tfrac{1}{2})^{2\mu+1}\, \frac{2\pi h(\alpha)}{\mu\Gamma(\mu)^2}\\ &\quad \times \int_{\xi_1}^{\xi_0} \xi^{-1}\, d[(1+\xi^2)^{1/2}]^{2\mu}\\ &= 2\pi i \alpha_\mu h(\alpha) \int_{\mathscr{M}_\zeta} (\zeta - \zeta^{-1})^{2\mu-1}\, \frac{d\zeta}{\zeta}, \qquad \text{where} \quad \xi = (x-\alpha)/y,\end{aligned}$$

and

$$\mathscr{M}_\zeta = \{\zeta \mid |\zeta| = 1;\, 0 \le \arg[\zeta] \le \cos^{-1}[\operatorname{Im}(\alpha)/y]\}. \tag{4.3.29}$$

To establish this result we note that the integral of the jump in value of $w(x, y)$ when z crosses Λ_1 from the left may be written as

$$\begin{aligned}&\frac{-4\pi}{\Gamma(\mu)^2}\, h(\alpha) \int_{z_1}^{z_0} ([x-\alpha]^2 + y^2)^{\mu-1} \left(\frac{-1}{2y}\right)^{2\mu} ([x-\alpha]\, dy - y\, dx)\\ &\quad = \frac{\pi}{2\mu}\, \frac{h(\alpha)}{\Gamma(\mu)^2} \int_{z_1}^{z_0} \left(\frac{y}{x-\alpha}\right) d\left\{\left(1 + \left[\frac{x-\alpha}{y}\right]^2\right)^\mu\right\}\\ &\quad = \frac{\pi}{2\mu}\, \frac{h(\alpha)}{\Gamma(\mu)^2} \int_{\xi_1}^{\xi_0} \xi^{-1}\, d\,[(1+\xi^2)^\mu].\end{aligned} \tag{4.3.30}$$

When μ is a half-integer, the jump integrals (4.3.30) may be evaluated as [G.13,14], [G.H.8, p. 46]

$$\begin{aligned}&\pi\, \frac{h(\alpha)}{\Gamma(\mu)^2} \left\{(\eta^2 - 1)^{1/2} \sum_{\nu=0}^{\mu-3/2} (-1)^\nu\, \frac{(2\mu-2;\, -2;\, \nu)}{(2\mu-1;\, -2;\, \nu+1)}\, \eta^{2(\mu-\nu-1)}\right.\\ &\quad \left. + (-1)^{\mu-\frac{1}{2}} \log[\eta + (\eta^2-1)^{1/2}]\right\}_{\eta=(\xi_1{}^2+1)^{1/2}}^{\eta=(\xi_0{}^2+1)^{1/2}}\end{aligned} \tag{4.3.31}$$

(μ is a half-integer),

and

$$\pi \frac{h(\alpha)}{\Gamma(\mu)^2}\left\{(\eta^2-1)^{1/2}\sum_{\nu=0}^{\mu-1}(-1)^\nu \frac{(2\mu-2;\ -2;\ \nu)}{(2\mu-1;\ -2;\ \nu+1)}\eta^{2(\mu-\nu-1)}\right\}_{\eta=(\xi_1^2+1)^{1/2}}^{\eta=(\xi_0^2+1)^{1/2}}$$

(μ is an integer)

(4.3.32)

where $(m;\ -d;\ \nu) = d^\nu\Gamma(m/d+1)/\Gamma(m/d-\nu+1)$.

Theorem 4.3.4 may be reinterpreted in terms of the composition on quasimultiplication [G.18], [B.24–26,22] for GASPT functions, which we define as

$$\begin{aligned} u_3(x, y) &= u_1(x, y)^* u_2(x, y) = \mathbf{A}_\mu[f_1(\sigma)f_2(\sigma)], \\ u_j(x, y) &= \mathbf{A}_\mu[f_j(\sigma)] \qquad (j = 1, 2, 3). \end{aligned} \tag{4.3.33}$$

(We note that quasimultiplication is commutative, associative, and distributive over ordinary addition.) Let

$$N(\alpha, \mu)h(\alpha) = \alpha_\mu \int_{\mathscr{L}+1}^{-1} (\zeta - \zeta^{-1})^{2\mu-1}\frac{d\zeta}{\zeta}\int_{\mathscr{C}_\sigma}\frac{h(\sigma)}{\sigma-\alpha}\,d\sigma, \tag{4.3.34}$$

where

$$N(\alpha, \mu) \overset{\text{def}}{\equiv} \int_{\mathscr{M}_\zeta} (\zeta - \zeta^{-1})^{2\mu-1}\frac{d\zeta}{\zeta},$$

and $h(\sigma)$ is entire. Furthermore, let $\operatorname{Re}\{w(x, y)\,dz\} \overset{\text{def}}{\equiv} \mathbf{A}_\mu[f(\sigma)\,d\sigma]$, and

$$\begin{aligned} \frac{1}{\rho_\mu(z, \alpha)} &\equiv \mathbf{A}_\mu \frac{1}{\sigma - \alpha} \\ &= \frac{\pi}{\Gamma(\mu)^2}\left(\frac{-1}{2y}\right)^{2\mu-1}\frac{1}{[(z-\alpha)(\bar{z}-\alpha)]^{1-\mu}}, \end{aligned} \tag{4.3.35}$$

then

$$\operatorname{Re}\{\tilde{w}(x, y)\,dz\}^*\left\{\frac{1}{\rho_\mu(z, \alpha)}\right\} = \mathbf{A}_\mu\left(\frac{f(\sigma)\,d\sigma}{\sigma - \alpha}\right). \tag{4.3.36}$$

The introduction of the terms $\rho_\mu(z, \alpha)$ suggests an expression for GASPT functions, corresponding to $\mathbf{A}_\mu$-associates having Laurent expansions about $\sigma = \alpha$. Suppose

$$g(\sigma) = \frac{b_{m+1}}{(\sigma - \alpha)^{m+1}} + \frac{b_m}{(\sigma - \alpha)^m} + \cdots + \frac{b_1}{\sigma - \alpha} + \sum_{j=0}^{\infty} c_j(\sigma - \alpha)^j, \quad (4.3.37)$$

then, for μ a half-integer, we have

$$\begin{aligned} G(x, y) &= \mathbf{A}_\mu g(\sigma) \\ &= \sum_{j=1}^{m+1} b_j \mathbf{A}_\mu(\sigma - \alpha)^{-j} + \sum_{j=0}^{\infty} c_j \mathbf{A}_\mu(\sigma - \alpha)^j \\ &= \sum_{j=1}^{m+1} \frac{(-1)^j b_j}{j!\,\Gamma(\mu)^2} \left(\frac{-1}{2y}\right)^{2\mu - 1} \frac{\partial^{j-1}}{\partial x^{j-1}} \{(z - \alpha)(\bar{z} - \alpha)\}^{\mu - 1} \\ &\quad + \sum_{j=0}^{\infty} c_j[(z - \alpha)(\bar{z} - \alpha)]^{j/2} C_j^\mu\left(\frac{x - \alpha}{[(z - \alpha)(\bar{z} - \alpha)]^{1/2}}\right). \quad (4.3.38) \end{aligned}$$

In general, however, we would write

$$G(x, y) = \sum_{j=1}^{m+1} b_j \left\{\frac{1}{\rho_\mu(z, \alpha)} *\right\}^j + \sum_{j=0}^{\infty} R(z, \alpha)^j C_j^\mu\left(\frac{x - \alpha}{R(z, \alpha)}\right) \quad (4.3.39)$$

where

$$\left\{\frac{1}{\rho_\mu} *\right\}^j = \frac{1}{\rho_\mu} * \frac{1}{\rho_\mu} * \cdots * \frac{1}{\rho_\mu}$$

(j terms), and $R(z, \alpha)^2 \equiv (z - \alpha)(\bar{z} - \alpha)$.

Theorem 4.3.5 suggests also the following analog of the argument principle in GASPT.

Theorem 4.3.6 *Let the $\mathbf{A}_\mu$ associate of $w(x, y)$ be $f'(\sigma)/f(\sigma)$, and suppose that $\mathscr{J}$ is a closed, Jordan contour in the z-plane, not passing through any zeros or poles of $f(z)$. Furthermore, let $f(z)$ have zeros at $\{a_p\}_{p=1}^m$ with multiplicities $\{r_p\}_{p=1}^m$ and poles at $\{b_q\}_{q=1}^n$ with multiplicities $\{s_q\}_{q=1}^n$, inside of $\mathscr{J}$. Then*

$$\begin{aligned} \frac{1}{4}\left(\frac{2}{iy}\right)^{2\mu} \Bigg\{ &\sum_{p=1}^{m} r_p \int_{\mathscr{J}} \{[x - \alpha_p]\, dy - y\, dx\}([x - \alpha_p]^2 + y^2)^{\mu - 1} \\ &- \sum_{q=1}^{n} s_q \int_{\mathscr{J}} \{[x - b_q]\, dy - y\, dx\}([x - b_q]^2 + y^2)^{\mu - 1} \end{aligned}$$

$$= \frac{1}{2\pi i} \int_{\substack{+1 \\ |\zeta|=1}}^{-1} n\{f[\mathscr{C}_\sigma(\zeta)]; 0\}[\zeta - \zeta^{-1}]^{2\mu-1} \frac{d\zeta}{\zeta}$$

$$= \sum_{p=1}^{m} r_p N(a_p; \mu) - \sum_{q=1}^{n} s_q N(b_q; \mu) \tag{4.3.40}$$

where $n\{\gamma; 0\}$ *is the winding number of* γ *with respect to* 0, *and* $f[\mathscr{C}_\sigma(\zeta)]$ *is the image of* $\mathscr{C}_\sigma$ *by* $f(\sigma)$ *for fixed* ζ. $\mathscr{C}_\sigma$ *is the image of* $\mathscr{J}$ *under the mapping* $z \to \sigma$ *for fixed* ζ.

Theorem 4.3.7 *Let the* $\mathbf{A}_\mu$ *associate of* $w(x, y)$ *be* $g(\sigma)f'(\sigma)/f(\sigma)$, *and suppose that* $\mathscr{J}$ *is a closed Jordan contour in the z-plane not passing through any of the zeros* $\{a_p\}_{p=1}^m$ *or poles* $\{b_q\}_{q=1}^n$ *of* $f(\sigma)$. *(The zeros and poles have the orders* r_p, s_q, *respectively.) Furthermore, let* $g(z)$ *be regular-analytic for* z *inside* $\mathscr{J}$, *then*

$$\int_{\mathscr{C}_\sigma} \mathbf{A}_\mu\left[\frac{f'}{f} g\, d\sigma\right] = \int_{\mathscr{C}_\sigma} \mathbf{A}_\mu\left[\frac{f'}{f}\right] * \mathbf{A}_\mu[g\, d\sigma]$$

$$= \int_{\mathscr{J}} \left\{ \sum_{p=1}^{m} \frac{r_p}{\rho_\mu(z; a_p)} - \sum_{q=1}^{n} \frac{s_q}{\rho_\mu(z; b_q)} \right\} * \{\text{Re } G(x, y)\, dz\}$$

$$= 2\pi i \alpha_\mu \left\{ \sum_{p=1}^{m} r_p g(a_p) N(a_p; \mu) - \sum_{q=1}^{n} s_q g(b_q) N(b_q; \mu) \right\},$$

where

$$G(x, y) = -\tfrac{1}{2}\mathbf{A}_\mu[g(\sigma)(\zeta - 1)^2\zeta^{-1}]. \tag{4.3.41}$$

4. *Generalized Axially Symmetric Elliptic Partial Differential Equations in Normal Form*

Introduction: The Cauchy Problem for Elliptic Equations

Henrici [H.5,6,8] has investigated elliptic partial differential equations of the form

$$\mathbf{e}(u) \equiv \Delta u + a(x, y)u_x + b(x, y)u_y + c(x, y)u = 0, \tag{4.4.1}$$

where Cauchy data is given on an analytic arc, $\mathscr{L}$, lying in a fundamental domain, $\mathfrak{S}$. He further assumes that this fundamental domain has a property which he refers to as *conformal symmetry* with respect to the carrier of the

Cauchy data. $\mathfrak{S}$ is defined to be conformally symmetric with respect to $\mathscr{L}$ if there exists a conformal mapping, $\zeta = F(z)$ (of $\mathfrak{S}$ into the ζ-plane) with the following conditions holding:

1. $F(\mathscr{L})$ is a segment of the real axis,
2. $\mathfrak{S} = \mathfrak{S}_{(+)} \cup \mathfrak{S}_{(-)}$ where $\mathrm{Im}\{F(\mathfrak{S}_{(+)})\} \subset R^{(+)}$ (upper half plane) and $\mathrm{Im}\{F(\mathfrak{S}_{(-)})\} \subset R^{(-)}$, (lower half plane),
3. $F(\mathfrak{S}_{(+)}) = F(\mathfrak{S}_{(-)})^*$.

In addition, the Cauchy data given on $\mathscr{L}$ is assumed to be of the form

$$\begin{aligned} u(x, y) &= \Phi(x + iy), \qquad z \in \mathscr{L}, \\ \mathbf{n} \cdot \frac{\partial u(x, y)}{\partial \mathbf{n}} &= \Psi(x + iy), \qquad z \in \mathscr{L}, \end{aligned} \tag{4.4.2}$$

($\mathbf{n}$ is a normal direction with respect to $\mathscr{L}$).

4. The data $\Phi(z)$, and $\Psi(z)$ are holomorphic for all $z \in \mathfrak{S}$.

Henrici's approach to this problem is to split up the general Cauchy problem with the data (4.4.2) into two partial problems. He seeks two solutions to the equation $\mathbf{e}[u] = 0$; the first solution is to satisfy the Cauchy data,

$$u_1(x, y) = \Phi(x + iy), \qquad \frac{\partial u_1}{\partial n}(x, y) = 0, \qquad \text{for} \quad z \in \mathscr{L}, \tag{4.4.3}$$

the second is to satisfy the Cauchy data,

$$u_2(x, y) = 0, \qquad \frac{\partial u_2(x, y)}{\partial n} = \Psi(x + iy), \qquad \text{for} \quad z \in \mathscr{L}. \tag{4.4.4}$$

It is clear that $u(x, y) = u_1(x, y) + u_2(x, y)$ is a solution of the Cauchy problem (4.4.1), (4.4.2).

If $\mathfrak{S}$ is a domain which is already symmetric with respect to conjugation, i.e., $\mathfrak{S} = \mathfrak{S}^*$, then the solutions $u_1(x, y)$, $u_2(x, y)$ have a particularly simple form. To see this let us use the customary transformation of $\mathbf{e}[u] = 0$ into the hyperbolic differential equation,

$$\mathbf{E}[U] \equiv U_{zz^*} + A(z, z^*)U_z + B(z, z^*)U_{z^*} + C(z, z^*)U = 0.$$

The initial data (4.4.3) and (4.4.4) become, respectively,

$$\begin{aligned} U_1(z, z^*) &= \Phi(z), && \text{on} \quad z = z^*, \\ \frac{\partial U_1(z, z^*)}{\partial z} - \frac{\partial U_1(z, z^*)}{\partial z^*} &= 0, && \text{on} \quad z = z^*, \end{aligned} \tag{4.4.5}$$

and

$$\begin{aligned} U_2(z, z^*) &= 0, && \text{on} \quad z = z^*, \\ \frac{\partial U_2(z, z^*)}{\partial z} - \frac{\partial U_2(z, z^*)}{\partial z^*} &= -i\Psi(z), && \text{on} \quad z = z^*. \end{aligned} \tag{4.4.6}$$

Following Henrici [H.6, p. 198] we pose that the two reduced problems may be solved by the functions

$$\begin{aligned} U_1(z, z^*) = {} & \tfrac{1}{2}[\Phi(z)R(z, z; z, z^*) + \Phi(z^*)R(z^*, z^*; z, z^*)] \\ & - \int_z^{z^*} \Phi(t)\Big\{[B(t, t) - A(t, t)]R(t, t, z, z^*) \\ & + \frac{1}{2}\left[\frac{\partial R}{\partial s}(t, s; z, z^*) - \frac{\partial R}{\partial s}(s, t; z, z^*)\right]_{s=t}\Big\}\, dt, \end{aligned} \tag{4.4.7}$$

$$U_2(z, z^*) = \frac{i}{2}\int_z^{z^*} \Psi(t)R(t, t; z, z^*)\, dt. \tag{4.4.8}$$

Clearly, because of the symmetry property of the Riemann function the $U_k(z, z^*)$ $(k = 1, 2)$ are solutions of $\mathbf{E}[U] = 0$; furthermore, if $\Phi(z)$, and $\Psi(z)$ are holomorphic in $\mathfrak{S}$, then $U_k(z, z^*)$ is holomorphic in $\mathfrak{S} \times \mathfrak{S}^*$. To see that these solutions satisfy the required initial data we make use of the formulas (3.5.6)–(3.5.10). We have, introducing the notation $R_k(\zeta_1, \zeta_2, \zeta_3, \zeta_4) = \partial/\partial\zeta_k\, R(\zeta_1, \zeta_2; \zeta_3, \zeta_4)$,

$$U_1(z, z) = \Phi(z)R(z, z; z, z) \equiv \Phi(z), \tag{4.4.9a}$$

$$\begin{aligned} \left.\frac{\partial U_1(z, z^*)}{\partial z}\right|_{z^*=z} &= \tfrac{1}{2}\{\Phi'(z) + \Phi(z)[R_1(z, z; z, z) + R_2(z, z; z, z) \\ &\quad + 2R_3(z, z; z, z)]\} + \Phi(z)\{[B(z, z) - A(z, z)] \\ &\quad + \tfrac{1}{2}[R_2(z, z; z, z) - R_1(z, z; z, z)]\} \\ &= \tfrac{1}{2}\Phi'(z) + \tfrac{1}{2}\Phi(z)[B(z, z) + A(z, z) - 2B(z, z)] \\ &\quad + \Phi(z)\{B(z, z) - A(z, z) + \tfrac{1}{2}[A(z, z) - B(z, z)]\} \\ &= \tfrac{1}{2}\Phi'(z), \end{aligned}$$

$$\left.\frac{\partial U_1(z, z^*)}{\partial z^*}\right|_{z^*=z} = \tfrac{1}{2}\{\Phi(z)R_4(z, z; z, z) + \Phi'(z) + \Phi(z)[R_1(z, z; z, z) + R_2(z, z; z, z) + R_4(z, z; z, z)]\}$$
$$- \Phi(z)\{[B(z, z) - A(z, z)] - \tfrac{1}{2}[R_2(z, z; z, z) - R_1(z, z; z, z)]\}$$
$$= \tfrac{1}{2}\Phi'(z) + \tfrac{1}{2}\Phi(z)\{-A(z, z) + B(z, z) + A(z, z) - A(z, z)\} - \{B(z, z) - A(z, z)\}\Phi(z) - \tfrac{1}{2}[A(z, z) - B(z, z)]\}$$
$$= \tfrac{1}{2}\Phi'(z);$$

hence

$$\frac{\partial U_1(z, z^*)}{\partial z} - \frac{\partial U_1(z, z^*)}{\partial z^*} = 0, \qquad \text{on} \quad z = z^*. \tag{4.4.9b}$$

Likewise, we have

$$U_2(z, z^*) = 0, \qquad \text{on} \quad z = z^*, \tag{4.4.10a}$$

$$\frac{\partial U_2(z, z^*)}{\partial z} - \frac{\partial U_2(z, z^*)}{\partial z^*} = -i\Psi(z), \qquad \text{on} \quad z = z^*, \tag{4.4.10b}$$

which are the required Cauchy conditions (4.4.6). The desired solution satisfying (4.4.2) (with data given on $z = z^*$) is then seen to be

$$u(x, y) = U_1(x + iy, x - iy) + U_2(x + iy, x - iy). \tag{4.4.11}$$

One notes by referring back to the representations (4.4.7) and (4.4.8) that since the data, i.e., $\Phi(z)$ and $\Psi(z)$, have a continuation to $\mathfrak{S}$, that $U(z, z^*) \equiv u(x, y)$ is holomorphic in the bicylinder $\mathfrak{S} \times \mathfrak{S}^*$.

We treat next the problem where data are given on an analytic curve $\mathscr{L} \subset \mathfrak{S}$, which is conformally mapped into a segment of the real axis by the mapping $\zeta = F(z)$, such that $F(\mathfrak{S}) = F(\mathfrak{S}^*)$. (Here $\mathfrak{S}^*$ is mapped by the conformal map $\zeta^* = \bar{F}(z^*)$). The initial data (4.4.2) given on $\mathscr{L}$ (in the z-plane) may be rewritten as initial data given on the real axis of the ζ-plane. Under this conformal mapping the differential equation $\mathbf{E}[U] = 0$ is transformed into a similar differential equation for the function $V(\zeta, \zeta^*) \equiv U(f(\zeta), \bar{f}(\zeta^*))$. Here $f(\zeta) \equiv F^{-1}(\zeta)$ and $\bar{f}(\zeta^*) \equiv \bar{F}^{-1}(\zeta^*)$. The function $V(\zeta, \zeta^*)$ may be seen to satisfy on $\zeta = \zeta^*$ the new Cauchy data,

$$V(\zeta, \zeta) = \Phi(\zeta) \equiv \phi(f(\zeta)), \tag{4.4.12}$$

and

$$\left.\frac{\partial V(\zeta, \zeta^*)}{\partial \zeta}\right|_{\zeta^*=\zeta} - \left.\frac{\partial V(\zeta, \zeta^*)}{\partial \zeta^*}\right|_{\zeta^*=\zeta} = \Psi(\zeta) \tag{4.4.13}$$

with

$$\Psi(\zeta) \equiv -i[f'(\zeta)\bar{f}(\zeta)]^{1/2} \times \psi(f(\zeta)).$$

Consequently, the Cauchy problem for conformally symmetric regions, $\mathfrak{S}$, (where the data is holomorphic in $\mathfrak{S}$) may be reduced in this manner to the Cauchy problem for data given on the real axis. This latter case was discussed in the above. For further details concerning this method the reader is directed to the original work by Henrici [H.6, pp. 196–200].

Generalized Axially Symmetric Elliptic Equations

In a later paper Henrici studied the construction of solutions to the singular differential equation,

$$\mathbf{l}_\nu[u] \equiv \frac{\partial^2 u}{\partial x^2} + \frac{\partial^2 u}{\partial y^2} + \frac{2\nu}{y}\frac{\partial u}{\partial y} + a(x)\frac{\partial u}{\partial x} + c(x)u = 0, \tag{4.4.14}$$

where $\nu > 0$, and $a(x)$, $c(x)$ are analytic functions of x alone. Following the approach of Bergman and Vekua he transforms this equation to the hyperbolic equation $\mathbf{E}[U] = 0$, where the coefficients now have the special form

$$\begin{aligned} A(z, z^*) &= \frac{1}{4}\left[a\left(\frac{z+z^*}{2}\right) - \frac{4\nu}{z-z^*}\right], \\ B(z, z^*) &= \frac{1}{4}\left[a\left(\frac{z+z^*}{2}\right) + \frac{4\nu}{z-z^*}\right], \\ C(z, z^*) &= \frac{1}{4}c\left(\frac{z+z^*}{2}\right). \end{aligned} \tag{4.4.15}$$

We note that the method of Vekua as applied to the differential equation $\mathbf{E}[U] = 0$ is valid, in general, only for the case of regular coefficients. Hence, Henrici's result provides an extension to the method of Vekua.

Lemma 4.4.1 (Henrici) *Let $u_0(x, y)$ be a solution of $\mathbf{l}_0[u] = 0$, which is defined in a domain $\mathfrak{S}$, with the property that if $z \in \mathfrak{S}$ then $z' = x + iyt \in \mathfrak{S}$, for $t \in [-1, +1]$. Then, for $\nu > 0$ the function*

$$u_\nu(x, y) = \alpha_\nu \int_0^\pi u^0(x, y \cos \gamma) \sin^{2\nu-1} \gamma \, d\gamma \tag{4.4.16}$$

is a solution of $\boldsymbol{l}_\nu[u] = 0$. *Furthermore,* $u^\nu(x, -y) = u^\nu(x, y)$, *and if*

$$\alpha_\nu^{-1} = \int_0^\pi \sin^{2\nu-1}\gamma \, d\gamma,$$

then $u^\nu(x, 0) = u^0(x, 0)$.

This may be seen by simply substituting the expression (4.4.16) into $\boldsymbol{l}_\nu[u] = 0$. The remaining conclusions are evident. Using the representations (4.4.7), (4.4.8), (4.4.11) of this section for the Cauchy data, $u^0(x, 0) = \Phi(x)$, $\partial u^{(0)}/\partial y(x, 0) = 0$, (where the usual analyticity conditions are assumed to hold on $\Phi(x)$ etc.) Henrici is able to obtain the following integral representation for such a solution of $\boldsymbol{l}_0[u] = 0$, i.e., for $U^{(0)}(z, z^*) \equiv u^{(0)}(x, y)$,

$$U^{(0)}(z, z^*) = \tfrac{1}{2}\{\Phi(z)R(z, z; z, z^*) + \Phi(z^*)R(z^*, z^*; z, z^*)\} + \frac{1}{2}\int_z^{z^*} \Phi(t)\{R_1(t, t; z, z^*) - R_2(t, t; z, z^*)\}\, dt. \tag{4.4.17}$$

He then uses Lemma 4.4.1 to obtain an integral representation for solutions $u^{(\nu)}(x, y) \equiv U^{(\nu)}(z, z^*)$ of $\boldsymbol{l}_\nu[u] = 0$, satisfying the above Cauchy data on $y = 0$, i.e.,

$$U^{(\nu)}(z, z^*) = \alpha_\nu \int_0^\pi U^{(0)}\left(z \cos^2 \frac{\gamma}{2} + z^* \sin^2 \frac{\gamma}{2}, z \sin^2 \frac{\gamma}{2} + z^* \cos^2 \frac{\gamma}{2}\right) \sin^{2\nu-1} \gamma \, d\gamma. \tag{4.4.18}$$

We rewrite this expression by using the auxiliary variables $\sigma = x + iy \cos \gamma$, $\sigma^* = x - iy \cos \gamma$, in the form

$$U^{(\nu)}(z, z^*) = \frac{\alpha_\nu}{2} \int_0^\pi \{\Phi(\sigma)R(\sigma, \sigma; \sigma, \sigma^*) + \Phi(\sigma^*)R(\sigma^*, \sigma^*; \sigma, \sigma^*)\} \times \sin^{2\nu-1} \gamma \, d\gamma + \frac{\alpha_\nu}{2} \int_0^\pi \left[\int_\sigma^{\sigma^*} \Phi(t)\{R_1(t, t; \sigma, \sigma^*) - R_2(t, t; \sigma, \sigma^*)\}\, dt\right] \sin^{2\nu-1} \gamma \, d\gamma, \tag{4.4.19}$$

which may be expressed alternately as,

$$U^{(v)}(z, z^*) = \alpha_v \int_0^\pi \Phi(\sigma) R(\sigma, \sigma; \sigma, \sigma^*) \sin^{2v-1} \gamma \, d\gamma$$
$$- \frac{i\alpha_v}{2}(z - z^*) \int_0^\pi \left[\int_0^{\pi-\delta} \Phi(\tau)\{R_1(\tau, \tau; \sigma, \sigma^*)\right.$$
$$\left. - R_2(\tau, \tau; \sigma, \sigma^*)\} \sin \delta \, d\delta\} \right] \sin^{2v-1} \gamma \, d\gamma, \qquad (4.4.20)$$

where the auxiliary variable, τ, is defined as $\tau = x + iy \cos \delta$. Finally, by interchanging orders of integration in (4.4.20), one has

$$U^{(v)}(z, z^*) = \alpha_v \int_0^\pi \Phi(\sigma) K_v(z, z^*; \gamma) \, d\gamma, \qquad (4.4.21)$$

with

$$K_v(z, z^*; \gamma) = R(\sigma, \sigma; \sigma, \sigma^*) \sin^{2v-1} \gamma - \frac{i(z - z^*)}{2} \sin \gamma$$
$$\times \int_0^\gamma \{R_1(\sigma, \sigma; \tau, \tau^*) - R_2(\sigma, \sigma; \tau, \tau^*)\} \sin^{v-1} \delta \, d\delta. \qquad (4.4.22)$$

The representation for solutions to the Cauchy initial value problem associated with (4.4.14) having the above data is then given by (4.4.21), (4.4.22). This result (in slightly modified form), is due to Henrici [H.8, pp. 19–23]; the reader who is interested in further details is referred to this reference. Henrici has shown that this representation for $u^{(v)}(x, y) \equiv U^{(v)}(z, z^*)$ yields an analytic continuation of the solution $u^{(v)}(x, y)$, to the bicylinder $\mathfrak{S} \times \mathfrak{S}^*$, providing that $\mathfrak{S}$ is symmetric with respect to conjugation, and the data, $\Phi(z)$ is holomorphic for $z \in \mathfrak{S}$.

By using the known Riemann function for the equation

$$\frac{\partial^2 u}{\partial x^2} + \frac{\partial^2 u}{\partial y^2} + \frac{2\mu}{x} \frac{\partial u}{\partial x} + k^2 u = 0,$$

namely,

$$R(t, t^*; z, z^*) = \left(\frac{t + t^*}{z + z^*}\right)^\mu \Phi_2\left(\mu, 1 - \mu, 1; X, -\frac{k^2 R^2}{4}\right),$$

Henrici [H.8] obtains, as a new result, a representation in the form (4.4.21), (4.4.22) for solutions of the equation

$$\frac{\partial^2 u}{\partial x^2} + \frac{\partial^2 u}{\partial y^2} + \frac{2\mu}{x}\frac{\partial u}{\partial x} + \frac{2\nu}{y}\frac{\partial u}{\partial y} + k^2 u = 0$$

with the usual Cauchy data, i.e., $u(x, 0) = \phi(x)$, $u_y(x, 0) = 0$; here Φ_2 is a confluent hypergeometric function of two variables [E.6, Vol. I, p. 225] defined by the power series

$$\Phi_2(\alpha, \beta, \gamma; x, y) = \sum_{m,n=0}^{\infty} \frac{(\alpha)_m(\beta)_m}{(\gamma)_{m+n}\, m!\, n!} x^m y^n,$$

and the auxiliary variables X and R are defined as

$$X = -\frac{(z-t)(z^*-t^*)}{(z+z^*)(t+t^*)}, \qquad \text{and} \qquad R^2 = (z-t)(z^*-t^*).$$

The kernel of (4.4.22) is found to be

$$K_\nu(z, z^*; \gamma) = \left(\frac{z+z^*}{2}\right)^{-\mu} \sigma^\mu \sin^{2\nu-1}\gamma$$
$$\times\, \Phi_2\left(\mu, 1-\mu, \nu; \frac{-y^2 \sin^2\gamma}{4x\sigma}, \frac{-k^2 y^2 \sin^2\gamma}{4}\right). \tag{4.4.23}$$

Henrici also shows that by setting either $\mu = 0$, $\nu = 0$ (or both) one obtains the already known representation for the corresponding partial differential equations with the above Cauchy data.

5. *The Generalized Biaxially Symmetric Helmholtz Equation (GBSHE)*

In this section we shall use Bergman's integral operator method to investigate solutions of the partial differential equation,

$$\mathbf{h}_{\mu\nu}[u] = \frac{\partial^2 u}{\partial x^2} + \frac{\partial^2 u}{\partial y^2} + \frac{2\mu}{x}\frac{\partial u}{\partial x} + \frac{2\nu}{y}\frac{\partial u}{\partial y} + k^2 u = 0 \qquad (\mu, \nu > 0). \quad \text{(GBSHE)}$$

(4.5.1)

In what follows we consider only the case where $\mu, \nu > 0$. Recently Colton

[C.4] has obtained uniqueness theorems for the case $\mu = 0$, $\nu < 0$, formulated in terms of the complex variable $\xi = \cos\theta$ which was introduced on pages 58 and 173.

We shall, following the terminology of Weinstein [W.6–15] refer to Eq. (4.5.1) as the generalized biaxially symmetric Helmholtz equation (GBSHE). One is led to consider this equation initially by seeking "mono-chromatic" solutions $U(X, Y, t) \equiv U_1(X, Y)e^{\pm ikt}$ of the $(m + n = (2\mu + 1) + (2\nu + 1))$-dimensional wave equation.

$$\left(\frac{\partial^2 U}{\partial {x_1}^2} + \cdots + \frac{\partial^2 U}{\partial {x_m}^2}\right) + \left(\frac{\partial^2 U}{\partial {y_1}^2} + \cdots + \frac{\partial^2 U}{\partial {y_n}^2}\right) = \frac{\partial^2 U}{\partial t^2}, \tag{4.5.2}$$

which depend solely on the variables $X^2 = ({x_1}^2 + \cdots + {x_m}^2)$, $Y^2 = ({y_1}^2 + \cdots + {y_n}^2)$. Henrici has studied (4.5.1) in [H.6,8], and using Henrici's representation, Gilbert and Howard [G.H.2,3] have investigated the analytic properties of solutions to (4.5.1).

We shall just consider those solutions of the GBSHE which are of class $\mathscr{C}^{(2)}$ in some neighborhood of the origin and even in x and in y. In this case for $u(x, y)$ to be a $\mathscr{C}^{(2)}[\Delta_\rho]$ solution, (i.e., $\mathscr{C}^{(2)}$ in the disk $\Delta_\rho \equiv \{z \mid |z| < \rho\}$), we must have that

$$u_x = 0, \qquad \text{on} \quad x = 0; \qquad u_y = 0, \qquad \text{on} \quad y = 0. \tag{4.5.3}$$

As the reader will recall from Section 4 of this chapter, Henrici has given an integral representation for solutions of (4.5.1), which furthermore may be used to construct a complete system of solutions. Referring to these results [H.8, p.25], we have, using standard notation (for instance see [E.6]), that

$$\begin{aligned} &P_n^{(\nu-\frac{1}{2},\,\mu-\frac{1}{2})}(\cos 2\theta)(kr)^{-\mu-\nu}J_{\mu+\nu+2n}(kr) \\ &\quad \equiv f_n(r, \cos 2\theta) \\ &\quad = \frac{\Gamma(\nu + n + \frac{1}{2})}{\Gamma(\nu)\Gamma(\frac{1}{2})\Gamma(n+1)} \int_0^\pi \{(k\sigma)^{-\mu-\nu}J_{\mu+\nu+2n}(k\sigma)\} \\ &\qquad \times \left\{\left(\frac{\sigma}{x}\right)^\mu \Phi_2(\mu, 1-\mu, \nu; \xi, \eta)\sin^{2\nu-1}\varphi\right\} d\varphi \end{aligned} \tag{4.5.4}$$

where

$$\sigma = x + iy\cos\varphi, \qquad x = r\cos\theta, \qquad y = r\sin\theta,$$

$$\xi = -\frac{y^2 \sin^2\varphi}{4x\sigma}, \qquad \eta = -\frac{k^2 y^2 \sin^2\varphi}{4}, \qquad k, \mu, \nu > 0, \qquad n = 0, 1, 2, \ldots.$$

It is known that an arbitrary solution to (4.5.1) of the class $\mathscr{C}^2[\Delta]$ may be represented in a series

$$w(r, \theta) = (kr)^{-\mu-\nu} \sum_{n=0}^{\infty} \frac{a_{2n} n!}{\Gamma(n+\nu+\frac{1}{2})} P_n^{(\nu-\frac{1}{2}, \mu-\frac{1}{2})}(\cos 2\theta) J_{\mu+\nu+2n}(kr); \quad (4.5.5)$$

also, it is well known (for instance see [E.6]) that an even analytic function regular about the origin may be expressed as a Neumann series of the type

$$f(\sigma) = \sigma^{-\mu-\nu} \sum_{n=0}^{\infty} a_{2n} J_{\mu+\nu+2n}(\sigma). \quad (4.5.6)$$

Hence, for r sufficiently small it follows that the class of analytic functions (4.5.6) may be mapped onto the class solutions (4.5.5) by an operator of the form

$$\begin{aligned} w(r, \theta) &\equiv u(x, y) \\ &\equiv \mathbf{H}_{\mu\nu} f \\ &\equiv a x^{-\mu} \int_{\mathscr{L}+1}^{-1} f(k\sigma)\sigma^{\mu} \left(\zeta - \frac{1}{\zeta}\right)^{2\nu-1} \Phi_2(\mu, 1-\mu, \nu; \xi, \eta) \frac{d\zeta}{\zeta}, \end{aligned} \quad (4.5.7)$$

with

$$\sigma = x + \frac{iy}{2}\left(\zeta + \frac{1}{\zeta}\right), \qquad \xi = \frac{y^2(\zeta - 1/\zeta)^2}{16x\sigma},$$

$$\eta = \frac{k^2 y^2(\zeta - 1/\zeta)}{16}, \qquad \mathscr{L} \equiv \{\zeta \mid \zeta = e^{i\phi}, 0 \le \phi \le \pi\},$$

and where the "normalizing constant" a is given by

$$a = \frac{2}{(2i)^{2\nu}\Gamma(\nu)\Gamma(\frac{1}{2})}.$$

For a justification of, and a motivation for, the replacement of the straight line path of integration by the given one, see Gilbert and Howard [G.H.3].

In [G.H.2,3] the present author and Howard introduced a method for constructing an inverse for the integral operator $\mathbf{H}_{\mu\nu}$ given above. We repeat this procedure below, since it is used as a standard technique in our further studies of partial differential equations by function theoretic methods.

It is useful to continue the arguments of the solutions $u(x, y)$ of (4.5.1) to complex values. Indeed a continuation of $r^2 = x^2 + y^2$, $\xi = \cos 2\theta = (x^2 - y^2)/(x^2 + y^2)$ to complex values allows one to obtain an inverse operator $\mathbf{H}_{\mu\nu}^{-1}$ which maps the class of solutions $\mathscr{C}^{(2)}[\Delta_\rho]$ back onto the class of analytic functions (4.5.6).

We consider next the problem of obtaining such an operator in the form

$$f(k\sigma) = \mathbf{H}_{\mu\nu}^{-1} u \equiv \int_{-1}^{1} K(\sigma, r, \xi) u\left[r\left(\frac{1+\xi}{2}\right)^{1/2}, r\left(\frac{1-\xi}{2}\right)^{1/2}\right] d\xi. \quad (4.5.8)$$

We try to determine K such that, formally integrating termwise, one obtains

$$(k\sigma)^{-\mu-\nu} \sum_{n=0}^{\infty} a_{2n} J_{\mu+\nu+2n}(k\sigma)$$
$$= (kr)^{-\mu-\nu} \int_{-1}^{1} K(\sigma, r, \xi)\left\{\sum_{0}^{\infty} \frac{a_{2n}\, n!\, P_n^{(\nu-\frac{1}{2}, \mu-\frac{1}{2})}(\xi)}{\Gamma(n+\nu+\frac{1}{2})} J_{\mu+\nu+2n}(kr)\right\} d\xi. \quad (4.5.9)$$

This may be done by recalling the orthogonality relation for the Jacobi polynomials

$$\int_{-1}^{1} (1-\xi)^{\nu-\frac{1}{2}}(1+\xi)^{\mu-\frac{1}{2}} P_n^{(\nu-\frac{1}{2}, \mu-\frac{1}{2})}(\xi) P_m^{(\nu-\frac{1}{2}, \mu-\frac{1}{2})}(\xi)\, d\xi$$
$$= \delta_{mn} \frac{2^{\mu+\nu}\Gamma(n+\nu+\frac{1}{2})\Gamma(n+\mu+\frac{1}{2})}{(2n+\mu+\nu)\Gamma(n+1)\Gamma(n+\mu+\nu)}. \quad (4.5.10)$$

Thus if we define†

$$K_n(\sigma, r, \xi) \equiv \frac{1}{2^{\mu+\nu}} b_n \left(\frac{kr}{k\sigma}\right)^{\mu+\nu} \frac{J_{\mu+\nu+2n}(k\sigma)}{J_{\mu+\nu+2n}(kr)}$$
$$\times P_n^{(\nu-\frac{1}{2}, \mu-\frac{1}{2})}(\xi)(1-\xi)^{\nu-\frac{1}{2}}(1+\xi)^{\mu-\frac{1}{2}}, \quad (4.5.11)$$

where

$$b_n = \frac{(2n+\mu+\nu)\Gamma(n+\mu+\nu)}{\Gamma(n+\mu+\frac{1}{2})},$$

† The case where certain of the quantities $J_{\mu+\nu+2n}(kr)$ may vanish is discussed somewhat further on.

we have

$$a_{2n}(k\sigma)^{-\mu-\nu}J_{\mu+\nu+2n}(k\sigma) = \int_{-1}^{1} K_n(\sigma, r, \xi)u\left(r\left(\frac{1+\xi}{2}\right)^{1/2}, r\left(\frac{1-\xi}{2}\right)^{1/2}\right) d\xi.$$

Hence,

$$f(k\sigma) = \int_{-1}^{1} K(\sigma, r, \xi)u\left(r\left(\frac{1+\xi}{2}\right)^{1/2}, r\left(\frac{1-\xi}{2}\right)^{1/2}\right) d\xi \tag{4.5.12}$$

where

$$K(\sigma, r, \xi) = \frac{1}{2^{\mu+\nu}}\left(\frac{r}{\sigma}\right)^{\mu+\nu}(1-\xi)^{\nu-\frac{1}{2}}(1+\xi)^{\mu-\frac{1}{2}}$$
$$\times \sum_{0}^{\infty}(2n+\mu+\nu)\frac{\Gamma(n+\mu+\nu)}{\Gamma(n+\mu+\frac{1}{2})}\frac{J_{\mu+\nu+2n}(k\sigma)}{J_{\mu+\nu+2n}(kr)}P_n^{(\nu-\frac{1}{2},\mu-\frac{1}{2})}(\xi).$$

We now show that these formal calculations can be justified, and also that K as a function of the complex variables, σ, r and ξ, is holomorphic in a certain polycylinder.

We note first that, except for factors independent of the parameter of summation, K_n can be written as

$$K_n(\sigma; r, \xi) = (2n+\mu+\nu)\frac{\Gamma(n+\mu+\nu)}{\Gamma(n+\mu+\frac{1}{2})}\frac{J_{\mu+\nu+2n}(k\sigma)}{J_{\mu+\nu+2n}(kr)}P_n^{(\nu-\frac{1}{2},\mu-\frac{1}{2})}(\xi).$$

But we have that (cf. [W.2, p. 225]) for all n sufficiently large

$$\frac{J_{\mu+\nu+2n}(k\sigma)}{J_{\mu+\nu+2n}(kr)} \sim \left(\frac{\sigma}{r}\right)^{2n+\mu+\nu}, \tag{4.5.13a}$$

and from Stirling's formula one has

$$\frac{\Gamma(n+\mu+\nu)}{\Gamma(n+\mu+\frac{1}{2})} \sim (n+\mu)^{\nu-\frac{1}{2}}. \tag{4.5.13b}$$

Hence there exists a positive integer, α say, such that for all n sufficiently large,

$$|K_n| \le n^{\alpha}\left|\frac{\sigma}{r}\right|^{2n}|P_n^{(\nu-\frac{1}{2},\mu-\frac{1}{2})}(\xi)|.$$

In order to investigate the domain of convergence for the kernel $K(\sigma; r, \xi)$ we consider the following comparison series (the generating function for the Jacobi polynomials), where $R \equiv (1 - 2t\xi + t^2)^{\frac{1}{2}}$,

$$\sum_{n=0}^{\infty} t^n P_n^{(\nu-\frac{1}{2},\, \mu-\frac{1}{2})}(\xi) = 2^{\mu+\nu-1} R^{-1}(1 - t + R)^{-\nu+\frac{1}{2}}(1 + t + R)^{-\mu+\frac{1}{2}}. \quad (4.5.14)$$

It may be easily seen that the series (4.5.14) converges uniformly and absolutely in the product space

$$\mathfrak{H}^{(2)} \equiv \{t \mid |t| \leq \rho(\varepsilon) < 1\} \times \mathfrak{E}(\varepsilon),$$

where

$$\mathfrak{E}(\varepsilon) \equiv \{\xi \mid |1 + \xi| + |1 - \xi| \leq 2 + \varepsilon\}$$

(for $\varepsilon > 0$ sufficiently small) to a holomorphic function of two complex variables.† We proceed as follows: for each ξ in the "slit ellipse" $\tilde{\mathfrak{E}}(\varepsilon) \equiv \mathfrak{E}(\varepsilon) - [-1, +1]$, we have the asymptotic estimate [S.6, p. 196]

$$|P_n^{(\alpha, \beta)}(\xi)|^{1/n} \approx |\xi + (\xi^2 - 1)^{1/2}|;$$

hence, for $|t| < |\xi - (\xi^2 - 1)^{1/2}|$, with $\xi \in \tilde{\mathfrak{E}}(\varepsilon)$ the generating function expansion (4.5.14) represents a holomorphic function of t. On the slit, $[-1, +1]$, itself we have the estimate $|P_n^{(\alpha, \beta)}(\xi)| \leq \binom{n+q-1}{n}$ where $q = \max(\alpha, \beta)$ (See [E.6, Vol. II, p. 206]); hence, here the series converges to a holomorphic function for all t such that $|t| < 1$. Consequently, for a given ellipse $\mathfrak{E}(\varepsilon_0)$, we may obtain a uniform bound by computing for some ξ_0 on its boundary the term $R_0^{-1} \equiv |\xi_0 + ({\xi_0}^2 - 1)^{1/2}|$. Then (4.5.14) is holomorphic in t for all $|t| < R_0$ and each fixed $\xi \in \mathfrak{E}(\varepsilon_0)$. By a theorem given in Szegö's book [S.6, p. 238], we know that the domain of convergence of a Jacobi series $f(\xi) = \sum_{n=0}^{\infty} a_n P_n^{(\nu-\frac{1}{2},\, \mu-\frac{1}{2})}(\xi)$ is the largest ellipse with foci at ± 1 in which the function is analytic-regular; moreover, the sum of the semiaxes of this ellipse, R_0, is given by $R_0 = \liminf_{n \to \infty} |a_n|^{-1/n}$. For the case of the series (4.5.14) $R_0 \equiv 1/|t|$. Since $|t|$ is taken to be $\leq \rho(\varepsilon) < 1$, we may take for $\rho(\varepsilon)$ the reciprocal of the sum of the semiaxes, namely

$$\rho(\varepsilon) = \left[1 + \frac{\varepsilon}{2} + \left(\varepsilon + \frac{\varepsilon^2}{4}\right)^{1/2}\right]^{-1} < 1.$$

† Clearly, the left hand side will converge as a power series in t and ξ in any circular bicylinder in which the right-hand side is regular.

Then for each fixed t, $|t| \le \rho(\varepsilon)$ the series (4.5.14) converges uniformly in the ellipse $\mathfrak{E}(\varepsilon)$ to a holomorphic function of ξ. Consequently, by Hartogs' theorem the series (4.5.14) is a holomorphic function in both ξ and t simultaneously.

In similar fashion (cf. [G.H.3]) the series

$$\sum_0^\infty n^\alpha \left(\frac{\sigma}{r}\right)^{2n} P_n^{(\nu-\frac{1}{2},\,\mu-\frac{1}{2})}(\xi)$$
$$= \left\{\left(t\frac{\partial}{\partial t}\right)^\alpha \sum_0^\infty t^n P_n^{(\nu-\frac{1}{2},\,\mu-\frac{1}{2})}(\xi)\right\}_{t=(\sigma/r)^2}$$
$$= \left\{\left(t\frac{\partial}{\partial t}\right)^\alpha (2^{\mu+\nu-1}R^{-1}(1-t+R)^{-\nu+\frac{1}{2}}(1+t+R)^{-\mu+\frac{1}{2}})\right\}_{t=(\sigma/r)^2} \tag{4.5.15}$$

is seen to converge absolutely and uniformly. Moreover it is clear from these considerations that K is bounded on the compact set

$$\mathfrak{H}^{(3)} \equiv \left\{(\sigma, r) \left| \left|\frac{\sigma}{r}\right| \le \rho(\varepsilon) < 1\right.\right\} \times \mathfrak{E}(\varepsilon),$$

and is seen to converge there to a holomorphic function of the three complex variables σ, r, and ξ. Indeed, K may be seen to be holomorphic in a somewhat larger set which does not intersect $\mathfrak{S} \equiv \{(\sigma, r, \xi) \,|\, r^2 - 2r\sigma\xi + \sigma^2 = 0\}$.

We remark that, in general, r, is usually considered as a fixed parameter such that it is not a root of the equations $J_{\mu+\nu+2n}(kr) = 0$. However, there may be times when we wish to vary r; in that case if r is ever a root of the equation, $J_{\mu+\nu+2n}(kr) = 0$ $(n = n_1, n_2, \ldots,)$ we rewrite the kernel as

$$K^1(\sigma, r, \xi) \equiv \sum_{\substack{n=0\\ n\neq n_i}}^{\infty} K_n(\sigma, r, \xi).$$

Using this modified kernel K^1, $\mathbf{H}_{\mu\nu}^{-1}$ maps u back onto f since in this case there is no term involving $J_{\mu+\nu+2n_i}$ in the series for u.

We next obtain a useful lemma concerning the singularities of K.

Lemma 4.5.1 *The kernel K used in the inverse operator $\mathbf{H}_{\mu\nu}^{-1} u$ is singular on the manifold whose points, $(\sigma, \xi) \in \mathbb{C}^2$ lie on the set*

$$\mathfrak{S}(r) \equiv \left\{(\sigma, \xi) \,|\, 1 - 2\xi\left(\frac{\sigma}{r}\right)^2 + \left(\frac{\sigma}{r}\right)^4 = 0\right\},$$

for each fixed r.

Proof From the preceding discussions we realize that the series representation for K does not converge on $\mathfrak{S}$. If r is a root of $J_{\mu+\nu+2n}(kr) = 0$ ($n = 1, 2, \ldots, N$) by definition we omit these terms from the kernel; thus the first N terms (N sufficiently large) form a well-defined holomorphic function in the σ, ξ variables, whereas the remaining terms approximate arbitrarily closely a function regular in $\mathfrak{H}^{(3)}$ but singularities on $\mathfrak{S}(r)$. We show this as follows. Let $t = \sigma/r$ and let us use the notation

$$K^1(\sigma, r, \xi) \equiv \sum_{\substack{n=0 \\ n \neq n_i}}^{N} K_n(\sigma, r, \xi) + \sum_{n=N+1}^{\infty} K_n(\sigma, r, \xi)$$

$$\equiv F_0(\sigma; r, \xi) + F_1(\sigma; r, \xi).$$

$F_0(\sigma; r, \xi)$ is as remarked above holomorphic in a neighborhood $\mathfrak{H}^{(3)}$, and F_1 may be estimated by

$$F_1(\sigma; r, \xi) = \sum_{n=N+1}^{\infty} k_n(\xi)\left(1 + O\left(\frac{1}{n}\right)\right)t^{2n+\mu+\nu}$$

in $\mathfrak{H}^{(3)}$, where $k_n(\xi) \equiv (n + \mu)^{\nu-1/2} P_n^{(\nu-\frac{1}{2}, \mu-\frac{1}{2})}(\xi)$. We assert now that the function $F_1(\sigma; r, \xi)$ has as a "first" set of singularities (moving away from the origin), the singularity manifold of the function given by the series (4.5.14). To make this point clear let us consider the term $k_n(\xi)(1 + O[1/n])$ to be the Taylor coefficient of F_1 expanded as a power series in t. Fabry's theorem on the location of singularities [D.4, p. 377] states, that if the $\{a_n\}$ are the Taylor coefficients of a power series, and the limit as $n \to \infty$ of the ratio, a_n/a_{n+1}, exists, and is equal to α, say, then this series, $\sum a_n z^n$, is singular at the point $z = \alpha$ on its circle of convergence. Applying this result to the above series for F_1 we have then as a singular point,

$$t = \lim_{n\to\infty} \frac{k_n(\xi)\left[1 + O\left(\frac{1}{n}\right)\right]}{k_{n+1}(\xi)\left[1 + O\left(\frac{1}{n}\right)\right]} = \{\xi - (\xi^2 - 1)^{1/2}\},$$

which follows directly from the asymptotic estimate given by Szegö [S.6, p. 190], namely

$$P_n^{(\alpha,\beta)}(\xi) \approx (\xi - 1)^{-\alpha/2}(\xi + 1)^{-\beta/2}\{(\xi + 1)^{1/2} + (\xi - 1)^{1/2}\}^{\alpha+\beta}$$
$$\cdot (2\pi n)^{-1/2}(\xi^2 - 1)^{-1/4}\{(\xi + (\xi^2 - 1)^{1/2}\}^{n+1/2},$$

where ξ is not to be contained on the slit from -1 to $+1$. We conclude by continuation of this analytic set (of singularities) and from the above that $t^2 - 2t\xi + 1 = 0$, with $t = \sigma/r$, are singular points of $F_1(\sigma; r, \xi)$.† It is indeed conceivable, that there might be additional singular points in the t-plane on the circle of convergence $|t| = |\xi - (\xi^2 - 1)^{\frac{1}{2}}|$. However, this topic is a detailed one and beyond the scope of the present work; the interested reader is referred to Gilbert [G.27]. The function given by (4.5.14) is singular only for the points (ξ, t) which satisfy the equations

$$(1) \qquad R^2 \equiv (1 - 2\xi t + t^2) = 0,$$

$$(2) \qquad 1 - t + R = 0,$$

$$(3) \qquad 1 + t + R = 0,$$

and indeed these points must also be singular points of F_1. The cases (1), (2), (3) imply, that (b'): $\{t(\xi - 1) = 0\}$, and (c'): $\{t(1 + \xi) = 0\}$ respectively. If $\xi \neq \pm 1$ the only possible singularities of the $\mathbf{H}_{\mu\nu}$-associate corresponding to (b'), (c') lie at $t = 0$. Since we deal with solutions regular at the origin (on the first Riemann sheet on which the solution is defined) we may ignore this case and consider only the case (1), i.e., $R = 0$.

We now list several theorems concerning the location of singularities of solutions of the GBSHE. The proofs are similar to those given in Gilbert [G.6,7,9,13,14,18] and the reader is referred to these papers for details.

Theorem 4.5.2 *Let $u(x, y) = \mathbf{H}_{\mu\nu} f$ where $f(k\sigma)$ is an even analytic function whose finite singularities are at $k\sigma = \pm\alpha$. Then the only possible singularities of $u(x, y)$ (except perhaps for points on the x and y axes) lie at $z = \pm\alpha/k$ and $\pm\bar{\alpha}/k$.*

Proof From [E.6, Vol. I, pp. 225, 229] it is known that the confluent hypergeometric function of two variables $\Phi_2(\mu, 1 - \mu, \nu; \xi, \eta)$ is entire. Hence, the only finite singularities of $u(x, y)$ for (x, y) over $\mathbb{C}^2$ must come either from the envelope method as applied to the singularities of $f(k\sigma)$, the endpoint-pinches, or a Hadamard-pinch at $\zeta = 0$. Since we are interested only in $u(x, y)$ on the first sheet of the Riemann space (ramified with respect to complex ξ) we may ignore the Hadamard pinch at $\zeta = 0$. This pinch suggests as candidates for singularities any point of the x-axis on other than the first Riemann sheet.

† The branch of $R = (1 - 2\xi t + t^2)^{\frac{1}{2}}$ which reduces to $+1$ as $t \to 0$ does not yield singularities of (4.5.14) of the form $1 \pm t + R = 0$. These latter singularities lie on another sheet of the Riemann space ramified with respect to the complex ξ-coordinate. This other branch of R contributes the singular planes $t = 0$, and $\xi = \pm 1$.

The endpoint-pinch and envelope method, as before, each yield the same sets as possible singularities of $u(x, y)$.

Indeed, by applying the envelope method (cf. Gilbert [G.6,9]) one sees that the only possible singularities of u must lie on the intersection

$$\{S(x, y, \varphi) \equiv (k\sigma - \alpha)(k\sigma + \alpha) = 0\} \cap \{\partial S/\partial\varphi = 0\}, \qquad \sigma = x + iy \cos \varphi.$$

Hence $(x + iy \cos \varphi)^2 - \alpha^2/k^2$, when differentiated and set equal to zero, gives $\sin \varphi = 0$. Using $\cos \varphi = \pm 1$ and $(x + iy \cos \varphi) = \pm\alpha/k$ one obtains the desired result immediately. (We use the $\sin \varphi$ representation for σ because of simplicity in computing the singularities.)

We also have

Theorem 4.5.3 *Let $u(x, y)$ be a solution of the* GBSHE *whose only finite singularities lie in the set*

$$\left\{\left(z^2 - \left(\frac{\alpha}{k}\right)^2\right)\left(z^2 - \left(\frac{\bar{\alpha}}{k}\right)^2\right) = 0\right\} \equiv \left\{(r, \xi) \mid \xi = \frac{1}{2}\left(\frac{r^2k^2}{\alpha^2} + \frac{\alpha^2}{k^2r^2}\right)\right\},$$
$$\xi = \cos 2\theta.$$

Then possible singularities of the $\mathbf{H}_{\mu\nu}$-associate $f(k\sigma)$ are at the points in the set $\{k\sigma = +\alpha, -\alpha, 0\}$.

For if u be singular at $\{(r, \xi) \mid \xi = \frac{1}{2}(r^2k^2/\alpha^2 + \alpha^2/k^2r^2)\}$ and if by Theorem 4.5.1, the kernel of the inverse operator has as a singularity manifold the set $\{(\xi, \sigma, r) \mid 1 - 2\xi(\sigma/r)^2 + (\sigma/r)^4 = 0\}$, then we know that possible singularities of $f(k\sigma)$ are on

$$\left\{\sigma \mid \tilde{S}(\sigma, r) \equiv r^4 - 2\left[\frac{1}{2}\left(\frac{r^2k^2}{\alpha^2} + \frac{\alpha^2}{k^2r^2}\right)\right]\sigma^2r^2 + \sigma^4 = 0\right\} \cap \left\{\sigma \,\middle|\, \frac{\partial\tilde{S}}{\partial r} = 0\right\}.$$

We get that

$$\frac{\partial\tilde{S}}{\partial r} = \frac{\partial}{\partial r}\left(r^4 - r^4\frac{k^2\sigma^2}{\alpha^2} - \frac{\alpha^2}{k^2}\sigma^2 + \sigma^4\right) = 4r^3\left[1 - \frac{k^2\sigma^2}{\alpha^2}\right].$$

Thus $\partial\tilde{S}/\partial r = 0$ gives $k\sigma = \pm\alpha$, or $r = 0$, which when introduced into $\tilde{S}(\sigma, r) = 0$, implies $\sigma^2(\sigma^2 - \alpha^2/k^2) = 0$ which is the desired result.

Combining these last two results we realize that each "possible singularity" of $u(x, y)$ is indeed an actual singularity, hence the following "fundamental" theorem concerning singularities of GBSHE functions.

Theorem 4.5.4 *A necessary and sufficient condition for $u(x, y)$ to be singular at $z = \pm\alpha/k$, $\pm\bar{\alpha}/k$ is for its $\mathbf{H}_{\mu\nu}$-associate, f, to be singular at $k\sigma = \alpha$, or $k\sigma = -\alpha$.*

Remark In order to see that Theorem 4.5.3 gave necessary and sufficient conditions for $u(x, y)$ to be singular it was not necessary to know *all* of the singularities of the kernel $K(\sigma, r, \xi)$ of the inverse operator. Because the kernel $\Phi_2(\mu, 1-\mu, \nu; \xi, \eta)$ of the operator $\mathbf{H}_{\mu\nu}$ was entire we were able to determine all candidates for singularities of $u(x, y)$. Hence, we merely need to know if *each* of these candidates does indeed map back, using the inverse operator, onto a given singularity of $f(k\sigma)$.

With this theorem one is able to transplant theorems about the location of singularities from classical function theory to the theory of solutions of the GBSHE. We may list results such as those given in Section 2 of the present chapter. An example is given below.

Theorem 4.5.5 *A* GBSHE *function $w(r, \theta)$ which has the series representation*

$$w(r, \theta) = (kr)^{-\mu-\nu} \sum_{n=0}^{\infty} \frac{a_{2n} n!}{\Gamma(n + \nu + \frac{1}{2})} P_n^{(\nu-\frac{1}{2}, \mu-\frac{1}{2})}(\cos 2\theta) J_{\mu+\nu+2n}(kr)$$

about $z = 0$ converges uniformly and absolutely in any compact subset of disk $\Delta_\rho \equiv \{|z| < 2\rho/k\}$, where

$$\rho^{-1} = \limsup_{n\to\infty} \left(\frac{a_{2n}}{\Gamma(2n + \mu + \nu + \frac{1}{2})}\right)^{1/2n}.$$

Proof First we recall that the GBSHE associate has the form (4.5.6), namely (for k set equal to 1),

$$f(\sigma) = \sigma^{-\mu-\nu} \sum_{n=0}^{\infty} a_{2n} J_{\mu+\nu+2n}(\sigma).$$

We may associate with $f(\sigma)$ another analytic function

$$g(z) = \sum_{n=0}^{\infty} \frac{a_{2n} z^{2n}}{\Gamma(2n + \mu + \nu + \frac{1}{2})}$$

by means of the integral transform

$$f(\sigma) = \frac{2^{1-\mu-\nu}}{\sqrt{\pi}} \int_0^1 (1-t^2)^{\mu+\nu-\frac{1}{2}} \cos(\sigma t) g\left(\frac{\sigma}{2}[1-t^2]\right) dt.$$

This follows immediately from the following integral representation for the Bessel functions [E.6, Vol. II, p. 14]

$$\Gamma(\nu + \tfrac{1}{2}) J_\nu(z) = \frac{2}{\sqrt{\pi}} \left(\frac{z}{2}\right)^\nu \int_0^{\pi/2} \cos(z \sin \varphi)(\cos \varphi)^{2\nu} \, d\varphi.$$

Let us consider the case where $g(z)$ has a finite singularity at $z = \alpha$, then $g((\sigma/2)[1 - t^2])$ has the singularity manifold

$$\{S(\sigma; t) \equiv \sigma[1 - t^2] - 2\alpha = 0\}.$$

The envelope method predicts a possible singularity of $f(\sigma)$ at

$$\{S = 0\} \cap \{\partial S/\partial t = 0\} = \{\sigma = 2\alpha\}.$$

The integrand also has singularities at $t = \pm 1$ which, however, do not yield finite singularities of $f(\sigma)$, when we compute their Hadamard "pinch" with $S(\sigma; t) = 0$. We conclude that on the first sheet of the Riemann surface of $f(\sigma)$ the closest singularity to the origin is at $\sigma = 2\alpha$. and that $w(r, \theta)$ must converge in the disk $|r| < 2|\alpha|$.

In the following we shall consider a special case of GBSHE functions, namely where $\mu = 0$, which is the generalized axially symmetric Helmholtz equation (GASHE). Here we obtain results about the order and growth of solutions that are somewhat more concise than are obtained for GBSHE. For further details about the GBSHE case the reader is directed to the papers by the present author with Howard [G.H.2,3].

Let $u(x, y)$ be a solution of the differential equation,

$$\mathbf{H}_{0\nu} u \equiv \frac{\partial^2 u}{\partial x^2} + \frac{\partial^2 u}{\partial y^2} + \frac{2\nu}{y} \frac{\partial u}{\partial y} + k^2 u = 0. \tag{4.5.16}$$

In this case one is able to obtain an integral operator which generates solutions from analytic functions by considering $\lim_{\mu \to 0} \mathbf{H}_{\mu\nu} f \equiv \mathbf{H}_{0\nu} f$; see for instance Henrici [H.8] or the review of these results in the previous section, and for a slight modification of this representation, [G.H.2]. The representation we shall use here is the one in [G.H.2], namely

$$\mathbf{H}_\nu f \equiv c_{\nu k} \int_{\substack{+1 \\ |\zeta|=1}}^{-1} J_{\nu-1}\left(\frac{ky[\zeta - 1/\zeta]}{2i}\right) f(k\sigma)\left(\zeta - \frac{1}{\zeta}\right)^\nu \frac{d\zeta}{\zeta} \tag{4.5.17}$$

where $\sigma = x + \frac{1}{2}iy[\zeta + 1/\zeta]$ as usual,

$$c_{\nu k} \equiv \frac{-(iky)^{1-\nu}}{2} \frac{\Gamma(\nu + \frac{1}{2})}{\Gamma(\frac{1}{2})},$$

and the integration path is the upper unit semicircle from $+1$ to -1. The operator $\mathbf{H}_\nu$ maps the class of analytic functions regular about the origin,

$$f(k\sigma) = (k\sigma)^{-\nu} \sum_{n=0}^{\infty} a_n J_{\nu+n}(k\sigma) \tag{4.5.18}$$

onto the class of regular solutions about the origin, expressed as a Bessel–Gegenbauer series,

$$u(x, y) \equiv w(r, \theta) = \Gamma(2\nu)(kr)^{-\nu} \sum_{n=0}^{\infty} \frac{a_n n!}{\Gamma(2\nu + n)} J_{\nu+n}(kr) C_n^\nu(\cos\theta). \tag{4.5.19}$$

That this set of solutions is complete "in the sense of Cauchy sequences" can be seen immediately from the fact that $\mathbf{H}_\nu$ is a *continuous* operator, and the monomials σ^n are complete with respect to a simply connected neighborhood of the origin.

For the case of the GASHE function (4.5.19) all of the previous theorems about singularities and domains of regularity for GBSHE functions hold, and we refer the reader to [G.H.2] for further details. However, in the case of the GASHE functions we may obtain growth estimates for entire solutions which are quite similar to those obtained by the present author for the solutions of Weinstein's (GASPT) equation.

We decide to call any GASHE or GBSHE function entire if its radius of convergence, i.e., the radius of convergence of its associated analytic function, is infinite.

This definition is suggested by the following argument. If $g(z)$ is singular at $z = \alpha$, then the closest singularity of $f(\sigma)$ to the origin is at $z = 2\alpha$. Hence, letting $\alpha \to \infty$ we conclude

$$\limsup_{n\to\infty} \left(\frac{|a_{2n}|}{\Gamma(2n + \mu + \nu + \frac{1}{2})}\right)^{\frac{1}{2}n} \to 0.$$

Suppose on the other hand that

$$\limsup_{n\to\infty}\left(\frac{\Gamma(2n+\mu+\nu+\frac{1}{2})}{|a_{2n}|}\right)^{\frac{1}{2}n} \to L \neq 0;$$

then $g(z)$ must have a finite singularity, and hence $f(\sigma)$ can not be entire. Hence our definition is justified.

Suppose that $f(k\sigma)$ is regular-analytic in a neighborhood of $|\sigma| \leq R$; then we may obtain a bound for $|w(r, \theta)|$ in terms of the maximum modulus $\tilde{M}(R)$ of $f(k\sigma)$ on $|\sigma| = R$. For instance, we have

$$\begin{aligned} |w(r,\theta)| &\leq \left|\frac{ky}{2}\right|^{1-\nu} \frac{\Gamma(\nu+\frac{1}{2})}{\sqrt{\pi}} \int_0^{\pi} |J_{\nu-1}(ky\sin\varphi) f(k\sigma)| \sin^{\nu}\varphi \, d\varphi \\ &\leq \frac{\tilde{M}(R)}{\sqrt{\pi}} \frac{\Gamma(\nu+\frac{1}{2})}{\Gamma(\nu)} \int_0^{\pi} \sin^{2\nu-1}\varphi \, d\varphi, \end{aligned} \tag{4.5.20}$$

since

$$|J_{\nu}(z)| \leq \left|\frac{z}{2}\right|^{\nu} \frac{e^{|y|}}{\Gamma(\nu+1)} \qquad \text{with} \quad y = \operatorname{Im}(z). \tag{4.5.21}$$

Expression (4.5.20) further reduces to

$$|w(r,\theta)| \leq \frac{\tilde{M}(R)}{\sqrt{\pi}} \frac{\Gamma(\nu+\frac{1}{2})}{\Gamma(\nu)} \frac{\Gamma(\nu)\Gamma(\frac{1}{2})}{\Gamma(\nu+\frac{1}{2})} = \tilde{M}(R). \tag{4.5.22}$$

Lemma 4.5.6 *Let $w(r, \theta)$ be a* GASHE *function defined in the disk $r \leq R$ by the operator $\mathbf{H}_{\mu\nu}$. Furthermore, let the associate function $f(k\sigma)$ have a maximum modulus $\tilde{M}(R)$ on $|\sigma| = R$. Then*

$$|w(r,\theta)| \leq \tilde{M}(R). \tag{4.5.23}$$

With information of this type we are able to obtain upper and lower bounds for the maximum modulus of an entire GASHE function. For instance, Gilbert and Howard [G.H.2] have proved the following result, which is an extension of the bounds obtained for the case of GASPT. We include this case here in order to show the reader what type of estimates are involved in our computations. It will be apparent that this method may be extended to a wide class of elliptic equations, providing we have a suitable kernel for the inverse integral operator.

Theorem 4.5.7 *Let $w(r, \theta)$ be an entire* GASHE *function with a series representation* (4.5.19); *then for R sufficiently large and any $\varepsilon > 0$ there exists a $\lambda \geq 0$ such that the maximum modulus $M(R)$ is bounded above by the inequality $M(R) < \exp R^{\lambda+\varepsilon}$; and if the order of the associate, f, of w is $\lambda > 1$, then the maximum modulus is bounded below by* $\exp R^{\lambda-\varepsilon} < M(R)$.

Proof As we argued earlier in the case of GASPT, if $w(r, \theta)$ is entire its $\mathbf{H}_{\mu\nu}$-associate, $f(k\sigma)$ is entire; hence, there exists a $\lambda \geq 0$ such that $|f(k\sigma)| < \exp R^{\lambda+\varepsilon}$, for arbitrary $\varepsilon > 0$, when R is sufficiently large. Using Lemma 4.5.5 we obtain $|w(r, \theta)| < \exp R^{\lambda+\varepsilon}$ for $r < R$. In order to obtain a lower bound for the maximum modulus $M(R)$, we consider the inverse operator $\mathbf{H}_\nu^{-1}$, which is given in [G.H.2, p. 348] as

$$\mathbf{H}_\nu^{-1}u \equiv \Gamma(2\nu)(kr)^{-1}\int_{-1}^{+1} K(\sigma, r, \xi)u(r\xi, r(1-\xi^2)^{1/2})\, d\xi,$$

with

$$K(\sigma; r, \xi) \equiv \sum_{m=0}^{\infty} K_m(\sigma, r, \xi) \tag{4.5.24}$$

$$= a_\nu\left(\frac{r}{\sigma}\right)^\nu (1-\xi^2)^{\nu-\frac{1}{2}} \sum_{m=0}^{\infty} (\nu+m)\frac{J_{\nu+m}(k\sigma)}{J_{\nu+m}(kr)} C_m^\nu(\xi),$$

providing kr is not a zero of $J_{\nu+m}(x)$. In the case that kr *is* a zero it must be one of a $J_{\nu+m}(x)$ for some integer $m \leq N(r) < \infty$. In this case we delete this term from our series expansion for $K(\sigma, r, \xi)$ and write

$$K(\sigma, r, \xi) = K'(\sigma, r, \xi) \equiv \sum_{\substack{m=0\\ m\neq m_i}}^{\infty} K_m(\sigma, r, \xi) \tag{4.5.25}$$

where m_i is an integer such that $J_{\nu+m_i}(kr) = 0$. For further details concerning this the reader is directed to [G.H.2, p. 350].

Using our definition of the inverse operator we obtain the estimates

$$|f(k\sigma)| \leq \Gamma(2\nu)M(R)\int_{-1}^{+1} |K(\sigma, R, \xi)|\, d\xi \tag{4.5.26}$$

for $|\sigma| \leq \rho < R$, and where we bound $|K(\sigma, r, \xi)|$ as follows:

$$K(\sigma, R, \xi) = \alpha_\nu\left(\frac{R}{\sigma}\right)^\nu (1-\xi^2)^{\nu-\frac{1}{2}}\left\{\sum_{m=0}^{N} (\nu+m)\frac{J_{\nu+m}(k\sigma)}{J_{\nu+m}(kR)} C_m^\nu(\xi)\right.$$

$$\left. + \sum_{m=N+1}^{\infty} (\nu+m)\frac{J_{\nu+m}(k\sigma)}{J_{\nu+m}(kR)} C_m^\nu(\xi)\right\}; \tag{4.5.27}$$

for any fixed R we can find an $N(R)$ so large such that we have the following approximation [W.2, p. 225]:

$$\frac{J_{\nu+m}(k\sigma)}{J_{\nu+m}(kR)} \approx \left(\frac{\sigma}{R}\right)^{\nu+m} \{1 + O(1/m)\}, \qquad \text{for} \quad m \geq N(R);$$

hence

$$K(\sigma, R, \xi) \approx \hat{K}_N(\sigma, R, \xi) + \alpha_\nu\{1 + O(1/N(R))\}(1 - \xi^2)^{\nu-\frac{1}{2}} \times \left(\frac{R}{\sigma}\right)^{\nu} \sum_{m=N+1}^{\infty} (\nu + m)\left(\frac{\sigma}{R}\right)^{\nu+m} C_m^\nu(\xi), \tag{4.5.28}$$

where $\hat{K}_N(\sigma, R, \xi)$ is the Nth partial sum which appears in (4.5.25). An upper bound for $|K(\sigma, R, \xi)|$ is thereby provided by

$$|K(\sigma, R, \xi)| \leq |\hat{K}_N(\sigma, R, \xi)| + 2\alpha_\nu |1 - \xi^2|^{\nu-\frac{1}{2}} \left|\frac{R}{\sigma}\right|^{\nu} \times \left\{\left|\sum_{m=0}^{\infty} (\nu + m)\left(\frac{\sigma}{R}\right)^{\nu+m} C_m^\nu(\xi)\right| + \left|\sum_{m=0}^{N} (\nu + m)\left(\frac{\sigma}{R}\right)^{\nu+m} C_m^\nu(\xi)\right|\right\} \tag{4.5.29}$$

$$\leq |\hat{K}_N(\sigma, R, \xi)| + \left|G_N\left(\frac{\sigma}{R}, \xi\right)\right| + \frac{2\alpha_\nu |1 - \xi^2|^{\nu-\frac{1}{2}} \left|1 - \dfrac{\sigma^2}{R^2}\right|}{\left|1 - 2\xi\dfrac{\sigma}{R} + \dfrac{\sigma^2}{R^2}\right|^{\nu+1}}, \tag{4.5.30}$$

where $G_N(\sigma/R, \xi)$ is the last term in (4.5.29), which we notice is a polynomial in σ/R, ξ. If we now introduce the complex notation $z = \mathrm{Re}^{i\theta}$, $\xi = \cos\theta$, we may rewrite (4.5.30) as

$$|K(\sigma, R, \xi)| \leq |\hat{K}_N| + 2|G_N| + \frac{\alpha_\nu |z\bar{z} - \sigma^2| \, |z - \bar{z}|^{2\nu}}{2^{2\nu-1}|(z - \sigma)(\bar{z} - \sigma)|^{\nu+1}}$$

$$\leq |\hat{K}_N| + 2|G_N| + 2^{2-2\nu} \frac{(R^2 + \rho^2)R^{2\nu}}{(R - \rho)^{2\nu+2}} \frac{\Gamma(2\nu)}{\Gamma(\nu + \frac{1}{2})^2}.$$

Using this estimate in (4.5.24) we find that

$$|f(k\sigma)| \leq \Gamma(2\nu)M(R)\left\{|\hat{K}_N| + 2|G_N| + \frac{\Gamma(2\nu)2^{2-2\nu}(R^2 + \rho^2)R^{2\nu}}{\Gamma(\nu + \frac{1}{2})^2(R - \rho)^{2\nu+2}}\right\},$$

for $|\sigma| \leq \rho < R$. If $\tilde{M}(\rho) = \exp(\rho^{\lambda})$ is the maximum modulus of $f(k\sigma)$ for $|\sigma| \leq \rho < R$ then

$$\exp(\rho^{\lambda-\varepsilon'}) < \tilde{M}(\rho) \leq \Gamma(2\nu)M(R)\left\{|\hat{K}_N| + 2|G_N| + \frac{\Gamma(2\nu)2^{2-2\nu}}{\Gamma(\nu+\frac{1}{2})^2}\frac{(R^2+\rho^2)R^{2\nu}}{(R-\rho)^{2\nu+2}}\right\},$$

for all $\varepsilon' > 0$. Now by setting $\rho = \rho_0 = \theta R$ $(0 < \theta < 1)$ we have then, for some $\varepsilon > 0$ and R large enough,

$$\exp(R^{\lambda-\varepsilon}) = \frac{(1-\theta)^{2\nu+2}\exp(\rho_0^{\lambda-\varepsilon'})}{\Gamma(2\nu)\left\{(1-\theta)^{2\nu+2}[|\hat{K}_N| + 2|G_N|] + \dfrac{\Gamma(2\nu)2^{2-2\nu}}{\Gamma(\nu+\frac{1}{2})^2}(1+\theta^2)\right\}}$$
$$< M(R),$$

where $N = N(R)$. We wish to show that by choosing R large (and then consequently $N(R)$ large enough for the estimate (4.5.13b) to hold), that ε is of the same order of magnitude as ε'. We have

$$R^{-\varepsilon} = \frac{\rho_0^{\lambda-\varepsilon'}}{R^{\lambda}} + \frac{2\nu+2}{R^{\lambda}}\log(1-\theta) - \frac{\log\Gamma(2\nu)}{R^{\lambda}}$$
$$- \frac{1}{R^{\lambda}}\log\left\{(1-\theta)^{2\nu+2}[|\hat{K}_N| + 2|G_N|] + \frac{\Gamma(2\nu)2^{2-2\nu}}{\Gamma(\nu+\frac{1}{2})^2}(1+\theta^2)\right\}.$$

Hence, for large R,

$$R^{-\varepsilon} \approx \frac{\rho_0^{\lambda-\varepsilon'}}{R^{\lambda}} - \frac{1}{R^{\lambda}}\log[|\hat{K}_N| + 2|G_N|].$$

We assume now that R is large and held fixed, say $R = R_{\mu}$. Then we determine $N(R_{\mu})$ so that (4.5.28) holds for $m > N(R_{\mu})$, and we delete any term in the finite sum $\hat{K}_N(\sigma, R, \xi)$ for which $J_{\nu+m}(kR_{\mu})$, $m = 1, 2, \ldots, N(R_{\mu})$, vanishes in the denominator. This is the redefined kernel discussed above in (4.5.25), and is the correct one to use for the inversion. For further details concerning this point the reader is referred to the original paper by the present author with Howard [G.H.2].

We show now that

$$\frac{1}{R^{\lambda}}\log\{|\hat{K}_N| + 2|G_N|\} \to 0 \qquad \text{as} \quad R \to \infty, \qquad \text{if} \quad \lambda > 1.$$

We note that the approximation used in (4.5.28) will be valid for $N = N(R) \cong [kR]$, since the first zero of $J_\lambda(z)$ for λ large is $\lambda + O(\lambda^{1/3})$, and we can therefore divide the asymptotic expression for $J_{\nu+m}(k\sigma)$ and $J_{\nu+m}(kR)$. By use of the triangle inequality and known appraisals for Bessel functions and Gegenbauer polynomials, we have

$$|\hat{K}_N| \le |\nu + [kR]| \sum_{m=0}^{[kR]} \frac{(\frac{1}{2}kR)^{\nu+m} e^{kR} \Gamma(2\nu + m)}{\Gamma(\nu + 1)\, |J_{\nu+m}(kR)|\, \Gamma(m)\Gamma(m + 1)}. \quad (4.5.31)$$

Consider next the factors $|J_{\nu+m}(kR)|$, $m = 0, 1, \ldots, N = [kR]$. We note that in any interval of length π/k, call it $\mathfrak{J}$, say, each of the functions $J_{\nu+m}(kR)$, $m = 0, 1, \ldots, N$, has at most one zero. Hence, in $\mathfrak{J}$ there exists at least one point whose distance from all the zeros of the functions of the set $\{J_{\nu+m}(kR)\}$ is at least $\pi/2k[N + 2] = O(1/N)$.

By an inspection of known asymptotic formula for Bessel functions (cf. in particular, [M.O.1, p. 22–24] we see that, asymptotically, Bessel functions may be written as $J = \Psi(x)\Phi(x)$, where $\Psi(x) \to 0$ as $x \to \infty$, and $\Phi(x)$ is a linear combination of sines and cosines, with the coefficients bounded away from zero by constants independent of whatever parameters appear elsewhere. Moreover, for $0 \le m \le [kR]$, it is easy to show that $\Psi(x) = O(1/x^\alpha)$ with $\frac{1}{3} \le \alpha \le \frac{1}{2}$. We make this plausible by explicit calculations for $m \cong (kR)^{1/3}$, $m \cong (kR)^{2/3}$, $m \cong kR - (kR)^{1/3}$, and $m \cong kR$, and leave it to the reader to supply the details of a complete proof. For the case $m \cong (kR)^{1/3}$ one sees from [M.O.1, p. 22] that, since ν is fixed while R is large,

$$J_{\nu+(kR)^{1/3}}(kR) \cong J_{(kR)^{1/3}}(kR) \cong \left(\frac{2}{\pi kR}\right)^{1/2} (A \cos \varphi + B \sin \varphi).$$

Similarly, for $m = (kR)^{2/3}$ one uses the expressions [M.O.1, p. 24],

$$H_\nu^{(1)}(x) = \frac{w}{\sqrt{3}} \exp\left(\frac{i\pi}{6}\right) \exp\left(i\nu\left(w - \frac{w^3}{3} - \tan^{-1} w\right)\right) H_{1/3}^{(1)}(\tfrac{1}{3}\nu w^3) + O\left(\left|\frac{1}{\nu}\right|\right),$$

$$H_\nu^{(2)}(x) = \overline{H_\nu^{(1)}(x)},$$

where

$$w = \left(\frac{x^2}{\nu^2} - 1\right)^{1/2}, \qquad \frac{-\pi}{2} \le \arg w < \frac{\pi}{2}, \qquad \tan^{-1} w = w - \frac{w^3}{3} + \cdots,$$

to show that

$$w = \left(\frac{(kR)^2}{(kR)^{4/3}} - 1\right)^{1/2} \cong (kR)^{1/3}, \qquad vw^3 \cong (kR)^{5/3},$$

so

$$\begin{aligned} J_{v+(kR)^{2/3}}(kR) &\cong O((kR)^{1/3}/(kR)^{5/6})(A\cos\varphi + B\sin\varphi) \\ &= O((kR)^{-1/2})(A\cos\varphi + B\sin\varphi). \end{aligned}$$

A similar analysis for $m = kR - (kR)^{1/3}$ gives $w \cong O((kR)^{-1/3})$, so

$$J_{v+kR-(kR)^{1/3}}(kR) \cong O((kR)^{-1/3})(A\cos\varphi + B\sin\varphi).$$

Finally, for $m = kR$, we have, by known formulas (cf. Watson [W.2, p. 237]),

$$J_{v+kR}(kR) \sim J_{kR}(kR) = O(1/(kR)^{1/3}).$$

Hence we have an appraisal of the form

$$|J_{v+m}(kR)| \geq \frac{C}{(kR)^{3/2}} \qquad (m = 0, 1, \ldots, [kR]),$$

for some constant $C > 0$ independent of all parameters. The factor $1/kR$ is a contribution from the Φ portion of the general expression just given for Bessel functions; we assume, of course, that kR is such that none of the Bessel functions vanishes and so, by previous remarks, is distant by an amount $O(1/kR)$ from any zero. But sine and cosine have simple zeros, hence the result.

Returning to (4.5.31) we have $|\hat{K}_N| = O(R^{\frac{5}{2}+(v+kR)}e^{kR})$. It is trivial to verify that $|G_N| = O(R^N)$, and thus

$$\frac{1}{R^\lambda}\log[|\hat{K}_N| + 2|G_N|] \to 0$$

as $R \to \infty$, for $\lambda > 1$. From our previous estimate we have

$$\varepsilon \log R \cong -(\lambda - \varepsilon')\log \Omega R + \lambda \log R,$$

so

$$\varepsilon \sim \varepsilon' - (\lambda - \varepsilon')\frac{\log \Omega}{\log R}.$$

Consequently, for R sufficiently large ε' is of the same order of magnitude as ε. Hence we conclude that $\exp(R^{\lambda-\varepsilon}) < M(R)$ for $\varepsilon > 0$ and R sufficiently large. This proves the theorem.

We next prove a lemma which will be useful in obtaining growth estimates for solutions of the GASHE in terms of the Gegenbauer–Bessel coefficients.

Lemma 4.5.8 *Let $f(z)$ be an entire function whose order, λ, is greater than* 1, *having the following Neumann series representation:*

$$f(z) = z^{-\nu} \sum_{m=0}^{\infty} a_m J_{\nu+m}(z).$$

Then a necessary and sufficient condition for $f(z)$ to be of order at most λ is for the inequality

$$|a_n| \le n^{n(1-[1/\lambda-\varepsilon])}$$

to hold, for any $\varepsilon > 0$, provided n is sufficiently large.

Proof For proof of the necessity, suppose that $f(z)$ has the Taylor representation

$$f(z) = \sum_{m=0}^{\infty} b_m z^m.$$

We know then [D.4, p. 293] that $|b_n| \le n^{-n(1/2-\varepsilon')}$ for any $\varepsilon' > 0$ provided n is sufficiently large. The Taylor–Neumann coefficients are related [E.6, Vol. II, p. 66] by the expressions

$$a_n = 2^{\nu+n}(\nu+n) \sum_{s=0}^{[n/2]} 2^{-2s}\Gamma(\nu+n-s)\frac{b_{n-2s}}{s!}$$

and

$$b_m \Gamma(\nu+m+1) = 2^{-m-\nu} \sum_{p=0}^{[m/2]} (-1)^p \binom{\nu+m}{p} a_{m-2p}.$$

Thus, for some suitably chosen constant C, $|b_n| \le Cn^{-n(1/2-\lambda')}$ for all n; and we get from the above,

$$|a_n| \le C2^{\nu+n}(\nu+n) \sum_{s=0}^{[n/2]} 2^{-2s} \frac{\Gamma(\nu+n-s)}{\Gamma(s+1)} (n-2s)^{-(n-2s)(1/\lambda-\varepsilon')};$$

since the largest term, up to an $n \log n$ approximation,† occurs for $s = 0$, we have the estimate

$$|a_n| \leq C2^{v+n}(v+n)\left(\frac{n}{2}+1\right)\Gamma(v+n)n^{-n(1/\lambda-\varepsilon')},$$

so

$$\frac{\log|a_n|}{n \log n} \leq \frac{\log C + (v+n)\log 2 + \log(v+n) + \log(\tfrac{1}{2}n+1) + \log\Gamma(v+n) - n(1/\lambda - \varepsilon')\log n}{n \log n}.$$

As $n \to \infty$ this inequality takes the form

$$\frac{\log|a_n|}{n \log n} \leq O\left(\frac{1}{\log n}\right) + \frac{\log\Gamma(v+n)}{n \log n} - \left(\frac{1}{\lambda} - \varepsilon'\right),$$

or

$$\frac{\log|a_n|}{n \log n} \leq 1 - \left(\frac{1}{\lambda} - \varepsilon\right)$$

for any $\varepsilon > 0$. Hence, for any n sufficiently large,

$$|a_n| \leq n^{n(1-(1/\lambda-\varepsilon))},$$

where $\varepsilon > 0$; this is the desired result.

For the sufficiency suppose that $|a_n| \leq n^{(n-(1/\lambda-\varepsilon'))}$ for any $\varepsilon' > 0$ provided n is sufficiently large. Then we can bound $|b_m|$, for some suitable constant C, as follows:

$$|b_m|\,\Gamma(v+m+1) \leq 2^{-m-v}C\sum_{p=0}^{[m/2]}\binom{v+m}{p}(m-2p)^{(m-2p)(1-(1/\lambda-\varepsilon'))}.$$

† To justify this we have the following analysis. Let us assume $s = \theta n/2$, $0 < \theta < 1$. Then we may rewrite each term in this sum as

$$y_n(\theta) = 2^{-\theta n}\frac{\Gamma(v+n-\theta/2)}{\Gamma(\theta n/2+1)}(n(1-\theta))^{-(n[1-\theta])(1/\lambda-\varepsilon')};$$

as $n \to \infty$ the major term in the expression $\log y_n(\theta)$ is

$$[1 - 1/\lambda + \varepsilon' + \theta(1/\lambda - \varepsilon' - 1)]n \log n.$$

If $\lambda > 1$ the maximum of this term occurs (for all ε' sufficiently small) for θ in $[0, 1]$ at $\theta = 0$.

Again the largest term occurs at $p = 0$, up to an $m \log m$ approximation,† and we get

$$|b_m| \leq 2^{-m-\nu} C\left(\frac{m}{2}+1\right) \frac{m^{m(1-(1/\lambda-\varepsilon'))}}{\Gamma(\nu+m+1)}.$$

Hence as $m \to \infty$ we find that

$$\frac{\log|b_m|}{m \log m} \leq O\left(\frac{1}{\log m}\right) - \left(\frac{1}{\lambda} - \varepsilon'\right) \leq -\left(\frac{1}{\lambda} - \varepsilon\right) \qquad \text{for any} \quad \varepsilon > 0,$$

provided m is sufficiently large. But this is equivalent to saying that $f(z)$ has order at most λ, the desired result.

Finally we have the following theorem.

Theorem 4.5.9 *Let $w(r, \theta)$ be an entire* GASHE *function with a series representation in terms of Bessel–Gegenbauer functions as given in* (4.5.19), *with the expansion coefficients $a_n(n!)/\Gamma(2\nu + n)$. Suppose that*

$$|a_n| \leq n^{n(1-(1/\lambda-\varepsilon))}$$

for some $\lambda > 1$ and say $\varepsilon > 0$, provided n is sufficiently large. Then $|w(r, \theta)|$ is bounded by the inequality

$$|w(r, \theta)| < \exp(r^{\lambda+\varepsilon}) \qquad \textit{for} \quad r \to \infty.$$

This follows at once from Lemmas 4.5.5 and 4.5.7, where λ is the order of the associate f. We can also get a lower bound on the maximum modulus by use of Theorem 4.5.7.

6. *The Generalized Biaxially Symmetric Schrödinger Equation (GBSSE)*

In this section we investigate partial differential equations of the type

† In this case we set $p = \varphi m/2$, $0 < \varphi < 1$. Then

$$x_m(\varphi) \equiv \frac{2^{-2m-2}[m(1-\varphi)]^{m(1-\varphi)(1-1/\lambda+\varepsilon')}}{\Gamma((\varphi/2)m+1)\Gamma(\nu+m(\varphi/2))}.$$

Again collecting the major terms, one has, for $m \to \infty$,

$$\log x_m(\varphi) \sim [-1/\lambda + \varepsilon' + \varphi(1/\lambda - \varepsilon' - 1)] m \log m.$$

Hence, if $\lambda > 1$ (and ε' is sufficiently small), the maximum is at $\varphi = 0$.

$$\mathbf{S}_{\mu\nu}[\Psi] \equiv \Psi_{xx} + \frac{2\nu}{x}\Psi_x + \Psi_{yy} + \frac{2\mu}{y}\Psi_y + \{k^2 - V(r)\}\Psi = 0, \qquad \text{(GBSSE)} \tag{4.6.1}$$

where μ, $\nu \geq 0$, and

$$rV(r) = \sum_{\nu \geq 0} v_\nu r^\nu, \qquad v_0 > 0,$$

is an entire function of $r = +(x^2 + y^2)^{1/2}$. We obtain a separated system of solutions for this equation by introducing polar coordinates r, and $\theta = \cos^{-1}(x/r)$, namely solutions $\Psi(r, \theta) = R(r)\Theta(\theta)$ which satisfy

$$\mathbf{S}_{\mu\nu}[\Psi] \equiv \Psi_{rr} + \frac{(2[\mu + \nu] + 1)}{r}\Psi_r + \frac{1}{r^2}\Psi_{\theta\theta} + \left\{\frac{2\nu \operatorname{ctn}\theta}{r^2} - \frac{2\mu \tan\theta}{r^2}\right\}\Psi_\theta + \{k^2 - V(r)\}\Psi = 0. \tag{4.6.2}$$

If we introduce the new independent variable $\xi = \cos 2\theta$, (4.6.2) is seen to separate into the ordinary differential equations

$$r^2\ddot{R} + r(2[\mu + \nu] + 1)\dot{R} + \{[k^2 - V(r)]r^2 - \Lambda\}R = 0, \tag{4.6.3}$$

and

$$(1 - \xi^2)\ddot{X} + \{\mu - \nu - \xi(1 + \mu + \nu)\}\dot{X} + \frac{\Lambda}{4}X = 0, \tag{4.6.4}$$

where $X(\xi) \equiv \Theta(\frac{1}{2}\cos^{-1}\xi)$, and Λ is the separation constant. If Λ is taken to be $4n(n + \mu + \nu)$, (4.6.4) is recognized as Jacobi's differential equation, which as we recall has a regular solution, $P_n^{(\mu - \frac{1}{2}, \nu - \frac{1}{2})}(\xi)$ (Jacobi's polynomial), which is normalized by setting its value equal to $\binom{n + \mu - \frac{1}{2}}{n}$ at $\xi = 1$.

By setting $R(r) = r^{-(\mu+\nu)}W(r)$, Eq. (4.6.3) takes on the somewhat more convenient form

$$r^2\ddot{W} + r\dot{W} + \{r^2[k^2 - V(r)] - (2n + \mu + \nu)^2\}W = 0; \tag{4.6.5}$$

for $V(r) \equiv 0$ we recognize this as Bessel's equation, which has about $r = 0$ the regular solution $W_n(r) = J_{2n+\mu+\nu}(kr)$. Clearly, the indicial equation for (4.6.5) is the same (since $V(r)$ has at most a first order pole at $r = 0$) as that for Bessel's equation, namely [C.6, p. 238],

$$F(\alpha) \equiv \alpha(\alpha - 1) + \alpha - (2n + \mu + \nu)^2,$$

and we conclude that for r in a sufficiently small neighborhood of the origin the two solutions obtained by the regular singular point method are locally

$$R_{n,1}(r) \approx r^{2n} \approx r^{-(\mu+\nu)} W_{n,1}(r),$$

and (4.6.6)

$$R_{n,2}(r) \approx r^{-2(n+\mu+\nu)} \approx r^{-(\mu+\nu)} W_{n,2}(r).$$

The solutions $R_{n,k}(r)$ $(k = 1, 2)$ may be obtained in terms of power series representations by the Fuchsian method, computing the coefficients of the expansions by the usual recursive formulas

$$C_m^{(k)} = \frac{1}{F(\alpha + m)} \left\{ \sum_{p=0}^{m-1} C_p^{(k)} \tilde{v}_{m-p-1} \right\}$$

$$\tilde{v}_m = \begin{cases} v_m; & m \neq 1, \quad m \geq 0 \\ -k^2 + v_1, & m = 1, \end{cases} \tag{4.6.7}$$

$$R_{n,k}(r) = r^{\alpha} \sum_{m=0}^{\infty} C_m^{(k)} r^m \qquad (k = 1, 2). \tag{4.6.8}$$

We are interested in studying the asymptotic solutions $R_{n,1}(r)$ (the regular solutions determined about $r = 0$ by (4.6.7), (4.6.8)) in a closed interval $[0, p]$. Since $r = 0$ is a singular point, the standard method for doing this (as discussed, say in Erdélyi [E.8, p. 84] applies only to intervals $[\rho_0, \rho_1]$, $0 < \rho_0 < \rho_1 < \infty$. For convenience, we rewrite (4.6.3) in the form

$$\ddot{u} + \left\{ \left[k^2 - V(r) + \frac{\delta - \delta^2}{r} \right] - \left[\frac{2(2\delta - 1)}{r^2} \right] n - \left[\frac{4}{r^2} \right] n^2 \right\} u = 0, \tag{4.6.9}$$

where $u(r) = r^{\mu+\nu+\frac{1}{2}} R(r)$, and $\delta = \mu + \nu + \frac{1}{2}$. We seek an asymptotic solution as $n \to 0$ of the form

$$u_n(r) \approx \exp\left\{ \sum_{l=0}^{N} \beta_l(r) n^{1-l} \right\},$$

which is possible since the coefficient of n^2 is negative for $r \geq 0$ and $\neq \infty$; see Erdélyi [E.8, p. 87]. The coefficients $\beta_m(r)$ are seen to satisfy the system of equations

$$\beta_0'^2 = \frac{4}{r^2}$$

$$\beta_0'' + 2\beta_0'\beta_1 = \frac{2(2\delta - 1)}{r^2}$$

$$\beta_1'' + 2\beta_0'\beta_2' + \beta_1'^2 = -k^2 + V(r) + \frac{\delta^2 - \delta}{r^2}$$

$$2\beta_0'\beta_m' + \sum_{p=1}^{m-1} \beta_p'\beta_{m-p}' + \beta_{m-1}'' = 0, \qquad m \geq 3.$$

The asymptotic expansions for $n \geq N_0(\rho)$, which correspond to $\beta_0' = \pm 2/r$ respectively are $R_n^{(1)}(r) \approx e_n r^{2n}[1 + O(1/n)]$ and

$$R_n^{(2)}(r) \approx f_n r^{-(2(n+\delta)+1)}[1 + O(1/n)]$$

(where e_n and f_n are the leading constants in the expansions, and the $O(1/n)$ approximation is good in that part of the complex n-plane, where $\arg[n] < \pi/2$). The solution $R_n^{(1)}(r)$, whose asymptotic behavior we have found in the interval $[\rho_0, \rho_1]$ must, however, be a linear combination of $R_{n,1}(r)$ and $R_{n,2}(r)$. This is impossible, unless $R_n^{(1)}(r) =$ constant times $R_{n,1}(r)$. We normalize the functions $R_n^{(1)}(r)$ by setting $e_n = 1$ and shall refer, in the future, to those normalized functions as simply $R_n(r)$.

We next consider the system of solutions

$$\{R_n(r)P_n^{(\mu-\frac{1}{2}, \nu-\frac{1}{2})}(\cos 2\theta)\}_{n=0}^{\infty}.$$

Since the Jacobi polynomials $P_n^{(\alpha,\beta)}(\xi)$ form a closed system on $[-1, 1]$ with respect to the inner product

$$(f, g) = \int_{-1}^{+1} (1 - \xi)^\alpha (1 + \xi)^\beta fg \, d\xi$$

[E.6, Vol. II, p. 157], it is clear that for ρ sufficiently small, i.e., for $V(r) - k^2 \geq 0$ for $r \leq \rho$, that this system of solutions is complete with respect to Dirichlet data on the boundary $r = \rho$. (The Dirichlet data is taken to be symmetric with respect to the origin and the coordinate axes.) Indeed, any classical solution of (4.6.2) in the disk $r \leq \rho$ has a Fourier series expansion of the form,

$$\Psi(r, \theta) = \sum_{n=0}^{\infty} a_n \frac{R_n(r)}{R_n(\rho)} P_n^{(\mu-\frac{1}{2}, \nu-\frac{1}{2})}(\cos 2\theta)$$
$$a_n = (\phi(\xi), P_n^{(\mu-\frac{1}{2}, \nu-\frac{1}{2})}(\xi)), \tag{4.6.10}$$

where

$$(\phi, f) = \int_{-1}^{+1} (1-\xi)^{\nu-\frac{1}{2}}(1+\xi)^{\mu-\frac{1}{2}}\phi(\xi)f(\xi)\,d\xi < \infty,$$

and

$$\phi(\xi) \equiv \Psi(\rho, \tfrac{1}{2}\cos^{-1}\xi).$$

We shall now indicate how an integral operator may be constructed which generates solutions of the type given above. If we define as our kernel the formal sum

$$J^{(+)}(r, \xi; \zeta^{-1}) \equiv \sum_{n=0}^{\infty} \zeta^n R_n(r) P_n^{(\mu-\frac{1}{2}, \nu-\frac{1}{2})}(\xi), \tag{4.6.11}$$

then by formally integrating termwise it is seen that

$$f(\xi) = \sum_{n=0}^{\infty} b_n \zeta^n, \qquad b_n \equiv a_n / R_n(\rho)$$

is mapped by the integral operator ($\Psi = \mathbf{Q}_{\mu\nu} f$),

$$\mathbf{Q}_{\mu\nu} f \equiv \frac{1}{2\pi i} \int_{|\zeta| = r^2+\varepsilon} J^{(+)}(r, \xi; \zeta) f(\zeta) \frac{d\zeta}{\zeta} \tag{4.6.12}$$

($\varepsilon > 0$ is sufficiently small) onto the solution (4.6.10). In [G.27] it is shown, using certain estimates for the Jacobi polynomials as given in Szegö's book [S.6, pp. 206, 238], that $J^{(+)}(r, \xi; \zeta^{-1})$ is a holomorphic function of the three complex variables r, ξ, and ζ in the domain $\mathfrak{T}^3(\varepsilon) \equiv \{(r, \zeta) \,|\, |r^2\zeta| < a(\varepsilon) < 1\} \times \mathfrak{E}(\varepsilon)$, where $\mathfrak{E}(\varepsilon)$ is the ellipse $E(\varepsilon) \equiv \{\xi \,|\, |1+\xi| + |1-\xi| < 2+\varepsilon\}$. Indeed, using the arguments of p. 209, and the fact that

$$R_n(r) \approx r^{2n}\,\{1 + O\,(n^{-1})\},$$

we may show that $J^{(+)}(r, \xi; \zeta)$ is *equivalent* (up to multiplication by a holomorphic function) in a neighborhood of $\mathfrak{T}^3(\varepsilon)$ to the generating function for the Jacobi polynomials, i.e.,

$$J^{(+)}(r, \xi; \zeta^{-1}) \approx 2^{\mu+\nu-1} T^{-1} (1 - \zeta r^2 + T)^{-\nu+\frac{1}{2}} (1 + \zeta r^2 + T)^{-\mu+\frac{1}{2}}.$$

Here $T = (1 - 2r^2\xi\zeta + r^4\zeta^2)^{1/2}$ is taken to be 1 when $\zeta r^2 = 0$. Indeed, the *first* singular set of $J^{(+)}$, moving away from the origin on the initial Riemann sheet is exactly that given by the generating function above. The reader is referred back to p. 207 for further details concerning the estimates needed here.

The inverse operator $\mathbf{Q}_{\mu\nu}^{-1}$ is constructed as usual by employing certain orthogonality properties of the system of solutions. For instance, if we introduce as the kernel of the inverse operator the formal sum,

$$J^{(-)}(r, \xi; \zeta) \equiv \frac{(1-\xi)^{\nu-\frac{1}{2}}(1+\xi)^{\mu-\frac{1}{2}}}{2^{\mu+\nu}}$$

$$\times \sum_{n=0}^{\infty} \frac{(2n+\mu+\nu)n!\,\Gamma(n+\mu+\nu)}{\Gamma(n+\nu+\frac{1}{2})\Gamma(n+\mu+\frac{1}{2})} \frac{\zeta^n}{R_n(r)} P_n^{(\mu-\frac{1}{2}, \nu-\frac{1}{2})}(\xi)$$

then by using the orthogonality properties of the Jacobi polynomials we have

$$f(\zeta) = \mathbf{Q}_{\mu\nu}^{-1}\Psi \equiv \int_{-1}^{+1} J^{(-)}(r, \xi; \zeta)\Psi(r, \tfrac{1}{2}\cos^{-1}\xi)\, d\xi.$$

In [G.27] it is also shown that $J^{(-)}(r, \xi; \zeta)$ is equivalent to the kernel for the inverse operator given for the case of GBSPE, namely in the set $\tilde{\mathfrak{T}}(\varepsilon) \equiv \{(r, \zeta) \,|\, |\zeta/r^2| < a(\varepsilon) < 1\} \times \mathfrak{E}(\varepsilon)$ we have the equivalence

$$J^{(-)}(r, \xi; \zeta) \approx (1-\xi)^{-\nu+\frac{1}{2}}(1+\xi)^{-\mu+\frac{1}{2}}$$

$$\times \sum_{n=0}^{\infty} \frac{n!(2n+\mu+\nu)\Gamma(n+\mu+\nu)}{\Gamma(n+\mu+\frac{1}{2})\Gamma(n+\nu+\frac{1}{2})} P_n^{(\mu-\frac{1}{2}, \nu-\frac{1}{2})}(\xi)\left(\frac{\zeta}{r^2}\right)^n$$

which we have investigated earlier (4.1.23). In fact, we found that this series could be summed in closed form, using a generating function representation due to Brafman, on the set $\tilde{\mathfrak{T}}(\varepsilon) \equiv \{(r, \zeta) \,|\, |\zeta/r^2| < a(\varepsilon) < 1\} \times \mathfrak{E}(\varepsilon)$. Because of this correspondence between the kernels for the cases of GBSSE and GBSPE we obtain all of the theorems concerning singularities developed earlier for solutions of the present equation with representations of the form

$$\Psi(r, \theta) = \sum_{n=0}^{\infty} b_n R_n(r) P_n^{(\mu-\frac{1}{2}, \nu-\frac{1}{2})}(\cos 2\theta).$$

The reader is referred to [G.27] for further details.

It is also possible to obtain bounds and growth theorems for GBSSE of the type developed, in the previous section, for GASHE; this is also done in [G.27].

7. *The Generalized Axially Symmetric Helmholtz Equation in (N + 1) Variables (GASHN)*

In this section we shall investigate the analytic properties of solutions of the generalized axially symmetric, reduced wave equation in $(n+1)$ variables, namely

$$\mathbf{L}_{\lambda,s}^{(n)}[\Psi] \equiv \frac{\partial^2 \Psi}{\partial x_1{}^2} + \cdots + \frac{\partial^2 \Psi}{\partial x_n{}^2} + \frac{\partial^2 \Psi}{\partial \rho^2} + \frac{s}{\rho}\frac{\partial \Psi}{\partial \rho} + \lambda^2 \Psi = 0, \qquad (4.7.1)$$

where $s > -1$, and $\lambda \neq 0$ is real. When $\lambda = 0$ this equation is known as the equation of generalized axially symmetric potential theory (GASPN). The case where $\lambda = 0$ was investigated by Gilbert and Howard [G.H.4]; the general case (4.7.1) was investigated by the present author in [G.28].

If we introduce after Appell and deFeriet [A.deF.1, p. 211] the zonal coordinates

$$\begin{aligned} &x_1 = r\xi_1, \qquad x_2 = r\xi_2, \ldots, x_n = r\xi_n, \\ &\rho = r\left(1 - \sum_{i=1}^{n} \xi_i{}^2\right)^{1/2}, \qquad r^2 = x_1{}^2 + \cdots + x_n{}^2 + \rho^2, \end{aligned} \qquad (4.7.2)$$

into Eq. (4.7.1) we obtain

$$\begin{aligned} r^2(\mathbf{L}_{\lambda,s}^{(n)}[\Psi]) = \frac{1}{r^{n+s-2}}\frac{\partial}{\partial r}\left(r^{n+s}\frac{\partial \Psi}{\partial r}\right) + \lambda^2 r^2 \Psi + n(s-1)\Psi \\ + \sum_{j=1}^{n} \frac{\partial}{\partial \xi_j}\left\{\frac{\partial \Psi}{\partial \xi_j} - \xi_j\left(\sum_{k=1}^{n} \xi_k \frac{\partial \Psi}{\partial \xi_k} + (s-1)\Psi\right)\right\} = 0. \end{aligned} \qquad (4.7.3)$$

If one considers next those solutions of (4.7.3), which may be written in the form

$$\Psi(r;\xi) = R(r)V(\xi), \qquad V(\xi) \equiv V(\xi_1, \ldots, \xi_n),$$

we find that $R(r)$, and $V(\xi)$ must satisfy the equations

$$R''(r) + \frac{n+s}{r}R'(r) + \left(\lambda^2 - \frac{\mu(n+s+\mu-1)}{r^2}\right)R(r) = 0 \qquad (4.7.4)$$

and

$$(\mu + n)(\mu + s - 1)V + \sum_{j=1}^{n} \frac{\partial}{\partial \xi_j} \left\{ \frac{\partial V}{\partial \xi_j} - \xi_j \sum_{k=1}^{n} \left(\xi_k \frac{\partial V}{\partial \xi_k} + (s-1)V \right) \right\} = 0 \quad (4.7.5)$$

where we have taken $b \equiv \mu(n + s + \mu - 1)$ to be the constant of separation for our pair of equations resulting from (4.7.3). In this case a regular solution of (4.7.4) about $r = 0$ is seen to be

$$R(r) = r^{-\frac{1}{2}(n+s-1)} J_{\mu+\frac{1}{2}(n+s-1)}(\lambda r), \quad (4.7.6)$$

where $J_\nu(x)$ is a Bessel function of the first kind and νth order. Solutions of the partial differential equation (4.7.5) may be found which satisfy the following system of equations simultaneously (see Appell and deFeriet [A.deF.1, pp. 246–256]):

$$\frac{\partial}{\partial \xi_j} \left\{ \frac{\partial V}{\partial \xi_j} - \xi_j \left[\left(\sum_{k=1}^{n} \xi_k \frac{\partial V}{\partial \xi_j} \right) + (\mu + n + s - 1)V \right] \right\}$$
$$+ (m_j + 1) \left[\left(\sum_{k=1}^{n} \xi_k \frac{\partial V}{\partial \xi_k} \right) + (\mu + n + s - 1)V \right] = 0 \quad (4.7.7)$$
$$(j = 1, 2, \ldots, n)$$

where $m_1 + m_2 + \cdots + m_n = \mu$. There exists polynomial solutions of the system (4.7.7) for arbitrary s, namely the functions

$$V_M^{(s)}(\xi) \equiv V_M^{(s)}(\xi_1, \ldots, \xi_n) \qquad (M \equiv m_1, \ldots, m_n),$$

which are uniquely defined by their generating function [A.deF.1, p. 249]

$$(1 - 2(a, \xi) + \|a\|^2)^{\frac{1}{2}(-n-s+1)} = \sum_{M=0}^{\infty} a^M V_M^{(s)}(\xi), \quad (4.7.8)$$

where

$$(a, \xi) \equiv \sum_{i=1}^{n} a_i \xi_i, \qquad \|a\|^2 \equiv (a, a), \qquad a^M \equiv a_1^{m_1} \cdots a_n^{m_n},$$

and the summation is meant to be an n-fold sum over all indices $(m_1, \ldots, m_n)$ from 0 to ∞. It is also well known [A.deF.1, p. 249] that the functions $V_M^{(s)}$ are related to the Maxwell pole functions

$$W_M^{(s)}(\mathbf{X}) \equiv W_M^{(s)}(x_1, \ldots, x_n, \rho) = \frac{(-1)^\mu}{M!} \frac{\partial^\mu}{\partial x^M} \frac{1}{r^{n+s-1}},$$

namely

$$V_M^{(s)}(\xi) = r^{\mu+n+s-1} W_M^{(s)}(\mathbf{X}).$$

It is well kown that the family of functions

$$\begin{gathered}\Psi^M(\mathbf{X}) \equiv r^{-\frac{1}{2}(n+s-1)} J_{\mu+\frac{1}{2}(n+s-1)}(\lambda r) V_M^{(s)}(\xi) \\ ((m_1 + m_2 + \cdots + m_n) \equiv |M| = \mu)\end{gathered} \tag{4.7.9}$$

form a complete system with respect to the Dirichlet problem of Eq. (4.7.1) for the "hypersphere" $\{\mathbf{X} | \, \|\mathbf{X}\| \leq R_0\}$, when the data is continuously differentiable [E.6, Vol. II, p. 281]. The reader is referred to this work for further details and further references concerning the convergence of series of expansions in terms of the $V_M^{(s)}(\xi)$.

Following our standard approach, we wish to construct an integral operator which maps the class of monomials ζ^M onto the class of solutions (4.7.9). To this end we introduce as a kernel function the formal sum

$$K(r, \xi, \zeta) \equiv \left(\frac{\lambda r}{2}\right)^{-\frac{1}{2}(n+s-1)} \sum_{\mu=0}^{\infty} \sum_{|M|=\mu} \mu! \zeta^M J_{\mu+\frac{1}{2}(n+s-1)}(\lambda r) V_M^{(s)}(\xi), \tag{4.7.10}$$

which, if we integrate using Cauchy's formula for several complex variables, gives

$$\left(\frac{1}{2\pi i}\right)^n \int_{\mathscr{C}_1} \cdots \int_{\mathscr{C}_n} K(r, \xi, \zeta) \zeta^{-M} \frac{d\zeta}{\zeta} = \left(\frac{\lambda r}{2}\right)^{-\frac{1}{2}(n+s-1)} \mu! J_{\mu+\frac{1}{2}(n+s-1)}(\lambda r) V_M^{(s)}(\xi), \tag{4.7.11}$$

where we have taken $\zeta^{-K} \equiv \zeta_1^{-k_1} \cdots \zeta_n^{-k_n}$, and $d\zeta/\zeta \equiv d\zeta_1/\zeta_1 \cdots d\zeta_n/\zeta_n$. The $\mathscr{C}_k$ $(k = 1, 2, \ldots, n)$ are suitably chosen contours (enclosing $\zeta_k = 0$) and such that $\{\prod_{k=1}^n \mathscr{C}_k\}$ be outside a sufficiently large polycylinder.

If we consider for each fixed r, ξ the series for $K(r, \xi, \zeta)$ to be a power series in ζ^M where the coefficients are given by

$$a_M \equiv \left(\frac{\lambda r}{2}\right)^{-\frac{1}{2}(n+s-1)} \mu! J_{\mu+\frac{1}{2}(n+s-1)}(\lambda r) V_M^{(s)}(\xi), \tag{4.7.12}$$

we may study its domain of convergence for $\zeta \in \mathbb{C}^n$ by considering the associated radii of convergence, $r_1, \ldots, r_n$, which satisfy the relation

$$\overline{\lim_{\mu\to\infty}} |a_M r^M|^{1/\mu} = 1, \qquad r^M = r_1^{m_1} \cdots r_n^{m_n}.$$

By direct computation we can show that the associate radii of convergence for the coefficients a_M are the same as those associated with the generating function representation

$$\sum_{\mu=0}^{\infty} \sum_{|M|=\mu} \left(\frac{\lambda r\zeta}{2}\right)^M V_M^{(s)}(\xi) = \left[1 - 2\left(\frac{\lambda r\zeta}{2}, \xi\right) + \left\|\frac{\lambda r\zeta}{2}\right\|^2\right]^{-\frac{1}{2}(n+s-1)}. \quad (4.7.13)$$

Actually, since the generating function (4.7.13) is a holomorphic function of the $(2n+1)$ complex variables (r, ξ, ζ) whose only singularities lie on the analytic set

$$\mathfrak{S}^{(n)} \equiv \{(r, \xi) \mid 4 - 4(\lambda r\zeta, \xi) + \|\lambda r\zeta\|^2 = 0\}, \quad (4.7.14)$$

we may conclude, using Hartogs' theorem and the several variable analogue of Fabry's theorem (Theorem 1.3.7), that $K(r, \xi; \zeta)$ is also singular on the set $\mathfrak{S}^{(n)}$, [G.28].

From the above discussion, we realize that it is possible to construct the integral operator

$$\mathbf{W}f \equiv \mathbf{W}_{\lambda,s}^{(n)} f = \left(\frac{1}{2\pi i}\right)^n \int_{\mathfrak{D}^n} K(r, \xi; \zeta) f(\zeta) \frac{d\zeta}{\zeta} \quad (4.7.15a)$$

where

$$\mathfrak{D}^n \equiv \prod_{k=1}^{n} \mathscr{C}_k,$$

and

$$f(\zeta) = \sum_{\mu=0}^{\infty} \sum_{|M|=\mu} b_M \zeta^{-M}. \quad (4.7.15b)$$

If $f(\zeta)$ is defined by (4.7.15) then the solution, $\Psi(\mathbf{X})$ corresponding to it is

$$\Psi(\mathbf{X}) = \left(\frac{\lambda r}{2}\right)^{-\frac{1}{2}(n+s-1)} \sum_{\mu=0}^{\infty} \sum_{|M|=\mu} \mu!\, b_M J_{\mu+\frac{1}{2}(n+s-1)}(\lambda r) V_M^{(s)}. \quad (4.7.16)$$

We shall now indicate how one may find an integral operator $\mathbf{W}^{-1}$, which plays the role of an inverse operator for $\mathbf{W}$. Again we introduce a formal sum as a proposed kernel for an integral operator and then show that the formal sum exists, and that the integral representation has a meaning under certain restrictions of the variables and integration parameters. We introduce as our kernel,†

$$K_2(r, \xi; \zeta) \equiv \frac{\Gamma(\frac{1}{2}[n+s-1])\Gamma(s)}{2\pi^{n/2}\Gamma(\frac{1}{2}s+1)} \left(\frac{\lambda r}{2}\right)^{\frac{1}{2}(n+s-1)} (1 - \|\xi\|^2)^{\frac{1}{2}(s-1)}$$
$$\times \sum_{\mu=0}^{\infty} \sum_{|m|=\mu} \frac{\zeta^{-M} M!(2\mu+n+s)U_M^{(s)}(\xi)}{\Gamma(s+\mu)J_{\mu+\frac{1}{2}(n+s-1)}(\lambda r)\mu!}, \tag{4.7.17}$$

$(M! = m_1! \cdots m_n!)$ where it is clearly understood that r is not a root of $J_{\mu+\frac{1}{2}(n+s-1)}(\lambda r) = 0$ (which we shall show is an easily met request below). First, by formally integrating term-by-term and making use of the biorthogonal relation

$$\int_\Omega (1 - \|\xi\|^2)^{\frac{1}{2}(s-1)} V_M^{(s)}(\xi) U_L^{(s)}(\xi)\, d^n\xi$$
$$= \delta_{l_1}^{m_1} \cdots \delta_{l_n}^{m_n} \frac{2\pi^{n+2}\Gamma(\frac{1}{2}s+1)\Gamma(s+m)}{(2m+n+s-1)\Gamma(\frac{1}{2}[n+s-1])\Gamma(s)M!},$$

where $\Omega \equiv \{\xi \mid 1 \geq \|\xi\| \geq 0\}$, we note that one obtains

$$f(\zeta) = \mathbf{W}^{-1}\Psi \equiv \int_\Omega K_2(r, \xi; \zeta)\Psi(r, \xi)\, d^n\xi,$$

since

$$\int_\Omega K_2(r, \xi; \zeta) V_M^{(s)}(\xi)\, d^n\xi = \zeta^{-M}.$$

By considering the kernel $K_2(r, \xi; \zeta)$ as a power series in $(\lambda r\zeta/2)^{-1}$, and again using the several-variable analog of Fabry's theorem we may conclude that $K_2(r, \xi; \zeta)$ is a holomorphic function of $(2n+1)$ complex variables whose "first" singularities (moving away from the origin) lie on the set[G.28]

$$\mathfrak{A}^{(n)} \equiv \left\{(r, \xi) \middle| \left[\left(\frac{2}{\lambda r\zeta}, \xi\right) - 1\right]^2 + \left\|\frac{2}{\lambda r\zeta}\right\|^2 [1 - \|\xi\|^2] = 0\right\}.$$

† The functions $U_M^{(s)}(\xi)$ are defined by the generating function [A.deF.1]

$$\{[(\zeta, \xi) - 1]^2 + \|\zeta\|^2(1 - \|\xi\|^2)\}^{-s/2} = \sum_{M=0}^{\infty} \zeta^M U_M^{(s)}(\xi)$$
$$= \sum_{m_1, \ldots, m_n = 0} \zeta_1^{m_1} \cdots \zeta_n^{m_n} U_{m_1, \ldots, m_n}^{(s)}(\xi_1, \ldots, \xi_n).$$

Since, in a suitably defined region $K_2(r, \xi; \zeta)$ is seen to be a holomorphic function in $(r, \zeta) \in \mathbb{C}^{n+1}$ when $\xi \in \Omega$, we may introduce as our inverse integral operator,

$$\mathbf{W}^{-1}\Psi \equiv \int_\Omega K_2(r, \xi; \zeta)\Psi(r, \xi)\, d^n\xi, \qquad f(\zeta) = \mathbf{W}^{-1}\Psi.$$

Using the general approach, referred to in preceding sections as the *envelope method*, we are able to obtain certain results concerning the location of possible singularities. To this end let us define the function $\phi(r, \xi; \zeta')$ to be the "eliminant" between $4 - 4(\lambda r\zeta, \xi) + \|\lambda r\zeta\|^2 = 0$ and $S(\zeta) = 0$ where $S(\zeta) = 0$ describes the singularities of the analytic function $f(\zeta)$. We assume $S(\zeta)$ is regular with respect to one of its variables [F.4, p. 58], say, ζ_1, and hence $\phi(r, \xi, \zeta') \equiv \phi(r, \xi; \zeta_2, \ldots, \zeta_n)$. Furthermore, we define for $m = 2, 3, \ldots, n$,

$$\phi_m(r, \xi; \zeta) \equiv \left(\frac{\lambda r}{2}\zeta_m - \xi_m\right)\frac{\partial S(\zeta)}{\partial \zeta_1} - \left(\frac{\lambda r}{2}\zeta_1 - \xi_1\right)\frac{\partial S(\zeta)}{\partial \zeta_m};$$

furthermore, let us define the corresponding analytic sets

$$\mathfrak{H}_{1,0} \equiv \{(r, \xi) \mid \phi = 0\}$$

and

$$\mathfrak{H}_{1,\mu} \equiv \{(r, \xi) \mid \phi_\mu = 0\}, \qquad (\mu = 2, 3, \ldots, n)$$

The envelope method as applied to the singularities of the kernel $K_2(r, \xi; \zeta)$ and $\Psi(r, \xi)$ taken together yields the point set,

$$\mathfrak{A}_{(1)}^{(n-1)} \equiv \mathfrak{H}_{1,0} \bigcap \{\bigcap_{\mu=2}^{n} \mathfrak{H}_{1,\mu}\},$$

as candidates for singularities of $\Psi(\mathbf{X})$.

The envelope method as applied to the kernel alone implies the following simultaneous conditions for a singularity set,

$$4 - 4(\lambda r\zeta, \xi) + \|\lambda r\zeta\|^2 = 0,$$

and

$$\zeta_k = 2\xi_k/\lambda r, \qquad (k = 1, 2, \ldots, n),$$

or equivalently, as a set of possible singularities

$$\mathfrak{A}_2^{(n-1)} \equiv \{(r, \xi) \,|\, \|\xi\| = 1\} \equiv \{\mathbf{X} \,|\, \rho = 0\}.$$

This latter set of singularities, however, can not appear in the initial branch of the solution $\Psi(\mathbf{X})$, since by definition $\Psi(\mathbf{X})$ is regular in some neighborhood of the origin. This is analogous to the case of GASPT functions having singularities along the x-axis on *other* than the initial Riemann sheet.

In order to obtain the complete set of singularity candidates of $\Psi(\mathbf{X})$, we should apply a variation of Theorem 1.3.4 to the complete singularity manifold of the integral (4.7.15a). However, since we know only the singularities of the kernel $K(r, \xi; \zeta)$ on $\mathfrak{S}^{(n)}$, we are forced to consider instead the following manifold

$$\hat{\mathfrak{S}}_0^{(n)} \equiv \{\mathbf{X} \,|\, \hat{S}(r, \xi{:}\zeta) \equiv \zeta S(\zeta)[1 - (\lambda r\zeta, \xi) + \|(\lambda r/2)\zeta\|^2] = 0\}.$$

The set of all possible singularities which occur due to the singularity manifold $\hat{\mathfrak{S}}_0^{(n)}$ are found to lie on

$$\hat{\mathfrak{S}}^{(n)} \equiv \bigcap_{\mu=0}^{n} \hat{\mathfrak{S}}_\mu^{(n)},$$

where $\hat{\mathfrak{S}}_\mu^{(n)} \equiv \{\mathbf{X} \,|\, \partial\hat{S}/\partial\zeta_\mu = 0\}$. The set $\hat{\mathfrak{S}}^{(n)}$ contains an analytic set of singularities which approaches closest to the origin. Hence we list the following theorem concerning this singularity set:

Theorem 4.7.1 *Let $\Psi(\mathbf{X}) = \mathbf{W}f$ be a solution of the generalized axially symmetric, reduced wave equation* (4.7.1), *where $f(\zeta)$ is a holomorphic function of n complex variables. Furthermore, let us assume that the only singularities of $f(\zeta)$ at a finite distance from the origin lie on the analytic set $\mathfrak{S} \equiv \{\zeta \,|\, S(\zeta) = 0\}$. Then as a first set of "possible" singularities of $\Psi(\mathbf{X})$ one encounters moving away from the origin in $\mathbb{R}^{n+1}$ are those points lying on the set, $\{\hat{\mathfrak{S}}^{(n)} - \mathfrak{A}_{(2)}^{(n-1)}\} \bigcap \mathbb{R}^{n+1}$.*

We add that results concerning the location of singularities which depend on the expansion coefficients b_M of the series (4.7.16) may also be obtained by using extensions of the Bergman–Mandelbrojt [M.2], [B.27] criteria to n complex variables. Results of this kind have been employed by Gilbert [G.25] for harmonic functions of four variables, and also for the solutions of the present differential equation.

Similar results to those discussed above were obtained earlier for the partial differential equation, $\mathbf{L}_{0,s}^{(n)}[\Psi] = 0$, by the present author and Howard [G.H.4].

In this case we used the operator

$$\hat{\mathbf{A}}_n^{(s)} g \equiv \frac{r^{-(n+s-1)}}{(2\pi i)^n} \int_{\mathfrak{D}} \frac{g(\zeta r)\, d\zeta/\zeta}{[1 - 2(\zeta, \xi) + \|\zeta\|^2]^{\frac{1}{2}(n+s-1)}},$$

where

$$\mathfrak{D} \equiv \prod_{k=1}^{n} \mathscr{C}_k; \qquad (\zeta, \xi) = \sum_{i=1}^{n} \zeta_i \xi_i, \qquad \|\zeta\|^2 = (\zeta, \zeta),$$

and

$$d_\flat/\zeta \equiv \frac{d\zeta_1 \cdots d\zeta_n}{\zeta_1 \cdots \zeta_n}.$$

Here, the holomorphic function of n complex variables,

$$g(\zeta r) \equiv \sum_{k_1, \ldots, k_n = 0}^{\infty} a_{k_1 \cdots k_n} (\zeta_1 r)^{-k_1} \cdots (\zeta_n r)^{-k_n},$$

are seen to be mapped on solutions of $\mathbf{L}_{0,s}^{(n)}[\Psi] = 0$ having the form

$$\Psi(\mathbf{X}) \equiv \sum_{k_1, \ldots, k_n}^{\infty} a_{k_1 \cdots k_n} W_{k_1 \cdots k_n}^{(s)}(x_1, \ldots, x_n, \rho) = \hat{\mathbf{A}}_n^{(s)} g(\zeta r).\dagger$$

An inverse operator for $\hat{\mathbf{A}}_n^{(s)}$ also is obtained as the integral representation,

$$\hat{\mathbf{A}}_n^{(s)-1}\Psi = \frac{\Gamma(s)\Gamma(n+s-1)}{2\pi^{n/2}\Gamma(\frac{1}{2}s+1)} \int_\Omega \Psi(r,\xi) R(\xi; \zeta r) d^n\ \xi,$$

where

$$\Omega \equiv \{\xi \,|\, \|\xi\| \leq 1\},$$

and

$$R(\xi, \zeta r) \equiv (1 - \|\zeta\|^2)^{\frac{1}{2}(s-1)} \left\{ \sum_{K=0}^{\infty} \frac{k_1! \cdots k_n!(2k+n+s-1)}{\Gamma(k+s)(\zeta_1 r)^{k_1} \cdots (\zeta_n r)^{k_n}} U_K^{(s)}(\xi) \right\}.$$

† The functions $W_k^{(s)}(\mathbf{X})$ used here are the same Maxwell pole functions introduced earlier by $W_k^{(s)}(\mathbf{X}) \equiv r^{1-(\mu+n+s)} V_k^{(s)}(\xi)$.

Similar results to those described above concerning location of singularities have been obtained for the case of $\mathbf{L}_s^{(n)}[\Psi] = 0$.

Several additional operators for this equation were also obtained in [G.H.4]. These equations bear a close resemblance to the case where $n = 1$, i.e., GASPT, and because of this we mention them here.

Using the following integral representation for the $V_M^{(s)}(\xi)$ [A.deF.1, p. 256]

$$\frac{\pi^{n/2}\Gamma(s/2)}{\Gamma(\frac{1}{2}[n+s])} V_M^{(s)}(\xi) = \frac{\Gamma(n+s-1+\mu)(i)^\mu}{\Gamma(n+s-1)m_1!\cdots m_n!} \times \iint_\Omega \frac{t_1^{m_1}\cdots t_n^{m_n}[1-\|t\|^2]^{\frac{1}{2}(s-1)}\, d^n t}{[(1-\|\xi\|^2)^{1/2} + i(t,\xi)]^{n+s-1+\mu}},$$

one may represent solutions $\Psi(\mathbf{X})$ as

$$\begin{aligned}\Psi(\mathbf{X}) &\equiv \sum_{M=0}^{\infty} a_M W_M^{(s)}(\mathbf{X}) \\ &= \frac{\Gamma(\frac{1}{2}[n+s])r^{-(n+s-1)}}{\pi^{n/2}\Gamma(\frac{1}{2}s)\Gamma(n+s-1)} \\ &\quad \times \iint_\Omega \left\{ \sum_{M=0}^{\infty} \frac{a_M(i)^\mu \Gamma(n+s-1+\mu)}{m_1!\cdots m_n!} \frac{r^{-\mu} t_1^{m_1}\cdots t_n^{m_n}}{[(1-\|\xi\|^2)^{1/2}+i(t,\xi)]^\mu} \right\} \\ &\quad \times \frac{(1-\|t\|^2)^{\frac{1}{2}(s-1)}\, dt_1\cdots dt_n}{[(1-\|\xi\|^2)^{1/2}+i(t,\xi)]^{n+s-1}}\end{aligned}$$

(where $\mu = m_1 + \cdots + m_n$ with m_i nonnegative integers), which we write more compactly as

$$\Psi(\mathbf{X}) = \mathbf{A}f \equiv \alpha_{n,s} r^{-(n+s-1)} \iint_\Omega f\left(\frac{t}{r\sigma}\right) \frac{(1-\|t\|^2)^{\frac{1}{2}(s-1)}}{\sigma^{n+s-1}}\, d^n t$$

where $\alpha_{n,s}$ is the constant multiplying the integrand and $\sigma \equiv (1-\|\xi\|)^{1/2} + i(t,\xi)$. This representation is valid in the exterior of a hypersphere. Kelvin's transformation may be used to continue it to the interior of the hypersphere.

By means of the biorthogonality of the sets $\{V_M^{(s)}(\xi)\}$ and $\{U_M^{(s)}(\xi)\}$ we can generate an operator inverse to $\mathbf{A}$. Indeed, from [A.deF.1, p. 263], we have

$$\iint_\Omega (1-\|\xi\|^2)^{\frac{1}{2}(s-1)} V_M^{(s)}(\xi) U_K^{(s)}(\xi)\, d^n\xi = \delta_K^M \frac{2\pi^{n/2}\Gamma[\frac{1}{2}(s)+1]\Gamma(\mu+s)}{(2\mu+n+s-1)\Gamma(\frac{1}{2}[n+s-1])\Gamma(s)m_1!\cdots m_n!}.$$

By use of this we have that

$$\mathbf{A}^{-1}W \equiv \int_{\Omega} \cdots \int W(\mathbf{X})K(t/\sigma; r, \xi)\, d^n\xi$$
$$= f(t/r\sigma) \equiv f(t_1/r\sigma, \ldots, t_n/r\sigma),$$

where the kernel $K(t/\sigma; r, \xi)$ is given by

$$K(t/\sigma; r, \xi) \equiv \frac{r^{n+s-1}\Gamma(s)\Gamma(\frac{1}{2}[n+s-1])}{\Gamma[\frac{1}{2}(s)+1]2\pi^{n/2}} \sum_{\mu=0}^{\infty} \frac{(2\mu+n+s-1)m_1! \cdots m_n!}{\Gamma(\mu+s)}$$
$$\times \frac{t_1^{m_1} \cdots t_n^{m_n}}{\sigma^{\mu}} U_{m_1 \cdots m_n}^{(s)}(\xi_1, \ldots, \xi_n)$$
$$\equiv \frac{r^{n+s-1}\Gamma(s)\Gamma(\frac{1}{2}[n+s-1])}{\Gamma[\frac{1}{2}(s)+1]2\pi^{n/2}} \sum_{M=0} (2\mu+n+s-1) \frac{m!\, t^m}{\sigma^{\mu}} U_M^{(s)}(\xi).$$

We remark that we may extend these definitions of **A** and its inverse by introducing integration over n-dimensional chains, Γ, where we hold the boundary $\partial\Gamma \equiv \{t \mid \|t\| = 1\}$ fixed. Hence

$$W(\mathbf{X}) = \mathbf{A}f \equiv \alpha_{n,s} r^{-(n+s-1)} \int_{\Gamma} \frac{f(t/r\sigma)}{\sigma^{n+s-1}} (1 - \|t\|^2)^{\frac{1}{2}(s-1)}\, d^n t,$$

where $\partial\Gamma \equiv \{t \mid \|t\| = 1\}$, and

$$f(t/r\sigma) = \mathbf{A}^{-1}W \equiv \int_{G} W(\mathbf{X})K(t/\sigma; r, \xi)\, d^n\xi$$

where $\partial G \equiv \{\xi \mid \|\xi\| = 1\}$.†

Using the last operator defined above, this present author and Howard [G.H.4] were able to obtain growth theorems for entire solutions which were analogs of those obtained by the present author for GASPT. To this end we first introduce the notation

$$\mathfrak{D}_R \equiv \left\{(z) \middle| \left(\frac{z}{R}\right) \in \mathfrak{D} \subset \mathbb{C}^n\right\},$$

† One may then investigate the singularities of solutions represented by these operators using the preceding methods.

where $\mathfrak{D}$ is an arbitrary, n-circular domain, and

$$M[g; \mathfrak{D}_R] = \sup_{z \in \mathfrak{D}_R} |g(z)|,$$

where $g(z) = \sum_{K=0}^{\infty} a_{k_1,\ldots,k_n} z_1^{k_1}, \ldots, z_n^{k_n}$. We now consider the GASPN functions defined by $\hat{\mathbf{A}}f$ and $\mathbf{A}g$, where $f \equiv f(1/\zeta r)$, and $g \equiv g(t/r\sigma)$, respectively.

To be specific in the case of the operator $\hat{\mathbf{A}}$ let us choose for our n-circular domain the unit hypersphere in the maximum norm, i.e., $\Delta \equiv \{(z) \mid \|z\|_m \le 1\}$, where $\|z\|_m = \max_{1 \le k \le n} |z_k|$. We notice that if $(1/\zeta r) \in \Delta_R$ then $\max_{1 \le k \le n} |1/\zeta_k| < Rr$ or $(\zeta) \notin \Delta_{1/Rr}$ which follows from $\max_k |rR\zeta_k| \ge \min_k |rR\zeta_k| > 1$.

Let us now introduce

$$\tilde{M}[f; \Delta_{R^{-1}}] = \sup_{(\zeta r) \notin \Delta_{R^{-1}}} |f(1/\zeta r)|,$$

and take $R = 1/r$. We assume that r, and hence R, is fixed. Then, for $\|\zeta\|_m \ge 1$ and taking as our domain of integration the set $\prod_{k=1}^{n} \{\zeta_k = e^{i\theta_k}\}$ we have

$$|W(\mathbf{X})| \le \frac{r^{-(n+s-1)}}{(2\pi)^n} \int_0^{2\pi} \cdots \int_0^{2\pi} \frac{|f(1/\zeta r)| \, d\theta_1, \ldots, d\theta_n}{|1 - 2(\zeta, \xi) + \|\zeta\|^2|^{\frac{1}{2}(n+s-1)}}.$$

We now proceed to obtain a lower estimate for $I \equiv |1 - 2(\zeta, \xi) + \|\zeta\|^2|$ by considering its extreme as $\zeta_k = e^{i\theta_k}$ varies. Since the quantity $I \ge 0$ we have a minimum for $\zeta_k = \xi_k$ $(k = 1, \ldots, n)$ and this yields,

$$|1 - 2(\zeta, \xi) + \|\zeta\|^2| \ge |1 - \|\xi\|^2|;$$

hence,

$$|W(\mathbf{X})| \le \frac{r^{-(n+s-1)}}{(2\pi)^n} \int_0^{2\pi} \cdots \int_0^{2\pi} \tilde{M}[f; \Delta_{1/R}] \frac{d\theta_1, \ldots, d\theta_n}{|1 - \|\xi\|^2|^{\frac{1}{2}(n+s-1)}}$$

$$\le \frac{\tilde{M}[f; \Delta_{1/R}]}{\rho^{n+s-1}}.$$

Thus we have a bound for those x's and ρ such that $x_1^2 + \cdots + x_n^2 + \rho^2 = r^2$. But $W(\mathbf{X})$ satisfies a maximum principle and we therefore have

$$|W(\mathbf{X})| \le \frac{\tilde{M}[f; \Delta_{1/R}]}{\rho^{n+s-1}}$$

for all $x_1^2 + x_2^2 + \cdots + x_n^2 + \rho^2 \ge 1/R^2$. We list this result as a theorem.

Theorem 4.7.2 *Let $W(\mathbf{X})$ be a* GASPN *function whose* **A**-*associate* $f(1/\zeta r)$ *is holomorphic regular for* (ζr) *in the exterior of a (maximum–norm) hypersphere,* $\|z\|_m \le R$. *Furthermore, if* $\tilde{M}[f; \Delta_{1/R}] = \sup_{(\zeta r) \in \Delta_R} |f(1/\zeta r)|$, *and* $\|\mathbf{X}\|_e^2 \equiv x_1^2 + \cdots + x_n^2 + \rho^2$, *then*

$$|W(\mathbf{X})| \le \frac{\tilde{M}[f; \Delta_{1/R}]}{\rho^{n+s-1}}, \qquad \textit{for} \quad \|\mathbf{X}\|_e \ge \frac{1}{R} > 0.$$

We next consider the GASPN functions generated by $\mathbf{A}[g(t/r\sigma)]$. Again let us use as a reference domain the (euclidean) hypersphere $\|z\|_e \le R$. We notice, that

$$|\sigma|^2 = |(1 - \|\xi\|^2)^{1/2} + i(\xi, t)|^2 \ge |1 - \|\xi\|^2|$$

for ξ, t real, and hence that

$$\frac{|t_k|}{r\,|\sigma|} = \frac{|t_k|}{r\,|1 - \|\xi\|^2|^{1/2}} \le \frac{|t_k|}{\rho} \qquad (k = 1, \ldots, n).$$

We conclude that if $(t/\rho) \in \Delta_R$, i.e., $(t) \in \Delta_{\rho R}$, that $(t/r\sigma) \in \Delta_R$. Since the domain of integration is taken to be $\|t\|_e \le 1$ we must have $\rho R \ge 1$ if $(t/r\sigma) \in \Delta_R$ for all t in the domain of integration. We proceed as before to obtain the bound

$$|W(\mathbf{X})| \le \frac{\Gamma(\frac{1}{2}[n+s])r^{-(n+s-1)}}{\pi^{n/2}\Gamma(\frac{1}{2}s)\Gamma(n+s-1)} \int_\Omega \frac{|g(t/r\sigma)|(1 - \|t\|^2)^{\frac{1}{2}(s-1)}|\, d^n t}{|\sigma|^{n+s-1}}$$

$$\le \frac{\Gamma(\frac{1}{2}[n+s])}{\pi^{n/2}\Gamma(\frac{1}{2}s)\Gamma(n+s-1)} \frac{M[g; \Delta_R]}{\rho^{n+s-1}} \iint_{\|t\| \le 1} (1 - \|t\|^2)^{\frac{1}{2}(s-1)}|\, d^n t|$$

for $\|\mathbf{X}\|_e \ge \rho \ge 1/R$. Since this bound is essentially of the same type as given in Theorem 4.7.2, we will not list this result as a separate theorem.

For a conclusion we shall list some extensions of results obtained by Gol'dberg [F.4, p. 339] concerning the growth of entire functions in $\mathbb{C}^n$ to the case of GASPN functions. We recall the results of Gol'dberg below. Let

$$\lambda[\mathfrak{D}] = \overline{\lim_{R\to\infty}} \frac{\ln \ln M[f, \mathfrak{D}_R]}{\ln R}, \qquad \sigma[\mathfrak{D}] = \overline{\lim_{R\to\infty}} \frac{\ln M[f; \mathfrak{D}_R]}{R^{\lambda[\mathfrak{D}]}}.$$

be associated with the entire function $f(z) = \sum_{M=0}^{\infty} a_M z^M$; then one has

$$\lambda[\mathfrak{D}] \equiv \overline{\lim_{\|K\|_a \to \infty}} \frac{\|K\|_a \ln\|K\|_a}{-\ln|a_K|}$$

$$(e\lambda\sigma[\mathfrak{D}])^{1/\lambda} = \overline{\lim_{\|K\|_a}} \{\|K\|_a^{1/\lambda}(|a_K|\, d_K[\mathfrak{D}])^{1/\|K\|_a}\},$$

where $\|K\|_a = k_1 + \cdots + k_n$ is the "addition" norm, $d_K[\mathfrak{D}] = \sup_{(z) \in \mathfrak{D}} |z^K|$, and $z^K \equiv z_1^{k_1} \cdots z_n^{k_n}$. We list the following extension of Gol'dberg's results.

Theorem 4.7.3 *Let* $W(\mathbf{X})$ *be a* GASPN *function whose* $\hat{\mathbf{A}}$*-associate* $f(1/\zeta r)$ *is an entire function of the variables* $(1/\zeta r) \in \mathbb{C}^n$, *with the following expansion about* $(1/\zeta r) = (0)$,

$$f\left(\frac{1}{\zeta r}\right) = \sum_{K=0}^{\infty} a_{k_1, \ldots, k_n}(\zeta_1 r)^{-k_1} \cdots (\zeta_n r)^{-k_n}.$$

Then we have the bounds

$$|W(\mathbf{X})| \le \frac{\exp(R^{\lambda+\varepsilon})}{\rho^{n+s-1}}, \qquad \textit{for} \quad \|\mathbf{X}\|_e \ge \frac{1}{R} > 0,$$

for arbitrary $\varepsilon > 0$, *and*

$$|W(\mathbf{X})| \le \exp\{(\sigma[\Delta_R] + \varepsilon')R^{\lambda}\}, \qquad \textit{for} \quad \|\mathbf{X}\|_e \ge \frac{1}{R} > 0,$$

arbitrary $\varepsilon' > 0$, *and where*

$$\sigma[\Delta_R] = e^{-1}R^{\lambda-1} \overline{\lim_{\|K\|_a \to \infty}} \{\|K\|_a \cdot |a_K|^{\lambda/\|K\|_a}\}.$$

Proof These results are direct transplantations of the results of Gol'dberg if one computes in our case $d_K[\Delta_R] = \sup_{(z) \in \Delta_R} |z^K| = R^{k_1 + \cdots + k_n} = R^{\|K\|_a}$.

Similar bounds may be obtained for the case of solutions to the equations $\mathbf{L}_{\lambda, s}^{(n)}[\Psi] = 0$; this has been done by the present author in [G.28].

8. *Weinstein's Theory of Singular Differential Equations*

For a concluding section to this chapter we present a short survey of the theory of singular partial differential equations as developed by Weinstein. This approach is essentially different from the ones previously presented in this book; however, his is also a function theoretic approach and has certain points of similarity with the operator method. We include his ideas because of this, and also because no chapter on singular partial differential equations could be considered complete, at this time, without reference to these important results.

Two partial differential operators studied by Weinstein [W.6–15] are the generalized axially symmetric potential theory (GASPT) operator,

$$\mathbf{L}_{2\mu}^{(m)} \equiv \frac{\partial^2}{\partial {x_1}^2} + \cdots + \frac{\partial^2}{\partial {x_m}^2} + \frac{\partial^2}{\partial y^2} + \frac{2\mu}{y}\frac{\partial}{\partial y}, \tag{4.8.1}$$

and the Euler–Poisson–Darboux (EPD) operator,

$$\hat{\mathbf{L}}_{2\mu}^{(m)} \equiv \frac{\partial^2}{\partial {x_1}^2} + \cdots + \frac{\partial^2}{\partial {x_m}^2} - \frac{\partial^2}{\partial y^2} - \frac{2\mu}{y}\frac{\partial}{\partial y}; \tag{4.8.2}$$

where μ is a real parameter, $-\infty < \mu < \infty$. We shall in what follows usually not distinguish between these two operators and denote both by simply $\mathbf{L}_{2\mu}$. This is because in the Weinstein theory both operators are seen to have similar properties. Likewise we shall denote solutions of the associated partial differential equations by $u^{(2\mu)}(x, y) \equiv u^{(2\mu)}(x_1, \ldots, x_n, y)$. Weinstein [W.11–15] has shown that the solutions of these equations obey the following recursion formulas:

$$u_y^{(2\mu)}(x, y) = yu^{(2\mu+2)}(x, y), \tag{4.8.3}$$

$$u^{(2\mu)}(x, y) = y^{1-2\mu}u^{(2-2\mu)}(x, y), \tag{4.8.4}$$

which may be seen to be fundamental properties of the operator† $\mathbf{D}_{2\mu} \equiv \partial^2/\partial y^2 + 2\mu/y\, \partial/\partial y$. Equation (4.8.3) allows one to represent $u^{(2\mu)}(x, y)$ in terms of an integral operator [W.14], namely,

$$u^{(2\mu)}(x, y) = \int_b^y \eta u^{(2\mu+2)}(x, \eta)\, d\eta + \Phi(x, b), \tag{4.8.5}$$

where $u^{(2\mu)}(x, b) = \Phi(x, b)$. Using the operator $\mathbf{A}_\mu$, introduced earlier for the case $m = 1$ of (4.8.1), we may obtain the following representation from the Weinstein formulas:

† This operator has been referred to by Delsarte and Kapilevich as Bessel's operator; however, Weinstein has noted that it appeared earlier in the work of Euler and Poisson [W.14].

$$u^{(2\mu)}(x, y) = \int_b^y \eta \mathbf{A}_{\mu+1}[f(x + i\eta)]\, d\eta + \Phi(x, b)$$

$$= \mathbf{A}_{\mu+1}\left[\int_b^y \eta f(x + i\eta)\, d\eta\right] + \Phi(x, b). \qquad (4.8.6)$$

These operations are clearly valid for $\mathscr{C}^{(2)}$-solutions of (4.8.1) (with $m = 1$); furthermore, if b is taken as 0, our result has the particularly simple form

$$u^{(2\mu)}(x, y) = \mathbf{A}_{\mu+1}\left[\int_0^y \eta u^{(2\mu+2)}(x + i\eta, 0)\, d\eta\right] + u^{(2\mu)}(x, 0). \qquad (4.8.7)$$

By replacing y^α ($\alpha \neq 0$) by z, and $v(x, z) = u(x, z^{1/\alpha})$ one obtains Weinstein's third property [W.14] of the operator $\mathbf{D}_{2\mu}$,

$$\mathbf{D}_{2\mu}[u] = \alpha^2 z^{2(\alpha-1)/\alpha} \mathbf{D}_{(2\mu+\alpha-1)/\alpha}[v]. \qquad (4.8.8)$$

Another property of solutions to $\mathbf{L}_{2\mu}[u] = 0$ is the relation $1/t\; \partial u^{(2\mu)}/\partial t = u^{(2\mu+2)}$; using this in (4.8.7) gives us back $u^{(2\mu)}(x, y) = \mathbf{A}_{\mu+1}\, u^{(2\mu)}(x + iy, 0)$. The relations (4.8.3) and (4.8.4) for the solutions for (4.8.1) or (4.8.2) were seen to be consequences of the differential operator $\mathbf{D}_{2\mu}$, and hence these relations are true for more general equations of the form

$$\mathbf{D}_{2\mu}[u] = \mathbf{X}[u], \qquad (4.8.9)$$

where $\mathbf{X}$ is an arbitrary linear operator, which vanishes for $u = 0$, and does not contain derivatives with respect to y. Combining (4.8.4) with $1/y\; \partial u^{(2\mu)}/\partial y = u^{(2\mu+2)}$ yields

$$u^{(2\mu)}(x, y) = y^{1-2\mu}\left(\frac{1}{y}\frac{\partial}{\partial y}\right)^n [y^{2(\mu+n)-1} u^{(2\mu+2n)}(x, y)] \qquad (4.8.10)$$

$$(n = 0, 1, 2, \ldots) \quad \text{[W.14]}.$$

Equations of the type (4.8.2) occur in the study of mean values of a function on a hypersphere. Poisson showed that if $f(x_1, x_2, \ldots, x_m)$ was a $\mathscr{C}^{(2)}$ function of the variables $x_1, x_2, \ldots, x_m$ in a simply connected domain, $\mathfrak{D} \subset \mathbb{R}^m$, then the mean value of $f(x)$ on a hypersphere S of radius y, i.e.,

$$M(x, y; f) = \frac{1}{\omega_m y^{m-1}} \int_S f\, ds$$

$$= \frac{1}{\omega_m} \int_{\|\xi\|=1} f(x_1 + \xi_1 y, \ldots, x_m + \xi_m y)\, d\omega_m, \qquad (4.8.11)$$

(where $\omega_m = 2(\pi)^{m/2}/\Gamma(m/2)$ is the area of the m-dimensional unit sphere) satisfies the following EPD equation (of index $m-1$):

$$\frac{\partial^2 M}{\partial r^2} + \frac{m-1}{r}\frac{\partial M}{\partial r} = \frac{\partial^2 M}{\partial {x_1}^2} + \cdots + \frac{\partial^2 M}{\partial {x_m}^2} \equiv \Delta_x M = 0. \qquad (4.8.12)$$

Weinstein [W.13] showed that this result also held in the case where $\mathfrak{D}$ was not simply connected.

A natural question which arises in the case of the EPD equation is the representation of solutions for Cauchy problems. Weinstein [W.13] considered the case of singular Cauchy problems with the initial data

$$u(x, 0) = f(x), \qquad \frac{\partial u(x, 0)}{\partial r} = 0, \qquad (4.8.13)$$

and obtained the following representation for the unique solution [W.13]:

$$u^{(2\mu)}(x, y; f) = \frac{\omega_{2\mu+1-m}}{\omega_{2\mu+1}} \int_{\|\xi\|=1} f(x_1 + \xi_1 y, \ldots, x_m + \xi_m y) \times (1 - \|\xi\|^2)^{\frac{1}{2}(2\mu-m-1)}\, d\xi_1 \cdots d\xi_m. \qquad (4.8.14)$$

Diaz and Weinberger [W.13] later gave the alternate representation

$$u^{(2\mu)}(x, y; f) = \frac{2\Gamma(\mu + \frac{1}{2})}{\Gamma(\mu + \frac{1}{2}[1-m])\Gamma(m/2)} \int_0^1 M(x, ty; f) \times (1 - t^2)^{\mu - \frac{1}{2}(m+1)} t^{m-1}\, dt. \qquad (4.8.15)$$

As Weinstein has shown [W.13], the EPD equation for the case $m = 1$ is of great importance for solving radiation problems associated with the k-dimensional wave equation,

$$\frac{\partial^2 u}{\partial t^2} = \frac{\partial^2 u}{\partial {y_1}^2} + \cdots + \frac{\partial^2 u}{\partial {y_k}^2}. \qquad (4.8.16)$$

We note that the solutions of (4.8.16) depending solely on $x = t$, and $y = +({y_1}^2 + \cdots + {y_k}^2)^{1/2}$ satisfy (4.8.2) with $m = 1$, and $2\mu = k - 1$. The radiation problem associated with (4.8.16) is usually formulated as follows [W.12], [C.H.1, Vol. II, p. 695]: let $f(t)$ be a function which is identically zero for $t < 0$, and let us seek a solution to (4.8.16) satisfying

$$u(0, y_1, \ldots, y_n) = 0, \qquad \frac{\partial u(0, y_1, \ldots, y_n)}{\partial t} = 0,$$

and such that it has a singularity at $y = 0$. Furthermore, the singularity is to be of such a nature that

$$\lim_{y \to 0} \int \frac{\partial u}{\partial y}\, dS = -\omega_k f(t), \tag{4.8.17}$$

where the integration is taken over the k-dimensional hypersphere of radius y. As Weinstein has noted [W.12], the radiation problem consists in finding a solution to the EPD equation

$$\frac{\partial^2 u}{\partial x^2} = \frac{\partial^2 u}{\partial y^2} + \frac{k-1}{y}\frac{\partial u}{\partial y}$$

which is defined for $x < y$, has a singularity of type y^{2-k} at $y = 0$, and vanishes for $x = y$. From Eq. (4.9.4) it is seen that this problem may be reformulated in terms of an EPD equation of index $(3 - k)$. Indeed, we seek a solution $u^{(3-k)}(x, y)$, which is regular at $y = 0$, taking the values $f(x)$ on $y = 0$, and zero on $x = y$. Weinstein [W.12] obtained the solution of this generalized radiation problem for $u^{(3-k)}(x, y)$ for $2 < k < \infty$, and we list his result below.

Let β be a positive number such that $0 \leq \beta < 1$, and $k - 2 = n + \beta$, where n is a nonnegative integer. Then a solution to the reformulated or generalized radiation problem was found by Weinstein [W.12] to be of the form

$$u^{(3-k)}(x, y) = \frac{1}{\Gamma(k-2)} \int_0^{x-y} \mathbf{I}^{n+3-k} f^{(n+1)}(\xi)[(x-\xi)^2 - y^2]^{\frac{1}{2}(k-3)}\, d\xi$$
$$+ \frac{1}{\Gamma(n+4-k)} \sum_{l \geq \frac{1}{2}(k-3)}^{n} f^{(l)}(0) \frac{\partial^{n-l+1} A_{n+3-k}(x, y)}{\partial x^{n-l+1}}, \tag{4.8.18}$$

where

$$A_\alpha(x, y) = \frac{1}{\Gamma(k-2)} \int_0^{x-y} \xi^\alpha [(x-\xi)^2 - y^2]^{\frac{1}{2}(k-3)}\, d\xi, \qquad \alpha > 0.$$

Here $\mathbf{I}^{n+3-k}$ denotes a Riemann–Liouville integral; furthermore, it is assumed that $f(x)$ possesses $(n + 1)$ continuous derivatives for $k \geq 5$, and $(n + 3)$ continuous derivatives for $2 < k < 5$, and for $k \geq 2n + 3$ it is assumed that

$$f(0) = f'(0) = \cdots = f^{(n)}(0) = 0.$$

Returning to the case of GASPT (4.8.1) we consider in particular the case $m = 1$, where the differential equation implies the existence of a stream function satisfying the generalized Stokes–Beltrami equations, $y^{2\mu}u_x = v_y$, and $y^{2\mu}u_y = -v_x$. Weinstein has shown that given a stream function $v^{(2\mu)}$ one can determine uniquely, up to a multiplicative constant, a potential function, $u^{(2\mu+2)} = cy^{-1-2\mu}v^{(2\mu)}$. This fundamental result has been particularly useful in application to boundary value problems. For instance, in the study of incompressible, perfect fluids flowing about axially symmetric bodies, the Weinstein method [W.6] has led to a reduction of the problem from a complicated Neumann problem for the potential to a much simpler Dirichlet problem for the stream function (in a dimension two higher than the original problem posed). Indeed, Payne [P.1] has used the above mentioned method of Weinstein to solve the problem for the flow about a spindle. The reader is referred to this paper and to [W.6,8] for further details concerning this material.

References and Additional Reading

[A.4]
[A.5]
[A.F.1]
[A.G.1]
[A.W.1]
[B.1]
[B.2]
[B.14]
[B.18]
[B.22]
[B.29]
[B.30]
[B.31]
[B.32]
[B.33]
[B.38]
[B.42]
[B.B.1]
[B.D.1]
[B.E.1]
[C.5]
[C.E.1]
[E.4]
[E.6]
[E.7]
[E.8]
[E.9]
[G.9]
[G.13]
[G.14]
[G.16]
[G.18]
[G.20]
[G.21]
[G.22]
[G.26]
[G.27]
[G.28]
[G.H.2]
[G.H.3]
[G.H.4]
[G.H.5]
[G.H.7]
[H.4]
[H.5]
[H.6]
[H.7]
[H.8]
[H.10]
[H.12]
[H.M.1]
[L.10]
[L.11]
[M.1]
[M.F.1]
[M.O.1]
[N.1]
[N.4]
[N.6]
[P.1]
[R.1]
[R.2]
[S.6]
[S.7]
[W.2]
[W.3]
[W.4]
[W.6]
[W.7]
[W.8]
[W.9]
[W.10]
[W.11]
[W.12]
[W.13]
[W.14]
[W.15]
[W.W.1]

5

Applications of integral operators to scattering problems

1. *Potential Scattering in Quantum Mechanics*

One of the areas where knowledge of the analytic properties of solutions of partial differential equations (and integral equations) is of importance is in the quantum theoretical models for the scattering of particles. The methods developed in the previous chapters are particularly useful in shedding light on certain problems which occur in the study of these models. In order to illustrate how our results may be used in this direction we must first introduce to the nonphysicist reader certain concepts concerning our model for the nonrelativistic collision phenomena.†

In quantum mechanics it is frequently assumed that the probability density, $\Phi(\mathbf{X}, t)$, for a particle (or beam of particles) being directed at some target satisfies Schrödinger's partial differential equation,

$$i\,\frac{\partial \Phi(\mathbf{X}, t)}{\partial t} = -\Delta_3 \Phi(\mathbf{X}, t) + V(\mathbf{X})\Phi(\mathbf{X}, t). \qquad (5.1.1)$$

We have written Schrödinger's equation in "normalized" form by having chosen a suitable coordinate system, i.e., such that Planks' constant ($\hbar$) is 1 and the mass of the bombarding particle is $\frac{1}{2}$. The function $V(\mathbf{X})$ is called a *localized potential*, and its presence accounts for the interaction between the particle and target.‡ If one considers the case where a "steady state" beam

† The reader who is interested in further information concerning the physicists' approach to these problems should see in particular the books by Morse and Feshbach [M.F.1], Newton [N.12,13], and Omnes and Froissart [O.F.1].

‡ $V(\mathbf{X}) \equiv 0$ for points $\mathbf{X}$ outside of the target.

of particles bombards the target, one is then led to consider the time independent Schrödinger equation,

$$\Delta_3 \Psi(\mathbf{X}) + [k^2 - V(\mathbf{X})]\Psi(\mathbf{X}) = 0, \tag{5.1.2}$$

$k = \|\mathbf{K}\|$, where $\mathbf{K}$ is the momentum of the *wave* $\Phi(\mathbf{X}, t) = \Psi(\mathbf{X})e^{ikt}$.

We now pose the following scattering problem. Suppose $V(\mathbf{X}) \equiv V(r)$, and furthermore that the function $V(r)$ for $0 < r < \infty$ satisfies the conditions

$$\int_0^r s\,|V(s)|\,ds < \infty \qquad \text{and} \qquad \int_r^\infty |V(s)|\,ds < \infty, \tag{5.1.3}$$

then for $\|X\| = r$ sufficiently large can we find a solution of (5.1.2) of the form†

$$\Psi(\mathbf{X}) = \exp\{i(\mathbf{K}, \mathbf{X})\} + f(\theta)\frac{e^{ikr}}{r} + O(1/r^2). \tag{5.1.4}$$

An alternate way of posing this problem is to seek a function, $u \equiv \Psi - e^{ikz}$, that satisfies the Sommerfeld radiation condition [H.3, p. 107], [C.H.1, Vol. II, p. 318]

$$\lim_{r\to\infty} r\left|\frac{\partial u\,(\mathbf{X})}{\partial r} - iku(\mathbf{X})\right| = 0,$$

and also the finiteness condition, $|ru(\mathbf{X})| \leq$ constant for say, $r > r_0$.

Kuroda [K.8] has shown that indeed under the conditions (5.1.3) the well-known *phase shift formulas* (which we discuss below) hold true and that one may use them to construct a solution of the form (5.1.4). The $1/r$ factor in the second term is expected from the interpretation of $\Psi(\mathbf{X})$ as a probability density, which implies that the amplitude of the *scattered wave* must decrease like an inverse radius. The function $f(\theta)$ is referred to as the *scattering amplitude*, and it is the analyticity of this function we wish to investigate (Fig. 4).

The standard approach used by physicists [O.F.1, p. 16], [M.F.1, Vol. II, p. 1066], is to decompose the solution $\Psi(\mathbf{X})$ into its *partial wave amplitudes* (Fourier components) and to extract that part which corresponds to the incoming *plane wave*. The remainder is the scattered wave from which one

† For simplicity we usually assumed that the incoming particles' beam is parallel to the x_3-axis, i.e., $\mathbf{K} \equiv (0, 0, k)$.

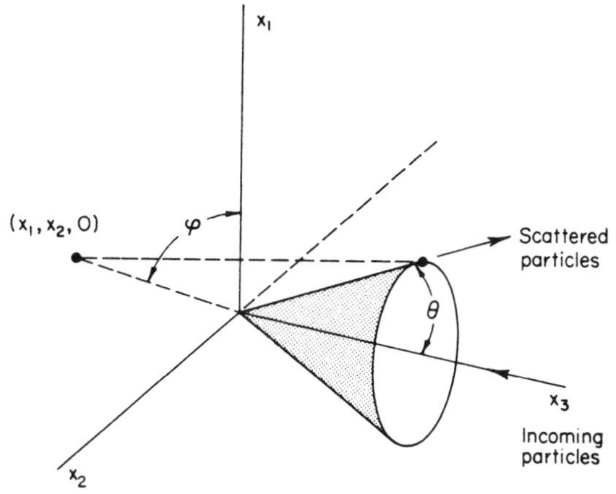

FIG. 4. Scattering symmetric with respect to the x_3-axis.

obtains the term $f(\theta)$. To this end let us suppose that the solution $\Psi(\mathbf{X})$ may be written in the form

$$\Psi(\mathbf{X}) \equiv \sum_{l=0}^{\infty} (2l+1)(i)^l \frac{y_l(r)}{kr} P_l(\cos\theta); \tag{5.1.5}$$

then the Fourier coefficients $y_n(r)$ must satisfy the ordinary differential equation

$$\frac{d^2 y_l(r)}{dr^2} + \left[k^2 - V(r) - \frac{l(l+1)}{r^2}\right] y_l(r) = 0. \tag{5.1.6}$$

If $V(r)$ is supposed identically zero for r sufficiently large we find the following asymptotic estimates† hold as $r \to \infty$:

$$y_l(r) \approx \beta_l \sin\left(kr - \frac{l\pi}{2} + \delta_l\right) = \frac{\beta_l}{2i}\left(\exp\left[ikr - \frac{il\pi}{2} + i\delta_l\right] - \exp\left[-ikr + \frac{il\pi}{2} - i\delta_l\right]\right).$$

The plane wave e^{ikx_3}, which we note is a solution of $\Delta_3\Psi + k^2\Psi = 0$, may be represented in terms of partial wave amplitudes by the classical identity [O.F.1, p. 18], [M.F.1, Vol. II, p. 1067]

† As was mentioned above, Kuroda showed that these estimates are valid whenever (5.1.3) hold.

$$e^{ikx_3} = \sum_{l=0}^{\infty} (2l+1)(i)^l j_l(kr) P_l(\cos\theta), \tag{5.1.7}$$

where

$$j_l(z) = (\pi/2z)^{1/2} J_{l+\frac{1}{2}}(z),$$

and $J_\nu(z)$ is a Bessel function of the first kind. [$j_l(z)$ is frequently referred to as a spherical Bessel function.]

The asymptotic condition on the scattered wave,

$$\Psi_s(\mathbf{X}) \equiv \Psi(\mathbf{X}) - e^{ikx_3} \approx f(\theta)\frac{e^{ikr}}{r} \tag{5.1.8}$$

as $r \to \infty$, is sufficient to determine the partial wave scattering amplitudes in terms of the phase shifts δ_l. This follows by using a well-known asymptotic expansion for Bessel functions of large argument (see Erdélyi [E.6], Vol. II, p. 85],

$$\begin{aligned} j_l(kr) &\approx \frac{1}{kr}\cos\left[kr - \frac{\pi}{2}(l+1)\right] \\ &\approx \frac{1}{2kr}\left(\exp\left[ikr - i\frac{\pi}{2}(l+1)\right] + \exp\left[-ikr + i\frac{\pi}{2}(l+1)\right]\right) \end{aligned} \tag{5.1.9}$$

as $r \to \infty$ in Eq. (5.1.8). We obtain

$$\begin{aligned} \Psi_s(\mathbf{X}) &= \frac{1}{kr}\sum_{l=0}^{\infty}(2l+1)(i)^l P_l(\cos\theta)\{y_l(r) - krj_l(kr)\} \\ &\approx \frac{1}{2kr}\sum_{l=0}^{\infty}(2l+1)(i)^l P_l(\cos\theta)\left\{-i\beta_l\left(\exp\left[+ikr - i\frac{l\pi}{2} + i\delta_l\right]\right.\right. \\ &\quad \left. - \exp\left[-ikr + i\frac{l\pi}{2} - i\delta_l\right]\right) - \exp\left[+ikr - i\frac{\pi}{2}(l+1)\right] \\ &\quad \left. - \exp\left[-ikr + \frac{i\pi}{2}(l+1)\right]\right\}, \end{aligned} \tag{5.1.10}$$

which in view of (5.1.8) necessitates that

$$\beta_l = e^{i\delta_l} \tag{5.1.11}$$

and hence

$$\Psi(\mathbf{X}) \approx e^{ikx_3} + \frac{1}{2kr}\sum_{l=0}^{\infty}(2l+1)P_l(\cos\theta)\exp\left(ikr - i\frac{\pi}{2}\right)[\exp(2i\delta_l) - 1]$$

$$\approx \exp(ikx_3) + \frac{1}{kr}\sum_{l=0}^{\infty}(2l+1)\exp(ikr + i\delta_l)\sin\delta_l\, P_l(\cos\theta). \qquad (5.1.12)$$

Hence $\Psi(\mathbf{X})$ has the desired asymptotic form with

$$f(\theta) \equiv A(k^2, \cos\theta) = \frac{1}{k}\sum_{l=0}^{\infty}(2l+1)\exp(i\delta_l(k))\sin\delta_l\, P_l(\cos\theta) \qquad (5.1.13)$$

where we have indicated the functional dependence of δ_l on the parameter k.

The physicist is interested in the behavior of the scattering amplitude $A(k^2, \xi)$ as a function of the complex variables k^2 and ξ. To this end he investigates the partial wave amplitudes,

$$a_l(k^2) = \frac{1}{k}e^{i\delta_l}\sin\delta_l, \qquad (5.1.14)$$

as an analytic function of k^2, and attempts to obtain further information concerning $A(k^2, \xi)$ as defined by the series (5.1.13). The customary way in which this is done is by employing the Sommerfeld–Watson representation [O.F.1, p. 45],

$$A(k^2, \xi) = \frac{i}{2}\int_{\infty}^{(0-)}\frac{(2l+1)a_l(k^2)P_l(-\xi)}{\sin\pi l}\,dl, \qquad (5.1.15)$$

where the symbol $\int_{\infty}^{(0-)}$ denotes integration along a contour starting at $+\infty$ on the real l-axis, encircling the origin in the negative sense, and then returning to its initial point. The physicist interested in evaluating (5.1.15) usually does so by deforming the path of integration into a straight line from $-c - i\infty$ to $-c + i\infty$ $(0 < c < 1)$, and then subtracting from this the sum of the residues of the integrand arising from the poles of $a_l(k^2)$ in the right-half plane $\operatorname{Re} l > 0$. These singularities of $a_l(k^2)$ are the celebrated *Regge poles*. This procedure yields the following result for each fixed $k \in \mathbb{C}^1$ [O.F.1, p. 46]:

$$A(k^2, \xi) = \frac{i}{2}\int_{-c-i\infty}^{-c+i\infty}\frac{(2l+1)a_l(k^2)}{\sin\pi l}P_l(-\xi)\,dl$$

$$+ \sum_{\nu}\frac{\gamma_\nu(k^2)P_{\alpha_\nu(k^2)}(-\xi)}{\sin\pi\alpha_\nu(k^2)}; \qquad (5.1.16)$$

here $\gamma_\nu(k^2)$ is the residue of $(2l + 1)a_l(k^2)/-\pi$ corresponding to the (Regge) pole in the l-plane at $l = \alpha_i(k^2)$. The usefulness of expression (5.1.16) is that it provides a convenient way to study the location of the singularities of $A(k^2, \xi)$.

Whenever a pole of $a_l(k^2)$ occurs for an integral value of $\alpha(k^2)$ this corresponds to a bound state for the scattered particle. (We remark here for the nonphysicist that integral values of l, and real values of $\frac{1}{4}k^2$, correspond to physical values of the angular momenta and energy respectively. The bound states occur for attractive potentials and hence correspond to energies.) Hence, it is of interest to study in the space of two complex variables the analytic sets given by the equations $l = \alpha(k^2)$. This set of points $(l, k^2) \in \mathbb{C}^2$ are called the *Regge trajectories*. If one considers the restriction of this set to $\operatorname{Im} k^2 = 0$ one obtains, as mentioned above, information concerning the bound states. On the other hand, if for $\operatorname{Im} k^2 = 0$, l does not take on integral values it is possible to interpret some of these singularities as "*shadow*" *metastable states*. Also, if for integral values of l, k^2 lies on the *nonphysical* sheet of the Riemann surface over the k^2-plane,† then one has a *resonance* [O.F.1, p. 47]. From this discussion we realize the importance of studying the purely mathematical problem of determining the singularity manifold of scattering amplitudes given by formal Legendre series

$$A(k^2, \xi) \equiv \sum_{l=0}^{\infty} a_l(k^2) P_l(\xi), \tag{5.1.17}$$

where the partial wave amplitudes $a_l(k^2)$ are to be considered as arbitrary analytic functions of k^2. Later we shall present formulas relating the $a_l(k^2)$ to the scattering potential $V(r)$, and use them to compute singularity manifolds for certain physically relevant potentials.

The ambition of the above program of investigation is to find suitable potentials, $V(r)$. By this we mean potentials which give rise to scattering amplitudes with the proper kind of singularities, i.e., singularities corresponding to known quantum states associated with a particular collision phenomenon; this program is frequently referred to as the *inverse scattering problem* [N.13]. In order to gain insight into the above questions the physicist frequently considers the direct scattering problem, i.e., the investigation of the various quantum states which correspond to reasonable (from a physical point of view) scattering potentials. To this end we present the following method for studying this problem, which has been introduced by Gilbert, Shieh, and Howard [G.S.1], [G.H.6].

† The physical and nonphysical sheets of this Riemann surface correspond to $\operatorname{Im} k > 0$ and $\operatorname{Im} k < 0$, respectively.

First, we notice that there exists a formal integral identity between the Legendre series,

$$A(k^2, \xi) = \sum_{l=0}^{\infty} a_l(k^2) P_l(\xi),$$

and the Taylor series,

$$B(k^2, z) = \sum_{l=0}^{\infty} a_l(k^2) z^l, \tag{5.1.18}$$

where the integral identity relating the two functions $A(k^2, \xi)$ and $B(k^2, z)$ is

$$A(k^2, \xi) = \mathbf{\Omega}[B] \equiv \frac{1}{2\pi i} \int_{|\zeta|=1} B(k^2, \xi + \tfrac{1}{2}(\zeta + \zeta^{-1})(\xi^2 - 1)^{1/2}) \frac{d\zeta}{\zeta}. \tag{5.1.19}$$

The reader will recall the similarity of this expression to the integral operator $\mathbf{A}_\mu$ of GASPT (generalized axially symmetric potential theory) in Chapter 4. Indeed, if r and $\cos\theta$ are replaced in this operator by 1 and ξ respectively (with $\mu = 1$) one obtains the integral operator $\mathbf{\Omega}$ given by (5.1.19). Using formula (5.1.19) and the wealth of information accumulated for GASPT one may obtain information concerning the singularities of $A(k^2, \xi)$ from information about the singularities of $B(k^2, z)$. For instance, if $B(k^2, z)$ has only polar singularities in the z-plane for each fixed value of k, then the singularities of $A(k^2, z)$ will be algebraic branch points; if in particular

$$B(k^2, z) = \sum_{\nu=1}^{\infty} \sum_{\mu=1}^{m_\nu} \frac{M_{\mu\nu}(k^2)}{[z - b_\nu(k^2)]^\mu}, \tag{5.1.20}$$

then by the residue theorem one has

$$A(k^2, \xi) = \sum_{\nu=1}^{\infty} \sum_{\mu=1}^{m_\nu} \frac{(-1)^{\mu-1}}{(\mu-1)!} M_{\mu\nu}(k^2) \frac{\partial^{\mu-1}}{\partial b_\nu^{\mu-1}} [b_\nu{}^2 - 2\xi b_\nu + 1]^{1/2}. \tag{5.1.21}$$

Since the series (5.1.18) is a power series and can easily be studied with regard to its singularities by the methods of Fabry [D.4, p. 377], Hadamard [D.4, p. 335], and Mandelbrojt [M.2], the reader will recall, in particular from Chapter 4, that an integral representation between the series for $A(k^2, \xi)$ and a power series, $B(k^2, z)$, permits a "translation of methods" for studying the analytic behavior of the function $A(k^2, \xi)$. Indeed, in our case we obtain numerous results by simply replacing $(r, \cos\theta)$ in our theorems for axially symmetric potentials by $(1, \xi)$ $(\mu = \frac{1}{2})$; we list a sampling of such theorems below. The first theorem we list was obtained by Nehari [N.6] who extended a result of Szegö [S.7] concerning the convergence of Legendre series. (Nehari's result concerned a Legendre series (5.1.17) where the a_l are simply constants and not functions of k^2 as we have assumed here.)

Theorem 5.1.1 (Nehari) *The necessary and sufficient conditions for $A(k^2, \xi)$ to be singular on the analytic manifold $\xi = \frac{1}{2}\{\delta(k^2) + \delta(k^2)^{-1}\}$ $(\xi \neq \pm 1)$ is that $B(k^2, z)$ is singular on $z = \delta(k^2)$.*

Theorem 5.1.2 [G.S.1] *Let $D_l^{(\mu)}(k^2)$ be defined as the following persymmetric determinant:*

$$D_l^{(\mu)}(k^2) \equiv \begin{vmatrix} a_l(k^2) & a_{l+1}(k^2) & \cdots & a_{l+\mu}(k^2) \\ a_{l+1}(k^2) & \cdot & \cdots & a_{l+\mu+1}(k^2) \\ \vdots & & & \\ a_{l+\mu}(k^2) & \cdot & \cdots & a_{l+2\mu}(k^2) \end{vmatrix} \tag{5.1.22}$$

$$L_\mu \equiv \lim_{l\to\infty} \sup |D_l^{(\mu)}(k^2)|^{1/l}, \tag{5.1.23}$$

and let $\mathfrak{E}(\rho)$ be the ellipse, $\mathfrak{E}(\rho) \equiv \{\xi \mid (\mathrm{Re}\,\xi)^2(\rho + 1/\rho)^{-2} + (\mathrm{Im}\,\xi)^2 \times (\rho - 1/\rho)^{-2} \leq \frac{1}{4}\}$. Then, we have the following possibilities concerning singularities of $A(k^2, \xi)$:

1. *If there exists a ν such that $\mu \geq \nu$, $L_\mu/L_{\mu-1} = 0$ (the ratios $L_\mu/L_{\mu-1}$ are monotone decreasing with respect to μ), then $A(k^2, \xi)$ has at most ν polelike branch points in the entire ξ-plane. Furthermore, these branch points have algebraic ramifications.*
2. *If $L_\mu/L_{\mu-1} \to 0$, $A(k^2, \xi)$ has just a finite number of polelike, algebraic, branch points in every compact set of the ξ-plane.*
3. *If $L_\mu/L_{\mu-1} \to R^{-1}$, $A(k^2, \xi)$ has just a finite number of polelike algebraic branch points in the ellipse, $\mathfrak{E}(\rho)$ $(\rho < R)$ but an infinite number of polelike branch points in a neighborhood of $\mathfrak{E}(R)$.*
4. *If $L_\mu/L_{\mu-1} \geq R^{-1}$ for $\mu \leq \nu$ and $L_\mu/L_{\mu-1} = R^{-1}$ for $\mu > \nu$ then (for each fixed k) $A(k^2, \xi)$ has in general a nonalgebraic, branch point on $\partial\, \mathfrak{E}(R)$.*

As in the case of GASPT we are able to list a Hadamard formula for the ellipse of convergence for $A(k^2, \xi)$.†

† The reader is directed to the proofs of the analogous theorems for the case of GASPT. If one considers the restriction $r = 1$ for $(r, \xi) \in \mathbb{C}^2$ $(r^2 = +(x^2 + y^2)^{1/2}$, $\xi = x/r)$, the above theorems are seen to be simply corollaries of those already developed for GASPT.

Theorem 5.1.3 [G.S.1] *For each fixed k, $A(k^2, \xi)$ converges uniformly and absolutely in any compact subset of the ellipse $\mathfrak{E}(\rho_0)$, where*

$$\rho_0(k)^{-1} = \overline{\lim_{l\to\infty}} |a_l(k)|^{1/l}.$$

Theorem 5.1.4 [G.H.7] *Let $A_1(k^2, \xi)$ and $A_2(k^2, \xi)$ be two scattering amplitudes defined by the series expansions,*

$$A_\nu(k^2, \xi) = \sum_{l=0}^{\infty} a_l^{(\nu)}(k^2) P_l(\xi) \qquad (\nu = 1, 2).$$

Furthermore, let us suppose that $A_\nu(k^2, \xi)$ $(\nu = 1, 2)$ is singular for

$$\xi = \tfrac{1}{2}\left[\alpha_\nu(k^2) + \frac{1}{\alpha_\nu(k^2)}\right] \qquad (\nu = 1, 2).$$

Then the scattering amplitude given by

$$A_3(k^2, \xi) = \sum_{l=0}^{\infty} a_l^{(1)}(k^2) a_l^{(2)}(k^2) P_l(\xi) \tag{5.1.24}$$

is singular for

$$\xi = \tfrac{1}{2}\left[\alpha_1(k^2)\alpha_2(k^2) + \frac{1}{\alpha_1(k^2)\alpha_2(k^2)}\right]. \tag{5.1.25}$$

Theorem 5.1.5 [G.H.6] *Let $A(k^2, \xi)$ be a scattering amplitude with the partial wave expansion* (5.1.17), *where for each $k^2 \in D \subset \mathbb{C}^1$ one has* $\limsup_{l\to\infty} |a_l(k^2)|^{1/l} = 0$. *Furthermore, if*

$$\lambda = \limsup_{l\to\infty} \frac{l \log l}{\log|a_l(k^2)|^{-1}},$$

then in the region $\mathfrak{D} \times \{\xi \mid |\xi|^2 + |\xi^2 - 1| \le R\}$ $A(k^2, \xi)$ satisfies the inequality

$$|A(k^2, \xi)| \le \exp R^{\lambda+\varepsilon},$$

where R is taken sufficiently large and $\varepsilon > 0$ is arbitrary.

In order to study the analytic behavior of the scattering amplitude one only needs to have information concerning the partial amplitudes as

$l \to +\infty$ through integral values. Newton, in his book [N.12, pp. 42, 32, 21], gives an asymptotic estimate when the scattering potential $V(r) \approx O(e^{-\mu r})$ as $r \to \infty$,

$$a_l(k^2) \approx -i\pi \int_0^\infty rV(r)[J_l(kr)]^2\, dr. \tag{5.1.26}$$

More complicated formulas are given for the general case where the scattering potential satisfies merely conditions (5.1.3); the reader interested in this aspect is directed to Newton's book [N.12], in particular, pages 32–33.

Example 1 We illustrate the use of the above theorems for locating singularities by several examples [G.S.1], [G.H.6].† For instance let us consider the case where $V(r)$ is an integrable function with compact support. In this case one may pass to the limit in the integral sign of (5.1.26) and obtain the estimates [N.12, p. 43],

$$a_l(k^2) \approx -i\pi\left(\frac{k}{2}\right)^{2l} \Gamma(l+1)^{-2} \int_0^\infty V(r) r^{1+2l}\, dr. \tag{5.1.27}$$

If the support of $V(r)$ lies in $[0, R]$ then by the mean value theorem for integrable functions [M.8, p. 184] we have for some R_0, where $0 < R_0 < R$,

$$a_l(k^2) \approx -i\pi\left(\frac{kR_0}{2}\right)^{2l} \frac{R_0}{\Gamma(l+1)^2} \int_0^R V(r)\, dr.$$

Hence, the series expansion for $A(k^2, \xi)$ converges in the ellipse $\mathfrak{E}(\rho)$, where

$$\begin{aligned} \rho &= \limsup_{l\to\infty} (|a_l(k^2)|^{1/l})^{-1} \\ &> \frac{1}{2}\left|\frac{2}{R_0 k}\right|^2 \times \left(\lim_{l\to\infty} \Gamma(l+1)^2 R_0^{-1} \left|\int_0^R V(r)\, dr\right|^{-1}\right)^{1/l} \end{aligned}$$

which tends to ∞ as $l \to \infty$. From this we conclude that scattering amplitudes $A(k^2, \xi)$ which correspond to integrable potentials with compact support are entire in the ξ-plane.

Example 2 If $V(r) = \exp(-a^2 r^2)$, then from Watson's book, [W.2, pp. 395–411], one may evaluate (5.1.26) to find

† In [G.H.6] several other scattering potentials are discussed. Tables are given relating scattering potentials, asymptotic forms for the partial waves, and singularities of the functions $B(k, z)$, and $A(k, z)$ in the complex z-plane.

$$a_l(k^2) \approx -\frac{i\pi}{2a^2}\exp(-k^2/a^2)I_l(k^2/2a^2),$$

where $I_l(z)$ is a modified Bessel function. Thus by using the asymptotic estimate [E.6, Vol. II, p. 86],

$$I_l(z) \approx \frac{1}{2\sqrt{\pi}}\left\{\sqrt{2}(l^2+z^2)^{-1/4}\exp[l^2+z^2]^{1/4} - l\sinh^{-1}\left(\frac{l}{z}\right)\right\}$$
$$\times\left\{1 - O\left(\frac{1}{l}\right)\right\}, \qquad z > 0,$$

we have

$$\lim_{l\to\infty}\frac{1}{l}\log I_l(z) = -\lim_{l\to\infty}\left[\sinh^{-1}\left(\frac{l}{z}\right)\right] = -\infty, \qquad z \geq 0.$$

Consequently, in this case the scattering amplitude

$$A(k^2, \xi) = \frac{1}{2a^2}\exp(-k^2/2a^2)\sum_{l=1}^{\infty} I_l(k^2/2a^2)P_l(\xi)$$

converges everywhere in the ξ-plane for k in the physical range. We restate this result as a corollary.

Corollary 5.1.6 [G.H.6] *There are no bound states occurring for nonrelativistic scattering with a potential of the form* $V(r) = \exp(-a^2r^2)$.

Example 3 If $V(r) = r^{\alpha-2}\exp(-a^2r^2)$ $(\alpha > 1)$, then using known results [W.2, pp. 395–411] one obtains

$$a_l(k^2) \approx \frac{-i\pi k^{2l}}{2^{2l}a^{2l+\alpha}}\frac{\Gamma(l+\alpha/2)}{\Gamma(l+1)^2}\,{}_2F_2(l+\tfrac{1}{2}, l+\alpha/2\,; l+1, 2l+1;\, -k^2/a^2),$$

where

$${}_2F_2(\alpha_1, \alpha_2; \beta_1, \beta_2; z) = \sum_{n=0}^{\infty}\frac{(\alpha_1)_n(\alpha_2)_n}{(\beta_1)_n(\beta_2)_n}\frac{z^n}{n!},$$

is a generalized hypergeometric function where $(\alpha)_n = \alpha(\alpha+1)\cdots(\alpha+n-1)$ $(n \geq 1)$ and $(\alpha)_0 \equiv 1$. In [G.H.6] it is shown that

$$\limsup_{l\to\infty} \left| \left(\frac{k}{2a}\right)^{2l} \frac{\Gamma(l+\alpha/2)}{\Gamma(l+1)^2} \, {}_2F_2(l+\tfrac{1}{2}, l+\alpha/2; l+1, 2l+1; -k^2/a^2) \right|^{1/l} = 0,$$

for all $k \neq \infty$, and consequently the scattering amplitude corresponding to a singular potential such as this one is still analytic-regular for ξ and k^2 lying in a compact subset of $\mathbb{C}^2$.

Example 4 For the case where the scattering potential is a superposition of Yukawa potentials, i.e.,

$$V(r) = \int_{\mu_0}^{\infty} \rho(\mu) \frac{e^{-\mu r}}{r} \, d\mu \qquad (\mu_0 > 0),$$

Newton has given the following asymptotic estimate [N.12, p. 44]

$$a_l(k^2) \approx O(l^{-1/2} e^{-2l\alpha}),$$

where

$$\alpha = \ln\left[\frac{\mu_0}{2k} + \left(1 + \frac{\mu_0^{\,2}}{4k^2}\right)^{1/2}\right], \qquad \text{and} \qquad |k| < \mu_0.$$

From the Cauchy–Hadamard formula and the Fabry theorem we compute the singularity of $B(k^2, z)$ in the z-plane to lie at

$$z = \{(\mu_0/2k) + [1 + (\mu_0^{\,2}/4k^2)]^{1/2}\}^2$$

where this holds for those complex k such that $|k| < \mu_0$. We choose the branch of the square root so that it is positive for $k > 0$, i.e., for physical k.

Theorem 5.1.1 then shows that the scattering amplitude is singular at the point

$$\begin{aligned}\xi &= \frac{1}{2}\left\{\left[\frac{\mu_0}{2k} + \left(1 + \frac{\mu_0^{\,2}}{4k^2}\right)^{1/2}\right]^2 + \left[\frac{\mu_0}{2k} + \left(1 + \frac{\mu_0^{\,2}}{4k^2}\right)^{1/2}\right]^{-2}\right\} \\ &= \frac{1}{2}\left\{\left[\frac{\mu_0}{2k} + \left(1 + \frac{\mu_0^{\,2}}{4k^2}\right)^{1/2}\right]^2 + \left[\frac{\mu_0}{2k} - \left(1 + \frac{\mu_0^{\,2}}{4k^2}\right)^{1/2}\right]^2\right\} \\ &= 1 + \frac{\mu_0^{\,2}}{2k^2}, \qquad |k| < \mu_0.\end{aligned}$$

This agrees with the known singularity in the momentum transfer plane at $t = 2k^2(z-1) = \mu_0{}^2$, which initiates a cut. The nature of this singularity may be studied by using Theorem 5.1.2 but the computations are rather detailed. The reader is referred to [G.H.6] to see how this may be done; however, we here state the result that in the case of Yukawa type potentials we have shown that $L_\nu/L_{\nu-1} = 1$, for all $\nu \geq 1$. This means that $B(k^2, z)$ has a nonpolar singularity at

$$z = \left\{\frac{\mu_0}{2k} + \left(1 + \frac{\mu_0{}^2}{4k^2}\right)^{1/2}\right\}^2$$

and hence this rules out the possibility of a pole-like branch point for $A(k^2, \xi)$ at $\xi = 1 + (\mu_0{}^2/2k^2)$.

Another method of investigating the nature of a singularity of $A(k^2, \xi)$ is to consider what happens to the value of the function when one passes around it on a small circle. For instance, if the function is multiple valued one can tell if it has algebraic or logarithmic ramification about such a branch point. Let us suppose that $B(k^2, z)$ has a singularity at $z = \delta(k^2)$ and consequently $A(k^2, \xi)$ is singular at $\xi = \xi_0 \equiv \frac{1}{2}(\delta + \delta^{-1})$ (we assume $\delta \neq 1$). We wish to study the possibility of ξ_0 being a branch point of $A(k^2, \xi)$. To this end we consider the following integral where $\varepsilon > 0$ is arbitrarily small,

$$A(k^2, \xi_0 + \varepsilon e^{2\pi i}) - A(k^2, \xi_0 + \varepsilon)$$

$$i\varepsilon \int_0^{2\pi} e^{i\theta} \frac{\partial A(k^2, \xi_0 + \varepsilon e^{i\theta})}{\partial \xi_0}\, d\theta = \frac{1}{2\pi i}\int_0^{2\pi} d\theta \left\{\int_{|\zeta|=1} \frac{\partial B(k^2, \sigma)}{\partial \sigma}\frac{\partial \sigma}{\partial \theta}\frac{d\zeta}{\zeta}\right\}, \tag{5.1.28}$$

where $\sigma = \sigma(\xi, \zeta) \equiv \xi + \frac{1}{2}(\xi^2 - 1)^{1/2}(\zeta + 1/\zeta)$. If the integrand is absolutely integrable on the product space $\{|\zeta| = 1\} \times \{0 \leq \theta \leq 2\pi\}$ (we have tacitly assumed much more by differentiating under the integral sign), then we may interchange orders of integration.

This is certainly satisfied if $B(k^2, \sigma)$ is $O([\sigma - \delta]^{-\alpha})$, $\alpha < 1$, about $\sigma = \delta$, which can be shown to be true by the method of dominants.

We consider the mapping $\xi \to \sigma$ for ζ fixed. Then the circle $|\xi - \xi_0| = \varepsilon$ is mapped onto the closed curve

$$\mathscr{C}_\phi \equiv \left\{\sigma \,|\, \sigma \approx \xi_0 + (\xi_0{}^2 - 1)^{1/2}\cos\phi + \varepsilon\left[e^{i\theta} + \frac{\xi_0}{(\xi_0^2 - 1)^{1/2}}\cos\phi\right]; \quad 0 \leq \theta < 2\pi\right\}$$

where $\phi = \arg \zeta$; the integral (5.1.28) becomes

$$A(k^2, \xi_0 + \varepsilon e^{2\pi i}) - A(k^2, \xi_0 + \varepsilon) = \frac{1}{2\pi} \int_0^{2\pi} d\phi \int_{\mathscr{C}_\phi} \frac{\partial B}{\partial \sigma} \, d\sigma.$$

Since $\xi_0 + (\xi_0^2 - 1)^{1/2} = \delta$ we may rewrite our expression for $\mathscr{C}_\phi$ as

$$\sigma - \delta = -(1 - \cos\phi)(\xi_0^2 - 1)^{1/2} + \varepsilon\left[e^{i\theta} + \frac{\xi_0}{(\xi_0^2 - 1)^{1/2}} \cos\phi\right] + O(\varepsilon^2),$$

where $\theta \in [0, 2\pi]$. We now subdivide the ϕ-interval from 0 to 2π into three parts $[0, \phi_1)$, (ϕ_1, ϕ_2), and $(\phi_2, 2\pi]$, where $\phi_1 < \phi_2$ are roots of the equation $(\xi_0 \neq 0, 1)$

$$\cos\phi = 1 + \frac{\varepsilon}{(\xi_0^2 - 1)^{1/2}}\left(1 + \frac{\xi_0}{(\xi_0^2 - 1)^{1/2}}\right) + O(\varepsilon^2).$$

It is clear that if $\phi \in [0, \phi_1)$ or $(\phi_2, 2\pi]$, the curve $\mathscr{C}_\phi$ winds about the point $\sigma = \delta$ exactly once; whereas, for $\phi \in (\phi_1, \phi_2)$, $\mathscr{C}_\phi$ does not contain $\sigma = \delta$. Hence, we may rewrite (making use of symmetry) our integral (5.1.28) as

$$\begin{aligned} A(k^2, \xi_0 + \varepsilon e^{2\pi i}) - A(k^2, \xi_0 + \varepsilon) &= \frac{1}{2\pi}\left[\int_0^{\phi_1} d\phi + \int_{\phi_1}^{2\pi} d\phi\right] \int_{\mathscr{C}_\phi} \frac{\partial B(k^2, \sigma)}{\partial \sigma} \, d\sigma \\ &= \frac{1}{\pi} \int_0^{\phi_1} d\phi \{B_L(k^2, \xi[\phi]) - B_0(k^2, \xi[\phi])\}, \end{aligned} \tag{5.1.29}$$

where $B_L(k^2, \sigma)$ is the branch obtained by passing over the cut

$$\Lambda \equiv \{\sigma \mid \sigma = \delta + i\lambda, \lambda \geq 0\}$$

from right to left. Clearly, the scattering amplitude $A(k^2, \xi)$ is single valued in a neighborhood of ξ_0 if the integral (5.1.29) vanishes. This approach has been used by Gilbert and Howard [G.H.6] to study the singularity of the scattering amplitude corresponding to a Yukawa potential about $\xi = (1 + \mu_0^2/4k^2)^{1/2}$. It has been shown that this point has a logarithmic ramification and the discontinuity across the branch cut has been computed in the above paper.

A natural question that arises in our study of the singularities of $A(k^2, \xi)$ is what type of singularity of $B(k^2, z)$ corresponds to a pole in the ξ-plane of

$A(k^2, \xi)$. To answer this question we return to our integral operators $\mathbf{\Omega}$ and $\mathbf{\Omega}^{-1}$. (The integral operator $\mathbf{\Omega}^{-1}$ may be obtained from $\mathbf{A}_\mu^{-1}$.) Let us consider the case where

$$A(k^2, \xi) \equiv \frac{1}{(\xi - \alpha[k^2])^m} + \text{entire function.}$$

Since no loss of generality occurs by assuming $m = 1$ (as we shall see) we consider those $B(k^2, z)$ defined by

$$B(k^2, z) = \mathbf{\Omega}^{-1}\left[\frac{1}{\xi - \alpha[k^2]}\right].$$

The entire part of $A(k^2, \xi)$ does not lead to finite singularities and hence may be ignored. This leads us to evaluate

$$\begin{aligned}
B(k^2, z) &= \frac{1 - z^2}{2}\int_{-1}^{+1}\frac{d\xi}{(\xi - \alpha[k^2])(1 - 2\xi z + z^2)^{3/2}} \\
&= \frac{1 - z^2}{(z^2 - 2z\alpha + 1)}\left[\frac{1}{(z^2 - 2\xi z + 1)^{1/2}}\right]_{\xi=-1}^{+1} + \frac{1 - z^2}{2(z^2 - 2z\alpha + 1)^{3/2}} \\
&\quad \times \left[\log\left(C_1\frac{(z^2 - 2\xi z + 1)^{1/2} - (z^2 - 2z\alpha + 1)^{1/2}}{(z^2 - 2\xi z + 1)^{1/2} + (z^2 - 2z\alpha + 1)^{1/2}}\right)\right]_{\xi=-1}^{+1} \\
&= \frac{-2}{z^2 - 2z\alpha + 1} + \frac{\frac{1}{2}(1 - z^2)}{(z^2 - 2z\alpha + 1)^{3/2}} \\
&\quad \times \log\left(\frac{1 + z\alpha + (z^2 - 2z\alpha + 1)^{1/2}}{1 + z\alpha - (z^2 - 2z\alpha + 1)^{1/2}}\right).
\end{aligned} \tag{5.1.30}$$

Hence, for z in a neighborhood of $z_0 = \frac{1}{2}(\alpha + 1/\alpha)$, $B(k^2, z)$ has the expansion

$$B(k^2, z) = \frac{1}{z\alpha - 1} + (1 - z^2)\sum_{m=0}^{\infty}\frac{(z^2 - 2\alpha z + 1)^m}{(2m + 3)(1 - z\alpha)^{2m+3}}.$$

which is clearly analytic regular. We conclude that there do not exist any polar singularities for scattering amplitudes of the form given above. In a similar way we may discuss the case where $A(k^2, \xi)$ has a pole of order m by writing

$$B(k^2, z) = \mathbf{\Omega}^{-1}\left[\frac{1}{(\xi - \alpha)^m}\right] = (m-1)!\,\frac{\partial^{m-1}}{\partial \alpha^{m-1}}\,\mathbf{\Omega}^{-1}\left[\frac{1}{\xi - \alpha}\right].$$

We list this result as a theorem.

Theorem 5.1.7 *There are no scattering amplitudes that have polar singularities of the form*

$$A(k^2, \xi) = \sum_{j=1}^{N} \frac{b_j[k]}{(\xi - \alpha_j[k])^{m_j}} + \text{entire function.}$$

2. *A Generalized Potential Scattering Problem*

In this section we will formally generalize known methods, the plane shift computations, which have been used for problem (5.1.2)–(5.1.4) to the higher dimensional problem

$$S[\Psi] \equiv \frac{\partial^2 \Psi}{\partial x_1{}^2} + \cdots + \frac{\partial^2 \Psi}{\partial x_n{}^2} + \frac{\partial^2 \Psi}{\partial \rho^2} + \frac{s}{\rho}\frac{\partial \Psi}{\partial \rho} + [k^2 - V(r)]\Psi = 0, \quad (5.2.1)$$

with the asymptotic condition

$$\Psi(\mathbf{X}) \approx e^{i(\mathbf{K},\,\mathbf{x})} + \frac{f(k;\theta)}{r^{\frac{1}{2}(n+s)}}\, e^{ikr} + O\left(\frac{1}{r^{\frac{1}{2}(n+s)+1}}\right). \quad (5.2.2)$$

Here $\mathbf{K} \equiv (k_1, \ldots, k_n)$ is the propagation vector of the incident wave, $\mathbf{x} \equiv (x_1, \ldots, x_n)$, $\mathbf{X} \equiv (x_1, \ldots, x_n, \rho)$, $r = \|\mathbf{X}\|$, and $\theta \equiv (\theta_1, \ldots, \theta_n)$ is the (multiple) scattering angle. The term $r^{-\frac{1}{2}(n+s)}$ is necessary in the coefficient of the scattering amplitude because of the physical interpretation of $\Psi(\mathbf{X})$ as a probability density; however, this factor is also implied by the generalized Sommerfeld radiation condition [H.3, p. 107],

$$\lim_{r \to \infty} \left[r^{\frac{1}{2}(n+s)} \left| \frac{\partial u(\mathbf{X})}{\partial r} - iku(\mathbf{X}) \right| \right] \to 0.$$

We now seek a formal solution of (5.2.1)–(5.2.2), and to this end recall (in modified form) a generating function (see [E.6, Vol. II, p. 282] for the polynomials $V_M^{(s)}(\xi)$, namely,

$$e^{i(\mathbf{K},\mathbf{x})} = r^{-\frac{1}{2}(n+s-1)}2^{\frac{1}{2}(n+s-1)}\Gamma(\tfrac{1}{2}[n+s-1])$$
$$\times \sum_M i^m\left(m + \frac{n+s-1}{2}\right)K^M k^{-m-\frac{1}{2}(n+s-1)} J_{m+\frac{1}{2}(n+s-1)}(rk)V_M^{(s)}(\xi), \tag{5.2.3}$$

where $m = m_1 + m_2 + \cdots + m_n$, $M \equiv (m_1, m_2, \ldots, m_n)$ $k = \|\mathbf{K}\|$ etc., and the remaining notation is the same as used before.† (We note that (5.2.3) is indeed a solution of (5.2.1) with $V(r) \equiv 0$.) When $s = n = 1$, this results in the well-known expansion formula for a plane wave in terms of its "partial waves," i.e., Eq. (5.1.7).

Defining a generalized, spherical Bessel function as

$$J_m^{(n,s)}(rk) \equiv \tfrac{1}{2}\Gamma(\tfrac{1}{2}[n+s-1])\left(\frac{2}{rk}\right)^{\frac{1}{2}(n+s-1)} J_{m+\frac{1}{2}(n+s-1)}(kr) \tag{5.2.4}$$

and introducing the function

$$Y_m^{(n,s)}(r) \equiv i^m r^{\frac{1}{2}(n+s)}(2m+n+s-1)J_m^{(n,s)}(rk), \tag{5.2.5}$$

we may rewrite (5.2.3) as

$$e^{i(\mathbf{K},\mathbf{x})} = \sum_M \frac{Y_m^{(n,s)}(r)}{r^{\frac{1}{2}(n+s)}} V_M^{(s)}(\xi).$$

Following the phase shift approach used in ordinary potential scattering (Section 1 of the present chapter), we seek a solution to (5.2.1)–(5.2.2) by the separation of variables method, considering those solutions which may be expressed in the form $\Psi(\mathbf{X}) = f(r)P(\xi)$. We find that $f(r)$ must be a solution of

$$\frac{d^2 f}{dr^2} + \frac{n+s}{r}\frac{df}{dr} + \left[k^2 - V(r) - \frac{(m+n+s-1)}{r}\right] f = 0,$$

with $P(\xi) \equiv V_M^{(s)}(\xi)$. For convenience we replace $f(r)$ by $y(r) \times r^{-\frac{1}{2}(n+s)}$; we find that $y(r; n, m, s)$ must satisfy

$$\frac{d^2 y}{dr^2} + \left[k^2 - V(r) - \frac{m(m+n+s-1)}{r^2} + \frac{\left(\frac{n+s}{2}\right)\left(\frac{n+s}{2} - 1\right)}{r^2}\right] y = 0. \tag{5.2.6}$$

† We denote $k_1^{m1} k_2^{m2} \cdots k_n^{mn}$ by K^M.

Using the usual arguments [O.F.1] the asymptotic form of $y(r; n, m, s)$ may be computed as $r \to \infty$:

$$y(r; n, m, s) \approx \frac{G_m}{2i}\left\{\exp\left(ikr - im\frac{\pi}{2} + i\delta_m\right) - \exp\left(-ikr + im\frac{\pi}{2} - i\delta_m\right)\right\}, \tag{5.2.7}$$

wnere G_m is a constant and δ_m is the so-called phase shift factor which occurs because of the scattering. The asymptotic form of $Y_m^{(n,s)}(r)$ can be computed using a known formula for the Bessel functions [E.6, Vol. II, p. 85],

$$Y_m^{(n,s)}(r) \approx \frac{1}{2}\frac{i^m}{(2\pi k)}(2m + n + s - 1)\Gamma\left(\frac{n + s - 1}{2}\right)\left(\frac{2}{k}\right)^{\frac{1}{2}(n+s-1)}$$
$$\times \exp\left(-i\frac{\pi}{4}(n + s)\right)\left\{e^{ikr} + \exp\left(-ikr + im\pi + i(n + s)\frac{\pi}{2}\right)\right\}$$
$$+ O(r^{-3/2}). \tag{5.2.8}$$

The partial wave amplitudes of the scattered wave are now obtained by identifying the incoming components of (5.2.7) and (5.2.8), and then computing the scattered partial wave as

$$y_m^{\text{scat}}(r) \equiv y(r; n, m, s) - Y_m^{(n,s)}(r).$$

This procedure leads to a determination of the constants G_m as

$$G_m = \frac{1}{2\sqrt{\pi}}\exp\left(i(2m + n + s - 2)\frac{\pi}{4}\right)$$
$$\times (2m + n + s - 1)\Gamma\left(\frac{n + s - 1}{2}\right)\left(\frac{2}{k}\right)^{\frac{1}{2}(n+s)} e^{i\delta_m}, \tag{5.2.9}$$

and the partial waves

$$y_m^{\text{scat}}(r) = \frac{e^{i\delta_m + ikr}}{2\sqrt{\pi}}\Gamma\left(\frac{n + s - 1}{2}\right)\left(\frac{2}{k}\right)^{\frac{1}{2}(n+s)}$$
$$\times (2m + n + s - 1)\sin\left\{\delta_m + \frac{\pi}{4}(n + s - 2)\right\}. \tag{5.2.10}$$

The formulas (5.2.9) and (5.2.10) reduce to well-known results in the theory of potential scattering when $n = s = 1$. The above allows us to rewrite (5.2.2) in the form

$$\Psi(\mathbf{X}) = r^{-\frac{1}{2}(n+s)} \sum_M Y_m^{(n,s)}(r) V_M^{(s)}(\xi) + r^{-\frac{1}{2}(n+s)} \sum_M y_m^{\text{scat}}(r) V_M^{(s)}(\xi)$$
$$\underset{r\to\infty}{\approx} e^{i(\mathbf{K},\mathbf{x})} + \frac{e^{ikr}}{r^{\frac{1}{2}(n+s)}} f(k, \xi) \tag{5.2.11}$$

with

$$f(k, \xi) = \frac{1}{2\sqrt{\pi}} \Gamma\left(\frac{n+s-1}{2}\right) \left(\frac{2}{k}\right)^{\frac{1}{2}(n+s)} \sum_M (2m + n + s - 1) e^{i\delta_m}$$
$$\times \sin\left\{\delta_m + \frac{\pi}{4}(n + s - 2)\right\} V_M^{(s)}(\xi). \tag{5.2.12}$$

We recall at this point the generating function representation given for the $V_M^{(s)}(\xi)$ in Section 7 of Chapter 4,

$$[1 - 2(\zeta, \xi) + \|\zeta\|^2]^{-\frac{1}{2}(n+s-1)} = \sum_M V_M^{(s)}(\xi)\zeta^M.$$

Formally, we have then that

$$F(\xi) \equiv \sum_M a_M V_M^{(s)}(\xi) = \left(\frac{1}{2\pi i}\right)^n \int_{\mathfrak{D}} \frac{g(\zeta)\, d\zeta/\zeta}{[1 - 2(\zeta, \xi) + \|\zeta\|^2]^{\frac{1}{2}(n+s-1)}}, \tag{5.2.13}$$

where $\mathfrak{D} = \prod_{s=1}^n \mathscr{L}_s$; the integration is a multiple Cauchy integral over suitably chosen closed contours $\mathscr{L}_s$ and

$$g(\zeta) \equiv \sum_M a_M \zeta^{-M}$$

is a holomorphic function of n complex variables in a neighborhood of $1/\zeta \equiv (1/\zeta_1, \ldots, 1/\zeta_n) = (0, 0, \ldots, 0)$.

As we have seen in the earlier chapters, in particular Chapter 4, integral representation of the form (5.2.13) can be used to study the possible singularities of the form (5.2.12); indeed our problem is reduced to an investigation of the singularities of the function

$$g(k, \zeta) = \frac{1}{2\sqrt{\pi}} \Gamma\left(\frac{n+s-1}{2}\right) \left(\frac{2}{k}\right)^{\frac{1}{2}(n+s)} \sum_M (2m + n + s - 1) e^{i\delta_m}$$
$$\times \sin\left\{\delta_m + \frac{\pi}{4}(n + s - 2)\right\} \zeta^{-M}. \tag{5.2.14}$$

The coefficients of this series depend on $M = (m_1, \ldots, m_n)$ in a very simple manner, i.e., on $m = m_1 + \cdots + m_n$, and hence computation of the "first" singular set of $g(k, \zeta)$ is relatively simple.

In his book, Newton [N.12, p. 42] gives an asymptotic expression as $m \to \infty$ for the partial wave in terms of the scattering potential $V(r)$. A similar result can be obtained for our case, from which one may compute the first singular set of $g(k, \zeta)$ and then also of the scattering amplitude.

3. *Single Channel Scattering of Particles with Spin*

In Section 5.1 we investigated the scattering of particles without spin by means of Schrödinger's equation. The solution of this equation may be considered to be the composite wave function corresponding to a plane wave plus a particle scattered by an infinite mass "target-particle," or on the other hand, the composite wave function for two particles in a center of mass coordinate frame. We assume as before that the local (scattering) potential $V(\mathbf{X})$ is a function of $r = \|\mathbf{X}\|$ alone, and that $V(r)$ obeys the conditions (5.1.3).

Let $\mathbf{k}$ and $\mathbf{k}'$ be the momenta of the incident beam and scattered particle respectively, and let us return to the problem of scattering particles of spin zero as discussed in Section 1. We remark that Eq. (5.1.13) may be written in the alternate form,

$$A(\mathbf{k}; \mathbf{k}') \equiv A(k^2, \cos\theta) = \sum_{l=0}^{\infty} (2l+1) a_l(k^2) P_l(\hat{\mathbf{k}} \cdot \hat{\mathbf{k}}'), \qquad (5.3.1)$$

where $\hat{\mathbf{k}}$ and $\hat{\mathbf{k}}'$ are unit vectors in the $\mathbf{k}$ and $\mathbf{k}'$ directions respectively. From the addition formula for Legendre functions [C.6, p. 307],†

$$P_l(\hat{\mathbf{k}} \cdot \hat{\mathbf{k}}') = P_0(\hat{\mathbf{z}} \cdot \hat{\mathbf{k}}) P_0(\hat{\mathbf{z}} \cdot \hat{\mathbf{k}}') + 2 \sum_{m=1}^{+l} \frac{(l-m)!}{(l+m)!} P_l^m(\hat{\mathbf{z}} \cdot \hat{\mathbf{k}}) P_l^m(\hat{\mathbf{z}} \cdot \hat{\mathbf{k}}') \cdot \cos m(\varphi - \varphi') \qquad (5.3.2)$$

and the identity

$$\frac{(n-m)!}{(n+m)!} P_n^m(\xi) = P_n^{-m}(\xi),$$

† Here $\hat{\mathbf{z}}$ is a unit vector in the z-direction; θ, φ and θ', φ' are the coordinates on the unit sphere of the momenta $\hat{\mathbf{k}}$ and $\hat{\mathbf{k}}'$ respectively. We note in particular that $\cos\theta = \mathbf{z} \cdot \mathbf{k}$, and $\cos\theta' = \hat{\mathbf{z}} \cdot \hat{\mathbf{k}}'$.

we may rewrite (5.3.1) as

$$A(\mathbf{k};\mathbf{k}') = \sum_{l=0}^{\infty} \sum_{m=-l}^{+l} (2l+1) a_l(k^2) \frac{(l-m)!}{(l+m)!} P_l^m(\hat{\mathbf{z}} \cdot \hat{\mathbf{k}}) P_l^m(\hat{\mathbf{z}} \cdot \hat{\mathbf{k}}') e^{im(\varphi - \varphi')}. \quad (5.3.3)$$

By introducing the following normalization for the spherical harmonics [N.13, p. 31],

$$Y_l^m(\hat{\mathbf{k}}) = (-1)^m i^l \left[\frac{2l+1}{4\pi} \frac{(l-m)!}{(l+m)!}\right]^{1/2} e^{im\varphi} P_l^m(\hat{\mathbf{z}} \cdot \hat{\mathbf{k}}), \quad (5.3.4)$$

Eq. (5.3.3) has the further representation

$$A(\mathbf{k};\mathbf{k}') = 4\pi \sum_{l=0}^{\infty} \sum_{m=-l}^{+l} a_l(k^2) Y_l^m(\hat{\mathbf{k}}) \overline{Y_l^m}(\hat{\mathbf{k}}'), \quad (5.3.5)$$

where the complex conjugate spherical harmonic is defined by $\overline{Y_l^m(\hat{\mathbf{k}}')} = (-1)^{l+m} Y_l^{-m}(\hat{\mathbf{k}}')$.

In what follows we shall show that the representation (5.3.5) for the scattering amplitude is a special case of a more general expression, and that its simplified form is a direct result of the fact that it is a rotationally invariant function of $\mathbf{k}$, and $\mathbf{k}'$ for the case of particles with spin zero scattered by a radially symmetric potential.

The plane wave expansion (5.1.7) may be rewritten in our present notation (here using $\mathbf{r}$ instead of $\mathbf{X}$ as the radial vector) as

$$\begin{aligned} e^{i(\mathbf{k},\mathbf{r})} &= \frac{4\pi}{kr} \sum_{l=0}^{\infty} \sum_{m=-l}^{+l} i^l j_l(kr) Y_l^m(\hat{\mathbf{r}}) \overline{Y_l^m(\hat{\mathbf{k}})} \\ &= \sum_{l=0}^{\infty} (2l+1) i^l j_l(kr) P_l(\hat{\mathbf{k}} \cdot \hat{\mathbf{r}}), \end{aligned} \quad (5.3.6)$$

and the solution $\Psi(\mathbf{X})$ given by (5.1.5) may be expressed as

$$\Psi(\mathbf{r}) = \frac{4\pi}{kr} \sum_{l=0}^{\infty} \sum_{m=-l}^{+l} i^l y_l(\mathbf{r}) Y_l^m(\hat{\mathbf{r}}) \overline{Y_l^m}(\hat{\mathbf{k}}). \quad (5.3.7)$$

It is clear that under the conditions (5.1.3) on $V(r)$ one may proceed from (5.3.7) and (5.3.6) and obtain the expression (5.3.5) exactly as was done in Sect. 1. One may use this fact in order to obtain the expression analogous to (5.3.5) for the scattering amplitude in the case where the particles have spin.

The functions $Y_l^m(\hat{\mathbf{r}})$ are eigenfunctions of the total, orbital angular momentum operator $\mathbf{L}^2$ and its z-component $\mathbf{L}_z$ [N.13, p. 32], i.e.,

$$\mathbf{L}^2 Y_l^m(\hat{\mathbf{r}}) \equiv -\left[\csc\theta \frac{\partial}{\partial\theta} \sin\theta \frac{\partial}{\partial\theta} + \csc^2\theta \frac{\partial^2}{\partial\varphi^2}\right] Y_l^m(\hat{\mathbf{r}}) = l(l+1) Y_l^m(\hat{\mathbf{r}}), \quad (5.3.8)$$

$$\mathbf{L}_z Y_l^m(\hat{\mathbf{r}}) \equiv -i \frac{\partial}{\partial\varphi} Y_l^m(\hat{\mathbf{r}}) = m Y_l^m(\hat{\mathbf{r}}). \quad (5.3.9)$$

For the problem of scattering of particles without spin the orbital angular momentum and its z-component are "good" quantum numbers, i.e., in this scattering phenomenon the orbital angular momentum and its z-component are preserved. In order to discuss the case of particles with spin we introduce, following the approach of Newton [N.13, Chapter 15], the functions

$$\mathscr{Y}_{jls}^M(\hat{\mathbf{r}}) = \sum_{m,\,\nu} C(l, s, j; m, \nu, M) Y_l^m(\hat{\mathbf{r}}) \chi_\nu^s, \quad (5.3.10)$$

where χ_ν^s is an eigenstate of the spin operator $\mathbf{S}^2$ and its z-component $\mathbf{S}_z$, i.e., $\mathbf{S}^2\chi_\nu^s = s(s+1)\chi_\nu^s$, and $\mathbf{S}_z\chi_\nu^s = \nu\chi_\nu^s$. (We remark that χ_ν^s will be an eigenstate of the operator $\mathbf{S}_z$ only if the z-axis is chosen in the direction of the particle's spin. The reader interested in further details is referred to [N.13] and in particular section (8.3.2) of that work.) The numbers $C(lsj; m\nu M)$ are known as the Clebsch–Gordan coefficients and are determined by the requirement that the functions $\mathscr{Y}_{jls}^M(\hat{\mathbf{r}})$ are to be eigenstates of the total angular momentum operator (spin plus orbital angular momentum) and its z-component, i.e.,

$$\mathbf{J}^2 \mathscr{Y}_{jls}^M(\hat{\mathbf{r}}) \equiv (\mathbf{L} + \mathbf{S})^2 \mathscr{Y}_{jls}^M(\hat{\mathbf{r}}) = j(j+1) \mathscr{Y}_{jls}^M(\hat{\mathbf{r}}), \quad (5.3.11)$$

$$\mathbf{J}_z \mathscr{Y}_{jls}^M(\hat{\mathbf{r}}) = (\mathbf{L}_z + \mathbf{S}_z) \mathscr{Y}_{jls}^M(\hat{\mathbf{r}}) = M \mathscr{Y}_{jls}^M(\hat{\mathbf{r}}). \quad (5.3.12)$$

In other words, we are seeking a unitary transformation from the space of functions $Y_l^m(\hat{\mathbf{r}})\chi_\nu^s$ (which diagonalize the operators $\mathbf{L}^2$, $\mathbf{S}^2$, $\mathbf{L}_z$, and $\mathbf{S}_z$), to the space of the functions (which diagonalize the operators $\mathbf{J}^2$, $\mathbf{L}^2$, $\mathbf{J}_z^2$, and $\mathbf{S}^2$.) The Clebsch–Gordan coefficients are known to satisfy certain orthogonality conditions [R.4, Chapter III], [N.13, Chapter 15],

$$\sum_{m,\,\nu} C(l, s, j; m, \nu, M) C(l, s, j'; m, \nu, M) = \delta_{jj'}\,\delta_{MM'}, \quad (5.3.13)$$

which becomes

$$\sum_m C(l, s, j; m, M - m, M)C(l, s, j'; m, M - m, M) = \delta_{jj'}, \qquad (5.3.14)$$

$$\sum_j C(l, s, j; m, M - m, M)C(l, s, j; m', M - m', M') = \delta_{mm'} \delta_{MM'}. \qquad (5.3.15)$$

There are, furthermore, conditions on the range of their parameters; for instance, l, s, and j must be numbers which form the sides of a triangle, also $j_{min} \leq j \leq j_{max}$, where $j_{min} = |l - s|$ and $j_{max} = l + s$. (The reader wishing a more detailed discussion of these conditions is referred to [R.3,4] above.)

We now seek a function $\Psi_s(\mathbf{r}; \mathbf{k}, s, \nu)$, which obeys an asymptotic condition equivalent to (5.1.8). To this end we formally reexpress the plane wave $e^{i(\mathbf{k}, \mathbf{r})}$ expansion in terms of the functions $\mathscr{Y}_{jls}^M(\hat{\mathbf{r}})$ and $\mathscr{Z}_j^M(l, s, \nu; \hat{\mathbf{k}}) \equiv i^{-l} \chi_\nu^{s\dagger} \cdot \mathscr{Y}_{jls}^M(\hat{\mathbf{k}})$. (Here $\chi_\nu^{s\dagger}$ is the Hermitian adjoint to χ_ν^s, and the "dot" indicates an inner product in the "spin space" [N.13, p. 445].) First, however, we must obtain representations for the spherical harmonics $Y_l^m(\hat{\mathbf{r}})$, and $Y_l^m(\hat{\mathbf{k}})$ in terms of the functions $\mathscr{Y}_{jls}^M(\hat{\mathbf{r}})$ and $\mathscr{Z}_j^M(l, s, \nu; \hat{\mathbf{k}})$. This may be done by employing the orthogonality relations for the Clebsch–Gordan coefficients (5.3.13)–(5.3.15). One obtains from (5.3.15), that

$$\sum_{j, M} \mathscr{Y}_{jls}^M(\hat{\mathbf{k}})C(l, s, j; m, \nu, M)$$

$$= \sum_{j, M} C(l, s, j; m, \nu, M) \sum_{m', \nu'} C(l, s, j; m', \nu', M)Y_l^{m'}(\hat{\mathbf{k}})\chi_{\nu'}^s$$

$$= \sum_{m', \nu'} \left\{ \sum_{j, M} C(l, s, j; m, \nu, M)C(l, s, j; m', \nu', M) \right\} Y_l^{m'}(\hat{\mathbf{k}})\chi_{\nu'}^s$$

$$= \chi_\nu^s Y_l^m(\hat{\mathbf{k}}), \qquad (5.3.16)$$

and that

$$\overline{Y_l^m}(\hat{\mathbf{k}}) = (-i)^l \sum_{j, M} \overline{\mathscr{Z}_j^M}(l, s, \nu; \hat{\mathbf{k}})C(l, s, j; m, \nu, M). \qquad (5.3.17)$$

Using (5.3.16) and (5.3.17) we may expand the plane wave in terms of the $\mathscr{Y}_{jls}^M(\hat{\mathbf{r}})$ and $\mathscr{Z}_j^M(l, s, \nu; \hat{\mathbf{k}})$ as

$$\Psi_0(\mathbf{k}, \mathbf{r}; s, \nu) \equiv \chi_\nu^s e^{i(\mathbf{k}, \mathbf{r})}$$

$$= 4\pi \sum_{l=0}^{\infty} \sum_{j, M} j_l(kr)\mathscr{Y}_{jls}^M(\hat{\mathbf{r}})\overline{\mathscr{Z}_j^M}(lsv; \hat{\mathbf{k}}). \qquad (5.3.18)$$

If the Hamiltonian is invariant under rotations then it commutes with the components of the total angular momentum and also with $\mathbf{J}^2$ itself; consequently, j and M are good quantum numbers in this case [N.13, p. 446]. One then expects to find a general representation for the full-wave function $\Psi(\mathbf{r}; k, s, \nu)$ in the form

$$\Psi(\mathbf{r}; k, s, \nu) = \frac{4\pi}{kr}\left\{\sum_l \sum_{j,M}\left[\sum_{l',s'} \Psi^j_{ls,l's'}(k, r)\mathscr{Y}^M_{jl's'}(\hat{\mathbf{r}})\right]\overline{\mathscr{Z}_j{}^M(lsv; \hat{\mathbf{k}})}\right\}. \qquad (5.3.19)$$

Newton [N.13, p. 446] gives such a representation for incoming $^{(+)}$ and outgoing $^{(-)}$ solutions, where the radial parts are seen to satisfy the Lippmann–Schwinger integral equations

$$\Psi^{j(\pm)}_{l's',ls}(k, r) = krj(kr)\,\delta_{ll'}\,\delta_{ss'}$$
$$+ \sum_{l''s''}\int_0^\infty dr'\; G^{\pm}_{l'}(k; r, r')\mathscr{V}^j_{l's',l''s''}(r')\Psi^{j(\pm)}_{l''s'',ls}(k, r'), \qquad (5.3.20)$$

with

$$\mathscr{V}^j_{l's',l''s''}(r) = 2\mu\int d\Omega\;\overline{\mathscr{Y}^M_{jl's'}(\hat{\mathbf{r}})}\mathbf{H}'\mathscr{Y}^M_{jl''s''}(\hat{\mathbf{r}}),$$

and where the integration is over the unit sphere. $\mathbf{H}'$ is the interaction Hamiltonian, and the $G_l{}^{\pm}(k, r, r')$ are the Fourier components of the free Green's function given by [N.13, p. 298]

$$G_l{}^{\pm}(k, r, r') = \begin{cases} -e^{\mp i\pi l}rj_l(kr)W_l^{(\pm)}(kr'); & r < r' \\ -e^{\mp i\pi l}r'j_l(kr')W_l^{(\pm)}(kr); & r > r', \end{cases} \qquad (5.3.21)$$

where

$$W_l^{(+)}(z) = ie^{i\pi l}\left(\frac{\pi z}{2}\right)^{1/2} H^{(1)}_{l+\frac{1}{2}}(z) = ie^{i\pi l}zh_l{}^{(1)}(z),$$

$W_l^{(-)}(z) \equiv W_l^{(+)}(-z)$ and $H_\nu^{(1)}(z)$ is a Hankel function of the first kind [N.13, p. 38]. (For a discussion of Hankel functions see [E.6, Vol. II, p. 4]. The Fourier component $G_l{}^{\pm}(k; r, r')$ is known to satisfy the asymptotic condition [N.13, p. 299]

$$G_l{}^{\pm}(k; r, r') \approx -e^{\mp i\pi l/2}rj_l(kr')e^{\pm ikr} \quad \text{as} \quad r \to \infty, \qquad (5.3.22)$$

from which one may obtain the asymptotic components of the wave function, and hence the scattering amplitude. Proceeding as was done in Section 5.1 one may separate the outgoing part of the wave function and obtain a representation for the scattering amplitude in the form [N.13, p. 447]

$$A(\mathbf{k}', s', v'; \mathbf{k}, s, v) = 4\pi \sum_{j, M, l, l'} \mathscr{Y}_j{}^M(l's'v'; \hat{\mathbf{k}}) a^j_{l's', ls}(k) \overline{\mathscr{Y}_j{}^M(lsv; \mathbf{k})} \quad (5.3.23)$$

with the partial-wave amplitudes

$$a^j_{l's', ls} = \frac{S^j_{l's', ls} - \delta_{ll'}\,\delta_{ss'}}{2ik},$$

where

$$S^j_{l's', ls} = \delta_{ll'}\,\delta_{ss'} - 2ik^{-1} \sum_{l''s''} \int_0^\infty dr\; kr j_l(kr) \mathscr{V}^j_{l's', l''s''}(r) \Psi^{(+)}_{l''s'', ls}(k, r). \quad (5.3.24)$$

This brings us again to the point where the integral operator method may be employed in the theory of potential scattering. We wish to investigate the analytic properties of $A(\mathbf{k}'; \mathbf{k}) \equiv A(\mathbf{k}', s', v'; \mathbf{k}, s, v)$ in terms of the six complex variables $\mathbf{k}$ and $\mathbf{k}'$. This can clearly be accomplished by recalling the integral operator $\mathbf{B}_3$ and forming a suitable modification of it. From (2.2.2) we realize that

$$i^{m-l} e(l, m) Y_l{}^m(\hat{\mathbf{k}}) = \mathbf{B}_3[\tau^{-l-1}\zeta^m],$$

where

$$e(l, m) = \left(\frac{4\pi(l+m)!\,(l-m)!}{(2l+1)[l!]^2} \right)^{1/2},$$

and

$$\tau = \cos\theta + \frac{i}{2}\sin\theta \left[\frac{\zeta}{e^{i\varphi}} + \frac{e^{i\varphi}}{\zeta} \right].$$

Hence, series expansions of the form (5.3.23) may be generated from functions of four complex variables of the form

$$g(\tau, \sigma; \zeta, \eta) = \sum_{l=0}^{\infty} \sum_{l'=0}^{\infty} \sum_{m=-l}^{+l} \sum_{m'=-l'}^{+l'} b^j_{l's'ls}(k; m, v, m', v') \tau^{-l'-1} (\bar{\sigma})^{-l-1} \zeta^{m'} \eta^m, \quad (5.3.25)$$

where

$$b^j_{l's'ls}(k; m, \nu, m', \nu') \equiv \frac{i^{-(m'+m)}}{e(l', m')e(l, m)} \sum_{j, M} a^j_{l's'ls}(k) C(l's'j; m'\nu'M) C(lsj; m\nu M), \qquad (5.3.26)$$

and

$$\sigma = \cos\theta' + \frac{i}{2}\sin\theta' \left[\frac{\eta}{e^{i\varphi'}} + \frac{e^{i\varphi'}}{\eta}\right],$$

by an iterated, Bergman integral operator, i.e.,

$$\mathbf{B}_3 \mathbf{B}_3'[g] = A(\mathbf{k}', s', \nu'; \mathbf{k}, s, \nu). \qquad (5.3.27)$$

Here the operator $\mathbf{B}_3'$ operates on the primed variables and their auxiliary variables, σ and η.

It is clear how we may generalize previous results to handle this case. From Theorems 2.2.1 and 1.3.4 we immediately obtain the following:

Theorem 5.3.1 *Let $A(k', s', \nu'; k, s, \nu) = \mathbf{B}_3 \mathbf{B}_3' g$ be a scattering amplitude generated from the holomorphic function $g(\tau, \sigma; \zeta, \eta)$. Furthermore, let the singularity manifold of g have the global representation,*

$$\Phi(\tau, \sigma; \zeta, \eta) \equiv S(k, \hat{\mathbf{k}}, \hat{\mathbf{k}}'; \zeta, \eta) = 0,$$

where $\hat{\mathbf{k}}$ and $\hat{\mathbf{k}}'$ are unit momentum vectors with the angular coordinates θ, φ and θ', φ'. Then $A(\mathbf{k}'; \mathbf{k})$ is regular at all points $(k, \hat{\mathbf{k}}, \hat{\mathbf{k}}') \in \mathbb{C}^5$, which do not lie on the coincidence,

$$\mathfrak{S} \cap \mathfrak{S}_1 \cap \mathfrak{S}_2, \qquad (5.3.28)$$

where $\mathfrak{S} \equiv \{k, \hat{\mathbf{k}}, \hat{\mathbf{k}}' \mid S(k, \hat{\mathbf{k}}, \hat{\mathbf{k}}'; \zeta, \eta) = 0; (\zeta, \eta) \in \mathbb{C}^2\}$,

$$\mathfrak{S}_1 \equiv \left\{k, \hat{\mathbf{k}}, \hat{\mathbf{k}}' \,\middle|\, \frac{\partial S}{\partial \zeta} = 0; (\zeta, \eta) \in \mathbb{C}^2\right\},$$
$$\mathfrak{S}_2 \equiv \left\{k, \hat{\mathbf{k}}, \hat{\mathbf{k}}' \,\middle|\, \frac{\partial S}{\partial \eta} = 0; (\zeta, \eta) \in \mathbb{C}^2\right\}. \qquad (5.3.29)$$

Newton [N.13, p. 449], gives a much more simplified representation of the scattering amplitude (5.3.23) in terms of Wigner's rotation matrices. In the expression (5.3.23) both vectors **k** and **k**′ are represented in the same coordinate frame. By choosing **k** (the momentum of the incoming beam), as the new z-axis, and an arbitrary but fixed direction normal to **k** as the new x-axis, one determines a more suitable coordinate frame in which the scattering amplitude has the expansion,

$$\begin{aligned} A(\mathbf{k}', s', v'; \mathbf{k}, s, v) &= A^h(\theta, \varphi; s'v', sv) \\ &= \sum_j (2j+1) a^j(s'v', sv) D^j_{v'v}(\varphi, \theta - \varphi) \\ &= e^{i(v-v')\varphi} \sum_j (2j+1) a^j(s'v', sv)\, d^j_{v'v}(\theta), \end{aligned} \tag{5.3.30}$$

where the partial amplitudes are now given by

$$\begin{aligned} &a^j(s'v', sv) \\ &= \sum_{l,l'} \frac{[(2l+1)(2l'+1)]^{1/2}}{2j+1} \cdot C(l', s', j; 0, v', v') a^j_{l's', ls} C(l, s, j; 0, v, v) \\ &= (-1)^{s+s'+v+v'} \sum_{l,l'} C(j, s', l'; -v', v', 0) a^j_{l's', ls} \cdot C(j, s, l; -v, v, 0). \end{aligned} \tag{5.3.31}$$

The functions $d^j_{v'v}(\theta)$ are the Wigner simplified rotation matrices and are given by [N.13, p. 449]

$$\begin{aligned} d^j_{vv'}(\theta) &= \left[\frac{(j+v')!(j-v')!}{(j+v)!(j-v)!}\right]^{1/2} \left(\cos\frac{\theta}{2}\right)^{v'+v} \left(\sin\frac{\theta}{2}\right)^{v'-v} \cdot P^{(v'-v,\, v'+v)}_{j-v'}(\cos\theta) \\ &= (-1)^{v'-v}\, d^j_{v'v}(\theta) \qquad \text{for} \quad v' \geq v. \end{aligned} \tag{5.3.32}$$

We may further simplify the representation, for the purpose of using the integral operator method, to the form

$$A(\mathbf{k}', \mathbf{k}) = e^{i(v-v')\varphi} \left(\cos\frac{\theta}{2}\right)^{v'+v} \left(\sin\frac{\theta}{2}\right)^{v'-v} \sum_j b_j P^{(v'-v,\, v'+v)}_{j-v'}(\cos\theta),$$

with

$$b_j \equiv a^j(s'v', sv)(2j+1) \left[\frac{(j+v')!(j-v')!}{(j+v)!(j-v)!}\right]^{1/2} \tag{5.3.33}$$

Hence, the study of the scattering amplitude $A(\mathbf{k}', \mathbf{k})$ in $\mathbb{C}^5$ can be reduced to a study of the functions

$$A^{(\nu,\nu')}(k, \xi) \equiv \sum_j b_j(k) P_{j-\nu'}^{(\nu'-\nu,\,\nu'+\nu)}(\xi),$$

for $(k, \xi) \in \mathbb{C}^2$. The functions $A^{(\nu,\nu')}(k, \xi)$, however, can be investigated using a simple modification of the operator $\mathbf{G}_{\mu\nu}$ (4.1.21).

Let $g(\sigma) = \sigma^{-[\nu']} f(\sigma) = \sigma^{-[\nu']} \sum_{n=0}^{\infty} \sigma^n a_n$, where the sum is taken over integers. Then by Eqs. (4.1.19), (4.1.20) we have, since $j - \nu' = [j] - [\nu']$ is an integer, that†

$$\begin{aligned} A^{(\nu,\nu')}(k, \xi) &= \mathbf{G}^{(\nu,\nu')} g \\ &\equiv \frac{1}{2\pi i} \int_{|\zeta|=\varepsilon} g(\sigma)\left(1 + \zeta\left(\frac{\xi+1}{\xi-1}\right)^{1/2}\right)^{\nu'-\nu} \left(1 + \zeta\left(\frac{\xi-1}{\xi+1}\right)^{1/2}\right)^{\nu'+\nu} d\zeta, \end{aligned} \tag{5.3.34}$$

with $\sigma = (\xi + \frac{1}{2}(\xi^2 - 1)^{1/2}[\zeta + 1/\zeta])$. Here, the path of integration is taken sufficiently small as in the case of $\mathbf{G}_{\mu\nu}$; indeed ε may be chosen so that

$$\varepsilon < \min\left\{\left|\frac{\xi+1}{\xi-1}\right|^{1/2}, \left|\frac{\xi-1}{\xi+1}\right|^{1/2}\right\}.$$

The investigation of the singularities of the above integral then depends on the usual process of continuing along a curve in the analytic plane $k = k_0$, while one deforms the contour $|\zeta| = \varepsilon$ to avoid encroaching singularities. One obtains the following result:

Theorem 5.3.2 *Let $A^{(\nu,\nu')}(k, \xi)$ be a scattering amplitude generated by the integral operator, $\mathbf{G}^{(\nu,\nu')}$, acting on $g(\sigma)$. Furthermore, let $\sigma = \alpha(k)$ be the only singularity of $g(\sigma)$ ($\alpha \neq 0$). Then $A^{(\nu,\nu')}(k, \xi)$ is singular at the point ξ in the $k = k_0$ analytic plane, if and only if $\xi = \frac{1}{2}[\alpha(k_0) + 1/\alpha(k_0)]$.*

The proof of this result parallels the author's discussion of the case of GBSP functions, and the reader is directed to that work. We remark, that this result is the analog of Nehari's theorem (5.1.1) [N.6] for Legendre series (which is relevant to the zero spin case); however, our method of proof relies on the *envelope method* rather than Hadamard's method. Using the *envelope method*, we compute the eliminant between

† The notation $[j]$ means the largest integer such that $j \geq [j]$.

$$S(\xi, \zeta) \equiv \frac{\zeta^2}{2}(1-\xi^2)^{1/2} + \zeta(\xi - \alpha) + \tfrac{1}{2}(1-\xi^2)^{1/2} = 0$$

and

$$\partial S/\partial \zeta = 0,$$

which yields $(\xi - \alpha)^2 + 1 - \xi^2 = 0$, and hence our result.

Remark A further generalization of the scattering problem is provided by the abstract perturbation formulation due to Kuroda [K.8]. In his development of the scattering problem it is shown that the Weinstein determinant [W.5,16] is closely related to the change of bound-state energies by perturbations in the scattering potential.

4. *Inelastic Scattering and Multichannel Theory*

In a series of papers Newton and Jost [N.J.1], Newton [N.9,10], and Newton and Fonda [N.F.1] have used a matrix formulation of the multichannel theory to investigate various inelastic scattering phenomena. In this section we sketch this method as it was formulated by Newton [N.9] to apply to the case, say, of an electron being scattered by a hydrogen atom with infinitely heavy nucleus. Such a system satisfies the two-particle Schrödinger equation,

$$\left(\frac{1}{2m_1}\Delta_1 + \frac{1}{2m_2}\Delta_2 + V_{01} + V_{02} + V_{12}\right)\Psi(\mathbf{r}_1, \mathbf{r}_2) = E\Psi(\mathbf{r}_1, \mathbf{r}_2), \quad (5.4.1)$$

where the Δ_k $(k = 1, 2)$ are the Laplacian operators for the kth particle, and the V_{ij} are the respective potentials between particles 1, 2 and the nucleus (0). Here we have set $\hbar = 1$ as before; however, since different masses will occur in the channels due to the inelastic scattering we do not set $m_1 = m_2 = 1$.

The solutions of the hydrogen atom by itself are well known and satisfy the partial differential equation

$$(\Delta_2 + V_{02})\Psi_\alpha(\mathbf{r}_2) = E_\alpha \Psi_\alpha(\mathbf{r}_2), \quad (5.4.2)$$

where the E_α are the eigenvalues. Newton [N.9] uses this system of solutions $\Psi_\alpha(\mathbf{r}_2)$ in order to reduce (5.4.1) to a finite system† of coupled, partial differential equations in the $\mathbf{r}_1$-variables,

† The reader is directed to the above mentioned work for a discussion of why one can truncate the infinite system.

$$\sum_{\beta} \mathbf{H}_{\beta\alpha} \varphi_\beta(\mathbf{r}_1) = \varphi_\alpha(\mathbf{r}_1)\varepsilon_\alpha, \tag{5.4.3}$$

where

$$\varepsilon_\alpha = E - E_\alpha,$$

$$\mathbf{H}_{\beta\alpha} = \left(\frac{1}{2m_1}\Delta_1 + V_{01}\right)\delta_{\beta\alpha} + \int d\mathbf{r}_2\, \Psi_\beta(\mathbf{r}_2)V_{12}(|\mathbf{r}_1 - \mathbf{r}_2|)\overline{\Psi_\alpha(\mathbf{r}_2)},$$

$$\varphi_\alpha(\mathbf{r}_1) = \int d\mathbf{r}_2\, \Psi_\alpha(\mathbf{r}_2)\Psi(\mathbf{r}_1, \mathbf{r}_2).$$

By expanding $\varphi_\alpha(\mathbf{r}_1)$ in terms of the spherical harmonics $Y_l^m(\hat{\mathbf{r}}_1)$, Eq. (5.4.3) may be further reduced to the system of ordinary differential equations [N.9],

$$-\tfrac{1}{2}\varphi''_{\alpha lm}(r_1)M_\alpha^{-1} + l(l+1)r_1^{-2}M_\alpha^{-1} + \sum_{\beta, l', m'} \varphi_{\beta, l', m'}(r_1)\mathscr{V}_{\beta l'm', \alpha lm}(r_1) = \varphi_{\alpha lm}(r_1)\varepsilon_\alpha, \tag{5.4.4}$$

where

$$\mathscr{V}_{\beta l'm', \alpha lm}(r_1) = \int_0^\infty dr_2\, r_2^{\,2} R_\alpha(r_2)R_\beta(r_2)W_{\beta l'm', \alpha lm}(r_1, r_2),$$

and

$$W_{\beta l'm', \alpha lm}(r_1, r_2) = \int d\Omega_1\, d\Omega_2\, \overline{Y_l^m}(\hat{\mathbf{r}}_1)V_{12}(|\mathbf{r}_1 - \mathbf{r}_2|)\overline{Y_{L_\alpha}^{M_\alpha}}(\hat{\mathbf{r}}_2)Y_{L_\beta}^{M_\beta}(\hat{\mathbf{r}}_2).$$

The above systems of equations may be rewritten as matrix ordinary differential equations; for instance (5.4.4) takes the form,

$$-\tfrac{1}{2}\varphi'' M^{-1} + \varphi\mathscr{V} = \varphi\varepsilon, \tag{5.4.5}$$

where M^{-1} is the inverse of the diagonal matrix $M = (M_\alpha \delta_{\alpha\beta})$, and $\mathscr{V}$ is a matrix including the centrifugal terms, $[l(l+1)r_1^{-2}M_\alpha^{-1}]$. As in previous sections one seeks a solution which has the proper asymptotic behavior. Here, we shall require that the matrix solution, φ, to (5.4.5) satisfies the matrix condition [N.9, p. 33],

$$\varphi \sim e^{i\mathbf{K}\cdot\mathbf{r}} + \frac{A(\theta, \varphi)}{r} e^{iKr}, \tag{5.4.6}$$

where **K**, and K are diagonal matrices with vector and scalar entries respectively. From our decompositions, (5.4.3) and (5.4.4), it is clear that the *matrix* scattering amplitude will have a representation of the form

$$A(\theta, \varphi) = 4\pi \sum_{lml'm'} \overline{Y_l^{\,m}(\hat{K})} a_{lm,\,l'm'}\, Y_{l'}^{m'}(\hat{K}'), \tag{5.4.7}$$

where $\hat{K}$ and $\hat{K}'$ are diagonal matrices with unit vector entries. The investigation of the analytic properties of the matrix scattering amplitude is then seen to be reduced to the study of matrix holomorphic functions. Indeed, if $g(\tau, \sigma; \zeta, \eta)$ has the Taylor series development

$$g(\tau, \sigma; \zeta, \eta) = \sum_{l=0}^{\infty} \sum_{l'=0}^{\infty} \sum_{m=-l}^{+l} \sum_{m'=-l'}^{+l'} b_{lml'm'} \bar{\tau}^{-l-1} \sigma^{-l'-1} \zeta^m \eta^{m'},$$

with $b_{lml'm'} = [a_{lml'm'}][e(l, m)e(l', m')]^{-1}$, where $a_{lml'm'}$ and $b_{lml'm'}$ are matrices, then the matrix scattering amplitude (5.4.7) is given by

$$A(\theta, \varphi) = \mathbf{B}_3 \mathbf{B}_3{}' g.$$

Theorem 5.3.1 may then be applied to the matrix entries of $A(\theta, \varphi)$ and $g(\tau, \sigma; \zeta, \eta)$. One obtains, in this way, a complete function theory for the case of the inelastic scattering amplitudes.

5. *Relativistic Scattering*

The approach that was used to study nonrelativistic scattering in the preceding sections depended on a quantum mechanical model called potential scattering. The reader will recall that for this model we asked that the total wave function (incident plus scattered wave) satisfy Schrödinger's equation and the outgoing Sommerfeld condition. From this solution we were then able to extract the scattering amplitude as a certain coefficient in the asymptotic expansion of the solution. Our interest was primarily in the analytic properties of this scattering amplitude as a function of the two complex variables k and ξ. This case we were able to investigate with relative ease because a partial differential equation provides us with a means of analytically continuing its solutions.

For the case of relativistic scattering the formulation of the problem is not so simple. Schrödinger's equation is no longer applicable and we must use a quantum field-theoretical model. The approach we shall use is essentially an *axiomatic field theory* where one postulates that the quantum field has certain rather fundamental properties and attempts to proceed from there. We shall ask that the scattering amplitude obey certain analyticity requirements known as the *Mandelstam hypothesis* and certain boundary conditions embodied in the concept called *unitarity*. However, before proceeding with a direct mathematical formulation we wish to introduce some new concepts and notations regarding the physical problem.

In what follows we shall only consider the case of *elastic* two-body interactions, i.e., where two particles (1) and (2) interact, conserving both energy and momentum, to produce two other particles (3) and (4). We shall, furthermore, assume that the particles involved are always *spinless*. We shall refer to p_1, p_2, p_3, p_4, and m_1, m_2, m_3, m_4 as the *four-momenta* and masses of the respective particles. We indicate schematically this scattering phenomena in Fig. 5 where we have represented all of the particles as incoming. It is

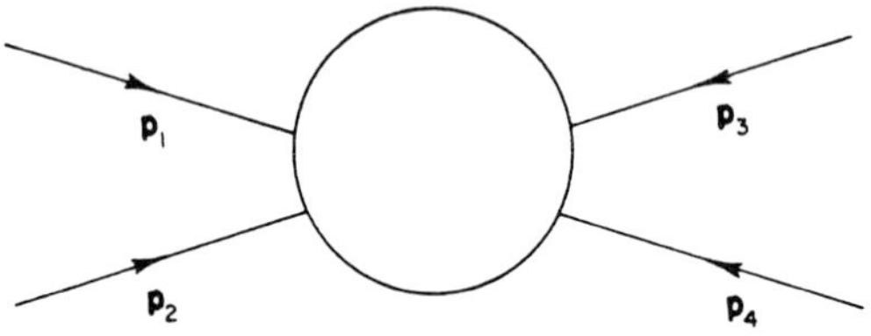

FIGURE 5

convenient for our discussion to introduce certain new variables s, t, u, which are traditionally defined to be

$$
\begin{aligned}
s &= \|p_1 + p_2\|^2 = \|p_3 + p_4\|^2, \\
t &= \|p_1 - p_3\|^2 = \|p_2 - p_4\|^2, \\
u &= \|p_1 - p_4\|^2 = \|p_2 - p_3\|^2.
\end{aligned}
\tag{5.5.1}
$$

The first of these equations states that the four-momentum is conserved, i.e., convervation of energy and the three-dimensional momentum. If the masses m_1 and m_2 are equal then in the center-of-mass coordinate system one has

$$t = \|p_1 - p_3\|^2 = (p_1{}^0 - p_3{}^0)^2 - |\mathbf{p}_1 - \mathbf{p}_3|^2 = -|\mathbf{p}_1 - \mathbf{p}_3|^2$$

since the energies $p_1{}^0$ and $p_3{}^0$ are equal.† Hence, in this coordinate system we have that $(-t)$ is the square of the momentum transfer between the particles (1) and (3). Likewise, when m_1 and m_2 are equal, the variable $(-u)$

† The norm indicated here is the Minkowski norm with

$$\|p\|^2 \equiv (p^{(0)})^2 - (p^{(1)})^2 - (p^{(2)})^2 - (p^{(3)})^2 = (p^{(0)})^2 - |\mathbf{p}|^2.$$

may be considered as the momentum transfer between particles (1) and (4). For the purposes of exposition, and for illustrating how the integral operator methods may be used in relativistic scattering, we shall consider in what follows that $m_1 = m_2 = m_3 = m_4 = m$.

One then has

$$s = \|p_1 + p_2\|^2 = (p_1^{(0)} + p_2^{(0)})^2 + |\mathbf{p}_1 + \mathbf{p}_2|^2 = 4(k^2 + m^2), \quad (5.5.2)$$

where k is the *center-of-mass momentum*. Likewise, we have for t and u that

$$\begin{aligned} t = -|\mathbf{p}_1 - \mathbf{p}_3|^2 &= -|\mathbf{p}_1|^2 - |\mathbf{p}_3|^2 + 2\mathbf{p}_1 \cdot \mathbf{p}_3 \\ &= -2k^2(1 - \cos\theta), \end{aligned} \quad (5.5.3)$$

and

$$\begin{aligned} u = -|\mathbf{p}_1 - \mathbf{p}_4|^2 &= -|\mathbf{p}_1|^2 - |\mathbf{p}_4|^2 + 2\mathbf{p}_1 \cdot \mathbf{p}_4 \\ &= -2k^2(1 - \cos[\pi - \theta]) \\ &= -2k^2(1 + \cos\theta). \end{aligned} \quad (5.5.4)$$

Here θ is taken to be the angle between the three-dimensional momenta $\mathbf{p}_1$ and $\mathbf{p}_3$, i.e., the *scattering angle*. In the study of nonrelativistic scattering using the potential scattering model we were concerned with the study of the analytic properties of the scattering amplitude $A(k, \cos\theta)$ in the space of the two complex variables k and ξ. According to Mandelstam's hypothesis, the relativistic scattering amplitude is a function of s, t, u, and by using the identities (5.5.2)–(5.5.4) it also becomes a function of k and ξ,

$$A(k, \xi) \equiv \Phi(4[k^2 + m^2], -2k^2[1 - \xi], -2k^2[1 + \xi]). \quad (5.5.5)$$

The first part of Mandelstam's hypothesis is that the scattering amplitude $\Phi(s, t, u)$ is a holomorphic function of s, t, and u, whose sole singularities are either polar points or ramification points lying on analytic planes of the following types:

$$\begin{aligned} &(i)\ s = \operatorname{Re}[s_0], && (t, u) \in \mathbb{C}^2 \\ &(ii)\ t = \operatorname{Re}[t_0], && (s, u) \in \mathbb{C}^2 \\ &(iii)\ u = \operatorname{Re}[u_0], && (s, t) \in \mathbb{C}^2, \end{aligned} \quad (5.5.6)$$

and where the ramification points have the associated cuts

$$s \geq \mathrm{Re}[s_1], \quad (t, u) \in \mathbb{C}^2, \qquad \text{and} \qquad s \leq \mathrm{Re}[s_2], \quad (t, u) \in \mathbb{C}^2,$$

etc. In other words, the singular points are not points where s, t, and u are simultaneously complex. This hypothesis was suggested by perturbation theory calculations [O.F.1, p. 80] and because singularities of this type were seen to occur both as bound-state and threshold (which indicate the production of particles) type singularities. The second part of Mandelstam's hypothesis is that $\Phi(s, t, u)$ has a representation (in the case of elastic scattering) as a Cauchy integral of the form

$$\begin{aligned}\Phi(s, t, u) = {} & \frac{1}{\pi^2}\int_{4m^2}^{\infty}\int_{4m^2}^{\infty}\frac{ds'\,dt'\,\Phi_{st}(s', t')}{(s-s')(t-t')} \\ & + \frac{1}{\pi^2}\int_{4m^2}^{\infty}\int_{4m^2}^{\infty}\frac{ds'\,du'\,\Phi_{su}(s', u')}{(s'-s)(u'-u)} \\ & + \frac{1}{\pi^2}\int_{4m^2}^{\infty}\int_{4m^2}^{\infty}\frac{dt'\,du'\,\Phi_{tu}(t', u')}{(t'-t)(u'-u)},\end{aligned} \tag{5.5.7}$$

where the *density functions* Φ_{st}, Φ_{su}, Φ_{tu} are all taken to be the same because of the *crossing symmetry*. (A particle on one side of the scattering interaction may be replaced by its *antiparticle* on the other side.)

Let us denote the scattering amplitude as $\hat{T}(p_1, p_2, p_3, p_4)$ where p_1, p_2 are the incoming momenta and p_3, p_4 are the outgoing momenta (Fig. 6). Then according to Omnes [O.1] and Zimmerman [Z.2] the unitarity of the S-matrix implies that $\hat{T}(p_1, p_2, p_3, p_4)$ satisfies the following integral condition,

$$\begin{aligned}\mathrm{Im}\ \hat{T}(p_1, p_2, p_3, p_4) = {} & \tfrac{1}{2}\int d^4q_1\,\theta(q_1{}^0)\,\delta(\|q_1\|^2 - m^2) \\ & \times \int d^4q_2\,\theta(q_2{}^0)\,\delta(\|q_2\|^2 - m^2)\,\delta(p_1 + p_2 - q_1 - q_2) \\ & \times \hat{T}(p_1, p_2, q_1, q_2)\hat{T}^*(q_1, q_2, p_3, p_4),\end{aligned} \tag{5.5.8}$$

in the elastic region, $4m^2 \leq S \leq 16m^2$. Here the integration is over the two particle four-space, and the symbols $\theta(q)$, and $\delta(q)$ refer to the unit and Dirac measures respectively.

The Mandelstam hypothesis says that $\hat{T}(p_1, p_2, p_3, p_4)$ is the boundary value of a holomorphic function of s, t, and u. Consequently, $\hat{T}(p_1, p_2, p_3, p_4)$ is a function of the form $\hat{T}(p_1, p_2, p_3, p_4) = T(\|p_1 + p_2\|^2, -|\mathbf{p}_1 - \mathbf{p}_3|^2, -|\mathbf{p}_1 - \mathbf{p}_4|^2) \equiv T(s, t, u)$. If $\Phi(s, t, u)$ is this holomorphic function (defined in a domain with the cuts (5.5.6)), then one has

$$T(s, t, u) = \lim_{\varepsilon \to 0^+} \Phi(s + i\varepsilon, t, u), \tag{5.5.9}$$

where $s \geq 4m^2$, and $0 \leq -(t+u) \leq s - 4m^2$. The crossing symmetry implies similar limits hold with respect to t and u.

If we introduce the integration parameters,

$$\begin{aligned} t' &= -|\mathbf{q}_1 - \mathbf{p}_1|, \qquad u' = -|\mathbf{q}_1 - \mathbf{p}_2|, \\ t'' &= -|\mathbf{q}_1 - \mathbf{p}_3|, \qquad u'' = -|\mathbf{q}_1 - \mathbf{p}_4|, \end{aligned} \tag{5.5.10}$$

the unitarity integral may be rewritten as

$$\begin{aligned} \operatorname{Im} \Phi(s, t, u) = \int d^4 q_1 \int d^4 q_2 \, \theta(q_1{}^0)\, \delta(\|q_1\|^2 - m^2) \theta(q_2{}^0)\, \delta(\|q_2\|^2 - m^2) \\ \times \Phi^*(s, t'', u'')\Phi(s, t', u')\, \delta^4(p_1 + p_2 - q_1 - q_2). \end{aligned} \tag{5.5.11}$$

This expression may in turn be simplified by replacing the measures $\theta(q_i{}^0)\, \delta(\|q_i\|^2 - m^2)$ by $\frac{1}{2}(|\mathbf{q}_i|^2 + m^2)^{-1/2}\, \delta(q_i{}^0 - [|\mathbf{q}_i|^2 + m^2]^{1/2})$, $(i = 1, 2)$ and performing the $dq_1{}^0\, d^4 q_2$ integration in the center-of-mass coordinate frame, $\mathbf{p}_1 + \mathbf{p}_2 = 0$. One obtains

$$\begin{aligned} \operatorname{Im} \Phi(s, t, u) = \tfrac{1}{4} \int d^3 \mathbf{q}_1 (|\mathbf{q}_1|^2 + m^2)^{-1}\, \delta(s^{1/2} - 2[|\mathbf{q}_1|^2 + m^2]^{1/2}) \\ \times \Phi^*(s, t'', u'')\Phi(s, t', u'). \end{aligned}$$

The condition imposed by the Dirac measure is that $s = 4(|\mathbf{q}_1|^2 + m^2)$, i.e., condition (5.5.2). Introducing the scattering angles θ_1, θ_2 by means of $t' = -2|q_1|^2(1 - \cos\theta_1)$, $t'' = -2|q_1|^2(1 - \cos\theta_2)$, we may express the above integral as

$$\begin{aligned} \operatorname{Im} \Phi(s, t, u) = \tfrac{1}{4} \int |\mathbf{q}_1|^2\, d|\mathbf{q}_1|\, \delta(s^{1/2} - 2[|\mathbf{q}_1|^2 + m^2]^{1/2}) \int_{-1}^{+1} d\cos\theta_1 \\ \times \int_0^{2\pi} d\varphi_1\, \Phi(s, -2\,|\mathbf{q}_1|^2(1 - \cos\theta_1), -2|\mathbf{q}_1|^2(1 + \cos\theta_1)) \\ \times \Phi^*(s, -2\,|\mathbf{q}_1|^2(1 - \cos\theta_2), -2\,|\mathbf{q}_1|^2(1 + \cos\theta_2)). \end{aligned}$$

By choosing the z-axis along the direction of the momentum $\mathbf{p}_1$ (Fig. 6) and using the following convention

$$\begin{aligned} \mathbf{p}_3 &= |\mathbf{p}_3|(\sin\theta\cos\varphi, \sin\theta\sin\varphi, \cos\theta) \\ \mathbf{q}_i &= |\mathbf{q}_i|(\sin\theta_i\cos\varphi_i, \sin\theta_i\sin\varphi_i, \cos\theta_i) \qquad (i = 1, 2), \end{aligned}$$

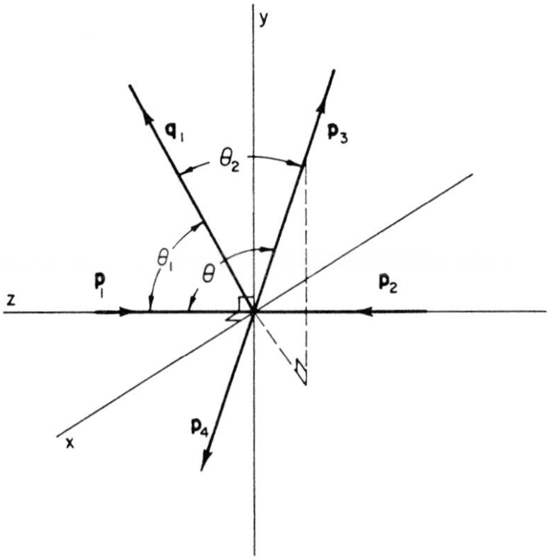

FIGURE 6

we note θ_1 and θ_2 are the scattering angles between the momenta $(\mathbf{q}_1, \mathbf{p}_1)$ and the momenta $(\mathbf{q}_1, \mathbf{p}_3)$, respectively; indeed, one has

$$\cos\theta_2 = \frac{\mathbf{q}_1 \cdot \mathbf{p}_3}{|\mathbf{q}_1| \cdot |\mathbf{p}_3|} = \sin\theta_1 \cos\varphi_1 \sin\theta \cos\varphi$$
$$+ \sin\theta_1 \sin\varphi_1 \sin\theta \sin\varphi + \cos\theta_1 \cos\theta$$
$$= \sin\theta_1 \sin\theta \cos(\varphi_1 - \varphi) + \cos\theta_1 \cos\theta.$$

One may, furthermore, choose the original coordinate system so that in addition to having the z-axis coincide with the $\mathbf{p}_1$ direction, the x-axis coincides with the ray of angle φ. To further simplify our notation we introduce $\Phi(s; \cos\theta) \equiv \Phi(s, -2k^2(1-\cos\theta), -2k^2(1+\cos\theta))$, etc., and recall that in the center-of-mass system that $k = |\mathbf{q}_i| = |\mathbf{p}_i|$ $(i = 1, 2)$. Performing the $d|\mathbf{q}_1|$ integration we obtain

$$\operatorname{Im} \Phi(s; \cos\theta) = \frac{1}{8}\left(\frac{s-4m^2}{s}\right)^{1/2} \int_{-1}^{+1} d\cos\theta_1 \int_0^{2\pi} d\varphi_1 \, \Phi(s; \cos\theta_1)$$
$$\times \Phi^*(s; \cos\theta_1 \cos\theta + \sin\theta_1 \sin\theta \cos\varphi_1). \qquad (5.5.12)$$

By introducing a term

$$\int_{-1}^{+1} d\cos\theta_2 \, \delta(\cos\theta_2 - \cos\theta_1 \cos\theta - \sin\theta_1 \sin\theta \cos\varphi_1)$$

into the integral and integrating with respect to the φ_1-variable one may obtain the alternate representation [A.2, p. 519], [Z.2, p. 260]

$$\operatorname{Im} \Phi(s; \cos\theta) = \frac{1}{8}\left(\frac{s-4m^2}{s}\right)^{1/2} \int_{-1}^{+1} d\cos\theta_1 \int_{-1}^{+1} d\cos\theta_2 \times \frac{\theta[k(\cos\theta, \cos\theta_1, \cos\theta_2)]}{[k(\cos\theta, \cos\theta_1, \cos\theta_2)]^{1/2}} \Phi(s; \cos\theta_1)\Phi^*(s; \cos\theta_2),$$

where

$$k(\cos\theta, \cos\theta_1, \cos\theta_2) = 1 - \cos^2\theta - \cos^2\theta_1 - \cos^2\theta_2 + 2\cos\theta\cos\theta_1\cos\theta_2. \quad (5.5.13)$$

The characteristic function for the negative real axis, θ, serves only to indicate the domain of integration and we may remove it by performing the integration over a chain $\Gamma(\xi)$ whose boundary $\partial\Gamma(\xi)$ is given by the characteristic function to be,

$$\partial\Gamma(\xi) \equiv \{(\xi_1, \xi_2) \mid 1 - \xi_1{}^2 - \xi_2{}^2 - \xi^2 + 2\xi_1\xi_2\xi = 0;\ \xi\text{-fixed};\ (\xi_1, \xi_2) \in \mathbb{R}^2\}$$

and where we have set $\xi_i = \cos\theta_i$ $(i = 1, 2)$ and $\xi = \cos\theta$. We remark that the transition from an iterated integral to a multiple integral over a chain is valid providing the integrand is absolutely integrable. One then has

$$\Phi(s;\xi) - \Phi^*(s;\xi) = \frac{i}{4}\left(\frac{s-m^2}{s}\right)^{1/2} \int_{\Gamma(\xi)} \frac{d\xi_1\, d\xi_2\, \Phi^*(s;\xi_1)\Phi(s;\xi_2)}{(1 - \xi_1{}^2 - \xi_2{}^2 - \xi^2 + 2\xi_1\xi_2\xi)^{1/2}},$$

where $\xi = \cos\theta$, and $(s, \xi) \in [4m^2, 16m^2] \times [-1, +1]$.

For physical reasons [A.2], [A.G.H.1], [S.W.1], [Z.2] it is reasonable to assume that this relationship may be extended in a bicylindrical region $\mathfrak{B}^+ \equiv \mathfrak{D}^+[4m^2, 16m^2] \times \mathcal{N}[-1, +1]$, where $\mathfrak{D}^+[4m^2, 16m^2]$ is a domain in the upper-half s-plane which contains the closed interval $[4m^2, 16m^2]$ as part of its boundary. $\mathcal{N}[-1, +1]$ is a neighborhood of the closed interval $[-1, +1]$. The continuation of the boundary values $\Phi^*(s;\xi)$ on $[4m^2, 16m^2] \times [-1, +1]$ to the bicylinder $\mathfrak{B}^+$, using the rule $\Phi^*(s;\xi) \equiv \Phi(s^*;\xi)$, we denote by $\Phi_2(s;\xi)$. Our unitarity condition then may be written as

$$\Phi(s;\xi) = \Phi_2(s;\xi) + \frac{i}{4}\left(\frac{s-4m^2}{s}\right)^{1/2} \int_{\Gamma(\xi)} \frac{d\xi_1\, d\xi_2\, \Phi_2(s;\xi_1)\Phi(s;\xi_2)}{(1 - \xi_1{}^2 - \xi_2{}^2 - \xi^2 + 2\xi\xi_1\xi_2)^{1/2}}. \quad (5.5.14)$$

dition, $s + t + u = 4m^2$, the function $\Phi(s;\, \xi)$ is seen to be singular only on the sets [Z.2, p. 251],†

$$\mathfrak{L}^{[3]}{}_1 \equiv \{(s, \xi) \mid s \geq 4m^2;\ \xi \in \mathbb{C}^1\}$$
$$\mathfrak{L}^{[3]}{}_2 \equiv \left\{(s, \xi) \mid \xi = \pm\left(1 + \frac{2t}{s - 4m^2}\right),\ t \geq 4m^2;\ s \in \mathbb{C}^1\right\}. \tag{5.5.21}$$

Remark As it is pointed out in [Z.2, p. 252], because of the crossing symmetry, $\Phi(s;\, \xi)$ is an even function of ξ, which is the reason for the negative sign appearing in $\xi = \pm[1 + 2t/(s - 4m^2)]$. Correspondingly, the function $f(s;\, z)$ will be singular on

$$\mathfrak{m}^{[3]}{}_1 \equiv \{(s, z) \mid s \geq 4m^2;\ z \in \mathbb{C}^1\}$$
$$\mathfrak{m}^{[3]}{}_2 \equiv \left\{(s, z) \mid z = \pm\left[1 + \frac{2t}{s - 4m^2} \pm \left(\frac{4t^2}{(s - 4m^2)^2} + \frac{4t}{s - 4m^2}\right)^{1/2}\right],\ t \geq 4m^2;\ s \in \mathbb{C}^1\right\}. \tag{5.5.22}$$

In particular, we consider as possible singularities of $f(s;\, z)$, the analytic sets

$$\mathfrak{m}_{\beta_\mu} = \left\{(s, z) \mid z = \pm\left[1 + \frac{2\beta_\mu}{s - 4m^2} \pm \left(\frac{4\beta_\mu{}^2}{(s - 4m^2)^2} + \frac{4\beta_\mu}{s - 4m^2}\right)^{1/2}\right];\ s \in \mathbb{C}^1\right\},$$
$$\beta_\mu > 4m^2 \quad (\mu \in I). \tag{5.5.23}$$

It may be seen from (5.5.19) that $s = 4m^2$ is a singularity of $f_2(s;\, z)$. To this end, we first compute the coefficients of the powers of z,

$$\phi_{l,\,2}(s) = \phi_l(s)\left[1 + \frac{i\pi}{8}(2l + 1)\phi_l(s)\left(\frac{s - 4m^2}{s}\right)^{1/2}\right]^{-1}. \tag{5.5.24}$$

Next, we wish to show that $\phi_l(s)$ has a square root ramification at $s = 4m^2$ and that $\phi_{l,\,2}(s)$ is $\phi_l(s)$ on the second sheet of the s-plane. Let s^0 be an interior point of the interval $(0, 4m^2)$, and let ε be a small positive number. Then in order to prove that $\phi_{l,\,2}(s)$ is the continuation of $\phi_l(s)$ about its

† The superscript enclosed in brackets indicate the real dimensionality of the set. If no superscripts are used, then the set is an analytic set of codimension one.

square root type branch point we wish to prove $\phi_{l,2}(s^0 - i\varepsilon) = \phi_l(s^0 + i\varepsilon)$ as $\varepsilon \to 0$. From (5.5.24) we obtain at $s = s^0 + i\varepsilon$,

$$\phi_{l,2}(s^0 + i\varepsilon) = \phi_l(s^0 + i\varepsilon)\left[1 + \frac{i\pi}{8}(2l + 1)\phi_l(s^0 + i\varepsilon)\left(\frac{s^0 + i\varepsilon - 4m^2}{s^0 + i\varepsilon}\right)^{1/2}\right]^{-1}. \tag{5.5.25}$$

Likewise, at $s = s^0 - i\varepsilon$ one has

$$\phi_{l,2}(s^0 - i\varepsilon) = \phi_l(s^0 - i\varepsilon)\left[1 + \frac{i\pi}{8}(2l + 1)\phi_l(s^0 - i\varepsilon)\left(\frac{s^0 - i\varepsilon - 4m^2}{s^0 - i\varepsilon}\right)^{1/2}\right]^{-1},$$

which becomes, upon using the continuation condition,

$$\phi_{l,2}(s^0 + i\varepsilon) = \phi_l(s^0 - i\varepsilon) \qquad \text{as} \quad \varepsilon \to 0,$$

$$\phi_{l,2}(s^0 - i\varepsilon) = \phi_{l,2}(s^0 + i\varepsilon) \times \left[1 + \frac{i\pi}{8}(2l + 1)\phi_{l,2}(s^0 + i\varepsilon)(-1)\left(\frac{s^0 + i\varepsilon - 4m^2}{s^0 + i\varepsilon}\right)^{1/2}\right]^{-1}.$$

The minus sign occurring before the square root radical indicates that the branch obtained at $s^0 + i\varepsilon$ corresponds to the second sheet of the Riemann surface. Solving expression (5.5.25) for $\phi_l(s^0 + i\varepsilon)$ one obtains,

$$\phi_l(s^0 + i\varepsilon) = \phi_{l,2}(s^0 + i\varepsilon) \times \left[1 - \frac{i\pi}{8}(2l + 1)\phi_{l,2}(s^0 + i\varepsilon)\left(\frac{s^0 + i\varepsilon - 4m^2}{s^0 + i\varepsilon}\right)^{1/2}\right]^{-1},$$

which, when subtracted from the equation for $\phi_{l,2}(s^0 - i\varepsilon)$, yields

$$\phi_{l,2}(s^0 - i\varepsilon) - \phi_l(s^0 + i\varepsilon) \equiv 0.$$

From the above discussion we realize that for each fixed z, $f_2(s; z)$ is the continuation of $f(s; z)$ onto the second sheet of the Riemann surface, about the square root branch point at $s = 4m^2$, and that $f_2(s^0 - i0; z) \equiv f(s^0 + i0; z)$.

Lemma 5.5.1 *The functions $f(s; z)$ and $f_2(s; z)$ which satisfy* (5.5.19) *and* (5.5.20) *are singular on the analytic set* $\mathfrak{P}_1 \equiv \{(s; z) \mid s = 4m^2;\ z \in \mathbb{C}^1\}$.

Corollary 5.5.2 *The functions $\Phi(s; \xi)$ and $\Phi_2(s; \xi)$, which are related to $f(s; z)$ and $f_2(s; z)$ as described above, are singular on the analytic sets*

$$\mathfrak{L}(4m^2) \equiv \{(s, \xi) \mid s = 4m^2; \xi \in \mathbb{C}^1\},$$

$$\mathfrak{M}(4m^2) \equiv \left\{(s, \xi) \mid \xi = \pm\left(1 + \frac{8m^2}{s - 4m^2}\right); s \in \mathbb{C}^1\right\}.$$

If $\Phi(s, t, u)$ is singular at $s = 4m^2$, then by the crossing symmetry it is also singular at $t = 4m^2$ and $u = 4m^2$. If $f(s; z)$ is singular at $s = 4m^2$, then $\Phi(s; \xi)$ is also singular at $s = 4m^2$. That $\Phi(s; \xi)$ is also singular on $\mathfrak{M}(4m^2)$ follows then from the crossing symmetry and the equations (5.5.2)–(5.5.4).

We now develop a sequence of lemmas which hold for arbitrary functions satisfying (5.5.20) and the crossing symmetry condition.

Lemma 5.5.3 (The First Consistency Condition) *Let $f(s; z)$ and $f_2(s; z)$ be singular only on the analytic sets $\mathfrak{S} \equiv \{(s, z) \mid z = \Psi(s); s \in \mathbb{C}^1\}$ and $\mathfrak{S}_2 \equiv \{(s, z) \mid z = \Psi_2(s); s \in \mathbb{C}^1\}$ respectively. Then $f(s; z)$ and $f_2(s; z)$ are singular on the same set*, i.e., $\mathfrak{S} \equiv \mathfrak{S}_2$.

Proof The right-hand side of (5.5.19) is singular at $\mathfrak{S}$ plus the (possible) singularities due to the integrand. The singularities of the integrand arising from the pinching of the singularities of $f_2(s; z/\zeta)$ and

$$[\zeta^{-1} f(s; \zeta) + 2\, \partial f/\partial\zeta(s; \zeta)]$$

lie on the analytic set

$$\mathfrak{R} \equiv \{(s, z) \mid z = \Psi(s)\Psi_2(s); s \in \mathbb{C}^1\}.$$

Hence the singularities of the right-hand side are contained in the union $\mathfrak{S} \cup \mathfrak{R}$. In order for the singularities of $f_2(s; z)$ to be *consistent* with those of the right-hand side of (5.5.19) we must then have

$$\mathfrak{S}_2 \equiv \{(s, z) \mid z = \Psi_2(s)\} \subset \{(s, z) \mid z = \Psi(s)\Psi_2(s)\} \cup \{(s, z) \mid z = \Psi(s)\} = \mathfrak{R} \cup \mathfrak{S}.$$

This means $\mathfrak{S}_2$ must be one of the prime terms in the decomposition of the analytic set representing the (possible) singularities of the right-hand side. This is clearly impossible unless either $\Psi_2(s) \equiv \Psi(s)$, $\Psi(s) \equiv 1$ or $\Psi_2(s) \equiv 0$. If $\Psi(s) \equiv 1$, then, since this would be an *actual* singularity of $f(s; z)$ we may show by use of (5.5.20) that $f_2(s; z)$ must *also* be singular at $z = 1$. Arguing as above, with the representation (5.5.20), we obtain the following inclusion relation:

$$\mathfrak{S} \subset \mathfrak{S}_2 \cup \{(s, z) \mid z = \Psi_2(s)\Psi(s)\} = \mathfrak{R} \cup \mathfrak{S}.$$

But, if $\Psi(s) = 1$, we must then have $\mathfrak{S} \subset \mathfrak{S}_2$, which is impossible unless $\mathfrak{S} \equiv \mathfrak{S}_2$. A similar argument holds for $\Psi_2(s) \equiv 0$. This proves our result.

Lemma 5.5.4 (The Second Consistency Condition) [A.G.H.1] *Suppose that the only finite singularities of $f(s; z)$ and $f_2(s; z)$ are contained on the analytic sets,* $\mathfrak{S} \equiv \{(s, z) \mid z = \Psi(s)\}$ *and* $\mathfrak{S}_2 \equiv \{(s, z) \mid z = \Psi_2(s)\}$, with $\mathfrak{S} \not\equiv \mathfrak{S}_2$. *Then $f(s; z)$ and $f_2(s; z)$ are either both singular on $\mathfrak{S} \cup \mathfrak{S}_2$, or* $\mathfrak{S}_2 \equiv \mathfrak{S} \equiv \varnothing$.

Proof If $f(s; z)$ is singular on $\mathfrak{S}$, then by (5.5.19) $f_2(s; z)$ has $\mathfrak{S}$ as a possible singularity. By (5.5.20) $f_2(s; z)$ being singular on $\mathfrak{S}$ implies $f(s; z)$ has $\mathfrak{S}$ as a possible singularity. However, if it is *given* that $\mathfrak{S}$ is a singularity of $f(s; z)$, then $\mathfrak{S}$ must also be a singularity of $f_2(s; z)$. A similar argument holds for $\mathfrak{S}_2$, and this proves the first part of the lemma. If $f(s; z)$ being singular on $\mathfrak{S}_2$ violates the hypothesis (5.5.22) that $\mathfrak{S}_2 \subset \mathfrak{m}^{[3]}{}_1 \cup \mathfrak{m}^{[3]}{}_2$, then $f_2(s; z)$ cannot be singular either on $\mathfrak{S}_2$. This contradicts our hypothesis unless $\Psi_2(s) \equiv \infty$ and $\mathfrak{S}_2$ is the empty set, i.e., there are no finite singularities of the form $z = \Psi_2(s)$.

Remark Lemma 5.5.4 states that $f_2(s; z)$ is singular whenever $f(s; z)$ is singular. A similar result holds for $\Phi_2(s; \xi)$ and $\Phi(s; \xi)$.

This might have alternately been argued by rewriting (5.5.19) as

$$\begin{aligned} f_2(s; z) - f(s; z) &\equiv F(s; z) \\ &= -\frac{1}{16}\left(\frac{s - 4m^2}{s}\right)^{1/2} \int_{\mathscr{L}} [\zeta^{-1} f(s; \zeta) + 2f_\zeta(s; \zeta)] f_2\left(s; \frac{z}{\zeta}\right) d\zeta \end{aligned}$$

and considering the singularities of the right- and left-hand sides. The *actual* singularities of the right- and left-hand sides must, of course, be the same. The possible singularities of the right-hand side are all contained in the analytic set $\mathfrak{R}$; the singularities of the left-hand side are contained in $\mathfrak{S} \cup \mathfrak{S}_2$. Since the possible singularities contain the actual singularities, the actual singularities are a subset of $(\mathfrak{S} \cap \mathfrak{S}_2) \cap \mathfrak{R}$. However, unless the singularities of $f(s; z)$ and $f_2(s; z)$ cancel, we also have $\mathfrak{S} \cup \mathfrak{S}_2 \subset \mathfrak{R}$. We conclude from this that unless the coordinate planes $z = 0$, $z = 1$ are singularities for *both*

$f(s; z)$ and $f_2(s; z)$, the actual singularities form a denumerable set of isolated points. In this latter case, since the singularities of an analytic function of several complex variables are not isolated, $F(s; z)$ is seen to be entire. In the former case, we note that both $f(s; z)$ and $f_2(s; z)$ are regular for $|z| < \varepsilon$, ε sufficiently small and $(s, z) \notin \mathfrak{m}_1^{[3]}, \mathfrak{m}_2^{[3]}$; hence $z = 0$ can not be a singularity surface. Likewise, $z = 1$ can not be a singularity surface for $f(s; z,) f_2(s; z)$, since this would imply $\Phi(s; \xi)$, $\Phi_2(s; \xi)$ are singular on $\xi = 1$, which contradicts the hypothesis that these functions are regular in the region $\mathfrak{B}^+$. We conclude that $F(s; z)$ is entire under both circumstances.

Lemma 5.5.5 (The Third Consistency Condition) [A.G.H.1] *Suppose $\mathfrak{S}$ and $\mathfrak{S}_2$ ($\mathfrak{S} \not\equiv \mathfrak{S}_2$) are the only candidates for finite singularities of $f(s; z)$ and $f_2(s; z)$ respectively. Then $f(s; z)$ and $f_2(s; z)$ are entire.*

Proof The hypothesis of this lemma states that $f(s; z)$ *may* be singular on $\mathfrak{S}$ but is singular nowhere else, and $f_2(s; z)$ *may* be singular on $\mathfrak{S}_2$ but is singular nowhere else. Using the previous consistency lemma and its notation we realize that the actual singularities of the $F(s; z)$ and its integral representation must be the same. Hence, since the possible singularities of the left-hand side must be included in $\mathfrak{S} \cup \mathfrak{S}_2$, those of the right-hand side must be contained in $\mathfrak{R}$. The actual singularities of both sides must lie in $(\mathfrak{S} \cup \mathfrak{S}_2) \cap \mathfrak{R}$, which is in general a denumerable set of isolated points. This proves our result.

Lemma 5.5.6 *Let $f(s; z)$ and $f_2(s; z)$ have polar singularities on the analytic sets $\mathfrak{S} \equiv \{(s, z) \mid z = \Psi(s)\}$ and $\mathfrak{S}_2 \equiv \{(s, z) \mid z = \Psi_2(s)\}$ respectively; furthermore, let the orders of these polar singularities be p and q respectively. Then either $f(s; z)$ or $f_2(s; z)$ or both have polar singularities of order $\geq (p + q - 1)$ on the set $\mathfrak{R} \equiv \{(s, z) \mid z = \Psi(s)\Psi_2(s)\}$, providing that, $\Psi(s)\Psi_2(s) \not\equiv \tilde{\Psi}(s)\tilde{\Psi}_2(s)$, where*

1. *$\tilde{\Psi}(s)$ and $\tilde{\Psi}_2(s)$ respectively define other singularities of $f(s; z)$ and $f_2(s; z)$,*
   or
2. *either $\tilde{\Psi}(s)$ or $\tilde{\Psi}_2(s)$ corresponds to a respective singularity of $f(s; z)$ or $f_2(s; z)$, and the other function corresponds to a point (s, z) outside the domain of holomorphy.*

Proof Instead of considering the function $F(s; z)$, defined above, it is sufficient to consider the related function

$$\tilde{F}(s; z) = -\frac{1}{16}\left(\frac{s - 4m^2}{s}\right)^{1/2} \int_{\mathscr{L}} f(s; \zeta) f_2\left(s; \frac{z}{\zeta}\right) \frac{d\zeta}{\zeta}. \tag{5.5.26}$$

For each fixed value of $s \neq 0, 4m^2$ the integral (5.5.26) is of the kind used in the Hadamard multiplication of singularities proof. Borel [D.4, p. 348] gave an extension of the original Hadamard theorem, which states (for functions of one complex variable) that if $f(z), f_2(z)$ are singular at α, β respectively and these are polar singularities (of orders p and q) then $\alpha\beta$ is a polar singularity of $F(z)$ of order $(p + q - 1)$, providing $\alpha\beta \neq \alpha'\beta'$ where (1) α', β' are other singularities of $f(z), f_2(z)$, or (2) α' is a singularity of $f(z)$ and β' is an external point, or (3) β' is a singularity of $f_2(z)$ and α' is an external point. The Borel theorem then provides us with the conclusion of our theorem as applied to the function $\tilde{F}(s; z)$, since if the result is true for each fixed s by meromorphic continuation it is true for all s. Since the singularities of $F(s; z)$ and $\tilde{F}(s; z)$ are the same, we conclude that either $f(s; z)$ or $f_2(s; z)$ has a polar singularity on $\mathfrak{R}$; however, we are unable to conclude that they are both singular there.

Corollary 5.5.7 *Under the conditions of Theorem* 5.5.6 *either* $f(s; z)$ *or* $f_2(s; z)$ *or both have polar singularities on the union of analytic sets* $\mathfrak{C} \equiv \bigcup_{l \geq 0} \bigcup_{m \geq 0} \{(s, z) \mid z = [\Psi(s)]^l [\Psi_2(s)]^m\}$.

Remark The conditions of Theorem 5.5.5 do not preclude the functions $\Phi(s; \xi)$ and $\Phi_2(s; \xi)$ being multivalued in the ξ-variable. Indeed, if $f(s; z)$, $f_2(s; z)$ have poles $\Phi(s; \xi)$, $\Phi_2(s; \xi)$ will have algebraic pole-like branch points as the corresponding singularities [G.S.1], [G.H.6].

Recalling our assumption (5.5.21) that $\Phi(s; \xi)$ was regular on $\mathbb{C}^2 - \{\mathfrak{L}^{[3]}{}_1 \cup \mathfrak{L}^{[3]}{}_2\}$, and hence $f(s; z)$ was regular on $\mathbb{C}^2 - \{\mathfrak{m}^{[3]}{}_1 \cup \mathfrak{m}^{[3]}{}_2\}$ (5.5.22) we may obtain a more precise result than Corollary 5.5.7 concerning the function $f_2(s; z)$.

Theorem 5.5.8 *The function* $f_2(s; z)$ *defined by* (5.5.19), *and the condition of crossing symmetry, is singular on an infinite family of analytic sets.*

Proof By Lemma 5.5.1 $f(s; z)$ and $f_2(s; z)$ are both singular at $s = 4m^2$; indeed, they have a square root ramification there. Consequently, because of crossing symmetry with respect to s, t, and u, $\Phi(s; \xi)$ has a square root ramification at $\xi = \pm(1 + 8m^2/[s - 4m^2])$, $s \in \mathbb{C}^1$. In Section 1 of this chapter [(5.1.20) and (5.1.21)], it was remarked that if

$$f(s; z) = \sum_{\nu=1}^{\infty} \sum_{\mu=1}^{m_\nu} \frac{M_{\mu\nu}(s)}{[z - b_\nu(s)]^\mu},$$

then a direct computation of $\boldsymbol{\Omega} f$ with the residue theorem produced that

$$\Phi(s; \xi) = \sum_{\nu=1}^{\infty} \sum_{\mu=1}^{M\nu} \frac{(-1)^{\mu+1}}{(\mu - 1)!} M_{\mu\nu}(s) \frac{\partial^{\mu-1}}{\partial b_\nu^{\mu-1}} [b_\nu{}^2(s) - 2zb_\nu(s) + 1]^{1/2}.$$

The square root, branch point at $\xi = 1 + 8m^2/(s - 4m^2)$, is seen thereby to correspond to a simple pole of $f(s; z)$ at

$$z = \Psi(s) \equiv \frac{s + 4m(m \pm \sqrt{s})}{s - 4m^2}.$$

By the above mentioned extension of the Borel theorem [D.4], Lemma 5.5.6, one realizes that either $f(s; z)$ or $f_2(s; z)$ or both will have polar singularities at the points satisfying $z = [\Psi(s)]^l$ $(l = 1, 2, \ldots)$. Since there are no restrictions on the location of the singularities of $f_2(s; z)$ made, implicitly or otherwise, in hypotheses, the conclusion follows.

Remark A further theorem due to Faber [D.4, pp. 349, 350] gives us a condition under which functions $f(z), f_2(z)$ with isolated essential singularities at α and β generated a function $\tilde{F}(z)$ (by the integral (5.5.26)) with an isolated essential singularity at $\alpha\beta$. The conditions of the theorem are the same as in the Borel extension, with the added stipulation that $f(z), f_2(z)$ are to be single valued in the neighborhoods of α, β respectively. Consequently, a substantially stronger result than Theorem 5.5.8 is possible, where one designates the polar and essential singularities.

Theorem 5.5.9 *Let $\Phi(s; \xi)$ and $\Phi_2(s; \xi)$ be singular at $\xi = \alpha(s)$ and $\xi = \alpha_2(s)$ respectively. Furthermore, let their **Ω**-associates be $f(s; z)$ and $f_2(s; z)$ respectively. Then $\Phi_2(s; \xi)$ is singular on the sets $\{(s, \xi) \mid \xi = \frac{1}{2}[\eta^p \eta_2{}^q + \eta^{-p} \eta_2^{-q}]\}$ $(p + q = 1, 2, \ldots)$ where $\alpha = \frac{1}{2}[\eta + \eta^{-1}]$, $\alpha_2 = \frac{1}{2}[\eta_2 + \eta_2{}^{-1}]$.*

Proof According to Nehari's theorem [N.6] and (5.1.1) if $f(s; z)$ is singular at either $z = \alpha(s) + [\alpha^2(s) - 1]^{1/2}$ or $z = \alpha(s) - [\alpha^2(s) - 1]^{1/2}$ then $\Phi(s; \xi)$ is singular at $\xi = \alpha(s)$. According to (5.5.18), $f(s; z)$ and $f_2(s; z)$ have been chosen to have a Taylor series development about the origin in the z-variable. Hence $f(s; z)$ and $f_2(s; z)$ are regular (for suitable fixed s) in the disks $|z| < |\alpha(s) - [\alpha^2(s) - 1]^{1/2}|$ $|z| < |\alpha_2(s) - [\alpha_2{}^2(s) - 1]^{1/2}|$, respectively. Now the integral in (5.5.19) will be singular only at those points, which correspond to singularities of $f_2(s; z/\zeta)$ and $[\zeta^{-1} f(s; \zeta) + 2 f_\zeta(s; \zeta)] \equiv K(s; \zeta)$ coinciding in the ζ-plane, that is for

$$z = (\alpha(s) - [\alpha^2(s) - 1]^{1/2})(\alpha_2(s) - [\alpha_2{}^2(s) - 1]^{1/2}).$$

The corresponding singularity that the function $[\Phi(s; \xi) - \Phi_2(s; \xi)]$ has then is seen to be located at

$$\xi - (\xi^2 - 1)^{1/2} = (\alpha - [\alpha^2(s) - 1]^{1/2})(\alpha_2(s) - [\alpha_2{}^2(s) - 1]^{1/2}).$$

By introducing the auxiliary variables $\eta(s)$, $\eta_2(s)$, defined by $\alpha = \frac{1}{2}[\eta + 1/\eta]$, $\alpha_2 = [\eta_2 + 1/\eta_2]$ one obtains

$$\xi - (\xi^2 - 1)^{1/2} = \frac{1}{4}\left(\left[\eta + \frac{1}{\eta}\right] - \left[\eta - \frac{1}{\eta}\right]\right)\left(\left[\eta_2 + \frac{1}{\eta_2}\right] - \left[\eta_2 - \frac{1}{\eta_2}\right]\right) = (\eta\eta_2)^{-1}.$$

Hence either $\Phi(s;\xi)$ or $\Phi_2(s;\xi)$ must be singular at $\xi = \frac{1}{2}(\eta\eta_2 + 1/\eta\eta_2)$; since $\Phi_2(s;\xi)$ is singular whenever $\Phi(s;\xi)$ is, we conclude, $\Phi_2(s;\xi)$ must be singular here. Repeating the previous argument with $\xi = \alpha(s)$ and $\xi = \frac{1}{2}(\eta(s)\eta_2(s) + 1/\eta(s)\eta_2(s))$ as the singular points of $\Phi(s;\xi)$ and $\Phi_2(s;\xi)$, respectively, yields the further singularity of $\Phi_2(s;\xi)$ at

$$\xi = \tfrac{1}{2}(\eta(s)\eta_2{}^2(s) + \eta^{-1}(s)\eta_2^{-2}(s)).$$

Again, since, $\Phi_2(s;\xi)$ is singular at those singularities of $\Phi(s;\xi)$, we have $\Phi_2(s;\xi)$ singular also at $\xi = \alpha_2(s)$. Repeating the above argument with the respective singularities $\xi = \alpha_2(s)$, $\xi = \frac{1}{2}(\eta(s)\eta_2(s) + 1/\eta(s)\eta_2(s))$ yields $\xi = \frac{1}{2}(\eta^2(s)\eta_2(s) + \eta^{-2}(s)\eta_2^{-1}(s))$ as a singularity of $\Phi_2(s;\xi)$. Continuing in this manner gives the stated conclusion.

Remark If we introduce the auxiliary variables t and t_2 defined by $\cos t = \alpha$, $\cos t_2 = \alpha_2$, then it is easy to see that the singularity sets of the previous theorem may be written as

$$\{(s,\xi)\,|\,\xi = \cos[p\cos^{-1}\alpha(s) + q\cos^{-1}\alpha_2(s)];\ s \in \mathbb{C}^1\} \quad (p + q = 1, 2, \ldots).$$

Corollary 5.5.10 *The function $\Phi_2(s;\xi)$ is singular on the following set (n an integer):*

$$\bigcup_{n\geq 1}\left\{(s,\xi)\,|\,\xi = \pm\cos\left(n\cos^{-1}\left[1 + \frac{8m^2}{s - 4m^2}\right]\right)\right\}.$$

Proof This follows immediately from Theorem 5.5.9 and the discussion of the proof of Theorem 5.5.10.

6. *The Inverse Scattering Problem*

Newton [N.11,13] has given a general method for investigating the inverse scattering problem. His procedure relates the scattering potential $V(r)$, in the complex r-plane, with the unique solution of the integral equation for $K(r, r')$,

$$K(r, r') = f(r, r') - \int_0^r ds\, s^{-2} K(r, s) f(s, r'); \tag{5.6.1}$$

where $f(r, r')$ is given as an infinite series of Riccati-Bessel functions, $U_l(r) \equiv rj_l(r)$,

$$f(r, r') = \sum_{l=0}^{\infty} c_l\, U_l(r) U_l(r'). \tag{5.6.2}$$

The function $K(r, r')$ is seen to satisfy a partial differential equation of the form $\mathbf{D}_r K(r, r') - \mathbf{D}_{r'}^0 K(r, r') = 0$, where $\mathbf{D}_r{}^0 \equiv r^2(\partial^2/\partial r^2 + 1)$ and $\mathbf{D}_r \equiv \mathbf{D}_r{}^0 - rV(r)$, with

$$V(r) \equiv -\frac{2}{r}\frac{d}{dr}\left(\frac{K(r, r)}{r}\right). \tag{5.6.3}$$

This is Newton's formula for the corresponding scattering potential. By putting the series representation for $f(r, r')$ into the integral equation for $K(r, r')$, it is found that

$$K(r, r') = \sum_{l=0}^{\infty} c_l\, \varphi_l(r) U_l(r') \tag{5.6.4}$$

where the

$$\varphi_l(r) \equiv U_l(r) - \int_0^r ds\, s^{-2} K(r, s) U_l(s). \tag{5.6.5}$$

Remark $\mathbf{D}_r{}^0 U_l(r) = 0$, and $\mathbf{D}_r \varphi_l(r) = 0$.

By subsituting the series representation (5.6.4) into (5.6.5) Newton obtains an infinite set of coupled linear-algebraic equations equivalent to the integral equation (5.6.1),

$$\varphi_l(r) = U_l(r) - \sum_m L_{lm}(r) c_m\, \varphi_m(r),$$

with

$$L_{lm}(r) = \int_0^r ds\, s^{-2}\, U_l(s) U_m(s). \tag{5.6.6}$$

He then goes on to show (by using asymptotic expansions for $U_l(r)$ and $\varphi_l(r)$, as $r \to \infty$), how one may solve for the coefficients c_m in terms of the phase shifts δ_m. This procedure, however, entails the solving of an infinite system of coupled linear algebraic equations.

Sabatier [S.1,2] generalizes Newton's procedure by considering the functions

$$f(r, r') = \sum_{\mu \in I} c_\mu U_\mu(r) U_\mu(r'), \tag{5.6.7}$$

where the index set I is no longer the set of positive integers, but may correspond to an arbitrary discrete or continuous index from -1 to $+\infty$. Sabatier [S.2] places some restrictions on the coefficients c_μ; however, his restrictions still allow a fairly large class of potentials to be possible. For instance, the class of potentials contains the class of all potentials analytic in a disk about the origin with a slit along the negative real axis.

The study of the inverse scattering problem is concerned with the investigation of the analytic properties of $V(r)$, and hence $K(r, r')$ [S.2]. By using Newton's reduction it was shown that the coefficients c_μ were related to the phase shifts δ_μ, and this question is reduced to determining the analytic properties of the series (5.6.4), modulo solving an infinite set of coupled linear algebraic equations. Rather than discussing (5.6.4), however, it is more convenient to investigate the properties of the simpler function (5.6.2) in terms of the coefficients c_μ and to relate this information to the function $K(r, r')$ by Eq. (5.6.1). For instance, using a well-known integral representation for the Bessel functions [E.6, Vol. II, p. 14] we have,

$$f(r, r') = \frac{rr'}{2} \int_0^1 dt \int_0^1 ds \cos(rt) \cos(r's) g\left(\frac{rr'}{4} [1 - t^2][1 - s^2]\right), \tag{5.6.8}$$

where

$$g(\zeta) \equiv \sum_{l=0}^{\infty} \frac{c_l}{(l!)^2} \zeta^l. \tag{5.6.9}$$

Since $[\cos(rt) \cos(r't)]$ is entire, $f(r, r')$ will be regular in the set, $\{(r, r') \mid |rr'| < 4a\}$, if $g(\zeta)$ is regular in the disk $\{\zeta \mid |\zeta| < a\}$. More precisely, if $g(\zeta)$ has a singularity at $\zeta = \alpha$, then the only possible singularities of $f(r, r')$ must correspond to a coincidence of a singularity of $g(\frac{1}{4}rr'[1 - t^2][1 - s^2])$ at an end point of each integration path. The *envelope method* gives exactly this result also, since if we let

$$\chi\left(\frac{rr'}{4}, s, t\right) \equiv \frac{rr'}{4}[1 - t^2][1 - s^2] - \alpha = 0, \tag{5.6.10}$$

then the singularities of $f(r, r')$ must satisfy in addition $srr'[1 - t^2] = 0$, and $trr'[1 - s^2] = 0$. If $\alpha \neq 0$, then we must rule out $s = 1$, and $t = 1$, and we conclude that the singularity manifold of $f(r, r')$ lies on the analytic surface, $rr' = 4\alpha$.

In order to obtain full information concerning the singularities of $K(r, r')$ one needs only to make use of the development of the previous section, concerning the *consistency theorems* for integral equations, to relate the singularities of $f(r, r')$ to the possible singularities of $K(r, r')$.

References and Additional Reading

[A.2]
[A.3]
[A.G.1]
[A.G.H.1]
[B.37]
[B.39]
[B.S.2]
[B.O.T.1]
[D.4]
[G.22]
[G.27]
[G.28]
[G.H.5]
[G.H.6]
[G.H.A.1]
[G.S.1]
[J.1]
[K.1]
[K.2]
[K.T.1]
[K.W.1]
[L.1]
[L.2]
[L.P.1]
[M.8]
[M.F.1]
[N.9]
[N.10]
[N.11]
[N.12]
[N.13]
[N.F.1]
[N.J.1]
[O.1]
[O.F.1]
[P.S.2]
[R.3]
[R.4]
[S.1]
[S.2]
[S.6]
[S.7]
[S.W.1]
[W.2]
[W.5]
[W.12]
[W.16]
[W.S.1]
[W.W.1]
[Z.2]

Remark Added in Proof: An alternate approach to the potential scattering problem is contained in the elegant treatment given by Lax and Phillips [L.P.1], Chapter VI, whereby they relate the scattering matrix for the Schrödinger equation to the scattering matrix for the acoustic equation.

References

[A.1] Ahlfors, L., "Complex Analysis." McGraw-Hill, New York, 1953.

[A.2] Aks, S., Proof that scattering implies production in quantum field theory, *J. Math. Phys.* **6**, 516–532 (1965).

[A.3] Aks, S., The singularities of the scattering amplitude in potential theory, *Nuovo Cimento* [X] **38**, 1794–1814 (1965).

[A.4] Askey, R., Norm inequalities for some orthogonal series, *Bull. Amer. Math. Soc.* **72**, 808–823 (1966).

[A.5] Askey, R., A transplantation theorem for Jacobi coefficients, *Pacific J. Math.* **21**, 393–404 (1967).

[A.B.1] Aziz, A. K., and Bogdonowcz, A., A generalized Goursat problem for nonlinear hyperbolic partial differential equations. (To be published.)

[A.D.1] Aziz, A. K., and Diaz, J. B., On a mixed boundary value problem for linear hyperbolic partial differential equations in two independent variables, *Arch. Rational Mech. Anal.* **10**, 1–28 (1962).

[A.F.1] Appell, P., and de Fériet, J., "Fonctions hypergéométriques et Hypersphériques, Polynomes d'Hermite." Gauthier-Villars, Paris, 1926.

[A.G.1] Avila, G. S. S., and Gilbert, R. P., On the analytic properties of solutions of the equation $\Delta u + xu_x + yu_y + c(r)u = 0$, *Duke Math. J.* **34**, 353–362 (1967).

[A.G.2] Aziz, A. K., and Gilbert, R. P., A generalized Goursat problem for elliptic equations, *J. Reine Angew. Math.* **222**, 1–13 (1966).

[A.G.H.1] Aks, S., Gilbert, R. P., and Howard, H. C., Analytic properties of the elastic unitarity integral, *J. Math. Phys.* **6**, 1626–1634 (1965).

[A.G.H.2] Aziz, A. K., Gilbert, R. P., and Howard, H. C., A second order, nonlinear elliptic boundary value problem with generalized Goursat data, *Ann. Math. Pura Appl.* [IV] **72**, 325–341 (1966).

[A.W.1] Askey, R., and Wainger, S., A transplantation theorem between ultraspherical series, *Illinois J. Math.* **10**, 322–344 (1966).

[B.1] Bateman, H., "Partial Differential Equations of Mathematical Physics." Dover, New York, 1944.

[B.2] Bateman, H., "The Mathematical Analysis of Electrical and Optical Wave-Motion." Dover, New York, 1955.

[B.3] Bergman, S., Zur Theorie der ein- und mehrwertigen harmonischen Funktionen der dreidimensionalen Raumes, *Math. Z.* **24**, 641–669 (1926).

[B.4] Bergman, S., Zur Theorie der Algebraischen Potentialfunktionen des dreidimensionalen Raumes, *Math. Ann.* **99**, 629–659 (1928); **101**, 534–558 (1929).

[B.5] Bergman, S., Über Kurvenintegrale von Funktionen zweier komplexen Veränderlichen, die Differentialgleichungen $\Delta V + V = 0$ befriedigen, *Math. Z.* **32**, 386–406 (1930).

[B.6] Bergman, S., Über ein Verfahren zur Konstruktion der Naherungslösungen der Gleichung $\Delta u + \tau^2 u = 0$, *Prikl. Mat. Meh.* 97–107 (1936).

[B.7] Bergman, S., Zur Theorie der Funktionen, die eine linear partielle Differentialgleichung befriedigen, *Soviet Math. Dokl.* **15**, 227–230 (1937).

[B.8] Bergman, S., Zur Theorie der Funktionen, die eine linear partielle Differentialgleichung befriedigen, *Mat. Sb.* **44**, 1169–1198 (1937).

[B.9] Bergman, S., Sur un lien entre la théorie des équations aux derivées partielles elliptiques et celle des functions d'une variable complexe, *C. R. Acad. Sci. Paris* **205**, 1198–1200, 1360–1362 (1937).

[B.10] Bergman, S., The approximation of functions satisfying a linear partial differential equation, *Duke Math. J.* **6**, 537–561 (1940).

[B.11] Bergman, S., The hodograph method in the theory of compressible fluids. *Suppl. to* "Fluid Dynamics," by R. von Mises and K. O. Friedrichs. Brown Univ. Graduate School, Providence, Rhode Island, 1942.

[B.12] Bergman, S., A formula for the stream function of certain flows, *Proc. Nat. Acad. Sci. U.S.A.* **29**, 276–281 (1943).

[B.13] Bergman, S., Residue theorems of harmonic functions of three variables, *Bull. Amer. Math. Soc.* **49**, 163–174 (1943).

[B.14] Bergman, S., Two-dimensional subsonic flows of a compressible fluid and their singularities, *Trans. Amer. Math. Soc.* **62**, 452–498 (1947).

[B.15] Bergman, S., Sur les fonctions orthogonales de plusieurs variables complexes avec les applications à la théorie des fonctions analytiques, Wiley (Interscience), 1941 and *Mémor. Sci. Math.* **106** (1947).

[B.16] Bergman, S., Sur la fonction-noyau d'un domaine et ses applications dans la théorie des transformations pseudo-conformes, *Mémor. Sci. Math.* **108** (1948).

[B.17] Bergman, S., Classes of solutions of linear partial differential equations in three variables, *Duke Math. J.* **13**, 419–458 (1946).

[B.18] Bergman, S., Two-dimensional transonic flow patterns, *Amer. J. Math.* **70**, 856–891 (1948).

[B.19] Bergman, S., "The Kernel Function and Conformal Mapping" (Math. Surveys, Vol. 5). Amer. Math. Soc., Providence, Rhode Island, 1950.

[B.20] Bergman, S., "Multivalued Solutions of Linear Partial Differential Equations. Contributions to the theory of Riemann Surfaces" (Ann. Math. Studies, Vol. 30), pp. 229–245. Amer. Math. Soc., Providence, Rhode Island, 1953.

[B.21] Bergman, S., Multivalued harmonic functions, in three variables, *Comm. Pure Appl. Math.* **9**, 327–338 (1956).

[B.22] Bergman, S., "Integral Operators in the theory of Linear Partial Differential Equations" (Ergeb. Math. N.S., Vol. 23,). Springer, Berlin, 1961.

[B.23] Bergman, S., Applications of the method of the kernel functions for solving boundary-value problems, *Numer. Math.* **3**, 209–225 (1961).

[B.24] Bergman, S., Some properties of a harmonic function of three variables given by its series development, *Arch. Rational. Mech. Anal.* **8**, 207–222 (1961).

[B.25] Bergman, S., Sur les singularités des fonctions harmoniques de trois variables, *C. R. Acad. Sci. Paris* **254**, 3304–3305 (1962).

[B.26] Bergman, S., Integral operators in the study of an algebra and of a coefficient problem in the theory of three-dimensional harmonic functions, *Duke Math. J.* **30**, 447–60 (1963).

[B.27] Bergman, S., On the coefficient problem in the theory of a system of linear partial differential equations, *J. Analyse Math.* **10**, 249–274 (1963).

[B.28] Bergman, S., On integral operators generating stream functions of compressible fluids, *in* "Nonlinear Problems of Engineering," pp. 65–89. Academic Press, New York, 1964.

[B.29] Bergman, S., Application of integral operators to singular differential equations and to computations of compressible fluid flows, *in* "Numerical Solution of Partial Differential Equations." Academic Press, New York, 1966.

[B.30] Bers, L., Theory of pseudoanalytic functions (*lecture notes, mimeographed*). New York Univ., 1953.
[B.31] Bers, L., Local theory of pseudoanalytic functions, *in* "Lectures on Functions of a Complex Variable." Univ. Michigan Press, Ann Arbor, Michigan, 1955.
[B.32] Bers, L., Survey of local properties of solutions of elliptic partial differential equations, *Comm. Pure Appl. Math.* **10**, 339–350 (1956).
[B.33] Bers, L., Formal powers and power series, *Comm. Pure Appl. Math.* **10**, 693–711 (1956).
[B.34] Bers, L., An outline of the theory of pseudoanalytic functions, *Bull. Amer. Math. Soc.* **62**, 291–331 (1956).
[B.35] Bers, L., "Mathematical Aspects of Subsonic and Transonic Gas Dynamics." Wiley (Interscience), New York, 1958.
[B.36] Bers, L., Introduction to several complex variables (*lecture notes*). Courant Inst. Math. Sci., New York Univ., 1964.
[B.37] Bjorken, J. D., Thesis, Stanford Univ., Stanford, California.
[B.38] Brafman, F., Generating functions of Jacobi and related polynomials, *Proc. Amer. Math. Soc.* **2**, 942–949 (1951).
[B.39] Bremermann, H., Complex convexity, *Trans. Amer. Math. Soc.* **82**, 17–51 (1956).
[B.40] Bremermann, H., Construction of the envelopes of holomorphy of arbitrary domains, *Rev. Math. Hisp.-Amer.* [4] **17**, 1–26 (1957).
[B.41] Bremermann, H., On a generalized Dirichlet problem for plurisubharmonic functions and pseudo-convex domains, *Trans. Amer. Math. Soc.* **91**, 246–276 (1959).
[B.42] Burns, J. C., The iterated equation of generalized axially symmetric potential theory, I, II, III, *J. Austral. Math. Soc.* **7**, 263–300 (1967).
[B.B.1] Bergman, S., and Bojanic, R., Application of integral operators to the theory of partial differential equations with singular coefficients, *Arch. Rational. Mech. Anal.* **10**, 323–340 (1962).
[B.D.1] Bremermann, H. J., and Durand, L., III, On analytic continuation, multiplication, and Fourier transformations of Schwartz distributions, *J. Math. Phys.* **2**, 240–258 (1961).
[B.E.1] Bergman, S., and Epstein, B., Operator methods in the theory of compressible fluids, *J. Math. and Phys.* **26**, 195–222 (1948).
[B.G.1] Bergman, S., and Greenstone, L., Numerical determination by use of special computational devices of an integral operator in the theory of compressible fluids. I. Determination of the coefficients of the integral operator by the use of punch card machines, *J. Math. and Phys.* **26**, 1–9 (1947).
[B.H.1] Bergman, S., and Herriot, J. G., Numerical solution of boundary-value problems by the method of integral operators, *Numer. Math.* **7**, 42–65 (1965).
[B.M.1] Bochner, S. and Martin, W. T. "Several Complex Variables." Princeton Univ. Press, Princeton, New Jersey, 1948.
[B.O.T.1] Bremermann, H. J., Oehme, R., and Taylor, J. R., Proof of dispersion relations in quantum field theories, *Phys. Rev.* **109**, 2178–2190 (1958).
[B.S.1] Bergman, S., and Schiffer, M., "Kernel Functions and Elliptic Differential Equations in Mathematical Physics." Academic Press, New York, 1953.
[B.S.2] Bogoliubov, N. N., and Shirkov, D. V., "Introduction to the Theory of Quantized Fields." Wiley (Interscience), New York, 1959.
[B.T.1] Behnke, H., and Thullen, P., "Theorie der Funktionen mehrer Komplexer Veränderlichen" (Ergeb. Math., Vol. 3). Springer, Berlin, 1934.
[C.1] Carathéodory, C., "Theory of Functions," Vols. I and II. Chelsea, New York, 1960.
[C.2] Cartan, H., "Elementary Theory of Analytic Functions of One or Several Complex Variables." Addison-Wesley, Reading, Massachusetts, 1963.

[C.3] Christianovich, L. A., Approximate integration of equations of a supersonic fluid flow, *Prikl. Mat. Meh.* **11**, 215–222 (1947). (In Russian.)

[C.4] Colton, D. L., Uniqueness theorems for a class of singular partial differential equations. (Thesis, Univ. of Edinburgh, 1967.)

[C.5] Colton, D. L., On the Analytic Theory of a Class of Singular Partial Differential equations, *Proc. Symp. Analyt. Methods in Maths. Phys.* Indiana Univ. Press, Bloomington, Indiana, 1969.

[C.6] Copson, E. T., "Theory of Functions of a Complex Variable." Oxford Univ. Press, London, 1935.

[C.D.1] Chu, S. C., and Diaz, J. B., Remarks on a mixed boundary-value problem for linear hyperbolic differential equations in two independent variables, *Arch. Rational Mech. Anal.* **16**, 187–195 (1964).

[C.D.2] Chu, S. C., and Diaz, J. B., Remarks on a generalization of Banach's principle of contraction mappings, *J. Math. Anal. Appl.* **11**, 440–446 (1965).

[C.E.1] Copson, E. T., and Erdélyi, A., On a partial differential equation with two singular lines, *Arch. Rational Mech. Anal.* **2**, 76–86 (1958).

[C.G.1] Colton, D. L., and Gilbert, R. P., Singularities of Solutions to elliptic partial differential equations with analytic coefficients. *Quart. J. Math.* (1968).

[C.G.2] Colton, D. L., and Gilbert, R. P., Nonlinear analytic partial differential equations with generalized Goursat data. *Duke J. Math.*

[C.H.1] Courant, R. and Hilbert, D., "Methods of Mathematical Physics," Vols. I and II. Wiley (Interscience), New York, 1953, 1962.

[D.1] Diaz, J. B., On a class of partial differential equations of even order, *Amer. J. Math.* **68**, 611–659 (1946).

[D.2] Diaz, J, B., On an analogue of the Euler–Cauchy polygon method for the numerical solution of $u_{xy} = f(x, y, u, u_x, u_y)$, *Arch. Rational Mech. Anal.* **1**, 357–390 (1958).

[D.3] Diaz, J. B., On existence, uniqueness, and numerical evaluation of solutions of ordinary and hyperbolic differential equations, *Ann. Mat. Pura.Appl.* [IV] **52**, 163–181 (1960).

[D.4] Dienes, P., "The Taylor Series." Dover, New York, 1957.

[D.5] Dougall, J., A theorem of Sonine in Bessel functions, with two extensions to spherical harmonics, *Proc. Edinburgh Math. Soc.* **37**, 33–47 (1919).

[D.6] Duffin, R. J., Two-dimensional Hilbert Transforms, *Proc. Amer. Math. Soc.* **8**, 239–245 (1957).

[D.7] Duffin, R. J., Discreet potential theory, *Duke Math. J.* **20**, 233–251 (1953).

[D.8] Duffin, R. J., Basic properties of discreet analytic functions, *Duke Math. J.* **23**, 335–363 (1956).

[D.L.1] Diaz, J., and Ludford, G. S. S., Sur la solution des équations linéaires aux dérivées partielles par des intégrales définies, *C. R. Acad. Sci. Paris.* **238**, 1963–1964 (1954).

[D.L.2] Diaz, J., and Ludford, G. S. S., On two methods of generating solutions of linear partial differential equations by means of definite integrals, *Quart. Appl. Math.* **12**, 422–425 (1955).

[D.L.3] Diaz, J., and Ludford, G. S. S., On a theorem of Le Roux, *Canad. J. Math.* **8**, 82–85 (1956).

[D.L.4] Diaz, J., and Ludford, G. S. S., On the integration methods of Bergman and Le Roux, *Quart. Appl. Math.* **14**, 428–432 (1957).

[D.L.5] Diaz, J., and Ludford, G. S. S., On the Euler-Poisson-Darboux equation, integral operators, and the method of descent, *Proc. Conf. Differential Equations, College Park, Maryland, 1956.*

[D.R.1] Davis, P., and Rabinowitz, P., Some SEAC computations of subsonic flows by Bergman's method of integral operators, *Nat. Bur. Standards Rep.* 3313 (1954).

[D.S.1] Deeter, C. R., and Springer, G., Discrete harmonic kernels, *J. Math. Mech.* **14**, 413–438 (1965).

[D.S.2] Duffin, R. J., and Shelly, E. P., Difference equations of polyharmonic type, *Duke Math. J.* **25**, 209–238 (1958).

[E.1] Eichler, M. M. E., Allgemeine Integration linearer partieller Differentialgleichungen vom elliptischen Typ bei zwei Grundvariablen, *Abh. Math. Sem. Univ. Hamburg* **15**, 179–210 (1947).

[E.2] Eichler, M. M. E., On the differential equation $U_{xx} + U_{yy} + N(x)U = 0$, *Trans. Amer. Math. Soc.* **65**, 259–278 (1949).

[E.3] Eichler, M. M. E., Eine Modifikation der Riemannschen Integrationsmethode bei partiellen Differentialgleichungen von hyperbolischen Typ, *Math. Z.* **53**, 1–10 (1950).

[E.4] Erdélyi, A., The analytic theory of systems of partial differential equations, *Bull. Amer. Math. Soc.* **57**, 339–353 (1951).

[E.5] Erdélyi, A., "Tables of Integral Transforms," Vols. I and II. McGraw-Hill, New York, 1954.

[E.6] Erdélyi, A., *et al.*, "Higher Transcendental Functions," Vols. I, II, and III. McGraw-Hill, New York, 1953–1955.

[E.7] Erdélyi, A., Singularities of generalized axially symmetric potentials, *Comm. Pure Appl. Math* **9**, 403–414 (1956).

[E.8] Erdélyi, A., "Asymptotic Expansions." Dover, New York, 1956.

[E.9] Erdélyi, A., An application of fractional integrals, *J. Analyse Math.* **14**, 113–126 (1965).

[F.1] Floridan, H., Normale Integraloperatoren, *Monatsh. Math.* **69**, 18–29 (1965).

[F.2] Forsyth, A. R., "Theory of Functions of Two Complex Variables." Cambridge, Univ. Press, London, 1914.

[F.3] Friedman, A., "Generalized Functions and Partial Differential Equations." Prentice-Hall, Englewood Cliffs, New Jersey, 1963.

[F.4] Fuks, B. A., "Introduction to the Theory of Analytic Functions of Several Complex Variables" (Transl. Math. Monographs, Vol. 8). Amer. Math Soc., Providence, Rhode Island, 1963.

[F.5] Fuks, B. A., "Special Chapters in the Theory of Analytic Functions of Several Complex Variables" (Transl. Math. Monographs, Vol. 14). Amer. Math. Soc., Providence, Rhode Island, 1965.

[G.1] Garabedian, P. R., Applications of analytic continuation to the solution of boundary value problems, *J. Rational Mech. Anal.* **3**, 383–393 (1954).

[G.2] Garabedian, P. R., Partial differential equations with more than two independent variables in the complex domain, *J. Math. Mech.* **9**, 241–271 (1960).

[G.3] Garabedian, P. R., Analyticity and reflection for plane elliptic systems, *Comm. Pure Appl. Math.* **14**, 315–322 (1961).

[G.4] Garabedian, P. R., "Partial Differential Equations." Wiley, New York, 1964.

[G.5] Ghaffari, A. G., "The Hodograph Method in Gas Dynamics." Publ. No. 85, Faculty of Science, Univ. of Teheran, Taban Press, 1950.

[G.6] Gilbert, R. P., Singularities of three-dimensional harmonic functions, (Thesis, Carnegie Inst. Technol., June 1958.)

[G.7] Gilbert, R. P., Singularities of three-dimensional harmonic functions, *Pacific J. Math.* **10**, 1243–1255 (1960).

[G.8] Gilbert, R. P., Singularities of solutions to the wave equation in three dimensions, *J. Reine Angew. Math.* **205**, 75–81 (1960).

[G.9] Gilbert, R. P., On the singularities of generalized axially symmetric potentials, *Arch. Rational Mech. Anal.* **6**, 171–176 (1960).

[G.10] Gilbert, R. P., A note on harmonic functions in $(p+2)$ variables, *Arch. Rational Mech. Anal.* **8**, 223–227 (1961).

[G.11] Gilbert, R. P., On the geometric character of singularity manifolds for harmonic functions in three variables, I, *Arch. Rational Mech. Anal.* **9**, 352–360 (1962).

[G.12] Gilbert, R. P., A note on the singularities of harmonic functions in three variables, *Proc. Amer. Math. Soc.* **13**, 229–232 (1962).

[G.13] Gilbert, R. P., On generalized axially symmetric potentials, *J. Reine Angew. Math.* **212**, 158–168 (1963).

[G.14] Gilbert, R. P., Some properties of generalized axially symmetric potentials, *Amer. J. Math.* **84**, 475–484 (1962).

[G.15] Gilbert, R. P., On harmonic functions of four variables with rational P_4 associates, *Pacific J. Math.* **13**, 79–96 (1963).

[G.16] Gilbert, R. P., Poisson's equation and generalized axially symmetric potential theory, *Ann. Mat. Pura Appl.* [IV] **61**, 337–348 (1963).

[G.17] Gilbert, R. P., Harmonic functions in four variables with rational and algebraic P_4 associates, *Ann. Polon. Math.* **9**, 273–287 (1964).

[G.18] Gilbert, R. P., Composition formulas in generalized axially symmetric potential theory, *J. Math Mech.* **13**, 577–588 (1964).

[G.19] Gilbert, R. P., Operators which generate harmonic functions in three-variables, *Scripta Math.* **27**, 141–152 (1964).

[G.20] Gilbert, R. P., Integral operator methods in biaxially symmetric potential theory, *Contrib. Differential Equations* **2**, 441–456 (1963).

[G.21] Gilbert, R. P., Some inequalities for generalized axially symmetric potentials with entire and meromorphic associates, *Duke J. Math.* **32**, 239–246 (1965).

[G.22] Gilbert, R. P., Bergman's integral operator method in generalized axially symmetric potential theory, *J. Math. Phys.* **5**, 983–997 (1964).

[G.23] Gilbert, R. P., Multivalued harmonic functions of four variables, *J. Analyse Math.* **15**, 305–323 (1965).

[G.24] Gilbert, R. P., On a class of elliptic partial differential equations, *Pacific J. Math,* **14**, 1223–1236 (1964).

[G.25] Gilbert, R. P., On the location of singularities of a class of elliptic partial differential equations in four variables, *Canad. J. Math.* **17**, 676–688 (1965).

[G.26] Gilbert, R. P., On generalized axially symmetric potentials whose associates are distributions, *Scripta Math.* **27**, 245–256 (1964).

[G.27] Gilbert, R. P., On the analytic properties of solutions to a generalized Schrödinger equation. *J. Differential Equations* **3**, 59–77 (1967).

[G.28] Gilbert, R. P., An investigation of the analytic properties of solutions to the generalized axially symmetric, reduced wave equation in $(n+1)$-variables, with an application to the theory of potential scattering, *SIAM J. Appl. Math.* **16**, 13–50 (1968)

[G.H.1] Gilbert, R. P., and Howard, H. C., On certain classes of elliptic partial differential equations. Tech. Note BN–344, Inst. for Fluid Dynam. and Appl. Math., Univ. of Maryland, College Park, Maryland, 1963.

[G.H.2] Gilbert, R. P., and Howard, H. C., On solutions of the generalized axially symmetric wave equation represented by Bergman operators, *Proc. London Math. Soc.* **15**, 346–360 (1965).

[G.H.3] Gilbert, R. P., and Howard, H. C., On solutions of the generalized biaxially symmetric Helmholtz equation generated by integral operators, *J. Reine Angew. Math.* **218**, 109–120 (1965).

[G.H.4] Gilbert, R. P., and Howard, H. C., Integral operator methods for generalized axially symmetric potentials in $(n+1)$-variables, *J. Austral. Math. Soc.* **5**, 331–348 (1965).

[G.H.5] Gilbert, R. P., and Howard, H. C., A generalization of a theorem of Nehari, *Bull. Amer. Math. Soc.* **72**, 37–39 (1966).

[G.H.6] Gilbert, R. P., and Howard, H. C., Role of the integral operator method in the theory of potential scattering, *J. Math. Phys.* **8**, 141–148 (1967).

[G.H.7] Gilbert, R. P., and Howard, H. C., On the singularities of Sturm–Liouville expansions, *Proc. Symp. Analyt. Methods in Math. Phys.* Indiana Univ. Press, Bloomington, Indiana, 1969

[G.H.8] Grobner, W., and Hofreiter, N., "Integraltafel erster Teil." Springer, Vienna, 1949.

[G.H.A.1] Gilbert, R. P., Howard, H. C., and Aks, S., Singularities of analytic functions having integral representations with a remark about the elastic unitarity integral, *J. Math. Phys.* **6**, 1157–1162 (1965).

[G.K.L.1] Gilbert, R. P., Knight, R. B., and Lo, C. Y., Nonlinear, analytic partial differential equations with generalized Goursat data: II *Bull. Polytech. Inst. Jassy*, To appear.

[G.R.1] Gunning, R. C., and Rossi, H., "Analytic Functions of Several Complex Variables." Prentice-Hall, Englewood Cliffs, New Jersey, 1965.

[G.S.1] Gilbert, R. P., and Shieh, S. Y., A new method in the theory of potential scattering, *J. Math. Phys.* **7**, 431–433 (1966).

[H.1] Hadamard, J., Théorème sur les séries entières, *Acta Math.* **22**, 55–64 (1898).

[H.2] Hartogs, F., Zur Theorie der analytischen Funktionen mehrerer unabhängiger Veränderlicher, im besondere über die Darstellung derselben durch Reihen, welche nach Potenzen einer Veränderlichen fortschreiten, *Math. Ann.* **62**, 1–88 (1906).

[H.3] Hellwig, G., "Partial Differential Equations." Ginn (Blaisdell), Boston, 1960.

[H.4] Henrici, P., Zur Funktionentheorie der Wellengleichung, *Comment. Math. Helv.* **27**, 235–293 (1953).

[H.5] Henrici, P., Bergman's Integraloperateur erster Art und Riemannsche Funktion, *Z. Angew. Math. Phys.* **3**, 228–232 (1952).

[H.6] Henrici, P., A survey of I. N. Vekua's theory of elliptic partial differential equations with analytic coefficients, *Z. Angew. Math. Phys.* **8**, 169–203 (1957).

[H.7] Henrici, P., On the domain of regularity of generalized axially symmetric potentials, *Proc. Amer. Math. Soc.* **8**, 29–31 (1957).

[H.8] Henrici, P., Complete systems of solutions for a class of singular elliptic partial differential equations, *in* "Boundary Problems in Differential Equations." Univ. of Wisconsin Press, Madison, Wisconsin, 1960.

[H.9] Hille, E., "Analytic Function Theory," pp. 19–34, Vols. I and II. Ginn, Boston, 1959.

[H.10] Hobson, E. W., "The Theory of Spherical and Ellipsoidal Harmonics." Cambridge Univ. Press, London, 1931.

[H.11] Hormander, L., "An Introduction to Complex Analysis in Several Variables." Van Nostrand, Princeton, New Jersey, 1966.

[H.12] Hyman, M. A., Concerning analytic solutions of the generalized potential equation, *Koninkl. Ned. Acad. Wetenschap. Proc.* **57**, 408–413 (1954).

[H.M.1] Heins, A., and MacCamy, R. C., Integral representatives of axially symmetric potential functions, *Arch. Rational Mech. Anal.* **13**, 371–385 (1963).

[H.W.1] Hirschman, I. I., and Widder, D. V., "The Convolution Transform." Princeton Univ. Press, Princeton, New Jersey, 1955.

[J.1] Jost, R., "The General Theory of Quantized Fields." Amer. Math. Soc., Providence, Rhode Island, 1965.

[K.1] Källen, G., Properties of vacuum expectation values of field operators, *in* "Relations de Dispersion et Particules Élémentaires," pp. 389–454. Hermann, Paris, 1960.

[K.2] Källen, G., The analyticity domain of the four point function, *Nuclear Phys.* **25**, 568–603 (1961).

[K.3] Kisynski, J., Sur l'existence des solutions d'un problème de Z. Szmydt relatif a l'equation $\partial^2 u/\partial x\, \partial y = f(x, y, u, u_x, u_y)$, *Ann. Univ. Mariae Curie-Sklodowska. Sect. A* **12**, 67–109 (1958).

[K.4] Kreyszig, E., On singularities of solutions of partial differential equations in 3 variables, *Arch. Rational Mech. Anal.* **2**, 151–159 (1958).

[K.5] Kreyszig, E., Coefficient problems in systems of partial differential equations, *Arch. Rational Mech. Anal.* **1**, 283–94 (1958).

[K.6] Kreyszig, E., On regular and singular harmonic function of three variables, *Arch. Rational Mech. Anal.* **4**, 353–370 (1960).

[K.7] Kreyszig, E., Kanonische Integraloperatoren zur Erzeugung harmonischer Funktionen von vier Veranderlichen, *Arch. Math.* **14**, 193–203 (1963).

[K.8] Kuroda, S. T., On a paper of Green and Lanford, *J. Math. Phys.* **3**, 933–935 (1962).

[K.F.1] Kolmogorov, A. N., and Fomin, S. V., "Elements of the Theory of Functions and Functional Analysis," Vol. 1. Graylock Press, Rochester, New York, 1951.

[K.T.1] Källen, G., and Toll, J., Integral representations for the vacuum expectation value of three scalar local fields, *Helv. Phys. Acta* **33**, 753–772 (1960).

[K.W.1] Källen, G., and Wightman, A., The analytic properties of the vacuum expectation value of a product of three scalar local fields, *Mat.-Fys. Skr. Danske Vid. Selsk.* **1**, 1–58 (1965).

[L.1] Lanckau, E., Über eine elliptische Differentialgleichung. 2, Ordnung mit einem singularen Koeffizienten, *Wiss. Z. Martin-Luther Univ. Halle–Wittenberg. Math. Nat.* **12**, 51–60 (1963).

[L.2] Lanckau, E., Eine einheitliche Darstellung der Lösungen der Tricomischen Gleichung, *Z. Angew. Math. Phys.* **42**, 180–186 (1962).

[L.3] Lanckau, E., Berechnung von kompressiblen Strömungen durch ein Korrespondenzprinzip, *Arch. Mech. Stos.* **12**, 291–300 (1964).

[L.4] Landau, L. D., On analytic properties of vertex parts in quantum field theory, *Nuclear Phys.* **13**, 181–192 (1959).

[L.5] Landau, L. D., On the analytic properties of vertex parts in quantum field theory, *Soviet Phys. JETP.* **37**, 45–50 (1960).

[L.6] Lefschetz, S., "L'Analyse Situs et la Géometrie Algébrique. Gauthier-Villars, Paris, 1924.

[L.7] Lefschetz, S., "Algebraic Geometry." Princeton Univ. Press, Princeton, New Jersey, 1953.

[L.8] Leray, J., Problème de Cauchy, III, Le calcul différentiel et intégral sur une variété analytique complex, *Bull. Soc. Math. France* **87**, 81–180 (1959).

[L.9] Leray, J., Problème de Cauchy, IV, Un prolongement de la transformation de Laplace qui transforme la solution unitaire dun opérateur hyperbolique en sa solution élémentaire, *Bull. Soc. Math. France* **90**, 39–156 (1962).

[L.10] Lo, C. Y., Singular behavior of orthogonal polynomial series in several variables, *SIAM J. Appl. Math.* **16**, 167–180 (1968).

[L.11] Lo, C. Y., A bound for entire harmonic functions of three variables, *Quart. Appl. Math.* (To be published.)

[L.P.1] Lax, P. D., and Phillips, R. S., "Scattering Theory", Academic Press, New York, 1967.

[M.1] MacCamy, R. C., On the scattering of water waves by a circular disc, *Arch. Rational Mech. Anal.* **2**, 120–138 (1961).

[M.2] Mandelbrojt, S., Théorème général fournissant l'argument des points singuliers situés sur le cercle de convergence d'une série de Taylor, *C. R. Acad. Sci. Paris* **204**, 1456–1458 (1937).

[M.3] Mandelstam, S., Some rigorous analytic properties of transition amplitudes, *Nuovo Cimento* **15**, 658 (1960).

[M.4] Maric, V., On some properties of solutions of $\Delta\Psi + A(r^2)X\Psi + C(r^2)\Psi = 0$, *Pacific J. Math.* **14**, 217–224 (1964).

[M.5] Mitchell, J., Representation theorems for solutions of linear partial differential equations in 3 variables. *Arch. Rational Mech. Anal.* **3**, 439–459 (1959).

[M.6] Mitchell, J., Properties of harmonic functions of 3 real variables given by Bergman–Whittaker operators, *Canad. J. Math.* **15**, 157–168 (1963).

[M.7] Mitchell, J., Integral theorems for harmonic vectors in 3 real variables, *Math. Z.* **82**, 314–334 (1963).

[M.8] Munroe, M. E., "Introduction to Measure and Integration." Addison-Wesley, Reading, Massachusetts, 1953.

[M.F.1] Morse, P. M., and Feshbach, H., Methods of Theoretical Physics," Vols. I and II. McGraw-Hill, New York, 1953.

[M.O.1] Magnus, W., and Oberhettinger, F., "Formulas and Theorems for the Functions of Mathematical Physics." Chelsea, New York, 1949.

[N.1] Nazarov, G. I., An exact solution of an axial symmetric problem for an ideal fluid, *Prikl. Mat. Meh.* **23**, 388 (1959). (In Russian.)

[N.2] Nazarov, G. I., On the exact solutions of the problems of magneto-hydrodynamics, *J. Appl. Mech. Tech. Phys.* **2**, 63–72 (1959). (In Russian.)

[N.3] Nazarov, G. I., About the exact analytic solution of equations of two-dimensional supersonic flows of a fluid, *Trudy Tomsk. Gos. Univ. Ser. Meh.-Mat. Geom. Sb.* **163**, 115–124 (1963). (In Russian.)

[N.4] Nazarov, G. I., On general solution of axial symmetric problem of an incompressible fluid, *Trudy Tomsk. Gos. Univ. Ser. Meh.-Mat. Geom. Sb.* **163**, 125–132 (1963).

[N.5] Nazarov, G. I., Bergman's functions in the theory of flows of compressible fluids, *Trudy Tomsk. Gos. Univ. Ser. Meh.-Mat. Geom. Sb., Sc.* **49**, 3–13 (1964) (In Russian.)

[N.6] Nehari, Z., On the singularities of Legendre expansions, *J. Rational Mech. Anal.* **5**, 987–992 (1956).

[N.7] Nehari, Z., "Conformal Mapping." McGraw-Hill, New York, 1952.

[N.8] Nevanlinna, R., Le théoreme de Picard–Borel et la théorie des fonctions méromorphes. Gauthier-Villars, Paris, 1929.

[N.9] Newton, R. G., Inelastic scattering, *Ann. Phys.* **4**, 29–56 (1958).

[N.10] Newton, R. G., Structure of the many-channel S matrix, *J. Math. Phys.* **2**, 188–197 (1961).

[N.11] Newton, R. G., Construction of potentials from phase shifts at fixed energy, *J. Math. Phys.* **3**, 75–82 (1962).

[N.12] Newton, R. G., "The Complex j-Plane." Benjamin, New York, 1964.

[N.13] Newton, R. G., "Scattering Theory of Waves and Particles." McGraw-Hıll, New York, 1966.

[N.F.1] Newton, R. G., and Fonda, L., Theory of resonance reactions, *Ann. Phys.* **10**, 490–515 (1960).

[N.J.1] Newton, R. G., and Jost, R., The construction of potentials from the S-matrix for systems of differential equations, *Nuovo Cimento* **1**, 590–622 (1955).

[O.1] Omnes, R., Some remarks about unitarity, *Nuovo Cimento* **25**, 806–815 (1962).

[O.2] Osgood, W. F., "Lehrbuch der Funktionentheorie." Vols. 1 and 2. Leipzig and Berlin, 1938, 1929. Reprinted Chelsea, New York, 1965.

[O.F.1] Omes, R., and Froissart, M., "Mandelstram Theory and Regge Poles." Benjamin, New York, 1963.

[P.1] Payne, L. E., On axially symmetric flow and generalized electrostatics, *Quart. Appl. Math.* **10**, 197–202 (1952).

[P.2] Pepper, P. M., The algebraic character of a class of harmonic functions in three variables, *Proc. Amer. Math. Soc.* **1**, 90–98 (1950).

[P.3] Picard, E., "Surfaces Algébriques." Gauthier-Villars, Paris, 1905.

[P.S.1] Picard, E., and Simart, G., "Théorie des Fonctions Algébriques de Deux Variables Indépendantes," Vols. I and II. Gauthier-Villars, Paris, 1897.

[P.S.2] Polkinghorne, J. C., and Screaton, G. R., The analytic properties of perturbation theory, I, *Nuovo Cimento* **15**, 289–300 (1960).

[R.1] Ranger, K. B., Some integral transformation formulae for the Stokes–Beltrami equation, *J. Math. Mech.* **12**, 663–674 (1963).

[R.2] Ranger, K. B., On the construction of some integral operators for generalized axially symmetric harmonics and stream functions, *J. Math. Mech.* **14**, 383–402 (1965).

[R.3] Rose, M. E., "Multipole Fields," Wiley, New York 1955.

[R.4] Rose, M. E., "Elementary Theory of Angular Momentum." Wiley, New York, 1957.

[R.W.1] Rosenbloom, P. C., and Widder, D. V., Expansions in terms of heat polynomials and associated functions, *Trans. Amer. Math. Soc.* **92**, 220–266 (1959).

[S.1] Sabatier, P. C., A general method for the inverse scattering problem at fixed energy, *J. Math Phys.* (To be published.)

[S.2] Sabatier, P. C., Interpolation formulas in the angular momentum plane, *J. Math. Phys.* (To be published.)

[S.3] Schiffer, M., Analytical theory of subsonic and supersonic flows, *in* "Handbuch der Physik" (S. Flugge, ed.), Vol. 9, pp. 1–161. Springer, Berlin, 1960.

[S.4] Schwartz, L., "Théorie des Distributions." Hermann, Paris, 1966.

[S.5] Stark, J. M., Transonic flow patterns generated by Bergman's integral operator, *Internat. J. Nonlinear Mech.* (To be published.)

[S.6] Szegö, G., "Orthogonal Polynomials" (Colloq. Ser., Vol. 23). Amer. Math. Soc., Providence, Rhode Island, 1939.

[S.7] Szegö, G., On the singularities of zonal harmonic expansions, *J. Rational Mech. Anal.* **3**, 561–564 (1954).

[S.8] Szmydt, Z., Sur un généralization des problèmes classiques concernant un système d'équations différentielles hyperboliques du second order à deux variables indépendentes, *Bull. Acad. Polon. Sci. C1. III* **4** (1956).

[S.W.1] Streater, R. F., and Wightman, A. S., "PCT, Spin and Statistics, and All That." Benjamin, New York, 1963.

[T.1] Titchmarsh, E. C., "Theory of Functions." Oxford Univ. Press, London and New York, 1932.

[T.2] Troshin, V. T., The impact of a subsonic gas flow on a plate covering the entrance into a channel with parallel walls, *Izv. Acad. Sci. USSR (OTN)* **4**, 67–170 (1960). (In Russian.)

[V.1] Vekua, I. N., Sur la représentation générale des solutions des équations aux dérivées partielles du second ordre. *C. R. Acad. Sci. USSR* **17**, 295–299 (1937).

[V.2] Vekua, I. N., Allgemeine Darstellung der Lösung einer partiellen Differentialgleichung des ellipticshen Types, die in bezug auf den Laplaceschen operator linear ist. *Acad. Sci. USSR Fil. Georigienne, Travauc Inst. Math Tbilissi* **2**, 227–240 (1941).

[V.3] Vekua, I. N., "Novye metody resenija elliptceskikh uravneni" ("New Methods for Solving Elliptic Equations"). OGIZ, Moskow and Leningrad, 1948; Wiley, New York, 1967.

[V.4] Vekua, I. N., "Systeme von Differentialgleichungen erster ordnung vom elliptischen Typus und Randwertaufgaben." Deut. Verlag Wiss., Berlin, 1956.

[V.5] Vekua, I. N., On a version of the bending theory of elastic shells, Lecture Series, Institute for Fluid Dynamics and Applied Mathematics, Univ. of Maryland, 1964.

[V.6] Vekua, I. N., "Generalized analytic functions." Addison-Wesley, Reading, Massachusetts, 1962.

[V.K.1] von Krzywoblocki, M. Z., Bergman's linear integral operator method in the theory of compressible fluid flow, *Oester. Ing.-Arch.* **6**, 330–360 (1952); **7**, 336–370 (1953); **8**, 237–263 (1954); **10**, 1–38 (1956).

[V.K.2] von Krzywoblocki, M. Z., "Bergman's Linear Integral Operator Method in the Theory of Compressible Fluid Flow" (with an appendix by P. Davis and P. Rabinowitz). Springer, Berlin, 1960.

[V.K.3] von Krzywoblocki, M. Z., Integral operators in ordinary differential equations. *J. Reine Angew. Math.* **214/215**, 137–140 (1964).

[V.K.4] von Krzywoblocki, M. Z., On the generalized integral operator method in the subsonic diabatic flow of a compressible fluid. *Proc. IXth Intern. Congr. Appl. Mech., Univ. Libre de Bruxelles, Brussels, Belgium, Sept.*, 1956, Paper I–11, pp. 414–419 (1957).

[V.K.5] von Krzywoblocki, M. Z., Generalization of Bergman's linear integral operator method to diabatic flow. *J. Soc. Ind. Appl. Math.* **5** (No. 2), 47–65 (1957).

[V.K.6] von Krzywoblocki, M. Z., A general approximation method in the theory of plates of small deflection. *Quart. Appl. Math.* **6** (No. 1), 31–52 (1948).

[V.K.7] von Krzywoblocki, M. Z., Some recent developments in the theoretical aspects of the electromagnetic wave propagation. *Proc. XIVth Intern. Astronaut. Congr., Paris, 1963.* Published in 1965, Vol. II, No. 10, pp. 135–157.

[V.K.8] von Krzywoblocki, M. Z., Bergman's integral operator method in the theory of wave propagation through a stratified troposphere. "Nonlinear Vibrations Problems," Vol. 6, pp. 83–130. Inst. of Basic Tech. Problems, Polish Acad. of Sci., Dept. of Vibrations, Warsaw, 1966.

[V.M.1] von Mises, R., "Mathematical Theory of Compressible Fluid Flow" (completed by H. Geiringer and G. S. S. Ludford). Academic Press, New York, 1958.

[V.M.S.1] von Mises, R., and Schiffer, M., On Bergman's integration method in two-dimensional compressible fluid flow, *in* "Advances in Applied Mechanics," Vol. 1, pp. 249–285. Academic Press, New York, 1948.

[W.1] Walter, W., Über die Differentialgleichung $u_{xy} = f(x, y, u, u_x, u_y)$, I, *Math. Z.* **71**, 308–324 (1960); II, **73**, 436–453 (1960); III, **73**, 268–279 (1960).

[W.2] Watson, G. N., "A Treatise on the Theory of Bessel Functions." Cambridge Univ. Press, London and New York, 1962.

[W.3] Weinacht, R. J., Fundamental solutions for a class of singular equations, *Contrib. Differential Equations* **3**, 43–55 (1964).

[W.4] Weinacht, R. J., A mean value theorem in generalized axially symmetric potential theory, *Acc. Naz. Lincei* **38**, 610–613 (1965).

[W.5] Weinstein, A., Étude des spectres des équations aux dérivées partielles de la théorie des plaques élastiques, *Mémor. Sci. Math.* **88**, (1937).

[W.6] Weinstein, A., Discontinuous integrals and generalized potential theory, *Trans. Amer. Math. Soc.* **63**, 342–354 (1948).

[W.7] Weinstein, A., Transonic flow and generalized axially symmetric potential theory, *Proc. NOL Aeroballistic Res. Symp., Naval Ordnance Laboratory, White Oak, Maryland, 1949.*

[W.8] Weinstein, A., Generalized axially symmetric potential theory, *Bull. Amer. Math. Soc.* **59**, 20–38 (1953).

[W.9] Weinstein, A., The singular solutions and the Cauchy problem for generalized Tricomi equations, *Comm. Pure Appl. Math.* **7**, 105–116 (1954).

[W.10] Weinstein, A., On a class of partial differential equations of even order, *Ann. Math. Pura Appl.* [IV] **39**, 245–254 (1959).

[W.11] Weinstein, A., The method of axial symmetry in partial differential equations, *Atti con. internaz. Equazioni alle derivate parziali, Trieste, 1954.*

[W.12] Weinstein, A., The generalized radiation problem and the Euler–Poisson–Darboux equation, *Summa Brasiliensis Math.* **3**, (7), 125–147 (1955).

[W.13] Weinstein, A., On a Cauchy problem with subharmonic initial values, *Ann. Mat. Pura Appl.* [IV] **43**, 325–340 (1957).

[W.14] Weinstein, A., On a singular differential operator, *Ann. Mat. Pura Appl.* [IV] **49**, 359–366 (1960).

[W.15] Weinstein, A., Singular partial differential equations and their applications, *in* "Fluid Dynamics and Applied Mathematics." Gordon and Breach, New York, 1961.

[W.16] Weinstein, A., On the Sturm–Liouville theory and eigenvalues of intermediate problems, *Numer. Math.* **5**, 238–245 (1963).

[W.17] Weierstrass, K., "Vorlesungen über die Theorie der Abelschen Transcendenten." Mayer and Miller, Berlin, 1902.

[W.18] Wilczynski, E. H., "Projective Differential Geometry of Curves and Ruled Surfaces." Teubner, 1906 (reprinted Chelsea, New York,) 1962.

[W.19] White, A., Singularities of harmonic functions of three variables generated by Whittaker–Bergman operators, *Ann. Polon. Math.* **10**, 81–100 (1961).

[W.20] White, A., Singularities of a harmonic function of three variables given by its series development, MRC Tech. Rep. 312, April 1962.

[W.S.1] Wightman, A. S., and Schweber, S. S., Configuration space methods in relativistic quantum field theory, I, *Phys. Rev.* **98**, 812 (1955).

[W.W.1] Whittaker, E. T., and Watson, G. N., "A Course of Modern Analysis." Cambridge Univ. Press, London and New York, 1920.

[Z.1] Zariski, O., "Algebraic Surfaces." Chelsea, New York, 1948.

[Z.2] Zimmermann, W., Analytic behavior of the scattering amplitude at zero energy, *Nuovo Cimento* **21**, 249–273 (1961).

Subject Index

Mathematics in Science and Engineering

A Series of Monographs and Textbooks

Edited by RICHARD BELLMAN, *University of Southern California*

1. Tracy Y. Thomas. Concepts from Tensor Analysis and Differential Geometry. Second Edition. 1965
2. Tracy Y. Thomas. Plastic Flow and Fracture in Solids. 1961
3. Rutherford Aris. The Optimal Design of Chemical Reactors: A Study in Dynamic Programming. 1961
4. Joseph LaSalle and Solomon Lefschetz. Stability by Liapunov's Direct Method with Applications. 1961
5. George Leitmann (ed.). Optimization Techniques: With Applications to Aerospace Systems. 1962
6. Richard Bellman and Kenneth L. Cooke. Differential-Difference Equations. 1963
7. Frank A. Haight. Mathematical Theories of Traffic Flow. 1963
8. F. V. Atkinson. Discrete and Continuous Boundary Problems. 1964
9. A. Jeffrey and T. Taniuti. Non-Linear Wave Propagation: With Applications to Physics and Magnetohydrodynamics. 1964
10. Julius T. Tou. Optimum Design of Digital Control Systems. 1963
11. Harley Flanders. Differential Forms: With Applications to the Physical Sciences. 1963
12. Sanford M. Roberts. Dynamic Programming in Chemical Engineering and Process Control. 1964
13. Solomon Lefschetz. Stability of Nonlinear Control Systems. 1965
14. Dimitris N. Chorafas. Systems and Simulation. 1965
15. A. A. Pervozvanskii. Random Processes in Nonlinear Control Systems. 1965
16. Marshall C. Pease, III. Methods of Matrix Algebra. 1965
17. V. E. Benes. Mathematical Theory of Connecting Networks and Telephone Traffic. 1965
18. William F. Ames. Nonlinear Partial Differential Equations in Engineering. 1965
19. J. Aczel. Lectures on Functional Equations and Their Applications. 1966
20. R. E. Murphy. Adaptive Processes in Economic Systems. 1965
21. S. E. Dreyfus. Dynamic Programming and the Calculus of Variations. 1965
22. A. A. Fel'dbaum. Optimal Control Systems. 1965
23. A. Halanay. Differential Equations: Stability, Oscillations, Time Lags. 1966
24. M. Namik Oguztoreli. Time-Lag Control Systems. 1966
25. David Sworder. Optimal Adaptive Control Systems. 1966
26. Milton Ash. Optimal Shutdown Control of Nuclear Reactors. 1966
27. Dimitris N. Chorafas. Control System Functions and Programming Approaches (In Two Volumes). 1966
28. N. P. Erugin. Linear Systems of Ordinary Differential Equations. 1966
29. Solomon Marcus. Algebraic Linguistics; Analytical Models. 1967
30. A. M. Liapunov. Stability of Motion. 1966

31. George Leitmann (ed.). Topics in Optimization. 1967
32. Masanao Aoki. Optimization of Stochastic Systems. 1967
33. Harold J. Kushner. Stochastic Stability and Control. 1967
34. Minoru Urabe. Nonlinear Autonomous Oscillations. 1967
35. F. Calogero. Variable Phase Approach to Potential Scattering. 1967
36. A. Kaufmann. Graphs, Dynamic Programming, and Finite Games. 1967
37. A. Kaufmann and R. Cruon. Dynamic Programming: Sequential Scientific Management. 1967
38. J. H. Ahlberg, E. N. Nilson, and J. L. Walsh. The Theory of Splines and Their Applications. 1967
39. Y. Sawaragi, Y. Sunahara, and T. Nakamizo. Statistical Decision Theory in Adaptive Control Systems. 1967
40. Richard Bellman. Introduction to the Mathematical Theory of Control Processes Volume I. 1967 (Volumes II and III in preparation)
41. E. Stanley Lee. Quasilinearization and Invariant Imbedding. 1968
42. William Ames. Nonlinear Ordinary Differential Equations in Transport Processes. 1968
43. Willard Miller, Jr. Lie Theory and Special Functions. 1968
44. Paul B. Bailey, Lawrence F. Shampine, and Paul E. Waltman. Nonlinear Two Point Boundary Value Problems. 1968
45. Iu. P. Petrov. Variational Methods in Optimum Control Theory. 1968
46. O. A. Ladyzhenskaya and N. N. Ural'tseva. Linear and Quasilinear Elliptic Equations. 1968
47. A. Kaufmann and R. Faure. Introduction to Operations Research. 1968
48. C. A. Swanson. Comparison and Oscillation Theory of Linear Differential Equations. 1968
49. Robert Hermann. Differential Geometry and the Calculus of Variations. 1968
50. N. K. Jaiswal. Priority Queues. 1968
51. Hukukane Nikaido. Convex Structures and Economic Theory. 1968
52. K. S. Fu. Sequential Methods in Pattern Recognition and Machine Learning. 1968
53. Yudell L. Luke. The Special Functions and Their Approximations (In Two Volumes). 1969
54. Robert P. Gilbert. Function Theoretic Methods in Partial Differential Equations. 1969

In preparation

V. Lakshmikantham and S. Leela. Differential and Integral Inequalities

Masao Iri. Network Flow, Transportation, and Scheduling: Theory and Algorithms

S. Henry Hermes and Joseph P. LaSalle. Functional Analysis and Time Optimal Control